Engineering Drawing and Geometry

(On reverse) Stressed-skin aluminum dome building erected in Oklahoma City is 145 feet in diameter. Dome is composed of 625 diamond-shaped panels reinforced with aluminum struts (Kaiser Aluminum Photograph).

RANDOLPH P. HOELSCHER

Recently Professor and Head of the Department of General
Engineering, University of Illinois

CLIFFORD H. SPRINGER

Professor of General Engineering
University of Illinois

Engineering Drawing and Geometry

SECOND EDITION

JOHN WILEY & SONS, INC.
NEW YORK   LONDON

SECOND EDITION
THIRD PRINTING, APRIL, 1963

Copyright © 1956, 1961 by John Wiley & Sons, Inc.

Library of Congress Catalog Card Number: 61—11176
Printed in the United States of America

Preface

The first edition of this book was based on the successful organization and teaching methods of a department that has been in continuous existence for over fifty years. It has been one that has had conservative overlapping leadership of experienced men. Each of the authors has an average teaching experience of more than forty years plus many years of engineering practice. This experience comes to fruition in this textbook. It represents a philosophy of teaching in engineering drawing and the other graphical sciences that is in harmony with the trend in present-day engineering education.

We have had in mind throughout the preparation of this second edition several very definite objectives that have been approved by the leading authorities in this field. These may be stated very briefly as follows:

1. To provide a textbook so clear in its verbal discussion and pictorial illustration that it can be easily understood by the freshman student.

2. To make a textbook which presents the best in drafting practice but emphasizes the development of the reasoning process in its theoretical discussion rather than manual skill.

3. To provide the necessary material in one textbook to cover adequately the work in basic drawing courses, fundamental descriptive geometry, advanced courses for sophomores in the professional fields, and fundamental work in graphical computation.

4. To present the material in such a way that it will stimulate creative imagination, develop visual perception in three dimensions, and promote original thinking.

5. To eliminate all material that is not essential for engineering college students or useful in a reference work on drawing for practicing engineers.

6. To adhere rigorously to third quadrant projection, not only for the three principal views but for auxiliary views as well, which is the basis for the unification of drawing practice among the United States, Great Britain, and Canada.

Since this book is designed for engineers, thoroughness in the understanding of principles has been emphasized rather than manual skills. Although the engineer must have reasonable facility and know what technique is required to produce a satisfactory drawnig for reproduction, we have not attempted to teach perfectionism in lettering and manual skills. It is from the viewpoint of developing an engineer rather than a draftsman that the subject matter has been presented.

In Part 2 all the theory in descriptive geometry necessary for the successful solution of problems in design and drafting has been included. This theory has been so arranged that it may be used in a combined and integrated course in both drawing and descriptive geometry or in separate courses if so desired. One textbook with a uniform system of nomenclature is a distinct advantage over two books with different systems. All forms of pictorial drawings have been presented on an exact theoretical basis as well as by conventional constructions where these are appropriate.

In Chapter 15, which is devoted to descriptive geometry, the auxiliary plane method has been used almost exclusively. The revolution of an oblique plane has been used only where it is distinctly advantageous.

Part 3 includes five chapters on various types of graphical computation sometimes loosely referred to as graphics. Enough material has been included in this section for a three-credit-hour semester course in this field of ever-increasing importance in engineering.

The chapters in Part 4 have been designed for sophomore courses in the professional fields. The treatment is thorough and sufficiently detailed in character and explanation so that the student may do problems of a professional character without entering into theoretical design work. The problems, which have been included in each of these chapters, are not merely copy work but offer an excellent opportunity for the development of clear thinking and good judgment.

The development of visual perception in three dimensions and creative imagination has been attempted in all parts of the text. These qualities, however, can be fully developed only with the complete cooperation of the instructors.

The text has not been confined to the concepts of machine drawing but treats the subject from the broader base of engineering usage as a whole. Thus the first treatment of dimensioning in Chapter 9 is limited to practices which apply in all fields, and the subject of tolerances and limit dimensions is treated in Chapter 13 with especial reference to production drawings for interchangeable assembly. The latest concepts such as form and positional tolerancing have been adequately presented, as well as the maximum material concept.

Both upper-case and lower-case letters have been presented in the chapter on this subject, and both have been used in the illustrations. Although upper-case letters are used almost exclusively in the machine industry, it should not be overlooked that in civil engineering and architecture lower-case letters are widely used.

The larger page size has been adopted to permit the use of larger illustrations where necessary for clarity and to enable the book to lie open without weights.

The problem sections in each chapter are adequate for at least four semesters of work without repetition. Since efficiency in teaching requires the use of workbooks to economize the student's time, the space devoted to problems has been held to a minimum. In several chapters the problems have been presented in a new form so that the student must exercise his ingenuity and judgment in the solution. Problems of various degrees of difficulty have been included so that the instructor can meet the challenge of varying ability among his students. Workbooks in both engineering drawing and descriptive geometry to accompany this textbook are available from the Stipes Publishing Co., 10 Chester St., Champaign, Illinois. These workbooks have been designed to supplement and expedite the teaching principles of this text. Quiz questions which may be used as a study guide by students are also available. Enough material has been presented in the Appendix to provide the necessary data for the solution of any problems given in the text or the workbooks.

We are indebted to several of our colleagues for valuable assistance in the development of this book. The chapter on Architectural Drawing was prepared by Professor Wayne L. Shick, the chapter on Pipe Drawing by Professor Leonard D. Walker. Professor Stanley G. Hall prepared the chapter on Material Specification. Professor Jerry S. Dobrovolny has also given valuable assistance and suggestions in the preparation of this edition. To each of these men we wish to express our appreciation for their contributions to the usefulness of this book.

We are also indebted to Professor Albert Jorgensen of the University of Pennsylvania, a former colleague, for his critical review of the entire textbook and for the many valuable recommendations which he made. Our thanks go also to Professor H. H. Jordan for his help.

We also desire to express our appreciation to Mr. Howard Nelson for the generous use of his time in checking some of the problems and to Miss Grace Wilson for her professional drafting work in several sections of the book. Many valuable suggestions and criticisms were received from forty or more members of the staff of the University of Illinois both at Urbana and at the Chicago Undergraduate Division, who use this text daily. To these men and the many at other schools we wish to express our gratitude.

Many industrial concerns have contributed drawings for illustration purposes, for which credit has been given at the appropriate places.

R. P. Hoelscher
C. H. Springer

February, 1961
Urbana, Illinois

Contents

(Each chapter begins with page 01)

Part One
Basic Drawing

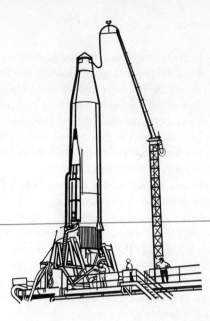

1

Introduction

1.1 Functions of engineering drawing. In order that the student may understand the purpose of studying engineering drawings, this chapter gives a very brief review of the scope of the subject and its place in engineering practice. In designing machines, factories, dams, bridges, missiles, and other structures for man's use, the engineer must first form a clear mental picture of the thing to be built. Before an estimate of the cost can be made or any work can be done on its actual construction he must convey his mental image to the shop man or contractor, furnishing him data which will give the exact sizes of all parts, the kinds of materials of which they are to be made, and the positions they are to occupy with respect to each other in the complete machine or structure. In addition he must indicate the finish required, the exactness with which the parts must be made, and many other types of information necessary to the builder of the project.

A little reflection serves to convince one that it would be an impossible task to describe in oral or written language a machine like the simplest gas engine, with data and dimensions sufficient to make possible its construction in the pattern shop, foundry, and machine shop. Engineering drawings, however, can supply all the information needed with the exactness and detail required. It is therefore one of the principal functions of drawing to convey ideas from the designing engineer to the fabricator. Since drawing serves the same purpose as the written language, namely, that of transmitting ideas from one man to another, engineering drawing is often referred to as the graphic means of communication.

Its quality of graphic description makes it the one

◄ Atlas intercontinental ballistic missile readied for test flight at Cape Canaveral, Florida (General Dynamics Corporation).

universal language and the only one understood by all civilized men. Like the written language it has its grammar and rhetoric in the rules and theory of projection, its idioms in conventionalized practices, and its abbreviations in symbols. As the written language has its forms of expression such as description, narration, exposition, and argumentation, so the graphic language has its various types of delineation.

1.2   Divisions of engineering drawing. The two main divisions of engineering drawing may be classified as projective drawings and non-projective drawings. Projective or projection drawings, which we shall discuss first, have to do with the description of the shape of objects. When this description is made with instruments such as the T-square, triangle, scale, and compass, it is usually referred to as a mechanical drawing since it is mechanically made.

If, on the other hand, the drawing is made without the aid of the draftsman's instruments it is called a freehand drawing or sketch. The term sketch as used in engineering does not imply in any way that ideas conveyed are sketchy, indefinite, or hazy. Quite the contrary is true, and one of the chief assets of an engineer is his ability to make clean-cut, accurate freehand sketches. Hence the whole broad field of engineering drawing is divided into instrumental and freehand drawing. The engineer should be competent in both so that he may direct the work of others.

1.3   Types of projection. Whether he uses the freehand or instrumental technique, the engineer may convey his ideas by one or more of three basic types of projection, namely, orthographic projection (Chapter 7), including the three types of axonometric (Chapter 17), oblique projection (Chapter 18), or perspective (Chapter 19). The type of projection he chooses will depend upon the purpose of the drawing and the person to whom he wishes to convey his ideas. If it is to another engineer or a skilled mechanic, he will use the multiview orthographic projection, commonly known as a shop drawing. On the other hand, if he must instruct the unskilled, clarify a complicated drawing, or make a popular appeal as in advertising, he will use one of the pictorial forms. These forms of expression are at his command if he has a thorough knowledge of projection.

1.4   Professional aspects. Though the foregoing discussion is basic to all types of engineering projection drawing, there are different practices in certain professional areas which differentiate drawings and give rise to the terms machine drawing, architectural drawing, structural drawing, map drawing, and the like. These differences, though quite definite, are nevertheless minor aspects of variation in the general practice of engineering drawings. They are discussed in detail in the chapters devoted to these subjects.

1.5   Standardization of drafting. In order to establish drafting practice throughout the country on a firm basis so that drawings made anywhere will have clear and unmistakable meaning everywhere, engineers have established standards in drafting. Those standards were set up first in industrial companies, later in engineering societies, and finally in a collective effort through the American Standards Association. The drafting procedures shown and recommended in this book reflect the latest revision of these American Standards, which are in general agreement with those of Great Britian and Canada.

The student should become familiar with the work of the American Standards Association and that of the professional engineering society with which he is most concerned, for it is only through this standardization that modern mass production is possible.

1.6   Legal aspects. The drawings for buildings, bridges, dams, and other major construction projects have always been the basis for legal contracts in which the builder agrees to erect the structure in accordance with the plans prepared by the engineer for the owner. Such drawings must always be clear and unmistakable in meaning. The drawing, in fact, becomes a legal document. If it is subject to more than one interpretation, litigation may arise causing unnecessary delay and expense.

In the machine industry, modern mass production has brought with it the letting of contracts for the manufacture of machine parts in large quantity. Machine parts, for interchangeable assembly, must be finished very accurately to the dimensions specified. The engineer can seldom go into his own shop and tell the foreman what he wants since the part may be produced in a plant hundreds of miles away. The drawing itself must tell the whole story. *It must be made not merely so that it can be understood but it must be so clear in its meaning that it cannot be misunderstood or misinterpreted either by accident or intention.*

This places on the young engineer who may make the drawing or direct the work of producing it a heavy responsibility to understand thoroughly both the fundamental theory and the conventional practice of drafting which he gains in his drawing courses.

1.7   Shop and construction methods. Before he can proceed very far in his profession the young engineer must become familiar with methods of manufacture in the shop or construction in the field. It is clearly a waste of time and money to make a drawing, however beautiful and accurate, of a part that cannot be made in the shop and made economically. Since shop courses have almost disappeared from engineering education, the young engineer as a part of his training in graphic expression should learn the simpler fundamentals of shop and construction methods as presented in several chapters of this book.

1.8   Dimensioning. A shape description of a part shown by one or more projected views is totally inadequate unless dimensions are given showing the exact size of each part and the location of parts in relation to each other. It is this phase of drawing which requires the greatest care and study. Engineers are giving a great deal of attention to the standardization of dimensioning so that there may be no ambiguity. *The dimensioning practice given in this book represents the most recently adopted American standards, as set forth in ASA Y14–1957.*

1.9   Non-projective drawings. With the constant development in science and technology the engineering designer requires more and more laboratory test data upon which to base his designs. The results of laboratory and field tests, although compiled originally in tabular form, are best understood and interpreted in the form of curves or charts and diagrams (Chapter 20). No theory of projection is involved in making such charts, but their construction and interpretation require a knowledge of the types of coordinate papers available and a knowledge of their meaning and engineering significance. This phase of drawing is particularly valuable to those engaged in research.

1.10   Graphical computation. Charts and diagrams used in engineering design frequently require a combination of mathematics and graphical construction. Some problems in calculus can be solved more effectively by graphical than by analytical methods.

Many engineering problems involve vector quantities and they lend themselves very well to graphical methods of solution. When these vectors are non-coplanar, graphical methods are less cumbersome than the analytical approach unless expensive computing machines are available.

It is often desirable, even necessary, to express the results of tests and experiments in the form of equations where no rational basis for such an equation exists from which it could be derived. In such cases graphical lay-

outs of the data may make it possible to obtain a satisfactory empirical equation.

1.11   Nomographs. Another phase of engineering drawing in modern practice lies in the construction and use of computation charts and nomographs. The work in almost any engineering office requires the repeated solution of certain equations with different quantities involved in the variables. A nomograph is a graphic device whereby a straight edge may be laid across the chart one or more times at the plotted position of the variables involved and the result read off on a calibrated scale. Only an engineer or mathematician can make a nomograph, but with a little instruction anyone can use it. This phase of engineering drawing is now receiving wider recognition, and it is a valuable tool for the engineer.

The five chapters of Part III of this textbook present enough material in this area for a two or three credit hour semester course. Special courses in nomography and other graphical methods are offered in many schools.

1.12   Value of drawing to the engineer. This preview of the field of modern engineering drawing gives some indication of its broad scope and usefulness as a working tool of the engineer. No matter how far reaching the research of scientists or engineers is in developing new ideas and concepts, little can be built or manufactured without drawings. If, for example, a factory is to be built to manufacture a new product, the usual procedure is to plan the manufacturing and machining operations, then determine the sequence and arrangements for assembling the product by referring to the drawings.

Only then can the whole sequence of operations be planned and machine sizes, types, and locations be determined to manufacture the product ecomomically. Then the plant can be designed to house the equipment and provide for the proper flow of materials.

Engineering drawing therefore is the basic tool with which all engineers must operate. For the young engineer the ability to present his ideas in neat, accurate, clean-cut drawing leads to professional advancement, for a well-made drawing inspires confidence in the ability of its maker. Later in his career as a designer or project engineer, he must direct others in the preparation of drawings and be responsible for the accuracy and correctness of them. Finally, as a manager, engineering executive or research man he will use and approve drawings long after his direct supervision of drafting has ended.

Cornerstone (Robert M. Mottar).

2

Lettering

2.1 Engineering lettering. The first essential to the use of the graphic language is a mastery of the art of lettering. Before a line drawing can serve a useful purpose, it must have placed upon it certain lettering in the form of dimensions, notes, and a title. This lettering may enhance or ruin the appearance of a drawing. If it is poorly made, mistakes may result and confidence in the draftsman or engineer making the drawing is reduced.

All engineers, except the architectural engineer, use a vertical or slant style of lettering as illustrated in Figs. 2–1 and 2–2. *This style of lettering is frequently referred to as single-stroke Gothic.*

2.2 Origin of the alphabet. The alphabet we use today had its origin in ancient hieroglyphics. Developed by the Egyptians into a cursive form, this was adopted by the Phoenicians, who produced an alphabet of twenty-two letters. This alphabet was transmitted in the course of time to the Greeks and by them to the Romans. Changes were made by each of these civilizations, due in part to the kinds of tools and materials available for recording the writings. The Roman capital alphabet finally evolved as shown in Fig. 2–30 at the close of this chapter, and has come down to us practically unchanged.

2.3 Style in lettering. All modern lettering is developed from one of the three basic styles, namely the roman, the Gothic, and the Text. When these letters are slanted in type setting they are referred to as italics. In this chapter we refer to any style as being either vertical or slant since that is the general practice in engineering.

a. Roman letters. Any letters composed of thin and thick strokes except Text letters (see paragraph *c* below) are called roman. See Figs. 2–30 and 2–32.

ABCDEFGHIJKLMNOPQRS
TUVWXYZ

abcdefghijklmnopqrstuvwxyz

Fig. 2–1. The single-stroke slant alphabet.

ABCDEFGHIJKLMNOPQRS
TUVWXYZ

abcdefghijklmnopqrstuvwxyz

Fig. 2–2. The single-stroke vertical alphabet.

b. Gothic letters. Letters having all strokes of uniform width are classified as Gothic. See Fig. 2–34. When the width of the strokes is such that it can be made with a single stroke of the lettering pen or pencil, the style is called single-stroke Gothic. This is the style used by engineers.

c. Text letters. These letters include all styles of Old English Text, German Text, and others designed for formal documents such as diplomas and scrolls. See Fig. 2–35.

2.4 Capitals and lower case. Each of the three basic styles may be further subdivided into capitals or upper case and small letters or lower case. See Figs. 2–1 and 2–2. The term "lower case" found its origin in the fact that formerly printers kept the small letters in the lower part of the letter case. *Therefore, in order to designate any style completely three items are necessary, namely, (1) basic form, (2) capital or lower case, and (3) vertical or slant.* Further classification would involve the terms single-stroke or "filled in" letters. Inscriptions in stone or metal may be incised, or cut into the material. They may also be embossed, or raised above the surrounding material.

2.5 Height of letters. *In speaking of the height of letters the height of the capital letters is meant.* The stems or ascenders of lower-case letters such as b, d, h, etc., are made the same height as the capitals except the letter t which is sometimes made a little shorter. *The body of the lower-case letters is made two-thirds the height of the capitals.* Numerals have the same height as the capitals. Thus on any drawing, if the height of of the capital letters is chosen as ³⁄₁₆ inch, the numerals will have the same height and the bodies of the lower-case letters will be ⅛ inch high. The stems of lower-case letters such as g, j, and p, which extend downward, are known as descenders. They go as far below the body of lower-case letters as the ascenders go above. These proportions of letters are obtained on a drawing by the use of guide lines.

2.6 Guide lines. In order to obtain perfect alignment and the correct height for different letters and numerals, guide lines must be drawn. They consist of three light parallel pencil lines ruled with T-square or triangle in the space to be occupied by the lettering. The space between the outside lines is made equal to the height of the letters. The third line is drawn between the other two at a distance equal to two-thirds the total height from the bottom guide lines as shown in Fig. 2–3. Only by the use of guide lines can the student attain uniform-

ity of height so essential in good lettering.

Guide lines may be ruled more rapidly by using the Braddock lettering triangle shown in Fig. 2–4. This triangle has six columns of small holes so placed that they give the proper spacing of guide lines for any line of lettering and also the proper spacing between lines when the lettering occupies more than a single line. The columns are numbered at the bottom from 3 to 8, consecutively. These numbers give the height of guide lines, made by the columns in thirty-seconds of an inch. Thus the column marked 6 produces guide lines ⁶⁄₃₂, or ³⁄₁₆, inch between the top and bottom lines.

To use the instrument, rest the hypotenuse against the T-square, place the pencil point through the lowest hole, and slide the triangle along the T-square. Move the pencil to the next hole above and slide the triangle in the opposite direction. Repeat for the third hole. The process is illustrated in Fig. 2–4.

The Ames lettering instrument is another popular device used in much the same manner, as illustrated in Fig. 2–5. This instrument permits a great latitude in the selection of the height of letters by rotating the dial and may also be used to give uniformly spaced lines for crosshatching an area by using the middle line of holes.

2.7 Slope. In vertical lettering, the stems are perpendicular to the line of lettering. In slant lettering, a

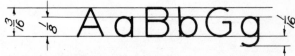

Fig. 2–3. Guide lines and height of letters.

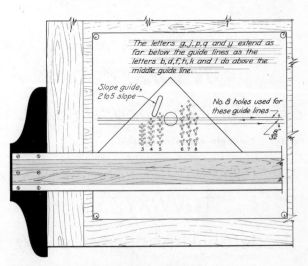

Fig. 2–4. The Braddock lettering triangle.

good appearance may be obtained at any angle between 65 and 75°. For standard slant lettering a slope of 67½° has been established. This slope may be obtained by drawing a triangle with a horizontal run of 2 to a vertical rise of 5, as shown in Fig. 2–6. In order to obtain uniformity of slope the beginner should draw light slope guide lines at random across any lettering exercise. The slot in the Braddock lettering triangle and one side of the Ames instrument give this slope.

2.8   Elements of the letters. The letters of the alphabet are composed mainly of two simple elements, with a few variations due to the shape of certain letters. The first of these elements is called the stem of the letter and is made with a single downward stroke of the pen. The second element is called the oval and is made with one or two strokes of the pen, depending upon the size of the letter being made.

2.8.1   *Stems.* Those straight lines, vertical or slant, which form a part of more than four-fifths of all the letters of the alphabet are called the stems. Those horizontal straight lines which form a part of such letters as A, E, F, and H are not classified as stems but must be made as carefully and neatly as the stems. Special instructions for making the individual letters are given later, but the following rules are applicable in forming all stems.

a. The stems must be uniform in weight or thickness and have a uniform height.

b. The stems must be perfectly straight without hooks or curls at either end.

c. The slopes of stems must be uniform and parallel to each other throughout any piece of lettering.

The width of the stroke is determined by the kind and size of pen being used rather than by the pressure placed upon the pen. Figure 2–7 shows examples of good and poor stems.

2.8.2   *Ovals.* The second element in lettering is a perfect ellipse with a well-determined ratio between its major and minor axes. In Fig. 2–8 the horizontal width of the parallelogram enclosing the ellipse is made five-sixths the height. The ellipse touches the four sides of the parallelogram at their midpoints. These proportions give what is termed a standard vertical or slant oval which, when properly combined with the stem, produces the normal or standard letter.

In making the oval, two strokes should be used beginning at the top and meeting at the bottom without a perceptible joint. The direction and character of the strokes are shown in Fig. 2–8.

It should be noted that in the vertical letters the major axis of the ellipse is vertical and joins the highest and lowest points of the ellipse. In slant letters the

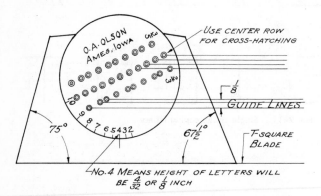

Fig. 2–5.   The Ames lettering instrument.

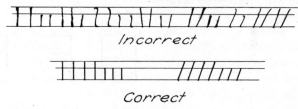

Incorrect

Correct

Fig. 2–7.   Stems of single-stroke letters.

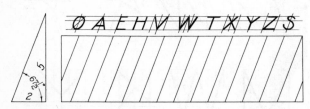

Fig. 2–6.   Slope guide lines.

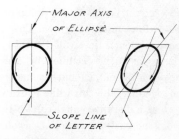

Fig. 2–8.   Direction of strokes in making the oval.

major axis of the ellipse makes an angle of approximately 45° with the horizontal and does not coincide with the slope line of the letter which would join the highest and lowest points on the letter. See Fig. 2–8.

2.9   Combination of stem and oval. When one has mastered the technique of the individual elements it becomes a simple task to combine them in forming such letters as a, b, d, p, n, r, and u. The secret of success lies chiefly in remembering that the stem becomes one side of the parallelogram shown in Fig. 2–8. In making the stem tangent to the ellipse it will be found that they must coincide with each other for some distance as shown in Fig. 2–9, but in no case should the thickness of the letter at the point of tangency be permitted to become greater than the thickness of the stem.

The weight of strokes of the stem and oval should be the same. The weight of the strokes may vary with the size of the letter, and a pen point should be chosen that will give the desired weight.

2.10   Position of the hand for lettering. Each person must determine for himself the best position of his hand for lettering. The following rules will serve as a guide in assisting the student to establish a good lettering technique:

a. The forearm should be completely supported by the desk at all times.

b. The pencil or pen should be held firmly but not tightly gripped. Straightening the forefinger along the pencil tends to relax the tight grip. See Fig. 2–10.

c. A hand motion made by rocking the hand will usually prove more satisfactory than a finger motion. The finger motion tends to cramp the hand.

d. For a right-handed person the forearm should make approximately 75 to 80° with the line of lettering.

With the exception of rule (*d*) above, these instructions apply also to left-handed persons.

2.11   Rule of stability. In order to avoid the appearance of being top-heavy, certain letters, such as A, B, E, F, and H, must have the horizontal cross-bar placed either above or below the center. *The position of the crossbar is arranged so that the white spaces within the letter appear balanced.* To give the appearance of being balanced the area in the upper part of the letter must actually be smaller than the lower area.

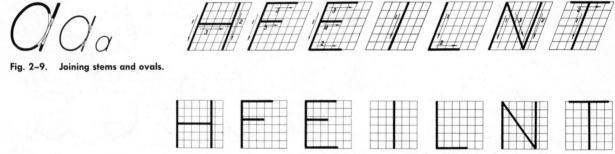

Fig. 2–9.   **Joining stems and ovals.**

Fig. 2–11.   **Single-stroke capital letters.**

Fig. 2–10.   **Position of hand for lettering.**

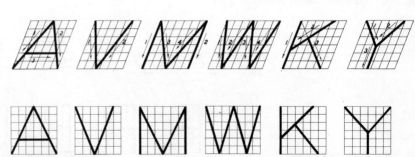

Fig. 2–12.   **Direction of strokes for making letters.**

Such letters as K, R, X, and Z must also have the base of the letter a bit wider than the top to give the feeling and appearance of stability. The various letters are discussed in detail in the following paragraphs.

2.12 Capital letters. The shape of the letters can be learned best by a study of Figs. 2–11 to 2–15 and the comments accompanying each figure. The letters have been placed within a parallelogram which is divided into six equal spaces both horizontally and vertically. The width of each letter can thus be determined at a glance. The direction and order of strokes have been indicated by numbered arrows on the individual letters. The same order applies to the vertical letters. *In general the strokes are made from top to bottom and from left to right.*

In Fig. 2–11, note that the crossbar of the H and the middle bar of E and F slightly above the center. This avoids a top-heavy appearance.

In Fig. 2–12, the crossbar of the A is placed below the middle. The third stroke of the K if extended would pass through the top of the first stroke. The branch of the Y is slightly below the middle. The second stroke of

the A and the first stroke of the V are almost vertical in slant lettering.

In the wide letters M and W the construction is different. The first and last strokes of the letter M are parallel; in the letter W alternate strokes are parallel. *Letters such as A, V, W, X, and Y should be constructed so that the slope lines bisect the angle between the strokes.*

In Fig. 2–13, the strokes of the X cross slightly above the center and the top line of the Z is shorter than the bottom.

In Fig. 2–14, all the letters are based on the ellipse. Almost one-half the right side of the ellipse is omitted to form the letter C. The G is similar with the addition of a horizontal line. The letter S lies entirely within the oval. The upper part should be smaller than the lower part to give the letter stability.

In Fig. 2–15, the letters P, R, and B should have the center horizontal line slightly above the middle, and the top of the R and B should be narrower than the bottom. Note that in the letters P, R, B, and D horizontal lines connect the stems to the ovals.

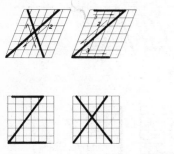

Fig. 2–13.   Direction of strokes for making X and Z.

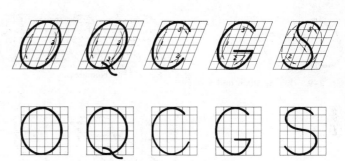

Fig. 2–14.   Capital letters based on the oval.

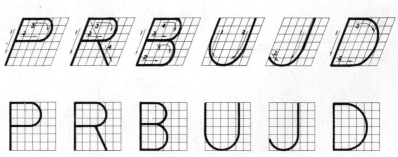

Fig. 2–15.   Capital letters involving partial ovals.

2.13 Numerals. In Fig. 2–16, note the similarity between the bottoms of 3, 5, and 8, also between the tops of 2 and 3. The top of most of the numerals is smaller than the bottom. The height of the interger numerals is always equal to the height of the capitals.

In fractions, as shown in Fig. 2–17, the height of the numbers in the numerator and denominator should be not less than two-thirds the height of the integer. A horizontal line should separate the numerals, and neither numerator nor denominator should touch this line. The same slope line should form the center line of both the numerator and denominator.

2.14 Small letters. The small, or lower-case, letters are also composed of straight lines, ovals, and combinations thereof, as shown in Figs. 2–18, to 2–21. The body of the lower-case letters is two-thirds the height of the capitals, and the long stems, with the exception of the letter t, are the same height as the capitals. The de-

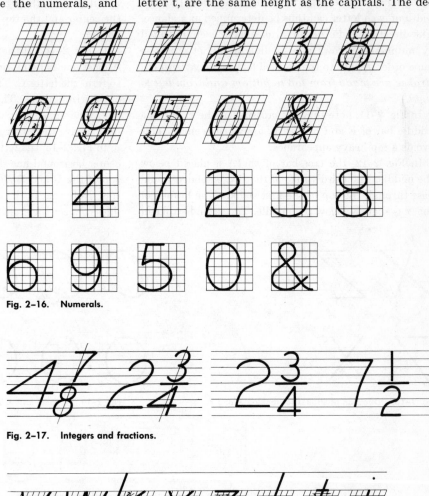

Fig. 2–16. Numerals.

Fig. 2–17. Integers and fractions.

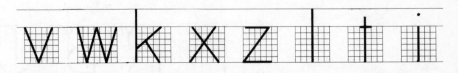

Fig. 2–18. Lower-case straight-stroke letters.

scenders for g, j, p, q, and y extend as far below the lower guide line as the ascenders extend above the body of the small letters.

The small letters in Fig. 2-18 are small counterparts of the capitals with the exception of i, k, l, and t; hence very little comment is necessary. Note that the small i has a dot over it whereas the capital I does not.

All the letters in Fig. 2-19 are based on the ellipse of the letter o. The stroke at the center of the letter e

should end horizontally. Care must be exercised to see that all ovals have the same basic slope and size. In the letters where stems are involved these must be tangent to the ovals.

In Figs. 2-20 and 2-21, the letters are formed by stems and partial ovals. The tops of the letters r and f and the bottom of the descenders on j, y, and g are all partial ovals. The letters s and u are the same as the capitals except for size.

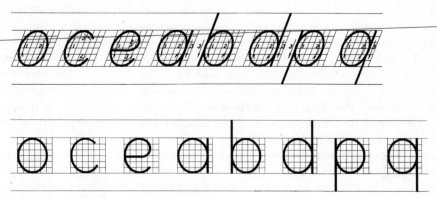

Fig. 2-19. Lower-case letters based on the oval.

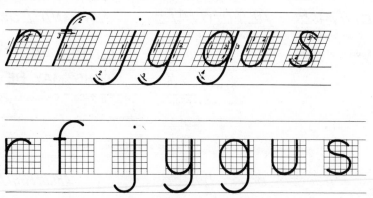

Fig. 2-20. Lower-case letters involving partial ovals.

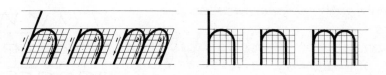

Fig. 2-21. Lower-case letters involving partial ovals.

2.15   Composition. Much of the poor lettering on drawing is due to the draftsman's lack of skill in composition. *Good composition requires that the white areas between the letters in a word appear to be equal and that the spaces between words appear uniform.* This spacing is a matter of judgment, and no rule of thumb can be given. It should be noted, however, that when certain letters such as L and T occur consecutively they must be spaced closer than usual. On the other hand, letters such as A and V or I and L must be placed farther apart, as shown in Fig. 2-22. In some sequences the width of the letters themselves should be modified.

The chief fault with beginners lies in making the space between letters too large. The most beautiful composition has the individual letters full and well rounded with the space between them small. A close inspection of the faults portrayed in the paragraph of lettering in Fig. 2-23 will aid the student to avoid the same mistakes. Spacing between words will be satisfactory if the minimum space is made equal to the width of the normal ellipse but not greater than the height of the letters being used.

2.15.1   *Large and small capitals.* In many engineering offices only capital letters are used for notes and legends on drawings. Some use one size of capitals throughout all lettering; others use initial capitals and smaller capitals two-thirds the height of the initial letters. This makes the lettering procedure easier and when well done presents a readable and pleasing appearance. See Fig. 2-24.

2.15.2   *Compressed and expanded lettering.* Where space limitations require, lettering may be expanded or compressed as illustrated in Fig. 2-25. In either case the change should be made in the letters themselves and not in the spacing between them.

2.16   Summary of principles. Good lettering depends upon the principle of uniformity. This involves consideration of six fundamentals, namely, weight, shape, style, slope, size, and spacing.

a. Uniformity of weight requires that all strokes in any composition have the same thickness. This is attained by careful and frequent filling of the pen and by uniform pressure upon the pen in making each stroke. Certain special lettering pens are very helpful in attain-

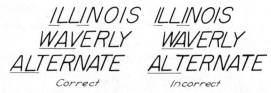

Fig. 2-22.   Spacing of letters.

LARGE AND SMALL CAPITALS ARE FREQUENTLY USED INSTEAD OF UPPER AND LOWER CASE LETTERS.

EITHER VERTICAL OR SLANT LETTERS MAY BE USED.

Fig. 2-24.   Composition with capital letters.

Make the letters broad but closely spaced. Open spacing is hard to read.

Even spacing is essential. Uneven spacing spoils the entire composition.

Use slope guide lines. Variable slope ruins the appearance of the lettering.

Compact uniform lettering is an asset to any drawing.

Fig. 2-23.   Study of composition of lettering.

ABCDEFGHIJKLMNOPQRSTUVWXYZ&
abcdefghijklmnopqrstuvwxyyz

ABCDEFGHIJ
KLMNOPQRS
TUVWXYZ&
abcdefghijklm
nopqrstuvwxyyz

Fig. 2-25.   Compressed and expanded alphabets.

ing this objective. In pencil work frequent sharpening of a soft pencil (H or 2H) is required.

b. Uniformity of shape requires a thorough knowledge of the correct letter shapes so that they are always made in the same way.

c. Uniformity of style prevents the indiscriminate mixing of Gothic and roman letters or the mixing of capitals and lower-case letters except for the legitimate purpose of initial capitals.

d. Uniformity of slope means that the stems and axes of all letters shall be parallel. This can be attained only through thoughtful practice and the use of slope lines for the beginner.

e. Uniformity of size may be attained by using guide lines and making sure that the letters actually touch both upper and lower guide lines but do not cross over them. The width of similar letters likewise must be uniform.

f. Uniformity of spacing requires that the white areas between letters appear equal and relatively small as compared with the size of the letter. The white areas between words must also appear equal.

2.17   Lettering pencils. For ruling guide lines a 4H or 5H pencil well sharpened is best. The actual lettering should be done with a well-sharpened H or 2H pencil. The soft pencils, containing more graphite, slide over the paper with less resistance and also produce a line dark enough to reproduce.

2.18   Lettering pens. Previous discussion has indicated that there should be some correlation between the size

of letter and the weight of strokes used in making the letters. The engineer will therefore need a selection of pens suitable for the range of lettering work he may be required to do.

The following pen points are recommended:

For very fine lines	Gillott 170 or 290
	Esterbrook 355 or 356
For heavier lines	Gillott 303 or 404
	Esterbrook 357 or 358

A few of the many special pens available are illustrated in Fig. 2-26.

2.18.1   *Use of the lettering pen.* To prepare a lettering pen for use, dip it in ink and wipe dry one or two times to remove the film of oil always found on new pens.

Wipe the pen clean frequently while using it, and always clean it thoroughly before putting it away.

It is better to fill the pen with the quill in the ink bottle stopper rather than by dipping the pen. This is particularly true of the Tank pens and all special lettering pens.

In lettering long notes on drawings, difficulty in maintaining uniform weight of strokes is encountered because the pen makes a lighter line when it is about to run dry than when it has been freshly filled. This can be alleviated somewhat by the use of Tank pens.

2.19   Mechanical lettering guides. Where mechanical precision and uniformity are desired as, for example, in titles of drawings or in any lettering on drawings to be

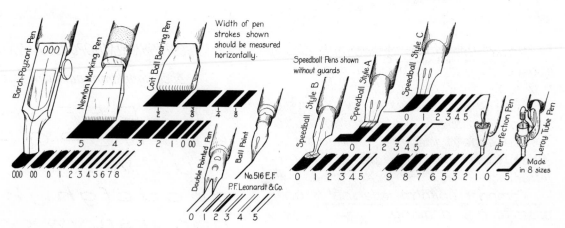

Fig. 2–26.   Special lettering pens.

reproduced photographically, mechanical lettering guides are very helpful.

The Wrico lettering guides consist of strips of transparent pyralin as shown in Fig. 2-27 with a series of openings so shaped that, when the point of the Wrico lettering pen is moved in contact with the side of the openings, the letters of the alphabet and the numerals may be formed. To construct most of the letters it is necessary to use two positions of the guide. These guides may be obtained in a wide variety of sizes and styles of lettering with a corresponding variety of pens to fit the various sizes of stencils.

The Le Roy lettering guides have the letters engraved in a template. The tracing point on the instrument is made to follow these engraved letters while the pen reproduces the letters above the template. This set is shown in Fig. 2-28.

In all these mechanical devices the spacing of letters and words must be done by eye. The engineer must therefore understand and observe all the rules for good composition.

2.20   Titles. In many industrial drafting rooms, printed title blocks are used, and the draftsman does not have to design the location or size of the title but merely letter in a few words in the space provided. Occasionally, however, it is necessary to design a complete title, and

therefore the draftsman must know what information should be contained in a title and how to make the layout. It is very frequently necessary to place subtitles under various parts of a drawing, and these layouts follow the same general principles.

A title should contain some or all of the following information:

Name of company and location.

Name of object or project shown on drawing.

Drawing number and/or contract number.

General notes and such items as material, finish, heat treatment, fillets, and tolerances as may be appropriate.

The name or initials of the draftsman, checker, and those who approve the drawing.

Scale and date.

The principal lines of the title or subtitle, such as the name of the company or name of the part, should always be in capital letters. The remaining lines may be in capitals or lower-case letters, depending upon the practice of the individual company. *Normally any title should be balanced about the center line, and words in any space should be centered in the space.*

Balancing of a title or subtitle may be done in several ways, one of which is to write the lines long hand, count the number of letters and the spaces between words,

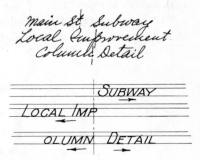

Fig. 2-29.   Balancing a subtitle.

Fig. 2-27.   Wrico lettering instruments. (Courtesy of Wood-Regan Instrument Co.)

Fig. 2-28.   Leroy lettering guides. (Courtesy Keuffel and Esser Co.)

and then starting from the center line work out both ways as indicated in Fig. 2–29. Others prefer to letter the line on scratch paper with sufficient care to obtain good spacing and determine the length. The center may be determined by measurement and the scratch copy placed below the line to be lettered on the drawing so that the spacing can be taken directly from the trial copy.

The size of lettering to be used will depend upon the space available and the amount of information to be placed therein. The most important items such as the name of the part or project should be most prominent, with other items such as company name and location in a descending order.

The size of lettering on a drawing may be influenced by the method of reproduction to be used. Thus, if the drawing is to be reproduced by the offset method and reduced, let us say, to one-half size, the lettering and dimensioning must be large enough to be legible on the finished reproduction.

2.21 Alphabets for special uses. In any engineering office occasions sometimes arise which require the use of more formal lettering than the single-stroke Gothic generally used on drawings. As an aid in solving these problems, the alphabets shown in Figs. 2–30 to 2–35 have been provided.

Figure 2–30 represents the first roman type of distinction used in England. It is said to have been cut by the printer Caslon in 1724. This cut is reproduced from Frederick Goudy's excellent work entitled *The Alphabet*.

Figure 2–31 shows typical alphabets used on architectural drawings. Although based on a single-stroke

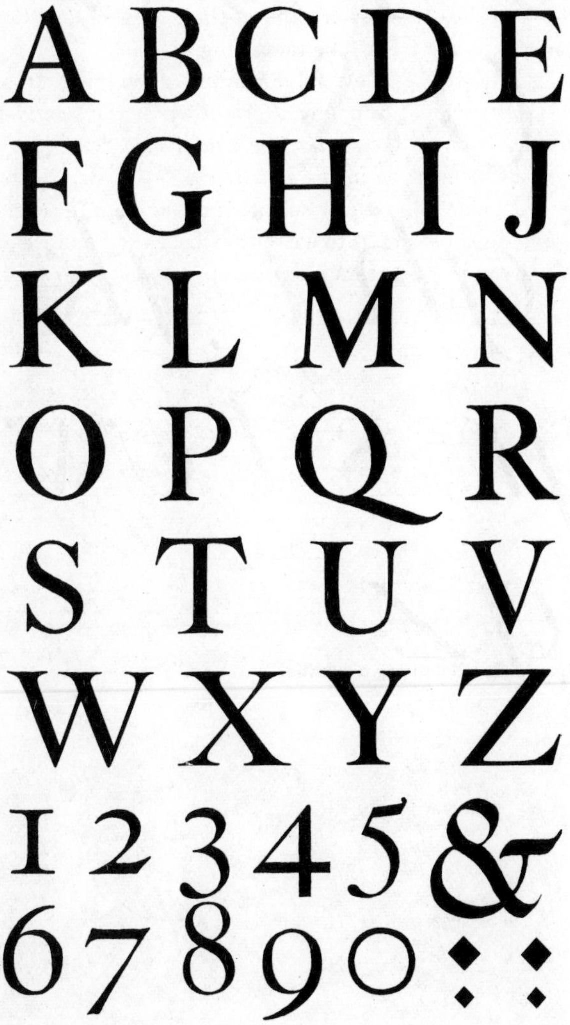

ABCDE
FGHIJ
KLMN
OPQR
STUV
WXYZ
1234&
67890 ❖

Fig. 2–30. Old roman type. (From *The Alphabet* by F. W. Goudy.)

ABCDEFGHIJKLMN
OPQRSTUVWXYZ&
1234567890
abcdefghijklmnop
qrstuvwxyz

Reserved and pleasing in appearance, yet simple enough for occasional use on engineering drawings.

ABCDEFGHIJKLMN
OPQRSTUVWXYZ&
1234567890
abcdefghijklmnopqr
stuvwxyz

Fig. 2–31. A style used in architectural drawing.

Fig. 2–32.   Modern roman slant letters.

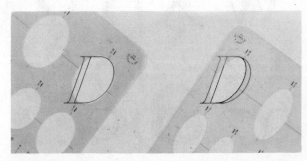

Fig. 2–33.   Use of ellipse guides in making roman lettering.

Gothic, it shows a freedom of design compatible with architectural work.

The Modern roman slant alphabet shown in Fig. 2–32 is used on maps and inscriptions. Its stately beauty can hardly be denied. It is recommended that when used in the larger sizes the outlines of the letters be constructed mechanically with ellipse guides as suggested in Fig. 2–33.

Figure 2–34 shows what may be done with speed and ease when conditions demand large uniform lettering.

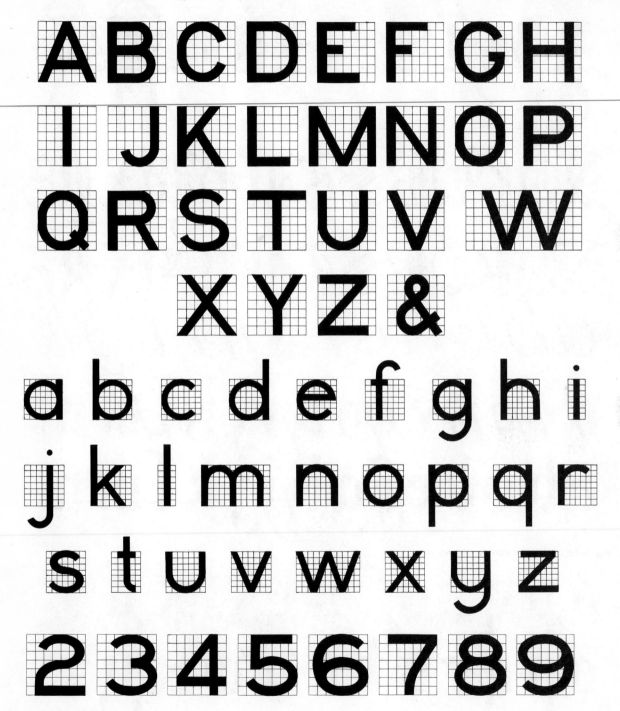

Fig. 2–34. Gothic letters.

A B C D E F G H I J K L M

A B C D E F G H I J K L M

N O P Q R S T U V W X Y Z

N O P Q R S T U V W X Y Z

a b c d e f g h i j k l m n

a b c d e f g h i j k l m n

o p q r s t u v w x y z

o p q r s t u v w x y z

The Gothic alphabets there shown are typical of what may be done by proper adaptations.

Gummed letters in either black or white and very similar to the letters shown in Fig. 2–34 may be purchased from the trade. These may be pasted upon paper, wood, glass, or other material very rapidly and are suitable for signs, names on office doors, and the like. The only skill required is that of proper spacing and alignment.

Figure 2–35 shows two forms of the Old English Text alphabet. It combines simplicity of design with a dignity of character sufficient to make it acceptable for ornamental work on certificates, diplomas, and memorials. The method of using the Speed-ball pen is shown in the figure.

◀ Fig. 2–35. Old English Text alphabets. (Courtesy Mr. Ross F. George.)
▼

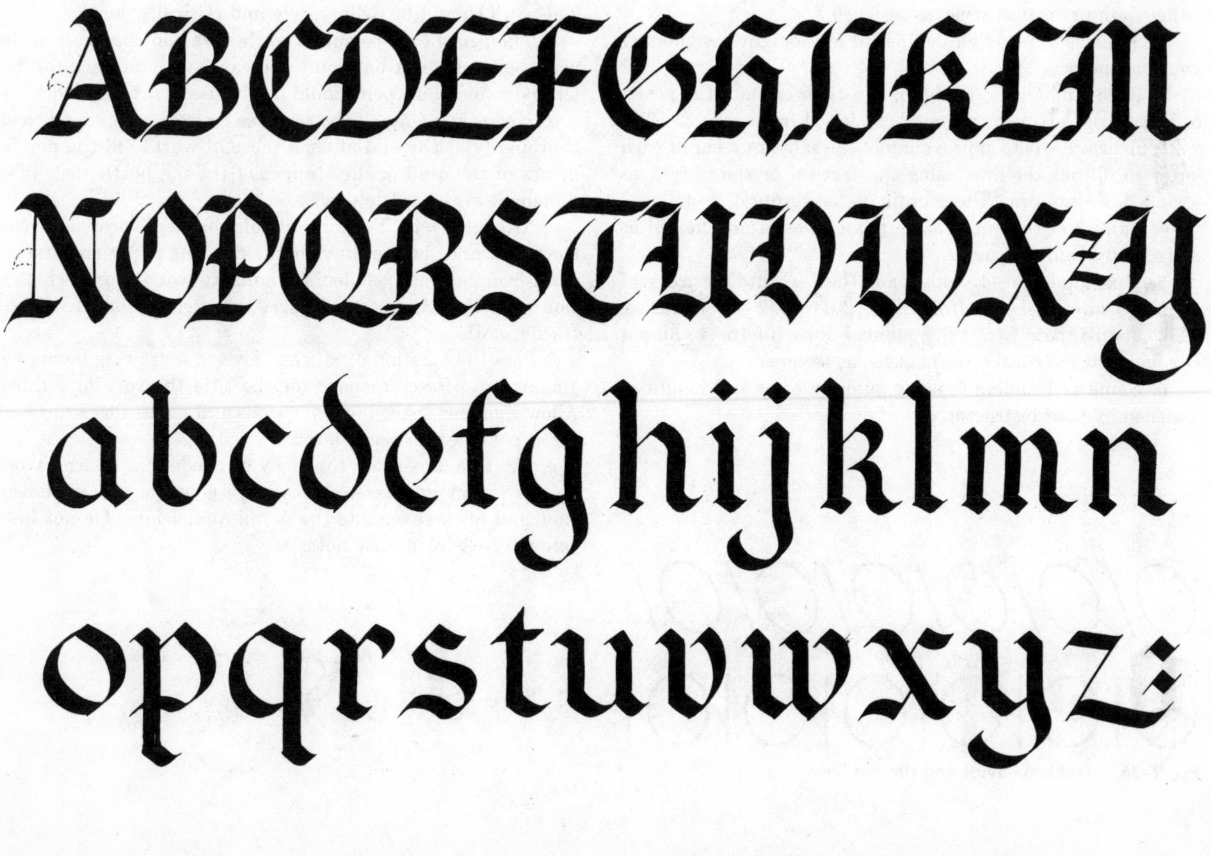

PROBLEMS

All lettering problems are to be done upon 8½ × 11 inch standard sheets unless otherwise directed by the instructor.

Divide the space inside the borderline of the selected sheet into four equal rectangles by means of horizontal and vertical center lines. Inside these spaces, rule guide lines as directed, and then do the exercises assigned from the following problems. Allow a margin of ½ inch at the top and on each side of the lettering space and a margin at the bottom as near ½ inch as the guide line layout will permit. It is recommended that the Braddock lettering triangle or Ames lettering instrument be used for ruling guide lines that are within the limits of these instruments.

Where the term "guide lines" occurs in the following problems, it will mean a set of three lines (see Fig. 2-3) whose overall height is that specified in the problem. The space between sets of guide lines will be as produced by the lettering triangle, or two-thirds the overall height of the guide lines if a lettering instrument is not available. It is recommended that lettering drills be not more than 10 to 20 minutes' duration.

1. Rule guide lines ⅜″ high and make an alternate series of smooth ovals and straight stems, as shown in Fig. 2-36. Make either slant or vertical style, as assigned.

2. Same as 1, using guide lines of any height assigned by your instructor.

3. Rule guide lines ³⁄₁₆″ high, and then execute the group of lower-case letters or numerals assigned from Figs. 2-19 to 2-21, inclusive. Make approximately the same number of each letter to fill out the line, using the vertical or slant style, as assigned. Do not draw the coordinate background.

4. Same as Problem 3, using guide lines of any height as assigned by your instructor.

5. Rule guide lines ³⁄₁₆″ high, and then execute the group of capital letters assigned from Figs. 2-11 to 2-15, inclusive. Make approximately the same number of each letter to fill out the line, using vertical or slant style, as assigned.

6. Same as Problem 5, using guide lines of any height as assigned by your instructor.

7. Rule guide lines ³⁄₁₆″ high, and then execute the letters of the alphabet in the order of their occurrence, as shown in Fig. 2-1 or 2-2. Fill out each line by repeating the alphabet as much as may be necessary.

8. Rule guide lines ³⁄₁₆″ high, and then make the numerals shown in Figs. 2-16 and 2-17. Repeat the numerals, and add additional fractions to fill out the space. Use vertical or slant style, as assigned.

9. Same as Problem 8, using guide lines of a height assigned by your instructor.

10. Rule guide lines ⁵⁄₃₂″ high, and then letter the material in one of the paragraphs assigned from the following group. The material is to be well balanced within the area reserved for it, whether done on regular lettering sheets or in connection with other drawing work. Use all capitals or initial capitals and lower-case letters as assigned.

a. In order that a piece of composition may look well, it must have uniformity in slope, weight, size, and spacing of the letters and words.

b. Control of the hand in lettering is best accomplished through short daily drills of from 10 to 20 minutes' duration. The work should be deliberately and critically done.

c. The pen should be suited to the size and character of the work being done. A ballpoint pen can hardly be used for fine letters; a fine-point pen should not be used for heavy work.

d. Keep the points of the pen free from dried ink, and clean thoroughly at the end of each piece of work. Fill the pen by means of the quill in the stopper of the ink bottle instead of dipping it in the bottle itself.

e. Triangles and T-square should be kept clean and free from dust and soot to prevent the drawing paper and tracing cloth from becoming soiled and unfit to work upon. Perspiration from the hands soon injures the surface qualities of the tracing cloth.

f. Plan the location of all the views of a drawing before beginning any. Reserve space for the title the very first thing. Allow generous space for dimensions and notes. Place these, as far as possible, between views.

g. Omit no dimension that may be needed for clearness, but do not repeat unnecessarily. Always give the overall dimension, and place it outside the detail dimensions. Do not hesitate to give explanatory notes.

Fig. 2-36. **Problem—ovals and straight lines.**

Drawing board and drafting instruments (Keuffel & Esser, Inc.).

3

Use and Care of Instruments

3.1 Introduction. The purpose of a drawing course is twofold: it aims first to give the student an understanding of the principles upon which drawing is based; and second, to give him instruction and practice in the use of his instruments, so that he may acquire a workmanlike facility in their manipulation. The engineer's objective is not to produce something that will just "get by" but rather to secure the best results, from the standpoint of correctness, accuracy, and appearance, in the least possible time.

To learn the correct form of handling instruments, one should study the proper use of them as explained in this chapter in order that awkward and useless movements may be avoided. No attempt has been made in this chapter to illustrate the hundreds of pieces of special drafting tools on the market. The engineer who learns to use the regular equipment discussed in this chapter can use the special tools without further instruction.

3.2 Regular equipment. The following list of equipment constitutes what is called a set or kit of instruments. The case of instruments is illustrated in Fig. 3–1.

Case of Instruments	*Other Equipment*
1 Large compass	1 T-square
1 Pen attachment	1 Architect's scale
1 Beam compass with attachments	1 Engineer's scale
1 Hair-spring divider	1 12″ 30–60° triangle
1 Ruling pen	1 8″ 30–60° triangle
1 Box of leads	1 6″ 45° Braddock lettering triangle
1 Screw driver	2 Irregular curves
	1 6″ protractor
	1 Erasing shield
	1 Eraser
	Assorted pencils and pen points

3.3 **Pencils.** Special pencils are used for drawing. They are of uniform size, hexagonal in shape, with varying size of lead as shown in Fig. 3-2. Eighteen degrees of hardness are supplied by the manufacturer, ranging from 7B, the softest and blackest in the order shown in the figure, to 9H which is the hardest and produces a thin gray line. From the diagram it will be noted that the softer pencils have the larger leads. Pencils can also be had with the lead in rectangular shape for wedge points. They are, however, not suited for general purposes.

Although all manufacturers use the same system of marking their pencils, it will be found that the pencils from different manufacturers having the same hardness number do not actually have the same hardness. It is for this reason that most draftsmen usually stick to one brand of pencil. Refill pencils, shown in Fig. 3-3, are also on the market together with refill leads of the varying degrees of hardness for the entire range.

For general layout work in drawing, the 4H and 5H pencils are most useful, and the harder varieties are used in graphic statics and other graphical computation methods where fine lines and extreme accuracy are required. For making a finished pencil drawing the H and 2H are more desirable since they give a sharp black line. For sketching and art work, the softer grades are used. The draftsman should learn to choose the quality of pencil appropriate to the work he has in hand.

More important, however, than the quality of the pencil is the condition in which it is kept. The proper shape for a pencil point is shown in Fig. 3-4. *The tapered wood portion should be about ⅞ inch long and ⅜ inch of lead should be exposed.* The lead should be brought to a point by means of a file or sandpaper. For a conical point as in (*a*), Fig. 3-4, the pencil should be rotated slowly while it is rubbed back and forth. The pencil should be inclined to the direction of motion, as shown in Fig. 3-5. To produce the wedge point, as in (*b*), Fig.

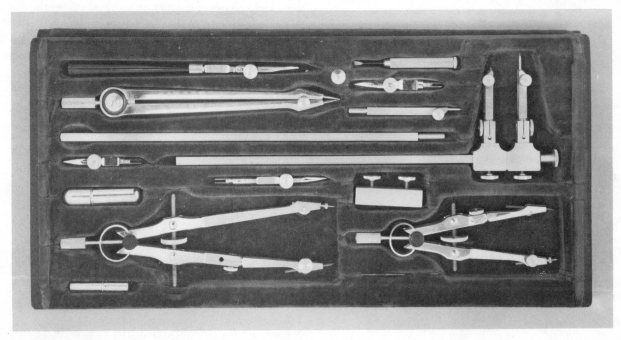

Fig. 3-1.   The engineer's case instruments.

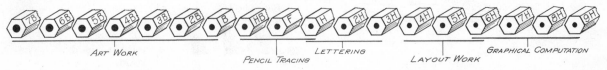

Fig. 3-2.   Grades of drawing pencils.

3-4, the opposite sides must be rubbed down. The bevel point, (c), is made by rubbing entirely on one side.

The wedge point is used for drawing long straight lines since it does not wear down so rapidly; its use, however, is limited to straight lines. The conical point may be used for all general drafting purposes and always should be used for lettering. The bevel point is recommended for use in the compass, as it has the same advantages there as the wedge point has for straight lines. It is also used with the softer pencils for purposes of shading. Since the drawing pencil wears away rapidly, the sandpaper pad or file should always be kept handy to resharpen the lead, and it should be used frequently.

Many drafting offices have pencil sharpeners of special design which remove only the wood and allow the lead to be shaped entirely by the sandpaper.

Experienced draftsmen, however, carry pocket knives and prefer to use them for sharpening their pencils. The only precaution necessary is not to nick the lead in

removing the wood since this will make a weak spot, causing the lead to break in service.

When using refill pencils, the lead should be filed down to a good point just as frequently as the regular pencil.

In drawing a straight line, the pencil should be held in a plane perpendicular to the paper along the edge of the T-square or triangle, and should be inclined at an angle of 60 to 75 degrees with the paper in the direction of motion. See Fig. 3-6. Note that the pencil is held in a little different manner from that used in lettering. The pencil should not be allowed to rock back and forth transversely to the direction of motion. For preliminary work, just enough pressure should be applied to the pencil to make a firm light line that can be readily seen, but not enough pressure to make a groove in the paper, as a groove cannot be erased and spoils the appearance of a drawing. The importance of clean-cut pencil work cannot be over emphasized; it tends toward both speed and accuracy. The proper direction for drawing lines in

Fig. 3-3.   Refill drawing pencil.

(a) CONICAL   (b) WEDGE   (c) BEVEL

Fig. 3-4.   Correct pencil point shapes.

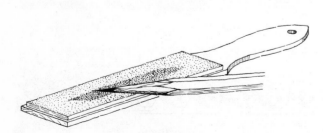

Fig. 3-5.   Sharpening the drawing pencil.

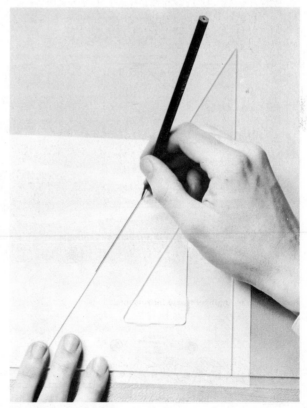

Fig. 3-6.   Drawing with the pencil.

various positions is shown in Figs. 3–7 and 3–8.

3.4 Erasers and erasing tools. *Only a pencil eraser should be used to remove lines made in error or to change lines because of an alteration in design.* This applies to both pencil and ink work since the pencil eraser will not destroy the surface of paper or cloth and the drawing can be repenciled or reinked over the erased spot without danger of blotting, provided a good quality of paper has been used. A grit eraser or razor blade or other sharp instrument, though working faster, will destroy the surface of the paper and ruin the drawing.

When there are many lines close together and only one needs to be removed or changed, the others may be protected by using an erasing shield, as shown in Fig. 3–9. One of the openings is placed over the line to be removed in such a way that other lines do not show, and then the erasure is made through this opening.

The razor blade and erasing knife or point shown in Fig. 3–10 have their legitimate use in checking over a drawing to remove ink lines when they may have overrun a bit and to remove small amounts of ink in places where it will not be necessary to ink over the spot again.

Because designs are sometimes changed only in some small detail, these portions are sometimes erased on the original and new parts drawn in. This requires extensive erasing at times, and a great deal of time can be saved by the use of a motor-driven eraser, one of which is shown in Fig. 3–9. There are a variety of types on the market. Care should be exercised in handling these erasers not to bear down too hard or too long in one spot, for so doing will frequently destroy the surface, particularly of cloth. A hole can be burned in the cloth very quickly by too much pressure. When extensive changes are required, a new tracing may be made by reproduction methods, omitting any desired portions of the original drawing.

Art gum, which is a softer variety of rubber, should be used to clean the drawing. One can rub over ink lines without removing them, but heavy scrubbing of a sheet with art gum destroys the lustre of the ink. It is therefore much better policy to keep the drawing paper clean in the first place and not depend upon art gum for this purpose. When cleaning is necessary, this should be done before the drawing is inked. Pencil drawings,

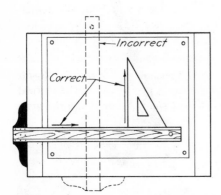

Fig. 3–7. Direction of ruling with T-square and triangle.

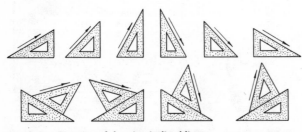

Fig. 3–8. Direction of drawing inclined lines.

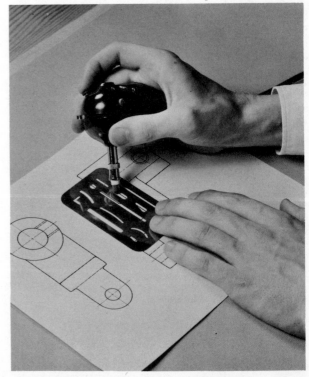

Fig. 3–9. Use of the erasing shield and motor eraser.

finished with a soft pencil which makes a deep black line, cannot be successfully cleaned with art gum since the pencil lines smudge very easily. It is far better to keep the drawing clean than to try to scrub it with art gum after it has been soiled. The following suggestions, if observed, will help to keep the drawing clean:

a. In moving the T-square, bear down on the head so that the blade is raised slightly from the paper.

b. The hands are always somewhat oily—keep them off the paper.

c. Use a hard pencil for layout work.

d. Pick up the triangles rather than slide them.

e. When finishing a drawing with a soft pencil, cover all views, except the one you are working on, with a clean sheet of paper.

f. Blow graphite particles, which flake off the soft pencil, from the sheet.

g. Use a brush or soft cloth to brush erasing crumbs off the sheet rather than the flat of the hand.

h. Use a hard smooth-surfaced paper if this is suitable for the type of drawing being made.

i. Use of a finely ground cleansing material on the drawing during work will keep both the drawing and instruments clean. Several varieties of this material may be purchased.

3.5 Letter pens. Although some draftsmen use the ruling pen for lettering, this is not a good practice. The regular pen holder with pen points similar to those used in writing should be used. A full discussion of lettering pens is given in Art. 2.18.

3.6 Drawing boards. Drawing boards vary greatly in size, from small ones which can be conveniently carried around, say 12 inches by 15 inches, to large vertical boards 6 or 7 feet high by 10 or 12 feet long. Regardless of size, the surface should be free from cracks and it should be a plane. Soft white pine or bass wood is a most suitable material since this will take thumb tacks or other fasteners. At least one edge should be straight as a base for the T-square.

3.7 T-square. The common T-square consists of two parts, the blade and the head, which should be rigidly fastened together. A variety of kinds and sizes may be obtained from the trade. Different lengths may be obtained, ranging from 18 inches to 72 inches.

The straightness of the blade may be tested by drawing a straight line between two points and then turning the blade over and drawing a line between the same two points, using the same edge as before as shown in Fig. 3–11. If the blade is true, the two lines will coincide.

To keep the T-square in good condition, careful handling is required. It should not be used as a hammer nor be allowed to drop to the floor. The upper or drawing edge should not be used as a guide for the knife in cutting paper. If the head should become loose, the screws must be removed and the two parts glued together. The screws may then be replaced, and the T-square is ready for use again.

3.8 Parallel rules. On large drawing boards, of both the horizontal and vertical type, a parallel rule permanently attached to the table is used in place of a T-square. This is simply a large straight edge which, by means of a wire-cable arrangement, always remains parallel to its previous position as it is moved up and down the board, as shown in Fig. 3–12. On the vertical boards there is a ledge at the bottom of the board to hold drafting tools.

Fig. 3–10.   Knife and penscratcher.

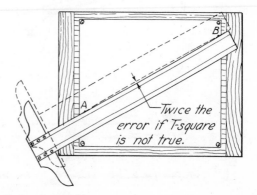

Twice the error if T-square is not true.

Fig. 3–11.   Testing the T-square.

3.9   Drafting machine. In many offices a drafting machine similar to the one shown in Fig. 3–13 is used in place of the T-square, triangles, and scales. In operation, this device keeps the two blades always parallel to their original position no matter where they are moved on the sheet. The two blades, which may be simple straight edges or straight edges with scales along them, are accurately set at right angles to each other. The blades are removable, and hence a variety of scales may be used. The adjusting head has a protractor with vernier attachment so that the blades may be set and clamped at any desired angle. Considerable saving of time results from the use of this machine.

3.10   Triangles. Triangles are the instruments used by the draftsman in connection with the T-square to draw lines at various angles with the horizontal. The two most common varieties which every draftsman should possess are the 30°–60° and the 45° triangles. With these two triangles, angles of 15, 30, 45, 60, 75, and 90 degrees with the horizontal can be drawn as shown in Fig. 3–14. The pencil or pen should be moved in the direction indicated by the arrows. Triangles range in size from 4 to 18 inches. The length of the long leg of the triangle determines the size. A thickness of about .08 of an inch is recommended.

3.11   Testing the triangles. The accuracy of the 90° angle of any triangle may be tested by drawing a vertical line through a point near the blade of the T-square, then turning the triangle over into the second position, as shown in Fig. 3–15, and drawing a second line through the same point. If the two lines coincide, the 90° angle is accurate.

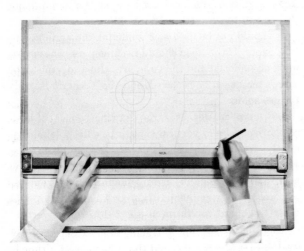

Fig. 3–12.   Parallel rule.

Fig. 3–13.   Drafting machine.

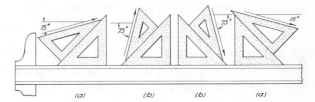

Fig. 3–14.   Drawing angles of 15 and 75 degrees.

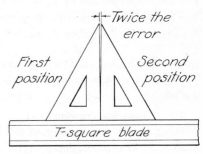

Fig. 3–15.   Testing right angle of triangle.

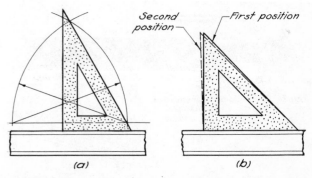

Fig. 3–16.   Testing 45- and 60-degree angles.

The 60° angle may be tested by drawing very accurately upon a given base line two arcs whose radii are slightly less than the hypotenuse of the 60° triangle, as shown in Fig. 3–16(a). Test the triangle to see if the hypotenuse passes through the two points indicated in the figure when resting on the T-square.

The 45° angle may be tested by drawing a 45° line through a point near the blade of the T-square and then turning the triangle over and bringing the other short edge on the T-square and drawing a second line through the point, as shown in Fig. 3–16(b). If the two lines coincide, the angle is exactly 45 degrees.

Besides drawing lines of various angles as indicated in Fig. 3–14, the triangles may be used in pairs or singly with a T-square to draw one line parallel to another as shown in Fig 3–17.

To draw one line perpendicular to another, bring the hypotenuse of the triangle into contact with the line, the other side being supported by a T-square or triangle. Rotate the triangle as shown in Fig. 3–18(a), and draw the second line perpendicular to the first. The same thing can be accomplished by placing the triangle with the hypotenuse in contact with the T-square as shown in Fig. 3–18(b) and sliding.

In drawing a line in any direction, the general rule may be laid down that the direction of motion of the pen or pencil should be away from the body of the draftsman and not toward it. To draw a straight line between any two points (not horizontal or vertical), place the pencil on one point, bring the triangle up to it, and then rotate the triangle about the pencil point as a pivot until the edge touches the other point. Then draw the line.

3.12   Standard drawing sheet sizes. Two series of drawing sheet sizes are recommended by the American Standards Association, Sectional Committee Y-14—1957 as listed:

Multiples of 8½ × 11		Multiples of 9 × 12	
Size	Letter Designation	Size	Letter Designation
8½ × 11	A	9 × 12	A
11 × 17	B	12 × 18	B
17 × 22	C	18 × 24	C
22 × 34	D	24 × 36	D
34 × 44	E	36 × 48	E

Both drawing paper and cloth can be obtained in cut sheets of these sizes as well as in rolls, varying in width from 24 inches to 54 inches by 6 inch increments.

3.13   Tracing paper and cloth. Many firms now make their drawings directly on tracing paper with pencil. The drawing is finished with a medium pencil (H or F), and blueprints are made directly from it. Tracing paper may be obtained in several weights and with corresponding transparency. A paper which has been oil treated is called vellum.

For somewhat greater permanence, pencil drawings are also made upon what is called a pencil tracing cloth. This cloth has been treated to make the surface white so that pencil lines show more clearly.

Regular tracing cloth has a bluish color and is quite transparent. It should be used exclusively for ink drawings since pencil lines do not show up well on this cloth. The cloth has a dull side and the opposite side is extremely glossy. The glossy side does not take ink so well, and it is recommended that the dull side be used for making tracings. Erasures of ink or pencil lines should be made only with a pencil eraser.

When the operation of tracing is to extend over several days it is recommended that one view at a time be fully completed rather than working over the entire area since the cloth is quite responsive to changes in the moisture content of the air and will expand or shrink a great deal from one day to the next.

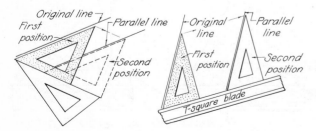

Fig. 3–17.   Drawing parallel lines.

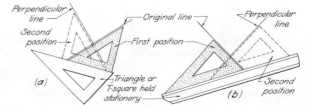

Fig. 3–18.   Drawing perpendicular lines.

Several materials that are dimensionally stable are now available. Glass cloth, Mylar, and Kronaflex are all used when it is necessary to avoid change of size in a drawing. They may be used for either pencil or ink.

3.14   Special paper fasteners. The drawing paper may be held on the board by means of fine wire staples. These are driven into the board by a special stapler. The staples are quite fine and do not damage the board as much as thumb tacks, and they offer little obstruction to the T-square and triangles.

Scotch tape may be used in fastening paper to the board by sticking small pieces of it across the corners of the paper. The tape is pliable and may be used several times before it loses its adhesive quality. The transparent cellophane tape is not recommended because it leaves the paper sticky and is a nuisance in the filing cabinet.

3.15   Scales. The size of the drawing paper upon which an engineer must work is quite limited, but the size of the object or project he may be required to draw may vary from a small fraction of an inch to hundreds or even thousands of feet in extent. As long as the object is considerably smaller than the convenient sizes of drafting paper, it should be drawn in its natural size. The drawing is then spoken of as a full-size drawing. If the object is larger it may be drawn one-half size; that is, 6 inches on the drawing will represent 1 foot on the object. Although the term half-size is not correct and the words one-half scale would be more accurate, the older term is still generally used. Likewise, a drawing may be made one-quarter size, which means that 3 inches on the drawing represent 1 foot on the object. In this way the size of a drawing may be greatly reduced. For one-half size drawings, the necessary reduction in dimensions could be made mentally and laid off on paper with a regular scale having $\frac{1}{16}$-inch divisions. But this is not necessary since scales have been made to represent such dimensions reduced to a great variety of sizes, as indicated in the list below.

Three kinds of scales are in common use in this country, namely, the architect's, the civil engineer's (or sim-ply engineer's), and the mechanical engineer's. All of them are made in both the triangular and flat shapes, shown in Fig. 3–19, and contain the following divisions:

Architect's Scales

Full size	$1'' = 0'1''$
Quarter size	$3'' = 1'-0''$
One-eighth	$1\frac{1}{2}'' = 1'-0''$
One-twelfth	$1'' = 1'-0''$
	$\frac{3}{4}'' = 1'-0''$
	$\frac{1}{2}'' = 1'-0''$
	$\frac{3}{8}'' = 1'-0''$
	$\frac{1}{4}'' = 1'-0''$
	$\frac{3}{16}'' = 1'-0''$
	$\frac{1}{8}'' = 1'-0''$
	$\frac{3}{32}'' = 1'-0''$

Civil Engineer's Scales	*Mechanical Engineer's Scales*
$1'' = 10.0'$*	$2'' = 1''$
$1'' = 20.0'$	$1\frac{1}{2}'' = 1''$
$1'' = 30.0'$	$1'' = 1''$
$1'' = 40.0'$	$\frac{3}{4}'' = 1''$
$1'' = 50.0'$	$\frac{1}{2}'' = 1''$
$1'' = 60.0'$	$\frac{1}{4}'' = 1''$
$1'' = 80.0'$	$\frac{1}{8}'' = 1''$
$1'' = 100.0'$	

* Or some integral power of 10' as, for example, 100' or 1000'. The civil engineer's scales are convenient for scaling forces in a vector diagram.

Scales are supplied either full-divided or open-divided. The civil engineer's scale is sometimes called a chain scale. The civil engineer's scales are always full-divided; that is, the same small subdivisions are carried throughout the length of the scale. The scales may also be used for the indicated values multiplied by any power of 10. The architect's and mechanical engineer's scales are almost always open-divided, which means that only the first major division at the end representing either 1 foot or 1 inch, as the case may be, is fully subdivided.

The better grades of scales are made of boxwood coated with a white material resembling ivory. These scales are engine-divided which means that each scale has been marked with a dividing engine which is the most accurate method. Cheaper scales are printed. The white coating is not essential to accuracy but it makes

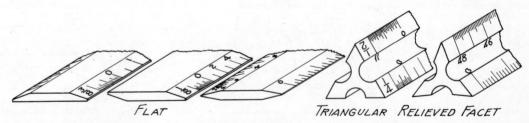

FLAT   TRIANGULAR   RELIEVED   FACET

Fig. 3–19.   Types of scales.

a better-looking scale.

3.15.1 *The architect's scale. The major end unit of these scales represents 1 foot. This is divided into twelve parts to represent inches.* On the larger sizes the inch division is further subdivided, as shown in Fig. 3–20. In this illustration the smallest subdivision represents ¼ inch, and eighths of an inch can be easily estimated. On the two smallest scales listed in the table the major end unit is divided into only six parts so that each of these subdivisions represents 2 inches.

3.15.2 *Civil engineer's scale.* Any one of the scales listed in the foregoing table may obtained on the flat-type scales, but the triangular scales carry only the first six. As indicated by the listing and as shown in Fig. 3–21, *the first scale 1″ = 10′-0″ has ten divisions to the inch and the successive scales have corresponding divisions, 20 to the inch, and so on.* This scale is very useful in graphic statics and nomography since the divisions may represent equal units of any quantity as pounds, tons, bushels, etc. Thus the 20-scale may be used to represent 20 feet, 200 pounds or a stress of 2000 pounds per square inch. In each case the smaller subdivisions have a corresponding meaning.

3.15.3 *Mechanical engineer's scale. On these scales the major end unit represents 1 inch and the subdivisions represent the commonly used fractions of an inch,* ½, ¼, ⅛, ¹⁄₁₆, *etc., as shown in Fig. 3–22. These scales may be obtained either open- or full-divided.*

3.15.4 *Decimal scale.* Much of the layout work in the aircraft industry must be done with great accuracy, and scales with divisions of one-hundredth inch are commonly used. Throughout industry in general there is a strong tendency toward decimal dimensioning rather than fractional figures. When parts are to be held to either plus or minus .01 inch, two-place decimals are used, and these are made in even numbers, that is, fiftieths of an inch so that when halved (diameters to radii) a two-place decimal results. A scale with graduations in fiftieths of an inch is shown in Fig. 3–23. One half-size and one quarter-size decimal scale may be used in the drafting room.

3.16 **Use of scales.** In Fig. 3–24 are shown two illustrations of the use of scales. Note that in all cases the inner end of the first subdivided unit is marked 0 and the numbering goes from that point toward the other end of the scale. There are two lines of numbers, one of

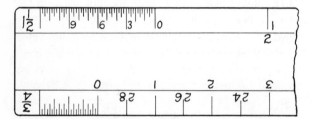

Fig. 3–20. Architect's scale.

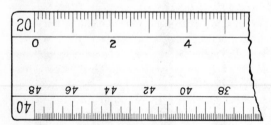

Fig. 3–21. Civil engineer's scale.

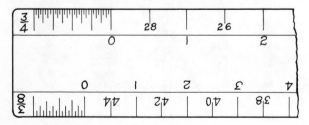

Fig. 3–22. Mechanical engineer's scale.

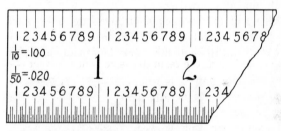

Fig. 3–23. Decimal scale.

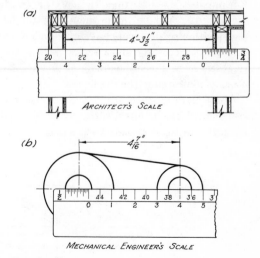

Fig. 3–24. Use of scales.

which applies to the scale at one end, and the other to the scale at the opposite end. The larger of these scales is always just twice the smaller. To mark off 4'-3½", set the scale with the division numbered 4 at one end and count off the 3½ inches in the subdivided unit at the other as shown in Fig. 3-24(a). Or again, to mark off 4⁷⁄₁₆ inches, set the mark numbered 4 at one end and count off the ⁷⁄₁₆-inch division in the opposite direction from the zero as shown in Fig. 3-24(b).

It should be clear, then, that to measure any distance to any one of the eighteen scales commonly available it is not necessary for the draftsman to do any arithmetical work. It is assumed, of course, that he knows that ⁷⁄₁₆" must lie halfway between the ⅜- and the ½-inch mark.

The draftsman not only is required to measure distances very accurately on his drawing, but he must frequently lay off a number of equal spaces. This should always be done with a scale rather than with a divider since a minute error in setting a divider may result in a large cumulative error. When the value of the equal spaces is one of the units on the scale, the scale should be set only once and all the divisions marked off rather than marking a few, then shifting the scale lengthwise and resetting and marking more. Shifting the scale may result in a cumulative error.

When a number of unequal distances are to be set off, the total of which lies within the length of the scale, it is best to add these distances arithmetically and then mark off the distances with the scale always at the same beginning or reference point. This avoids cumulative errors of setting.

To employ the scale properly, one should place the working edge farthest from him against the paper and then, looking down over it, mark off the required dimensions with a very sharp conical-pointed pencil, or a needle point as shown in Fig. 3-25. Note that a blunt pencil is of no value at all for this purpose, since the draftsman cannot see where the point actually touches the paper. The pencil or needle point should be held in a vertical position.

3.17 Case of instruments. Instruments may be purchased singly or in groups, in cases designed to hold them. An adequate set for general drafting purposes should contain approximately the items illustrated in Fig. 3-1.

The following paragraphs make clear the proper methods for handling the various pieces of the set, what to look for in selecting them, and how to care for them and keep them in proper working order. The use to which they are subjected and the care they receive, when not in use, determine to a large extent how long they will last.

3.18 Ruling pens. Ruling pens are supplied with two general types of points and several kinds of handles as shown in Fig. 3-26. The wide-pointed pens are called Swedish detail pens, or simply detail pens, but they are

Fig. 3-25. Laying off dimensions with a scale.

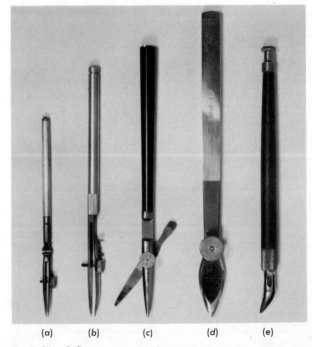

(a)   (b)   (c)   (d)   (e)

Fig. 3-26. Ruling pens.

no more useful for this purpose than any other. They serve best for drawing long, heavy borderlines since they hold more ink. Pens of any one type are specified by length, which is the overall length. The draftsman, if buying a single pen, can choose one that suits his hand.

The nibs of the pen, as the two blades are called, can be opened and closed by means of a screw. The spring pressure of the blades should be positive but not too strong or it will rapidly wear out the threads on the adjusting screw. A pen with undue friction on this screw should not be purchased.

Pens, with special devices for opening, are so arranged that the nibs are widely separated for cleaning and then closed again without changing the setting of the pen. See Fig. 3–26(b) and (c). This is quite desirable, but it gives an additional point of wear. The dials on pens a and c are useful in setting the pen to the same thickness

of line at any time. The steel in ruling pens should be reasonably hard so that the points of the nibs do not wear down too rapidly.

The narrow-pointed pens are the type commonly furnished in cases. Even in better sets these are seldom properly pointed, and, as well-pointed pens will, in time, wear down, the draftsman should know how to sharpen his pen. Figure 3–27(a) shows a point as it frequently comes from the manufacturer. This pen is entirely too pointed. It has a very high capillary action on the ink and holds it well away from the point of the pen. A point of this type will not permit the ink to start, even on a broad line.

After a few months of steady service, a good point will have a flat spot worn on one side as shown in Fig. 3–27 (b). Both of these errors can be corrected by proper grinding on a fine-grained oil stone.

The first operation in preparing the nibs for use consists of grinding them to an even length and then rounding them off so that the end has a parabolic shape, as shown in Fig. 3–27(c). This can be done by closing the nibs of the pen and then rubbing the nibs over an oil stone, keeping the pen in a plane perpendicular to the surface of the stone and rocking it back and forth in the direction of motion as the grinding proceeds, as shown in Fig. 3–28(a). The next operation is that of sharpen-

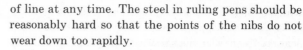

Capillary action holds ink from point

NIBS TOO POINTED
(a)

WORN NIBS
(b)

NIBS IN WORKING ORDER
(c)

Fig. 3–27. Ruling pen nibs.

(a)   (b)

Fig. 3–28. Sharpening the ruling pen.

ing the nibs. This must be done by grinding entirely from the outside, as shown in Fig. 3–28(*b*), until the edges of the nibs do not show any shiny flat spots when viewed edgewise. A magnifying glass is useful in making this examination. Care should be exercised in this operation to see that the nibs are not again made unequal in length, and also to avoid making them so sharp that they will cut the paper.

The ruling pen should be held in the same manner as the drawing pencil, that is, slightly inclined in the direction of motion and in a plane perpendicular to the paper through the line being drawn. Great care must be exercised to get and keep the correct position of the pen, since only a slight deviation is necessary to bring disastrous results. Figure 3–29 shows the right and wrong relations between the ruling pen and the triangle or T-square together with the type of line that results from such handling. Both nibs of the pen must touch the paper and when held perpendicular to the paper, the bevel of the nibs keeps the point at the proper distance from the triangle. *A white space should always show between the line and the T-square.*

The pen should be filled by placing the quill, which is in the stopper of the small ink bottle, between the nibs of the pen and letting the ink run into the pen as shown in Fig. 3–30. The ink should not stand more than ¼ inch high in the pen, as the weight of a higher column will frequently cause the ink to run out and make a blot.

Long lines should always be drawn with an arm move-

ment, coming to rest near the end of the line and finishing with a finger movement. Short lines, of course, are always drawn with a finger movement. The pressure upon the paper should be little more than the natural weight of the pen. Additional pressure serves only to tire the arm and fingers and groove the paper with no corresponding improvement in the flow of ink. Likewise, the side pressure upon the T-square or triangle should be just enough to ensure a firm and continuous contact. Too much side pressure will result in a line of varying width and may cause the T-square or triangle to slip. When inking with a triangle always use the far edge and have the adjusting screw of the pen on the side away from the ruling edge.

In inking straight lines and curves that join each other, *the curve should be inked first* and then care taken to stop the arc exactly at the tangent point as shown in Fig. 3–31. The ruling pen should then be lined up with the end of the arc by looking down squarely over the pen, as shown in the figure, before actually touching it to the paper. In order that the arc and straight line may have exactly the same width, which is absolutely necessary, a few sample arcs are made on scratch paper, which should be of the same kind as that on which the drawing is made. Then the width of the ruling pen is adjusted by drawing lines to these arcs and changing until a perfect match is secured. In all cases the ink line should straddle the pencil line over which it is drawn.

One of the common faults of beginners is that of run-

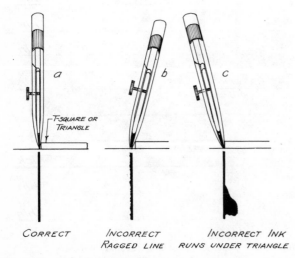

Fig. 3–29. Using the ruling pen.

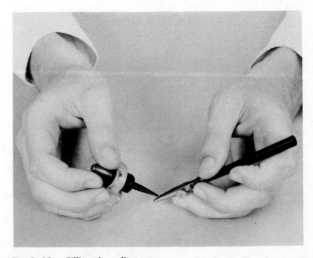

Fig. 3–30. Filling the ruling pen.

ning the lines beyond their proper stopping points. It should be remembered that the ink flows just a little ahead of the pen; therefore, when the line being drawn is to end upon another line, the pen must be stopped at the near side of the line. A little practice will enable the draftsman to determine just when to stop his pen to avoid overrunning.

3.19 Drawing ink. One cannot discuss the use of the ruling pen without giving consideration to drawing inks because the ink has a decided influence upon the results produced. Drawing inks may be obtained in black and a wide variety of colors. The black ink is a combination of carbon and a solvent. The carbon, however, is in suspension and not in solution; consequently it is a very thick ink. The solvent contains alcohol and evaporates very readily. The ink bottle should therefore always be kept tightly closed except when filling the pen. This practice also avoids upsetting an open ink bottle with the consequent damage to drawings and equipment. Most of the colored inks are true solutions and are much thinner than the black india ink. One must be particularly careful not to fill the pen too full with colored inks because the ink will run out of the pen much more readily when it touches the paper.

Since india ink dries very rapidly it forms little cakes of carbon on the inside of the nibs; therefore, the pen must be cleaned frequently while in use, and it should always be cleaned before it is put away. The pen is cleaned by inserting a piece of chamois or soft cloth

between the nibs while the ink is still moist and then pulling the cloth out. A clogged pen is one of the most common causes of poor lines. It should be noted also that due to evaporation the ink gradually thickens in the bottle and it then dries out so very rapidly in the pen that it is quite annoying and difficult to use. Ammonia may be used to thin the ink or a fresh bottle should be purchased. Another cause of poor lines is the presence of lint, dust, and dirt on the paper. The ruling pen will pick these up and cause a sudden widening of the line.

3.20 Inking on tracing cloth. If a pen is in proper working order and is properly held and the ink is fresh, it will produce a good line, except sometimes on tracing cloth and vellum, where a slightly oily surface may give trouble. This may be overcome by rubbing the surface with magnesium carbonate or powdered chalk and then wiping it clean with a cloth. Thereafter avoid touching the tracing cloth with the hands, for the hands may leave traces of oil on its surface. The presence of this oil film is indicated when the ink gathers up in small globules instead of flowing out in a smooth line.

In order to give a drawing "life and vigor" there must be a variation in the weight of the different lines employed. The outline of the object should stand out sharply, with the hidden lines somewhat less prominent. Dimension lines, auxiliary lines, center lines, and crosshatching should be still lighter. The weight and character of lines shown in Fig. 3–32 is that recommended by the American Standards Association. These weights of

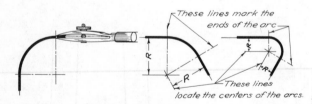

Fig. 3–31.   **Joining arcs and straight lines.**

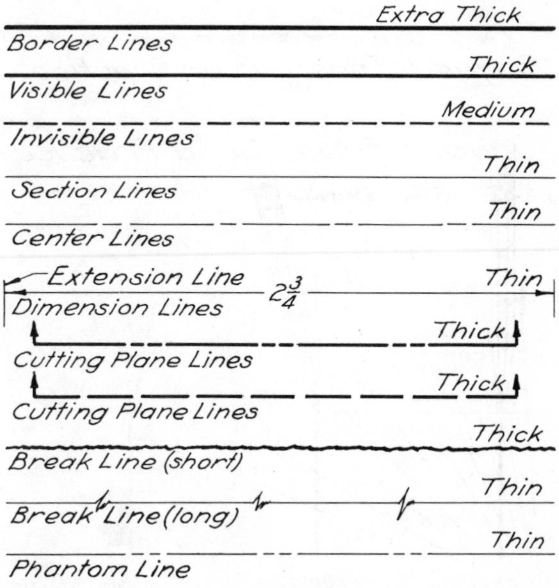

Border Lines	Extra Thick
Visible Lines	Thick
Invisible Lines	Medium
Section Lines	Thin
Center Lines	Thin
Extension Line / Dimension Lines	Thin
Cutting Plane Lines	Thick
Cutting Plane Lines	Thick
Break Line (short)	Thick
Break Line (long)	Thin
Phantom Line	Thin

Fig. 3–32.   **Proper weight of lines. (Courtesy American Standards Association.)**

lines may be varied somewhat in accordance with the size and nature of the drawing, but in any event three distinct weights should be maintained.

In drawing hidden lines or any other line of an interrupted character, the pen should be brought to a full stop before it is lifted from the paper. This will produce a square-ended line as shown in Fig. 3–33, whereas lifting the pen while it is in motion causes the line to fade out with a ragged end. The secret of making good-looking hidden lines lies in making the dashes of uniform length and the spaces between them also uniform but very small, say about one-thirty-second of an inch. Close adherence to the examples shown in Fig. 3–32 will produce the desired results.

When a number of lines converge to a point, the best practice is to run only the two outside lines to the point and stop all intermediate lines along the arc of a circle just large enough to prevent the lines from touching. If the converging lines are very numerous as in charts, two arcs may be used and alternate lines may be stopped on the inner and outer arcs as illustrated in Fig. 3–34.

3.21   Compass. The large compass is one of the most important instruments in the draftsman's kit. It should be adjusted before it is used for the first time and then maintained in that condition. One leg is arranged to hold either a lead or a pen. The pen should be put in the compass first and then the needle point adjusted so that it is about 1⁄32 of an inch longer than the pen as shown in Fig. 3–35. Thus when the needle point sinks into the paper the pen will be perpendicular to the paper and just touch it when the compass is held in a vertical position. The needle point, once adjusted, should not be changed again for the lead point. The lead point should be made to suit the needle point with the relationship the same as for the pen point. In this way, the compass can be quickly changed from pencil to ink work.

The lead for the compass should be of the same hardness as that used in pencil work. This means that several lead points should be kept on hand in the lead case to suit the varieties of pencil used. The lead should be sharpened to a bevel point on the outside as shown in Fig. 3–36, since it is easier to sharpen in this manner and permits the drawing of smaller circles.

In drawing small circles, the legs of the compass may be kept straight; but for the larger ones, one or both legs should be bent as in Fig. 3–37 in order that the pen may be perpendicular to and have both nibs touching the paper. The center is also perpendicular to the paper; and in this position it will not wear a large unsightly hole, as it otherwise would if several concentric circles were to be drawn. It is best in drawing circles to move the pen clockwise and to go around the circle only once,

Ragged Ends   Poor Practice

Square Ends   Good Practice

Fig. 3–33.   Hidden-line technique.

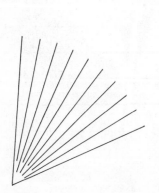

Fig. 3–34.   Drawing converging lines.

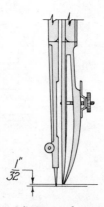

$\frac{I''}{32}$

Fig. 3–35.   Adjustment of compass points.

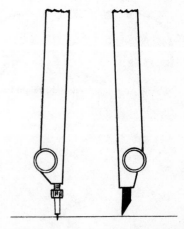

Fig. 3–36.   Sharpening compass lead.

when inking, although to secure good black pencil lines it may be necessary to go over the circle several times. When a number of concentric circles are to be drawn a horn center is very convenient. It definitely prevents wearing a large hole in the paper.

For circles larger than the compass will accommodate, the beam compass should be used. This requires more skill than handling the regular compass since both hands must be employed, one to hold the needle point at the center and the other to move the pencil or pen point as shown in Fig. 3–38.

With the beam compass, the radius of the circle is limited only by the length of the beam available. They can be purchased up to 60 inches or more in length.

3.22   Dividers. Dividers are used chiefly for transferring distances and occasionally for dividing spaces into equal parts. To set the divider it should be held as shown in Fig. 3–39. If the distance to be set permits, the second and third fingers are placed inside to help control the movement of the points. If the space to be set is small, the divider must first be opened wider than the space and then closed down to the proper measurement by pressure from the thumb and fingers; or the hair-spring adjustment may be used.

To step off distances, grasp the knurled top of the divider between the thumb and first finger and rotate first in one direction and then in the other. This avoids taking a new hold on the instrument, which would be necessary if it were always turned in the same direction. The points of the instrument should not be pushed through the paper, but instead only dents need be made. These may be identified by immediately touching them

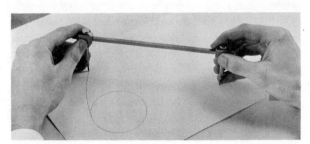
Fig. 3–38.   Drawing with beam compass.

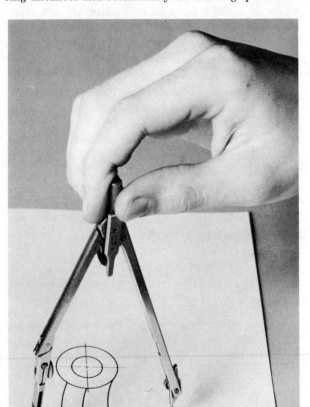
Fig. 3–37.   Drawing with compass.

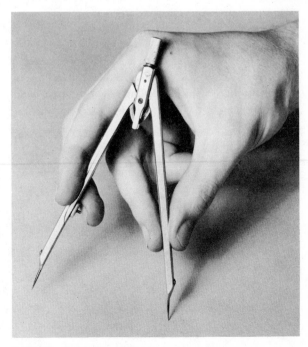
Fig. 3–39.   Setting the divider.

with a sharp, soft pencil to make a dot or by lightly encircling them, after which they readily can be found. The divider points should be kept sharp and of the same length; they should never be stuck in the drawing board when not in use.

3.23   Bow instruments. These small instruments which are used for drawing small arcs and circles can be obtained in a number of styles. Those with the adjusting screw on the outside are called side-adjusting; whereas those with the screw nut in the center are called center-adjusting. Which type to use is a matter of preference among draftsmen. These instruments are specified by the above names and by their overall height. The range of size varies from 3¾ to 6½ inches.

The most common fault with these instruments is the wearing and stripping of the threads on the adjusting screw. If the spring pressure is too great they will wear rapidly. This is the one place where oil may be used to advantage on a set of instruments. All excess should, of course, be carefully wiped off so that it does not get on the pen point or on the drawings. Except for the setting, the handling of these instruments is the same as for the large compass and divider. One of their chief advantages is the accuracy with which they may be set and the fact that they can be laid aside temporarily without danger of losing the setting. On the side-adjusting instruments only, the wear on the threads may be reduced by pinching the legs together to relieve the spring pressure when making large changes in the setting. It is also possible to spin the adjusting screw more rapidly in this manner.

3.24   Irregular curves. There is such a wide variety of irregular or French curves produced that it is impossible to give more than a sampling of the different kinds within the limits of this book. In Fig. 3–40 are shown a few curves of common usefulness which are simply designated as irregular curves.

The irregular curve is one of the most difficult instruments to use skillfully, especially when doing ink work. The skill required lies not only in the handling of the pen, but also to a considerable extent in the placing of the curve. If a curve is to be drawn through a series of points, the irregular curve should be made to fit as many of the points as possible at one time. This fitting of the curve to the points must be accomplished by trial. In no case should the line be drawn when the curve does not fit at least three points and have the proper curvature with regard to the next points on both sides. To accomplish this it is usually best to match as many points as possible, but not draw the entire distance. Then when the curve is moved forward the last two points should be rematched and a portion of the curve that was previously drawn can be retraced to avoid humps in the final curve. Figure 3–41 shows how the curve may be set several times to complete one curved line. In this figure two curves are used. Curve No. 1 fits the central part of the sine curve up to the point b. Curve No. 2 fits the upper part down to the point a'. An overlap occurs between the points a and b, and each curve should be used to the center of the space between these points. Note that points a' and b' on curve No. 2 if reversed would coincide with a and b and the upper portion of the curved line under No. 1. It will be seen that curve No. 2 comes tangent to the horizontal line at the top. Points of tangency should always be used as guides in setting the curve.

The ruling pen should be held perpendicular to the paper in drawing an irregular curve. This is particularly

Fig. 3–40.   Irregular curves.

Fig. 3–41.   Use of irregular curves.

true on curves of sharp radius where the pen must also be rotated between the fingers so that the same spot on the nibs remains in contact with the curve.

3.25 Technique of drafting. The technique of drafting refers not only to the fine points of a finished drawing but to every movement the draftsman makes from the time he gets his tools out until he finishes his drawing. As has been indicated before, speed, accuracy, and neatness are essential to good drafting.

All these qualities will be appreciably enhanced if the tools are neatly arranged in order on the desk so that they are easily found and readily accessible. A few points which should always be observed are the following:

a. Do not sharpen pencil over the drawing board.

b. Knock excess graphite off file or sandpaper pad on the leg of table or chair at a point near the floor. Do this immediately after sharpening the pencil.

c. Always keep pencil sharp.

d. Do not fill ruling pen or compass over the drawing board.

e. Do not have ink bottle on drawing board.

f. Put stopper in ink bottle immediately after filling pen.

g. Time will be saved by using a scale guard on the triangular scales to indicate the scale in use. Otherwise a good deal of time is lost hunting for the correct scale.

3.26 Pencil technique. To make a good pencil drawing on paper, tracing cloth, or tracing paper requires the same general technique in each case. The original layout of the problem should be made with a 4H or 5H pencil. The lines should be firm, light lines of the proper character, heavy enough to be clearly seen but not so heavy as to groove the paper. When the drawing is thus completed, all construction lines, overrunning corners, center lines which are too long, projecting lines, and the like should be erased. The drawing is then made rapidly a second time, with a soft pencil (3H to HB, depending upon the touch of the draftsman and the hardness of the working surface) in the same fashion and in the same order that one would ink a drawing. See paragraph below. The soft pencil must be resharpened frequently so that the same weight of line is maintained throughout the drawing. The lines should be dense and black. The T-square and triangles should not be permitted to slide over the soft, black lines since they will smudge the lines and ruin the drawing almost as badly as rubbing them across a wet ink line would do. With the softer pencils tiny flakes of graphite will be found to break off around the line. These can be blown off as each line is drawn and thus avoid smudging since it is

these particles rather than the imbedded line which cause the trouble.

Contrast between visible outlines, hidden lines, and dimension lines should be maintained. This may be done by using somewhat harder pencils for the lighter lines, by keeping the points much sharper, and by using a little less pressure.

3.27 Ink technique. In inking a drawing or making a tracing, a certain order or procedure should be followed to give the best results in the least time. A good drawing must have uniformity and contrast. That is to say, there must be uniformity among lines of any one kind and contrast between lines of different kinds. To obtain this result, the lines should be inked in the following order:

a. Visible outlines, all of the same weight.

    1. Circles and arcs of circles and other curved lines.

    2. Horizontal lines beginning at the top.

    3. Vertical lines beginning at the left.

    4. Inclined lines.

b. Invisible outlines in the same order as in (*a*) above.

c. Center lines in the same order as (*a*) above. Some draftsmen prefer to ink center lines first.

d. Crosshatching light lines, evenly spaced.

e. Dimension lines in the same order as in (*a*) above.

f. Dimensions, arrowheads, and other lettering.

g. Borderlines, title box, trim lines.

The importance of drawing arcs and circles first should not be overlooked for one can always make a straight line tangent to one or two arcs, but it is extremely difficult to make an arc or curve tangent to two straight lines, particularly if one of them should be just slightly out of place.

Uniformity between the weight or thickness of arcs and straight lines must be determined by trial on scratch paper, drawing the arcs of the desired thickness first and then later matching them with the ruling pen.

3.28 Section liners. For small areas the draftsman spaces his crosshatching by eye, but when the area is large or when the work is very important and is to be reproduced the crosshatching can be spaced with section liners.

The draftsman may construct devices of his own which will aid in the even spacing of crosshatching lines. By scratching a line on the triangle, say one-sixteenth of an inch from the edge and parallel to it, this line can be used as a guide in doing the pencil work. The first crosshatching line is drawn and then the triangle is moved up so that the line on the triangle is over the one on the drawing and a second line is drawn. Two or more lines can be made on the triangle to give different spacings or different spacings can be made on the various edges as illustrated in Fig. 3–42.

A small piece of heavy cardboard or thin veneer can be cut to the shape of the hole in the triangle but slightly smaller. By shifting the triangle and block alternately accurate spacing may be obtained. For small areas the center line of holes in the Ames lettering instrument may be used.

3.29   Protractors. Protractors may be obtained in small sizes, made of thin brass or celluloid or, in the more expensive varieties of polished steel having vernier attachments for accurate setting of the ruling edge. One of these is shown in Fig. 3–43. They are used to measure angles and are particularly useful in map work. The usual divisions are in degrees and fractions thereof, though other divisions such as percentage parts of a circle may be obtained.

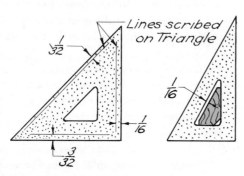

Fig. 3–42.   Aids in section lining.

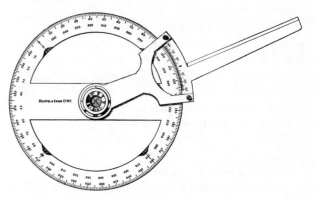

Fig. 3–43.   Protractor. (Courtesy Keuffel & Esser Co.)

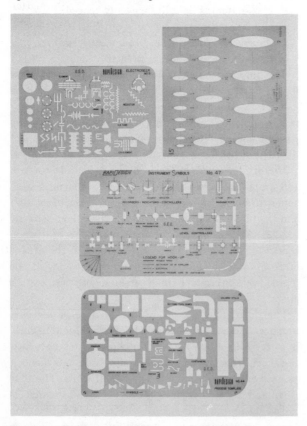

Fig. 3–44.   Special drafting tools.

Fig. 3–45.   Drop pen.

Fig. 3–46.   Contour pen.

3.30 Special celluloid tools. A variety of special celluloid forms are on the market whose purpose and usefulness is self-evident. A number of these are shown in Fig. 3-44. Ellipse guides which may be obtained in a wide variety of sizes are particularly useful in pictorial drawing. Circle guides are valuable time savers.

3.31 Drop pen. The drop pen shown in Fig. 3-45 is used for drawing very small circles. The pencil or pen point spins around the central axis. The top is held with the thumb and index finger, and the pen raised and lowered with the third finger. The third finger is then used to give it a spin when in place. This instrument is particularly useful to structural engineers in drawing rivet holes or heads.

3.32 Contour pen. The contour pen shown in Fig. 3-46 is used by map draftsmen in drawing contour lines which are quite irregular in shape. The pen swivels very freely on the axis which passes up through the handle. By holding it almost vertical, it can be made to follow any curved line no matter how sharply it turns.

PROBLEMS

Some individuals prefer to teach the use of instruments by exercises which allow the student to concentrate his entire attention upon acquiring skill. For those persons, Problems 1 to 5 have been presented. Others prefer to have the student learn to use his instruments on regular drawing problems. Problems 6 to 10 will supply this need, as well as problems chosen from other parts of the text.

In all cases the student should arrange the problems to form a well-balanced sheet. The scale is to be full size (8½ × 11 or 9 × 12-inch sheets) unless otherwise specified by the instructor. Show clearly the construction in all problems where construction is involved. Ink problems, unless otherwise directed.

Accuracy of construction is the primary aim. Geometrical problems are therefore very excellent material for training in accuracy. All problems should be constructed with a hard pencil sharpened to produce a hairline. In all tangency problems, exact tangency is to be secured even though this requires a slight shifting of the center of a circle from its geometrical location. Geometrical constructions will be found in Chapter 4 of this book.

1. On an A-size sheet of paper (8½″ × 11″) draw four rectangles of the size shown in Fig. 3-47 well balanced inside the borderline of your sheet. In the rectangles reproduce the patterns shown in Fig. 3-47(a), (b), (c), and (d). Repeat the patterns to cover the entire rectangle. Make all lines of thickness used for visible outlines except (d) where the proper weight for each type of line should be used. See Fig. 3-32.

2. Same as Problem 1. Copy patterns of Fig. 3-47(b), (d), (e), and (f).

3. Same as Problem 1. Copy patterns of Fig. 3-47(a), (c), (d), and (f).

4. Reproduce the patterns of Fig. 3-48(a) and (b). Have circles well balanced on your sheet. Thickness of lines to be that of section lines in Fig. 3-32.

5. Same as Problem 4. Copy patterns of Fig. 3-48(a) and (c).

6. Reproduce the pipe gasket of Fig. 3-51 to the scale specified by your instructor. Show construction for the location of centers of the 1-inch radius arcs, and mark tangency points of these arcs with the other circular arcs.

7. Reproduce the pump gasket of Fig. 3-52. Locate centers of small arcs, and locate tangency points with other arcs.

8. Draw the valve gasket of Fig. 3-49. Scale full size unless otherwise specified.

9. Draw the heavy-duty gasket of Fig. 3-50. Scale full size unless otherwise specified.

10. Reproduce one or more geometrical layout problems as assigned from the illustrations of Chapter 4.

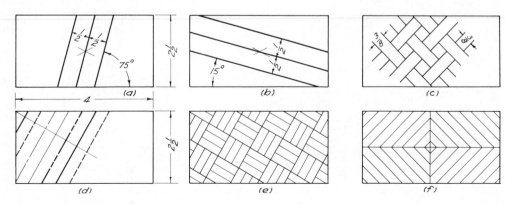

Fig. 3-47. Geometric patterns.

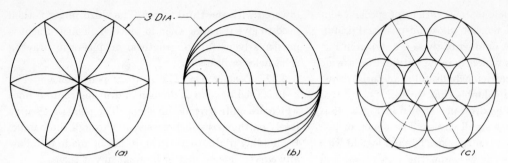

Fig. 3–48.   Circular patterns.

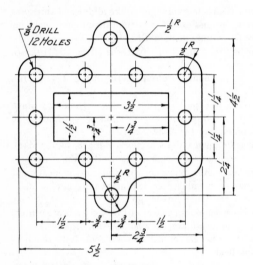

Fig. 3–49.   Valve gasket.

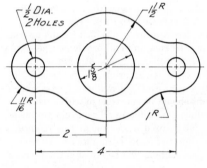

Fig. 3–51.   Pipe gasket.

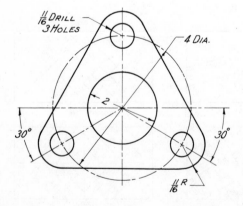

Fig. 3–50.   Heavy duty gasket.

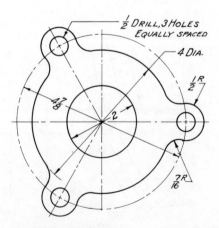

Fig. 3–52.   Pump gasket.

Freeway at Los Angeles, California (A. Devany, Inc.).

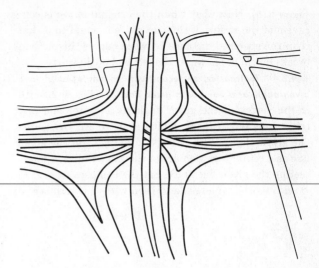

4

Geometrical Constructions

4.1 To be successful in drafting or design and in engineering practice in general, the engineer must have at his finger tips, ready for use without reference to a text book, many of the simple geometrical constructions shown in this chapter, most of which are commonly used in the drafting room, shop, or field. To help the student recognize the form in which geometrical constructions occur, practical applications have been shown along with theoretical constructions. When short-cut constructions are available, these have been indicated.

4.2 Constructions involving lines and angles. Sections 4.2 to 4.4 show only basic constructions in this classification. Practical applications are too evident to require illustration in most instances.

4.2.1 *To erect a perpendicular to a line by the use of triangles and T-square.* For ordinary purposes the method of drawing a perpendicular to a line shown in Art. 3.11, Fig. 3–18 is generally used. This is much more rapid than the geometrical constructions, but it is subject to whatever inaccuracy may exist in the triangle.

4.2.2 *To draw a straight line parallel to and at a given distance r from another line.* With the compass set to the specified distance and with centers on the given line near its ends, draw two arcs as shown in Fig. 4–1(*a*). A line drawn tangent to these arcs is parallel to the given line. For ordinary constructions in the drafting room the method of Art. 3.11, Fig. 3–17, is used.

4.2.3 *To draw a curved line parallel to another curve at a given distance away.* With a compass set at the given distance, and with centers upon the given curve, draw a series of arcs sufficiently close together so that a smooth curve can be drawn tangent to the arcs as shown in

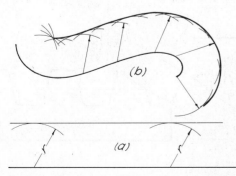

Fig. 4–1. Drawing parallel lines.

Fig. 4–1(*b*). Note that when the original curve is concave and the radius of the curvature is equal to or less than the specified distance between curves the method breaks down, as shown at the left end of the curve.

4.2.4   *To transfer, or reconstruct, an angle equal to a given angle at a point on a given line.* See Fig. 4–2. With *A* the vertex of the given angle as a center and any convenient length *R* as a radius, draw an arc, *CB,* across the given angle. With the given point *A′* on the given line as a center, draw an arc of the same radius *R* intersecting the given line at *B′*. Set the compass from *B* to *C* on the original angle, and then with this radius and

with *B′* as a center describe a short arc intersecting the first arc at *C′*. Draw *A′C′* to complete the angle.

4.2.5   *To transfer, or reconstruct, any plane figure.* If the plane figure consists entirely of straight lines as in Fig. 4–3, it may be divided into a series of triangles and the method of Section 4.2.4, Fig. 4–2, may be used. This consists of constructing a series of contiguous angles equal in turn to each one of those in the group of angles into which the original figure may be divided. To keep the construction lines outside the plane figure, note the single arc across all angles extended with its center at *A* and then *A′*. Having established the angles,

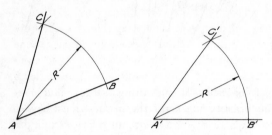

Fig. 4–2.   Constructing an angle equal to a given angle.

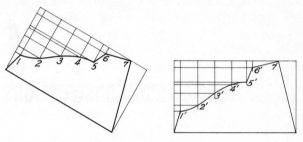

Fig. 4–4.   Reproducing a given plane figure.

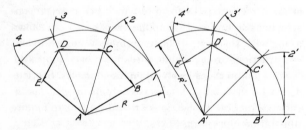

Fig. 4–3.   Reproducing a given plane figure.

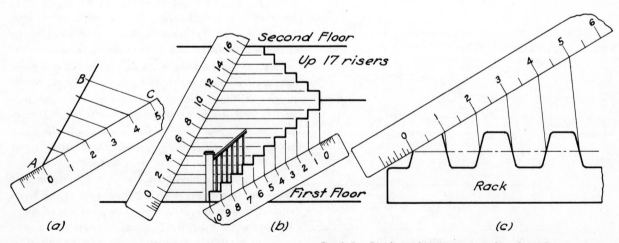

Fig. 4–5.   Dividing a line into any number of equal spaces.

$A'B'$ is made equal to AB, $A'C'$ equal to AC, and so on around the whole figure.

If the plane figure contains curves as boundaries, the coordinate method shown in Fig. 4–4 may be used. Construct a rectangle about the original figure, and draw rectangular coordinates through all corners and enough points on the curves, such as *1, 2,* and *3,* to locate accurately the curves. In the new designated position, reconstruct the rectangle and the coordinates, thus establishing all essential points such as *1'* and *2',* through which the new figure may be drawn.

4.2.6   To divide a line or space into any number of equal parts. For example, line AB in Fig. 4–5(*a*) is to be divided into 5 equal parts. Draw a base line AC making any convenient angle with AB, and on it lay off 5 convenient equal spaces. This may be done by the use of the draftsman's scale as shown. Connect the point B with the point 5, and then draw lines parallel to B–5 from the other four points to the line AB, thus dividing it into 5 equal parts. Common applications of this construction are shown in Fig. 4–5(*b*) and 4–5(*c*).

It should be emphasized that a given line may be divided into any number of unequal parts of known proportions or ratios in length by the above method simply by scaling the known ratios on the selected base line and completing the indicated constructions.

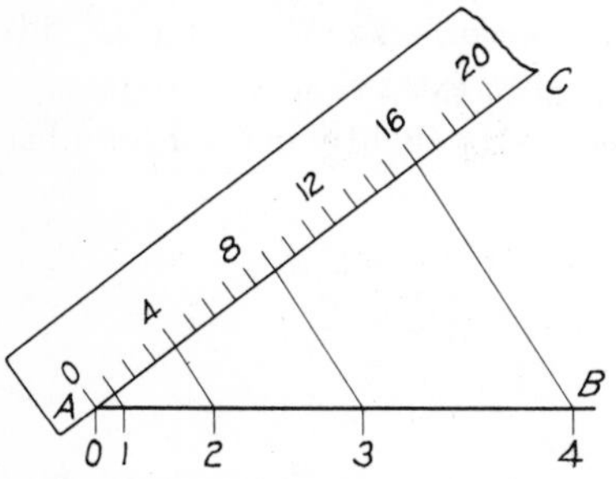

4.2.7   To divide a line so that it will represent varying integer values of an algebraic function to scale—a functional scale. The same principles of construction may be applied in this situation as dividing a line into equal parts; for example, to divide the line AB in Fig. 4–6 so that the sequential values of X^2 may be measured from it in correct scale. Draw a line AC making any convenient angle with AB, and on it, beginning at A as the zero point on the scale, lay off repetitively in convenient units the lengths *1, 4, 9,* etc. Connect the last point, in this case *16*, with B, and then draw lines parallel to B–16 from the other points, thus dividing AB into parts proportional to those on AC and hence in conformity to the problem specifications. If the points on AB are numbered *1, 2, 3,* etc., as shown, we have what is called a squared scale or scale of squares (values of the function X^2) commonly used in nomography. It should be emphasized that a functional scale can be laid out in the above manner for any exponential value that may be assigned to X.

This principle of the functional scale can be used to advantage in laying out a specified ellipse or its projections in orthographic, isometric, oblique, and perspective work, using the circle instead of a straight line as the layout base line. In Fig. 4–7(*a*), the horizontal grid lines on the base circle are transferred directly to the enclosing rectangle of the specified ellipse. By drawing a diagonal (a functional scale) across the horizontal lines, proportional spacings are obtained as shown in Step 2 of Fig. 4–7(*a*). Vertical lines can then be drawn through these points as in Step 3, Fig. 4–7(*b*).

Fig. 4–6.   Laying out a functional scale.

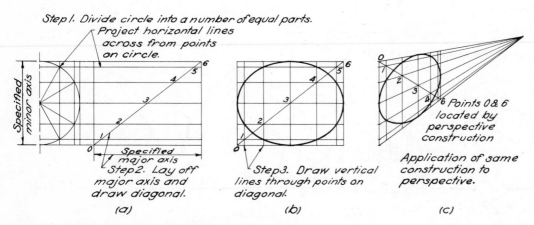

Fig. 4–7.   Proportioning a space by a diagonal to construct an ellipse.

A similar construction can be applied to speed up the projection of circles in perspective, as shown in Fig. 4–7(c). Here the corners of the enclosing perspective rectangle must be obtained by the usual perspective constructions and the base circle then constructed to fit the circumstances.

4.2.8 *To draw a line through point P passing through the intersections of lines AB and CD when their intersection is inaccessible.* With point P as one corner, draw any convenient triangle 1 in Fig. 4–8 having the other corners on the two given lines. At any other place, draw a similar triangle 2. The lines from P through the corresponding corner of triangle 2 will satisfy the requirement.

4.3   Construction of plane figures. Although the necessity for constructing the more complicated plane figures other than the triangle, square, and hexagon does not occur very often, several are included here for reference purposes.

4.3.1   *To construct a square.*

a. Length of sides given. Figure 4–9(a). Draw two lines, AB and AC, at right angles to each other. With their intersection A as the center and a radius equal to the length of the side, draw an arc locating corners B and C on the lines. With B and C as centers and the same radius, draw two intersecting arcs, locating the remaining corner D. Draw BD and CD, completing the square.

b. Second method. Figure 4–9(b). With a radius equal to one-half the side, draw a circle. Draw two center lines with T-square and triangle at right angles to each other, and then draw the four sides tangent to the circle and perpendicular to the center lines.

c. Length of diagonal given. Figure 4–9(c). Draw a circle with the length of the diagonal as a diameter. Through the center, draw two lines at right angles to each other. Connect the four points at which these lines intersect the circle.

4.3.2   *To construct a regular pentagon.*

a. Inscribed in a circle of given radius. In Fig. 4–10(a), bisect radius CA. With center O and radius OB, draw arc BD. With B as a center and radius BD, draw arc DE, and step off this distance five times around the circle. This method is empirical and will be in error less than 1 part in 1000.

b. Second method. Figure 4–10(b). Draw a diameter of the circle, and divide it into 5 equal parts. With ends A and B as centers and a radius equal to the diameter of the circle, draw two arcs until they intersect. From this point, C, draw a line through the second division point on the diameter, and continue it until it crosses the circle at D. The chord AD is one side of the polygon. Step off this distance the required number of times on the circle to locate the corners of the polygon. This method is empirical. It gives exact results for the square and hexagon and is only very slightly in error for other polygons.

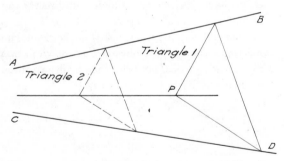

Fig. 4–8.   Intersecting lines when intersection is inaccessible.

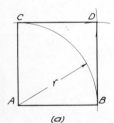 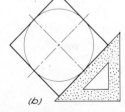 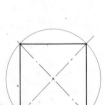

Fig. 4–9.   Constructing a square.

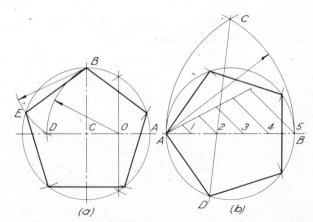

Fig. 4–10.   Constructing a pentagon.

c. Length of side given. See method of construction in paragraph 4.3.4(*a*) below. Figure 4–12.

4.3.3 To construct a hexagon.

a. Length of side given. Figure 4–11(*a*). Draw a circle with the length of a side as a radius. The diameter will be the distance across the corners. Step off the radius six times around the circle, and connect the points.

b. Distance across corners given. See Fig. 4–11(*b*). Draw a circle with the distance across the corners as a diameter, and, with the ends of the diameter as centers, draw two arcs as shown, thus locating six points including the ends of the diameter. Connect the six points on the circle to form the hexagon.

c. Distance across flats given. Figures 4–11(*c*) and 4–11(*d*). Draw a circle with the distance across flats as a diameter, and circumscribe a hexagon about the circle with a T-square and triangle.

4.3.4 To construct a regular polygon having any number of sides.

a. Given length of a side. Figure 4–12(*a*). Lay off side *AB* equal to given length, and, with *A* as a center and *AB* as a radius, draw a semicircle. Divide the semicircle into the required number of parts by trial. Through the point *A* and the second division point, draw a line *AC*, forming a second side of the polygon. Bisect *AC* and

AB. The intersection of these bisectors, *O,* is the center of a circle containing the corners of the polygon. Draw lines from *A* through the remaining points on the semicircle. These will cut the circumscribing circle in the required corners of the polygon. Connect the corners by straight lines.

b. Given circumscribed circle. Figure 4–12(*b*). With *C* the center of the given circumscribed circle as a vertex, construct an equilateral triangle with the other two corners, *A* and *B,* on the circumference. Rectify the arc *AB* by the method of Art. 4.4.7. For the methods of rectifying an arc and drawing an arc equal to length to a straight line, see paragraphs 4.4.7 and 4.4.8. Since the angle *ABC* is $2\pi/6$ radians, an angle of any size can be obtained by multiplying $2\pi/6$ by the appropriate fraction. Thus, for a polygon of seven sides, if we multiply $2\pi/6$ by $6/7$ we have $2\pi/7$ radians. Hence, if we take $6/7$ of *AD,* the rectified arc, and return this length, *AE,* to the circle, we have an arc equal to $1/7$ of the circle. Therefore, by connecting the end points of the arc and stepping this distance off on the circle in the usual way, the corners of the polygon are determined.

c. A third method for constructing a polygon having any number of sides is shown in Fig. 4–10(*b*) for the pentagon. This method will apply to any number of

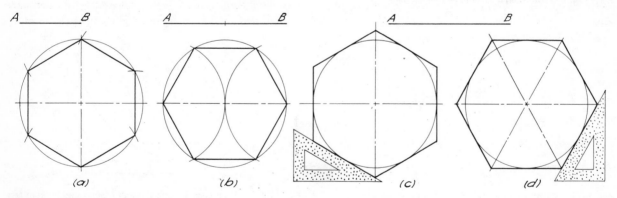

Fig. 4–11. Constructing a hexagon.

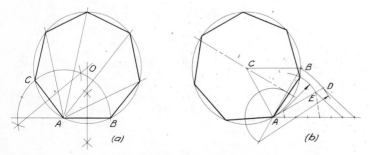

Fig. 4–12. Constructing a regular polygon of any given number of sides.

sides by simply dividing the diameter into a number of parts corresponding to the number of sides of the polygon, and proceeding as described for the pentagon.

4.4   Constructions involving the circle. Most numerous of the common geometrical constructions occurring in the drafting room are those involving the circle. One of the greatest helps in remembering the constructions involving circles is its definition, namely, a circle is the plane locus of a point at a given distance from a given point.

4.4.1   *To draw a circle through three points.* Figure 4–13. Connect the points A, B, and C by two intersecting lines AB and BC. Find the perpendicular bisector of each of these lines. The intersection of the bisectors is the center of the circle, since each bisector is the

locus of points equidistant from two of the given points, and hence their intersection is equidistant from all three.

4.4.2   *To draw a circle of radius r through a point and tangent to a straight line.* Figures 4–14(a) and (b). With the point A as a center and radius r, describe an arc. Draw a line parallel to the given line BC at a distance r from it. The intersection of the line and arc is the required center. An application to a drawing problem is shown in Fig. 4–14(b).

4.4.3   *To draw a circle of given radius r through a point and tangent to a circle.* Fig. 4–15(a) and (b). With the point A as a center and radius r, describe an arc. With the center of the circle C as a center and a radius R + r, describe a second arc. The intersection of these lines is the center of the required circle or arc.

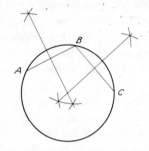

Fig. 4–13.   Constructing a circle through three points.

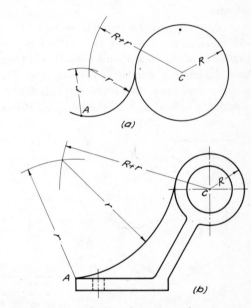

Fig. 4–15.   Constructing a circle through a point and tangent to a circle.

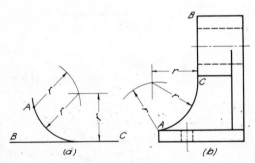

Fig. 4–14.   Constructing a circle through a point and tangent to a line.

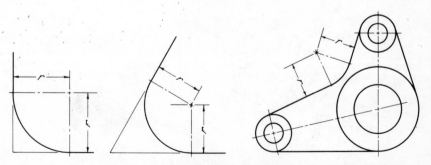

Fig. 4–16.   Constructing a circle tangent to two intersecting lines.

4.4.4   To draw a circle of radius r tangent to two straight lines. Figure 4-16. Draw a line parallel to each of the given lines at a distance r from each of them. The intersection of these lines is the center of the required circle or arc.

4.4.5   To draw a circle of radius r tangent to a straight line and another circle. Figure 4-17. Draw a line parallel to the given line at a distance r from it. Draw an arc of radius $R + r$ concentric with the given circle. The intersection of the line and arc is the required center.

4.4.6   To draw a circle of radius r tangent to two other circles.

a. *Tangent externally.* Figure 4-18(a). Draw two arcs respectively concentric with the given circles and with radii equal to $R + r$ and $R_1 + r$. The intersection of these arcs is the required center.

b. *Tangent internally.* Figure 4-18(b). In this case the radius of the tangent circle must be greater than that of either circle. Draw two arcs respectively concentric with the given circles with radii equal to $r - R$ and $r - R_1$. The intersection of these arcs is the required center. A practical application is shown in Fig. 4-18(c).

c. *Tangent internally to one and externally to the other.* Figure 4-19. As before, draw two arcs concentric with the given circles. For the circle tangent internally the radius is $r - R$, and for the one tangent externally the radius is $R_1 + r$. The intersection of these arcs locates the center of the tangent circle.

4.4.7   To rectify an arc.

a. *First method.* Figure 4-20. Divide the arc into a

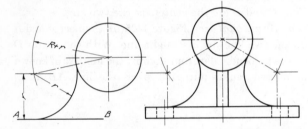

Fig. 4-17.   Constructing a circle tangent to a straight line and a circle.

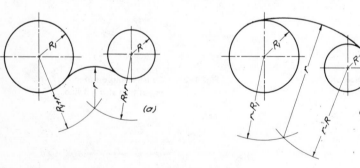

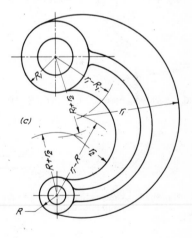

Fig. 4-18.   Constructing a circle tangent to two circles.

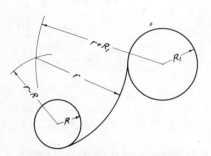

Fig. 4-19.   Constructing a circle tangent to two circles.

number of equal parts. With a divider set to one of these parts, step off the same number of divisions on a straight line. If 12 chords are used in a complete circle, the error will be less than 6 parts in 1000, assuming perfect setting of the dividers. The setting of the dividers should be checked by stepping off the correct number of times on the arc.

b. Second method. Figure 4–21. Draw the chord through the ends of the arc *AB*, and extend it beyond *A* so that *AE = ½AB*. Draw also a tangent to the circle at *A*. With *E* as a center and *EB* as a radius, draw an arc intersecting the tangent at *D*. *AD* is approximately equal in length to the arc *AB*. For angles up to 60° the error is less than 1 in 1000. This method is also used to show the path of travel of the end of a spring for clearance purposes. Figure 4–22.

4.4.8   To make a circular arc equal in length to a given straight line.

a. First method. Obviously the first method of the preceding paragraph could be easily reversed and needs no comment.

b. Second method. Figure 4–23. Lay off on a tangent to the given arc a length *AB* equal to the given line. Divide this length into 4 equal parts. With the first point *D* adjacent to the tangent point *A* as a center, draw an arc cutting the circle. The arc *AC* is equal in length to the line *AB* with an error of less than 6 parts in 1000, for angles less than 90°. This principle is used to determine the rebound limits of a spring. See Fig. 4–24.

4.4.9   To connect two straight parallel lines by a reverse curve at fixed points on the lines.

a. By equal arcs. In Fig. 4–25(*a*), connect by a straight line the points *A* and *B* at which the curve is to begin and end. Bisect *AB*, and then erect a perpendicular bisector of each half until they intersect the perpendiculars to the original lines drawn at *A* and *B*. These intersections *C* and *D* are the centers of the two arcs.

b. By unequal arcs. Figure 4–25(*b*). Connect *A* and *B* on the two lines by a straight line. With the center *D* on the perpendicular from *A*, draw the first arc of known or chosen radius until it crosses the line *AB* at *C*.

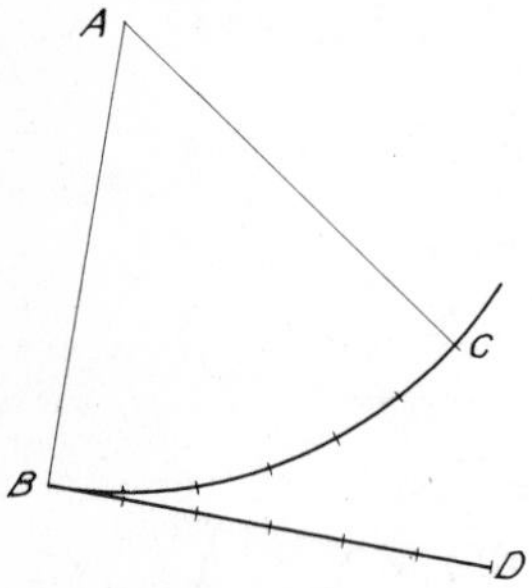

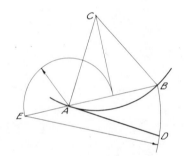

Fig. 4–20.   Rectifying an arc.

Fig. 4–21.   Alternate method of rectifying an arc.

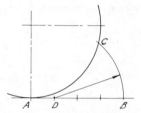

Fig. 4–23.   Constructing an arc equal to a straight line.

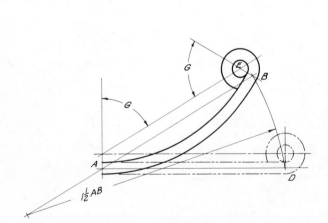

Fig. 4–22.   Application of rectifying an arc. (Courtesy C. S. Mobley, *Automotive Industries*.)

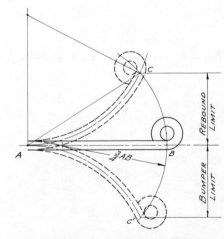

Fig. 4–24.   Application of Fig. 4–23. (Courtesy C. S. Mobley, *Automotive Industries*.)

Extend *DC* until it crosses the perpendicular from *B* at *E*. This locates the center for the second arc. Note that the problem resolved itself into drawing an arc tangent to a circle and a straight line.

4.4.10   *To connect two non-parallel lines by a reverse curve.* Figure 4–25(*c*). On the perpendicular from *B*, step off the chosen radius *BC,* and, with *C* as a center, draw an arc. On the perpendicular from *A,* draw *AD* equal to *BC* and on the same side of the line as *BC*. Join *D* and *C* by a straight line, and erect a perpendicular bisector of this line. Extend the bisector until it intersects the perpendicular from *A* at *F.* This is the center of the circle tangent to the line at *A* and to the other arc. Note that this construction resolves itself into drawing an arc tangent to two circles.

4.5   Construction of the conic sections. The ellipse, parabola, and hyperbola are usually called the conic sections although a straight line and a circle may also be cut from a cone. The conic sections may be defined and constructed with reference to a cone from which they may be cut by a plane or with reference to their properties as plane figures. Both methods will be used for each curve.

Basing the definition first on the right circular cone, an ellipse may be described as the section cut from the cone by a plane making an angle with the axis greater than that made by the elements but less than a right angle. This plane will cut all the elements. Figure 4–26.

The parabola is the section cut from a cone by a plane making an angle with the axis equal to the angle made by the elements of the cone with the axis. The cutting plane is therefore parallel to one of the elements.

The hyperbola is a section cut by a plane inclined to the axis at an angle less than the angle made by the elements. See Fig. 4–26. The section is usually taken parallel to the axis, which gives the hyperbola with two symmetric branches.

4.5.1   *To draw an ellipse.*

a. As a section of a cone. See Fig. 4–27. Draw a plane *AB* cutting the cone as specified above. Draw twelve elements of the cone, and find the line of intersection of plane and cone. This can readily be done since the plane shows edgewise in the front view and the points

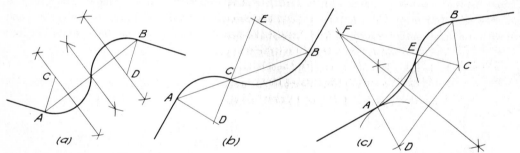

Fig. 4–25.   Connecting straight lines by a reverse curve.

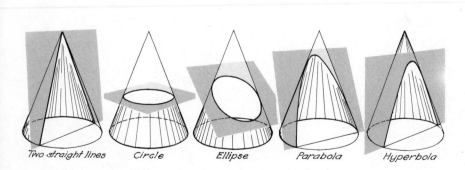

Fig. 4–26.   The conic sections.

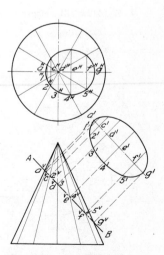

Fig. 4–27.   The ellipse as a section of a cone.

where the respective elements pierce the plane can be seen by inspection at 1^V, 2^V, 3^V, etc. By projecting these to the top view, the curve of intersection can be drawn. This is an ellipse but it is not the true shape of the one cut by the plane AB. To get the true shape of this ellipse, draw a center line parallel to AB at a convenient place. Project the points 1^V, 2^V, 3^V, etc., from the front view perpendicular to this center line, and measure distances from the center line equal to those of the corresponding points from the center line in the top view. A smooth curve through these points gives the true shape of the ellipse.

b. By definition as a locus. The ellipse is the locus of a point the sum of whose distances from the two known points, called the foci, is a constant, as in Fig. 4–28. A locus may be defined as the path of a point moving according to some given law or as the assemblage of all possible positions of the point or generating element. Given the foci F and F_1 and the constant sum, AB, which is also the major axis of the ellipse. Divide the space from F to the center into any convenient number of parts. Set the compass to the distance A–1, and, with F and F_1 as centers, describe four arcs. Then set the compass to B–1, and with the same centers describe four

arcs intersecting the first four. These intersections will lie on the ellipse. Repeat for the other points on the axis to determine as many points on the ellipse as desired. Draw a smooth curve through these points.

c. By the two-circle method. Major and minor axes given. Draw two concentric circles whose diameters are equal respectively to the major and minor axes of the ellipse. Divide each circle into 12 equal parts by drawing 30° and 60° radial lines, as shown in Fig. 4–29. From the point B where any radial line crosses the large circle, draw a line vertically down, and, from the point A where the same radial line cuts the small circle, draw a line horizontally outward until the line intersects the vertical line previously drawn from B. The intersection C of these lines determines a point on the ellipse.

d. With the major and minor axes given. This construction of an ellipse depends upon the construction of a circle shown in Fig. 4–30(a). Any oblique or perspective view of the construction in Fig. 4–30(a) will yield an ellipse similar to that shown in Fig. 4–30(b), but it is not necessary to make the perspective construction. Briefly, the construction is as follows. Draw the rectangle which will enclose the ellipse, also its vertical and horizontal center lines. Divide the short center line into

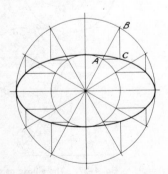

Fig. 4–28.   The ellipse constructed from foci.

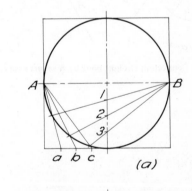

(a)

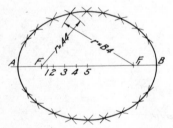

Fig. 4–29.   Two-circle method of constructing an ellipse.

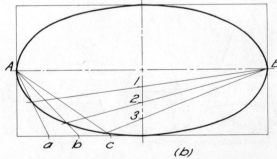

(b)

Fig. 4–30.   Ellipse by intersection of lines.

any number of equal parts and the side perpendicular to the center line into the same number of parts. Draw lines from the ends of the major axis through these points as indicated in the figure. Only the lines for one-quarter of the ellipse have been shown. The intersections of the lines locate points on the ellipse. The other quarters can be constructed in the same way. A construction based upon the same principles is shown for the parabola in Fig. 4–36(*a*) and for the hyperbola in Fig. 4–40(*a*).

e. With the conjugate axes given. The construction in Fig. 4–31 is similar to that of Fig. 4–30 and needs no further explanation. Other methods of construction for special situations are shown in Arts. 17.3(*c*) and 18.5(*b*).

f. By the four-center approximate method. In many cases an approximate ellipse can be drawn quickly with a compass and is quite satisfactory. Draw the enclosing rectangle and its center lines as in Fig. 4–32. Then draw the diagonal *BC* of one of the quarters of this rectangle. With center *O* draw an arc with radius *OA* cutting the minor axis at *E*. With center at *C* and radius *CE*, draw an arc cutting the diagonal *CB* at *F*. Construct the perpendicular bisector of *FB*, and extend the bisector until it cuts the center lines, thus locating two of the four centers. The remaining two may be located by symmetry.

g. By the trammel method. The trammel method is a very convenient method for plotting any number of points on an ellipse since it leaves the drawing free of all construction lines.

(1) First method. On the edge of a strip of paper, lay off the distance *cd* equal to the semiminor axis of the ellipse. Also lay off *ca* on the same side of *c* as the point *d* equal to the semimajor axis, as shown in Fig. 4–33(*a*). By moving the strip of paper so that *d* is on the major axis and *a* on the minor axis, *c* will always be on the ellipse. Any number of positions for *c* may be located, and a smooth curve through them will give the ellipse.

(2) Second method. This is like the preceding method except that *a* and *d* are laid off on opposite sides of *c*, as shown in Fig. 4–33(*b*). In all other respects the procedure is the same. This scheme is a little more accurate when the difference between the major and the minor axis is small.

4.5.2.   *To draw a five-centered arch.* The five-centered arch is used as a practical substitute for the elliptical arch. Draw the rectangle *ABCD* which will just enclose the arch, or half ellipse, as shown in Fig. 4–34. Draw the diagonals *AE* and *BE*. From *C* and *D*, draw lines

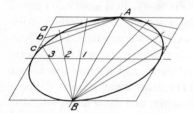

Fig. 4–31.   Ellipse constructed on conjugate axes.

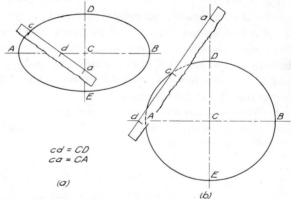

$cd = CD$
$ca = CA$

(*a*)

(*b*)

Fig. 4–33.   Ellipse by the trammel method.

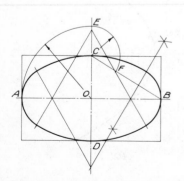

Fig. 4–32.   Four-center approximate ellipse.

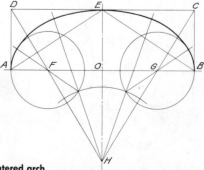

Fig. 4–34.   Five-centered arch.

perpendicular to BE and AE, respectively. The intersections of these lines with the center lines at F, G, and H locate the centers of osculating circles of the ellipse, giving three of the five centers. The other two may be selected at will within a limited range. A convenient method is to draw an arc with center at H and a radius equal to the difference between the radius of the large osculating circle and the diameter of the small one. Where this arc cuts the small osculating circles locates the centers of the arcs which will complete the gap between the large and small circles.

4.5.3 *To draw a parobola.* The parabola is one of the most useful curves not only in engineering computations but also in actual construction. Reflectors for light and sound are made in parabolic form, as are vertical curves on highways and railroads, just to mention two common applications.

a. As a section of a cone. Figure 4–35. Draw the cutting plane AB parallel to the outstanding element of the cone. Since this is an edgewise view of the cutting plane, the piercing points 1^V, 2^V, 3^V, etc., of the elements can be seen by inspection. On the half bottom view, construct the curve of intersection 1 to 6. This is a parabola, but it does not represent the true shape of the one cut by plane AB. To get the true shape, draw a center line EF at a convenient place parallel to AB, and project the points of intersection 1^V, 2^V, 3^V, etc., to it. Measure from this center line the corresponding distances in the bottom view as indicated in the figure for distances a and b. A smooth curve through the plotted points will be the true shape of the parabola.

b. With one point A at the vertex and two symmetrically placed points B and C given. Figure 4–36(a).

Divide BC into any even number of parts and the sides perpendicular to it into half as many parts. Through the points on BC, draw lines parallel to the axis, and, from A the vertex, draw lines to the points on the sides. The intersections of the lines in pairs locate points on the parabola. This construction is based on the perspective of the circle construction shown in Fig. 4–30(a).

c. With the focus and directrix given. The parabola may be described as the locus of a point the distance of which from the focus is always equal to the perpendicular distance from the directrix. With AB the directrix and F the focus in Fig. 4–36(b), a series of points may be located by fulfilling the condition specified above. Thus, for any given distance r, draw an arc with center at F and radius r. Likewise draw a line parallel to AB at r distance from it. The intersections of the arc and line locate two points on the curve. Locate a sufficient number of points to determine accurately the curve.

d. Tangent to two intersecting lines. This is the form in which the problem occurs in highway work, and the solution represents the methods of layout used by the surveyor in computing the curve. The construction is shown in Art. 25.31.

Another method of joining two straight lines by a parabola is shown in Fig. 4–37. This is an exact device based on the fact that a section of a hyperbolic paraboloid parallel to its axis gives a parabola. In the front view of Fig. 4–37, divide the lines $a^V c^V$ and $b^V d^V$ into the same number of equal parts, and number one toward the intersection and the other away from it. Connect points of the same number, and draw a smooth curve tangent to them. If the two tangents are equal, the curve is symmetrical about the bisector of the angle. If

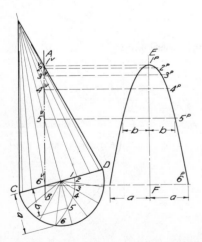

Fig. 4–35.   Parabola as a section of a cone.

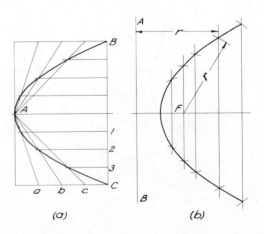

Fig. 4–36.   Parabola by intersection method.

the two tangents are unequal, the curve is still a parabola but the portion joining the lines is an unsymmetrical part.

4.5.4 *To draw a hyperbola.*

a. As a section of a cone. Figure 4–38. Draw two views of a right circular cone, and draw a cutting plane *AB* parallel to the axis so that it appears edgewise in the front view. Draw twelve or more elements of the cone,

and find where they pass through the cutting plane. This can be done by inspection in the front view. Project these points to the corresponding elements in the side view, and draw a smooth curve through the points thus found. The curve through these points will be an hyperbola.

b. With the asymptotes of the hyperbola and one point on the curve given. Figure 4–39(*a*). Through the

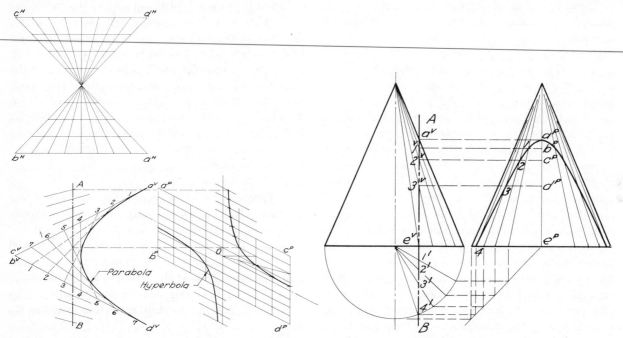

Fig. 4–37.   Parabola as an element of a hyperbolic paraboloid.

Fig. 4–38.   The hyperbola as a section of a cone.

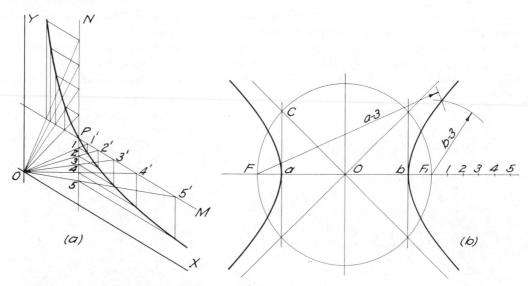

Fig. 4–39.   Hyperbola through a point with asymptotes given.

given point *P,* draw two lines *PM* and *PN* respectively parallel to the asymptotes. From the origin *O,* draw a series of radial lines intersecting *PN* in the points *1, 2, 3,* etc. and *PM* in corresponding points *1', 2', 3',* etc. The radial lines should be distributed on both sides of the given point *P.* Lines drawn through *1* and *1'* parallel to the corresponding asymptote will intersect on the hyperbola.

When the asymptotes are at right angles to each other, the hyperbola is called a rectangular or equilateral hyperbola. This curve occurs in thermodynamics in the study of the laws of expansion of gases. The side view of Fig. 4–37 shows how the foregoing construction is derived from cutting a section through a hyperbolic paraboloid with a cutting plane *AB* perpendicular to its axis. The two elements of the surface passing through the vertex *O* form the asymptotes of the curves.

c. With the foci and vertices of the hyperbola given. Figure 4–39(*b*). Draw the axis, and locate on it the foci *F* and *F₁* and the vertices *a* and *b.* Mark off a series of points on the axis as *1, 2, 3,* etc. Then with a radius *a–1* draw four arcs with *F* and *F₁* as centers. Do likewise with *b–1* as a radius intersecting the first four arcs. The intersections of the arcs are points on the curve. Repeat this process for as many points on the axis as you choose. Draw a smooth curve through the plotted points. Note that the constant difference between the radii is *ab.* The asymptotes of the curve can be located by drawing a circle having *FF₁,* the distance between foci, as its diameter. Lines drawn through the vertices *a* and *b* perpendicular to the axis intersect the circle at points on the asymptotes.

d. With the vertex A and two symmetrically placed points B and C on the curve given. Figure 4–40(*a*). This construction is derived from the perspective construction of a circle, the points of which have been formed by a series of intersecting lines, as shown in Fig. 4–30(*a*).

Since an infinite number of hyperbolas can be drawn through the three points specified in this construction, the point *P* in Fig. 4–40(*a*) may be selected at any convenient distance to the left of *A.*

If the problem is further restricted, as, for example, by specifying the diameter of the base of the cone through *B* and *C,* Fig. 4–40(*b*), then there is only one solution. With *B* as a center and the compass set to the radius of the base, strike an arc cutting the center line at *D.* Then with *D* as a center and the same radius, draw the arc *BJM.* Project *M* to *G* on the line *BC.* With center *E* and radius *EJ,* draw the arc *JN.* Project *N* across to *L.* Draw the line *GL* until it intersects the axis at *H.* This line *GH* is an asymptote of the hyperbola. Step off *HP* equal to *HA* to locate *P.* With point *P* located, the construction is as shown in Fig. 4–40(*a*).

The focus of the hyperbola may be obtained by drawing an arc with its center at *H* and radius *HL* to intersect the axis at *F.*

4.5.5 To draw any conic.

a. Through five given points. The solution of this problem, which occurs in joining surfaces as in aircraft work, is an application of Pascal's theorem which states, "Opposite pairs of sides of a hexagonal figure inscribed in a conic intersect in three points which lie in a straight line." Thus in Fig. 4–41 the sides *1–6* and *3–4* intersect at *A,* *1–2* and *4–5* intersect at *B,* and *2–3* and *5–6* intersect at *C,* and the line *ABC* is referred to as Pascal's line.

If only points *1–5* are known, any sixth point *X* may be found on the conic as follows:

1. Extend the opposite sides *1–2* and *4–5* until they intersect at *B.* This point must be on every Pascal line of the conic.

2. Draw another Pascal line through *B,* intersecting the lines *2–3* and *3–4* as at *C'* and *A'.*

3. Draw the remaining sides of the hexagon from *1*

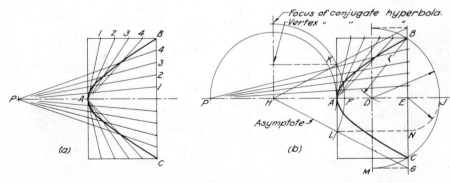

Fig. 4–40.   Hyperbola by intersection method.

to A' and from 5 to C', thus locating point X, the sixth corner, at their intersection.

As many points as desired may be located on the conic by drawing successive Pascal lines through B and proceeding as outlined above.

b. Tangent to two lines at given points and passing through a given third point. See Fig. 4-42(a). The same construction may be applied as in the preceding problem by simply assuming that the points *1* and *2*, and *4* and *5* have become coincident, thus establishing the tangents which can be extended to intersection at B on the Pascal line.

The sides of the hexagon *2-3* and *3-4* are again extended, and Pascal lines are drawn through B to intersect them. Thus in Fig. 4-42(a) the first Pascal line intersects *3-4* at A and *2-3* at C. Lines *1-A* and *5-C* intersect at *6*, a point on the curve. The second Pascal line cuts *3-4* at A' and *2-3* at C'. Lines *1-A'* and *5-C'* intersect at *6'*, another point on the curve.

c. Identifying a conic. It is sometimes desirable to know the nature of the conic constructed by methods *a* or *b* above. This can be done by selecting two points as A and B on the curve of Fig. 4-42(b) as far apart as possible and drawing tangents to the curve at these points until they intersect at C. Draw the chord AB, and bisect it at D. Draw CD, and find its midpoint E. If the curve goes through E, it is a parabola; if it lies between E and C, it is an hyperbola; and if it lies between E and D, it is an ellipse.

4.6 Tangency constructions. Many drafting problems require the construction of lines tangent to various curves. The most common solution involves the circle. Both practical and geometric methods are discussed in the following paragraphs.

4.6.1 *To draw a line tangent to a circle from a point on the circle.* Figure 4-43. Given the point P on the circle with center at C. With P as a center and radius equal to that of the circle PC, swing an arc cutting the circle at A. With A as a center and the same radius, swing a semicircle. Draw the line CA until it intersects this semicircle at B. The line BP is the required tangent.

This problem is usually solved in the drafting room by the method shown in Fig. 4-44. Bring a triangle resting on another straight edge up to the figure so that one of the edges of the right angle of the triangle coincides with the line BC joining the center and the point of tangency. See dotted line triangle. Then slide the triangle along the straight edge until the other leg of the right angle passes through B. This edge is tangent to the circle at B.

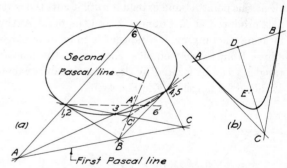

Fig. 4-42. Conic through a point and tangent to two lines at given points.

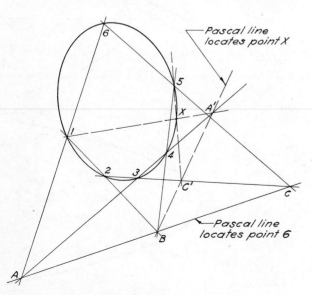

Fig. 4-41.   Conic through five points.

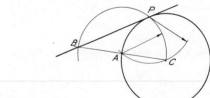

Fig. 4-43.   Line tangent to a circle.

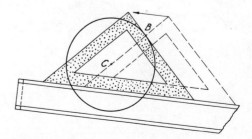

Fig. 4-44.   Draftsman's method of drawing a tangent to a circle.

4.6.2   To draw a straight line tangent to an ellipse from a point P on it. Figure 4–45(a). From P, draw lines to the two foci F and F_1, and extend one of these lines. The bisector of the external angle is the required tangent. If the foci are not given, they may be found by drawing an arc with a radius equal to the semimajor axis and with the center at the end of the minor axis as shown in Fig. 4–45(b).

Another method of drawing a tangent to an ellipse is shown in Fig. 4–46. This construction is based on the fact that an ellipse may be constructed as an oblique view of a circle. In such a view a tangent to the circle will appear as a tangent to the ellipse. By imagining the major axis of the ellipse as the axis of rotation, the intersection of the tangent and this axis remains in a fixed position. Therefore, with one-half the major axis as a radius, draw an arc BA_1D tangent to the ellipse as shown. Project the point A to the circle on a line perpendicular to the major axis. Draw a tangent to the circle at this point A_1, and extend it until it cuts the major axis produced at X. Connect X and the point A, thus locating the tangent. If a tangent is to be drawn to an ellipse from a point outside, such as Y, the point of tangency can be located by the same line of reasoning as shown for tangent YF in Fig. 4–46.

4.6.3   To draw a straight line tangent to a parabola from a point P on it. Figure 4–47. From the point P, draw a line to the focus F and a second line perpendicular to the directrix or parallel to the axis. The bisector of the angle between these lines is the required tangent.

One property of the parabola is that the tangent to the parabola at any point intersects the axis as far from the vertex as does the chord from the point of tangency drawn perpendicular to the axis, that is, $CD = DE$ in Fig. 4–48(a). Therefore, to draw a tangent at any point P on a parabola, drop a perpendicular from the point P to the axis at C. With a divider, step off on the axis a distance DE equal to CD. The tangent passes through point E.

Another method is illustrated in Fig. 4–48(b). Through the point P, draw a line parallel to the axis of the parabola. Draw two lines parallel to the axis on opposite sides of the line through P and at equal distances from it, cutting the parabola at A and C. Draw the line AC. The tangent through P will be parallel to this line.

4.6.4   To draw a straight line tangent to an hyperbola at point P on the curve. Figure 4–49. From the point P, draw two lines to the foci F and F_1. The bisector of the angle between these lines is the required straight line tangent.

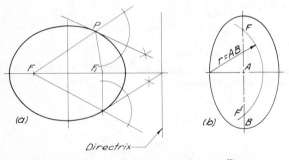

Fig. 4–45.   Use of foci in drawing tangents to an ellipse.

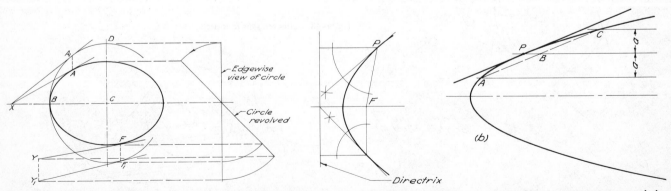

Fig. 4–46.   Alternate method: line tangent to an ellipse.   **Fig. 4–47.   Line tangent to a parabola.**   **Fig. 4–48.   Line tangent to a parabola.**

4.6.5 *To draw a tangent to any curve.* To draw a line tangent to any given curve at any given point O upon it. See Fig. 4-50. Assume any curve AOC, to which a line is to be drawn tangent at the point O. With O as a center, draw an arc ht of any convenient radius. Draw a number of secants from the point O to each side of the curve, as shown. From the point h on the secant Oa extended, lay off the distance hu equal to Oa. Proceed in like manner with each secant, laying off those distances on one side of O on the same side of the arc as hu, and those on the other side of O on the opposite side of the arc. Through the points thus obtained, draw a smooth curve. The intersection of this curve with the arc locates a second point on the tangent. Proof of this method depends upon the proposition that the tangent is the limiting position of the secant.

4.7 **Construction of other curves common in practical work.** Although the conic sections have a prominent place in engineering work, a number of other mathematical curves are widely used. Among these are the involute, the helix, the cycloids, and the spiral of Archimedes.

4.7.1 *To draw the involute.* The involute may be defined as a curve which would be described if a string were unwound from some geometrical surface with the string kept taut and the end point describing the curve. Three involutes are shown in Fig. 4-51, one each for a triangle, a square, and a circle. The involute need not begin on the surface although it may as in the triangle and the circle.

a. In the equilateral triangle, the curve consists of a series of 120° arcs with the radius increasing each time by the length of a side of the triangle. The corners of the triangle are the centers. This is also true for the square or any other figure with straight sides.

b. In the circle the circumference is divided into any convenient number of equal parts. Beginning at point *1* a tangent is drawn, and on it the length of the arc *0-1* is stepped off to locate *A*. At point *2* another tangent is drawn and a length equal to arc *0-1-2* is stepped off and so on for as many points as may be desired. A smooth curve is then drawn through these plotted points.

The involute is the basic curve for gear teeth and for the impeller of centrifugal pumps.

4.7.2 *To draw the cycloids.* The cycloids form a group of curves generated by the path of a fixed point on the circumference of a rolling circle. When the circle rolls on a straight line, the path of the point is called simply a

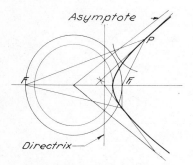

Fig. 4-49.   Line tangent to a hyperbola.

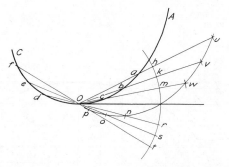

Fig. 4-50.   Line tangent to any curve.

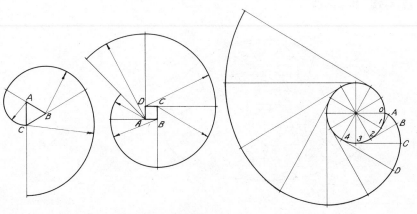

Fig. 4-51.   Involutes.

cycloid. If the circle rolls on the outside of another circle, the path of the point is called an epicycloid, whereas if the circle rolls on the inside of another circle the path of the point is called a hypocycloid. These curves have a practical application in the design of gear teeth. To draw the cycloid, in Fig. 4–52, divide the rolling circle into 12 or more equal parts and lay out on the straight line 12 divisions equal to the arcs of the circle. As the circle rolls along, the center will occupy successively the positions, *1, 2, 3,* etc., while the point on the circumference will rise to the elevation on the horizontal lines *A, B, C, D,* etc. The intersections of the circle in its successive positions with the horizontal lines will give the required points.

To draw the epicycloid and the hypocycloid, see Fig. 4–53. The constructions of the epicycloid and hypocycloid are quite similar to each other and can be readily grasped from the figure. Note that in both cases there is a separate line of centers for the rolling circles and, in place of the horizontal lines *A, B, C,* etc., we have the arcs *A, B, C,* etc.

4.7.3   *To draw the spiral of Archimedes.* In the spiral of Archimedes, the radius of curvature increases directly as the angle through which it rotates. We may assume an arbitrary amount by which the radius shall increase in passing through a certain angle. See Fig. 4–54. With any convenient point as a center, draw a circle and divide it into 12 equal parts. Divide the radius into the same number of equal parts. One of the divisions of the radius is then the increment by which the radius of curvature increases in passing through an angle of 30°. Then beginning at the center and intersecting radius 1^1 by arc *1,* and radius 2^1 by arc *2,* and so on, twelve points on the curve can be found. The curve thus generated is commonly used in cam design.

4.7.4   *To draw a helix.* For the definition and construction of this curve see Art. 10.2, Fig. 10–1.

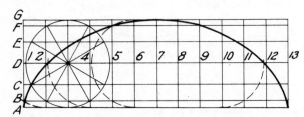

Fig. 4–52.   The cycloid.

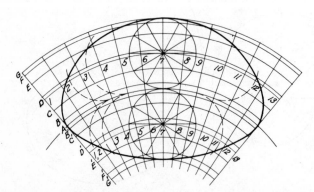

Fig. 4–53.   Epicycloid and hypocycloid.

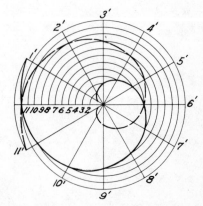

Fig. 4–54.   Spiral of Archimedes.

PROBLEMS

On an 8½ × 11 inch sheet, draw one or more problems from the following group as assigned by your instructor. First make a freehand sketch of the problems so that you can plan a well-balanced sheet. Make the geometric construction with a well-sharpened 4H pencil. Finish the drawing with an H pencil, making the final result stand out prominently. Leave the geometric construction in light lines. Finish problems in ink if so directed. Scale of drawings to be full size unless otherwise directed.

1. Draw a triangle having sides 1¼, 1½, and 2 inches long.

2. Draw a circle through the three corners of the triangle of Problem 1.

3. Draw a triangle having a base 3 inches long with angles of 60° at its ends.

4. Inscribe a circle in the triangle of Problem 3.

5. Inscribe a hexagon in a 3-inch-diameter circle.

6. Circumscribe a hexagon about a 2-inch-diameter circle.

7. Draw a pentagon inscribed in a 2-inch-diameter circle. See Fig. 4–10.

8. Draw a pentagon 1 inch on a side. See Fig. 4–12.

9. Draw a heptagon inscribed in a 2½-inch-diameter circle. See Fig. 4–10.

10. Draw a heptagon 1 inch on a side. See Fig. 4–12.

11. Draw two circles with their center on a horizontal line 3 inches apart. One circle is to be 1 inch in diameter and the other 1¼ inches. Draw a circle of 2-inch radius tangent to the two circles externally. See Fig. 4–18.

12. Same as Problem 11. Circle 3 inches in diameter tangent internally to the small circle and externally to the large one. See Fig. 4–19.

13. Same as Problem 11. Circle of 6-inch radius tangent internally to both circles. See Fig. 4–18.

14. Draw two horizontal parallel lines 1½ inches apart. Two points, 3 inches apart horizontally, one on each line, are to be connected by a reverse curve both parts of which have the same radius. See Fig. 4–25(a).

15. Draw two horizontal parallel lines 2 inches apart, and connect two points, one on each line, 3 inches apart on the shortest distance, by two arcs, one of which has a radius of 1½ inches. See Fig. 4–25(b).

16. Draw two intersecting lines making 120° with each other. Connect two points on these lines each 4 lines from their intersection by a parabola. See Fig. 25–35.

17. Draw a rectangle 4 inches by 2 inches, and draw a parabola through two corners and the midpoint of a long side. See Fig. 4–36.

18. Draw an ellipse with a major axis of 3 inches and a minor axis of 2 inches by the two-circle method. See Fig. 4–29.

19. Draw an ellipse inside a rectangle 4 inches by 2 inches by the method shown in Fig. 4–30(b).

20. Draw an ellipse have a major axis of 3½ inches and a minor axis of 2 inches by the trammel method. See Fig. 4–33.

21. Draw a rectangular hyperbola through a point whose coordinates are $x = 1$ inch and $y = 1$ inch from coordinates which are the asymptotes. See Fig. 4–39(a).

22. The foci of an hyperbola are 2 inches apart and the vertices 1¼ inches apart. Draw one branch of the hyperbola. See Fig. 4–39(b).

23. Draw a rectangle 4 inches by 2 inches, and then draw an hyperbola through two corners and the midpoint of the long side by the method of Fig. 4–40.

24. Draw one turn of an involute based on a circle 1½ inches in diameter. See Fig. 4–51.

25. Draw one turn of an involute based on a square ¾ inch on a side. See Fig. 4–51.

26. Draw two projections of a helix of 2-inch diameter and 3-inch pitch. See Fig. 10–1.

27. Draw a cycloid having a rolling circle 2 inches in diameter. See Fig. 4–52.

28. Draw an epicycloid having a rolling circle of 1-inch diameter rolling on a base circle having a 6-inch diameter. See Fig. 4–53.

29. Draw a spiral of Archimedes. Begin curve 1 inch from center, and use a radial increment of ¼ inch for each 30°. Make one-half turn, and draw also the symmetrical portion on the opposite side of the center line. See Fig. 4–54.

Aluminum plant used in the reduction of bauxite to alumina (Charles Rotkin).

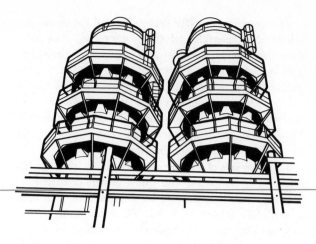

5

Geometric Projections

5.1   Origin of projection drawing. The representation of three-dimensional objects on two-dimensional surfaces by means of geometric drawings, such as plans and elevations, has involved a gradual change from crude pictorials of prehistoric man through a period of highly artistic drawings to the present well-developed types of industrial drawing. In the early days, most of the construction work was concerned with buildings and many very complicated buildings were erected. It is highly probable that drawings of some kind were made before construction was undertaken, although frequently construction problems were worked out by the mason or builder from general specifications as the work progressed. However, very few examples of these drawings have been preserved.

One early Egyptian drawing made on papyrus which shows two views of a shrine without dimensions has been found. An example of a drawing made for general instructions rather than a working drawing is the diagram plan of the monastery of St. Gall made in the ninth century.

Two elevations are in existence of the west front of the Cathedral of Orvieto, supposed to have been made by Lorenzo del Maitano of Siena soon after 1310, but again these are not true front views since each is in slight perspective. By the end of the fifteenth century, there were draftsmen who could make true elevations. One of the earliest examples of the use of plan and elevation is included in an album of drawings in the Vatican Library, drawn by Giuliano Da San Gallo. The date on the title page is 1465, but the book was not actually completed until 1490.

The drawings of early architects and engineers contained the basic idea of the theory that was to be developed into our modern forms of geometric projection. The system of right-angle projection on planes set up perpendicular to each other was first completely worked out by Gaspard Mongé in the eighteenth century and was used to solve geometric problems. The work of Mongé is the basis of descriptive geometry which has been called the theory of drawing.

5.2   Elements of projections. Three kinds of projection are used by engineers and other designers to portray objects which they propose to manufacture or projects which they intend to build. *They are called orthographic, oblique, and perspective projection.* In discussing any one of them, four distinct elements must be considered—namely, *the location of the point of sight, the direction of the lines of sight,* or projecting lines as they are also called, *the surface upon which the drawing is made, and the position of the object with relation to this surface or plane of projection.* No real understanding of the theory of projection can be had without considering the fullest relationships of these four determining factors. They are so definitely interrelated that any discussion of one of them must necessarily involve the others; hence any treatment of a single item should not be considered complete until all four have been finished in turn. A study of Fig. 5–1 will give a general idea of the meaning of these four elements and the methods of combining them to produce the three kinds of projection mentioned above.

The point of sight is the real or imaginary position of the eye of the observer, relative to the object and the plane of projection, from which the view or projection is obtained. This view point may be located at some finite distance from the object, as in perspective projection, or at an infinite distance as in orthographic and

oblique projection. See Fig. 5–1.

Projecting lines or lines of sight are the imaginary lines connecting the eye of the observer with points on the object. In orthographic and oblique projection these lines of sight are parallel, which means that the eye of the observer must be imagined at an infinite distance from the object. In perspective projection they converge to a finite point where the eye of the observer is located.

The plane of projection is the plane surface upon which the object is projected or drawn. The projection of an object is found by connecting the points where the lines of sight, or projecting lines, through definitive or significant points on the edges or contour lines of the object, pierce the plane of protection. On the cube there are eight such points (corners) and twelve such edge lines. On the sphere there is only a single contour circle, called a great circle, to be projected for each view. This will be a different circle for each view.

The object may be anything real or imaginary which it is desired to represent. Theoretically, it may have any relation whatever to the plane of projection, but, for practical reasons, in multiview drawing, the faces of the object are placed parallel to the principal planes of projection.

These relationships are more fully discussed in the chapters on orthographic, axonometric, oblique, and perspective drawing.

5.3   Projection of an object. The projection of any designated point of an object on a plane of projection is the point at which the line of sight through the point pierces the plane. Thus in the first drawing of Fig. 5–2, the projection, orthographic in this case, of corner A of the cube is at a^V in the plane of projection (the point of sight is considered at infinity in front of the plane of projection); similarly the projection of corner B is at b^V. The projection of the whole edge AB of the cube is

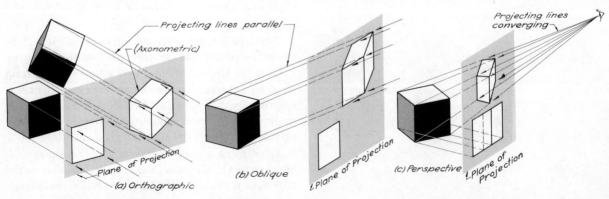

Fig. 5–1.   Three types of projections.

the line a^Vb^V in the plane of projection. The projection of the four boundary lines of the face $ABCD$, as well as all points and lines inside these boundaries of the face, is the line $a^Vb^Vc^Vd^V$. The point M is represented by m^V. Similarly, the projection of the face $ADEH$ is the line $a^Vd^Ve^Vh^V$. The face $CDEF$, being parallel to the plane of projection, will project in its true size as the square $c^Vd^Ve^Vf^V$. The projections of all twelve edge lines and of the enclosed areas of the six faces of the cube are simply the four sides of the square or the space enclosed within the square. Moreover, the projection of any point or line within the object, for instance, the point O, will fall within the boundaries of the square. This projected square is also known as a view of the object. These relationships and sizes are shown pictorially in (a) of Fig. 5–2 and hence in somewhat distorted fashion, but in (b), where the plane of projection has been rotated into the plane of the paper, they appear in true proportions as they should in orthographic projection.

From the foregoing the conclusion is drawn that the complete projection of any object on a plane can be obtained by finding the projections of all its outstanding or bounding points, lines, and faces.

As noted previously, the shape or appearance of the projection of an object will depend on the geometrical relationships of the four elements mentioned in Art. 5.2, most important of which is the relationship of the projecting lines to the plane of projection.

5.4   Projecting lines and plane of projection. Three possible relationships between projecting lines, or lines of sight as they are called, and the plane of projection are illustrated pictorially in Fig. 5–1. In the first illustration (a) the projecting lines are parallel to each other and perpendicular to the plane of projection. Projections made on the basis of this arrangement are called

orthographic projections. They show all distances, angles, and areas of an object that are parallel to the plane of projection in true dimensions or sizes. In the second illustration (b) the projecting lines are parallel to each other but oblique to the plane of projection. The type of projection obtained thereby is known as oblique projection for obvious reasons. In the third part of the figure (c) the projecting lines, or lines of sight, converge at a definite point so that all lines make different angles with the plane of projection, unless there are one or more planes of symmetry in the whole projective system. Projections based on this arrangement are called perspective projections.

5.5   The object and plane of projection. Although the three relationships of projecting lines and plane of projection discussed in Art. 5.4 determine the only basic differences between the three types of projections—orthographic, oblique, and perspective—it is important to give consideration to the various possible placements of the object with respect to the plane of projection in order to secure the most satisfactory appearance of the object and the most useful projection (drawing) for the purposes in mind.

5.5.1   Orthographic projection. *Any projection made by lines of sight that are perpendicular to the plane of projection is called an orthographic projection.*

In multiview orthographic projection it is customary to place the principal faces of the object, in other words, the three principal coordinate axes of the object, parallel or perpendicular to the planes of projection. See Fig. 5–2. Turning the principal axes of an object to various angles with the plane of projection gives rise to a type of orthographic projection that is called axonometric. If the axes of the object are turned so that they make equal angles with the plane of projection, the resulting

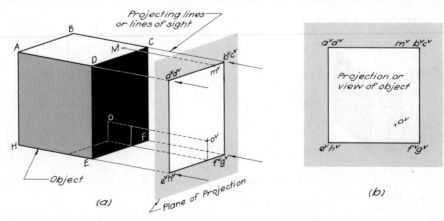

Fig. 5–2.   Orthographic projection.

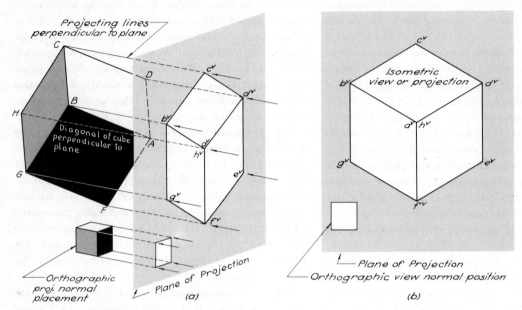

Fig. 5–3.   Axonometric projection. Isometric.

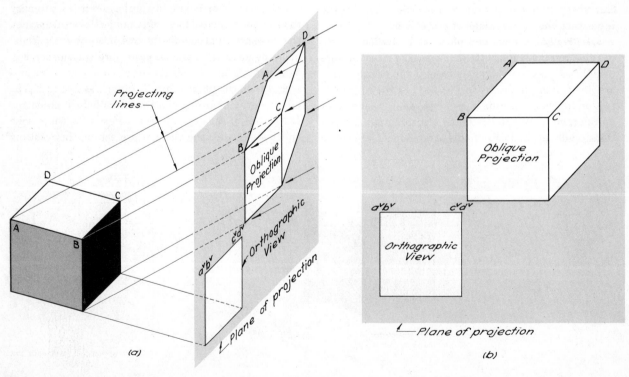

Fig. 5–4.   Oblique projection.

projection on the plane is known as isometric. See Fig. 5–3. The principal fact to be noted here about this particular type of axonometric projection is that measurements along or parallel to each projected axis are equally foreshortened, a very useful characteristic in making pictorial drawings that are to be scaled and dimensioned. Other inclinations of the coordinate axes of an object to the plane of projection produce axonometrics that are called dimetric or trimetric. Each of these subdivisions of orthographic projection, resulting from special placements of the object with respect to the plane of projection, is discussed fully in Chapter 17.

5.5.2   *Oblique projection.* *Any projection made by lines of sight that are parallel to each other and inclined to the plane of projection is called an oblique projection.*

In oblique projection a principal face of the object is almost always placed parallel to the plane of projection. This arrangement has marked advantages over other possible placements, principally in the speed and ease with which the drawing can be constructed. See Fig. 5–4. Circles, ellipses, and other plane figures in faces parallel to the plane of projection appear in true shape and size in the drawing and can be dimensioned as in orthographic projection. A detailed discussion of this type of projection will be found in Chapter 18.

5.5.3   *Perspective projection.* *Any projection made by lines of sight that converge to a point which is at a finite distance from the plane of projection is called a perspective projection.*

In perspective projection the objective is to obtain a pictorial drawing that will most clearly represent the shape and relative position of the several parts of an object as seen from a definite point of view. Therefore, the object may be turned to any desired angle with the plane of projection to produce the best effects. See Fig. 5–5. Full discussion of this type of projection will be found in Chapter 19.

5.6   Point of sight and views. Although it is possible to think of projections as strictly mechanical constructions, obtained by the use of projecting lines that fulfill certain geometrical conditions, meaningful drawings cannot be made without a definite conception of a point of sight and its location with respect to the object and the plane of projection. The relation of the projecting lines to one another depends upon the location of the point of sight, which may be assumed in either of two general positions. It may be at an infinite distance from the object or at a finite distance from it. If the point of sight is at infinity, the projecting lines must, as a result, be parallel to each other, as in the first and second drawings of Fig. 5–1, whereas, if the point of sight has a finite location, the projecting lines converge to this point as in the third drawing of Fig. 5–1.

This fact of a chosen point of sight from which the object is assumed to be seen, or viewed, and through which all projectors must pass, gives rise to the general practice of calling a projection of an object a view. In oblique, perspective, and axonometric forms of orthographic projection, one-view drawings are the rule. They show the main features of the object from a single point

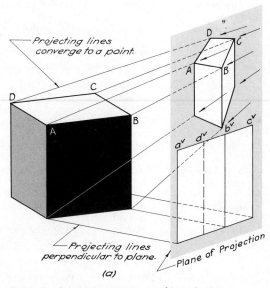

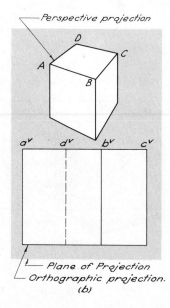

Fig. 5–5.   Perspective or scenographic projection.

of sight or viewpoint. Such drawings are often called pictorials because of the closeness with which they simulate camera pictures or the artist's paintings.

The engineer, however, must present his plans and specifications in more detail than can be shown with pictorial drawings. He must make several views or projections of the object he is designing and constructing. This is known as multiview drawing and is based on the principles of general orthographic projection explained in the preceding articles of this chapter. Hence there are in the engineer's drawings, top views, front views, side views, auxiliary views, and others. These are also known as plans, elevations, profiles, and auxiliaries, respectively.

In multiview orthographic projection, with which the next chapter is concerned, it will be shown in Chapter 7 that there must be a point of sight for each view of the object represented. Hence there is not just one point of sight and one plane of projection but as many of each as there are views to be made of the object. To obtain a top view, the point of sight must be above the object. For a front view, the point of sight must be in front of the object; for a right side view, it must be to the right of the object; and for a left side view, it must be to the left of the object. In each case, of course, the point of sight is theoretically at infinity in a direction perpendicular to the plane of projection. In the U.S.A. third quadrant projection is always used for shop drawings, in which case the plane of projection is between the object and the observer.

5.7   Summary. The kinds of projection discussed in this chapter, the relationships of the geometric elements entering into each type of projection, and the classification and name of each special form of projection are summarized in the following table. Each type is discussed in detail in succeeding chapters of this book.

TYPES OF PROJECTIONS

Major classifications	Subdivision	No. of planes of projection	Relation of lines of sight to plane of projection	Relation of lines of sight to each other	Location of point of sight in relation to plane of projection	Position of enclosing cube with relation to plane of projection
Orthographic	Multiple view	As many as necessary	Perpendicular	Parallel	Infinite distance	Faces parallel to planes
	Isometric	One	Perpendicular	Parallel	Infinite distance	Faces equally inclined to plane
	Dimetric	One	Perpendicular	Parallel	Infinite distance	Two faces equally inclined to plane
	Trimetric	One	Perpendicular	Parallel	Infinite distance	Three faces at different angles to plane
Oblique	Cavalier	One	45°	Parallel	Infinite distance	Principal face parallel to plane
	Cabinet	One	63°-26′	Parallel	Infinite distance	Principal face parallel to plane
	Clinographic	One	80°-32′	Parallel	Infinite distance	Principal face at angle of 18°-26′
	General	One	Any angle except those above	Parallel	Infinite distance	Principal face parallel to plane
Perspective	One-point	One	Various angles	Converge at a point	Finite distance	Principal face parallel to plane
	Two-point	One	Various angles	Converge at a point	Finite distance	Two faces inclined and one face perpendicular to plane
	Three-point	One	Various angles	Converge at a point	Finite distance	Three faces inclined to plane

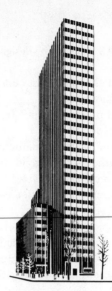

6

Sketching

6.1 Introduction. The accurately scaled engineering drawings, made with instruments, which are used for shop production and construction purposes are usually made by young engineers or professional draftsmen. The ideas are conceived and the designs are made by experienced engineers who must then convey his instructions to the draftsman. These instructions must be clear and concise so that the draftsman can complete the detailed working drawings.

Engineering designs, however, are usually complicated and require so much detailed information that the only practical method of conveying these ideas is by means of a drawing. It follows, therefore, that the engineer must be thoroughly familiar with all forms of projection used by the draftsman and he must be able to make some form of drawing much more rapidly than the detailed instrumental drawing. For this purpose the engineer uses freehand drawing.

Other than the fact that such drawings are made without instruments, they follow all the principles of projection described in Chapter 7 for multiview drawings. This chapter should be studied before making sketches. For pictorial drawings of various kinds, the student should refer to Chapters 17, 18, and 19. If the sketches are dimensioned, the principles of Chapter 9 on Basic Dimensioning should be followed.

6.2 Purpose of sketches. Technical sketches are used for a wide variety of purposes, among which the following are the more important:

a. To transmit information obtained in the field or factory to the drafting office. This occurs when repairs have to be made or when changes are contemplated in an existing structure.

◀ Skyscraper of glass (Corning Glass Works).

b. To transmit the ideas of the designer to the draftsman.

c. To make studies of the layout and views required for a mechanical drawing.

d. As a means of making preliminary studies of a design for functional operation.

e. As a basis for making computations of stress analysis for strength design. A good sketch is very important in making a correct analysis.

f. To provide a basis for discussion between engineers and workmen.

g. To furnish a picture of an object which will help to interpret the orthographic projections.

h. As shop drawings for manufacturing. These are usually made on coordinate tracing paper with non-actinic grid lines.

i. As a teaching aid when discussing problems in the classroom.

6.3 Materials for sketching. One of the advantages of sketching is that only a minimum of equipment is required.

a. Pencils and erasers. Most draftsmen prefer a soft pencil in the range from F to 2H. The H grade pencil is a good all-around tool. It should have a conical point and be frequently resharpened. A good eraser that will not smudge is very useful.

b. Papers. (1) Blank paper. For the experienced man blank paper of bond or ledger quality is satisfactory.

When away from the office, nothing else may be available.

(2) Rectangular coordinate paper. For multiview drawing, rectangular coordinate paper is an aid to the beginner, and in many offices it is regularly used (with non-actinic lines) to produce dimensioned working drawings for the shop. Coordinate papers can be obtained in a wide variety of divisions. For ordinary purposes, subdivisions of ⅛ or ¼ inch are satisfactory as shown in Fig. 6–1.

(3) Isometric ruled paper. For pictorial sketches, isometric paper provides a guide to give the correct position of the axes and for units of measurements in proportioning. See Fig. 6–2. For oblique sketches, rectangular coordinate paper is useful since the front face of an object will be the same as in multiview drawings. See Fig. 6–3.

(4) Perspective grids. Perspective grids can be obtained in a few different sizes and with varying coordinate rulings. These are used most frequently for larger projects. See Fig. 6–35.

6.4 Tools for measurement. Although freehand sketches are not made to scale, it is often necessary to make measurements, as for example, in an emergency when a broken part must be replaced or when working in the field.

a. Field work. A six-foot rule and sometimes a steel tape are necessary, not to mention the usual surveying instruments.

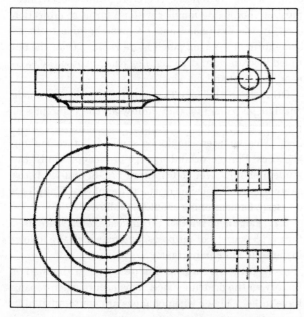

Fig. 6–1. Two-view sketch on rectangular coordinate paper.

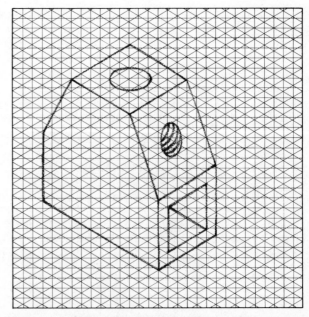

Fig. 6–2. Isometric sketch on isometric paper.

b. Shop work. Here it may be necessary to use the steel scale, calipers, micrometer calipers, surface gages, depth gages, and thread gages. The engineer should know how to use these tools to get the dimensions he needs.

6.5 Technique of sketching. As an aid in acquiring skill in sketching, the following suggestions will be helpful. These recommendations apply to any sketch whether it be done on plain paper or coordinate paper. The only difference is that with ruled papers the coordinate lines serve as guides for some of the lines. In other respects, the principles are the same.

a. The sketch stroke for straight lines. Experience has shown that it is very difficult to draw a long straight line in one stroke, whereas by using a series of short overlapping strokes a rough but straight line can be made readily. The sketch stroke, therefore, consists of a short light stroke made with an arm or finger movement as conditions dictate. The pencil should be held firmly, but not tightly, in a normal writing position with the fingers well away from the point of the pencil.

b. Horizontal lines. For drawing horizontal lines, the forearm should be approximately at right angles to the line being sketched, as shown in Fig. 6-4, with the short overlapping strokes being made from left to right. When sketching a line between two previously fixed points the draftsman should place his pencil on one point and sketch toward the other, always keeping his eye on the point toward which he is drawing. The eye should not be allowed to follow the point of the pencil. The first trial line should be made lightly with rather long sketch strokes, after which the strokes may be shortened and corrected until the proper position has been determined. The sketch strokes can then be erased with art gum or soft eraser to the point where they are just visible. A smooth line may then be drawn over the original line. For this drawing the eye should remain on the point of the pencil.

In appearance, the final sketch stroke should not resemble a mechanical line. It has a freedom and character that are entirely different from the clean-cut precision of the mechanically ruled line. The difference between ruled lines and the sketch line is illustrated in Fig. 6-5.

c. Vertical lines. The same type of stroke should be used for vertical lines as described above. When using the finger and wrist movement, the forearm should be placed in a comfortable position which usually varies from approximately parallel to the line, to an angle of 45° with the line being drawn, as shown in Fig. 6-6, with the overlapping strokes from top to bottom. Most draftsmen prefer to use the arm movement for horizontal lines

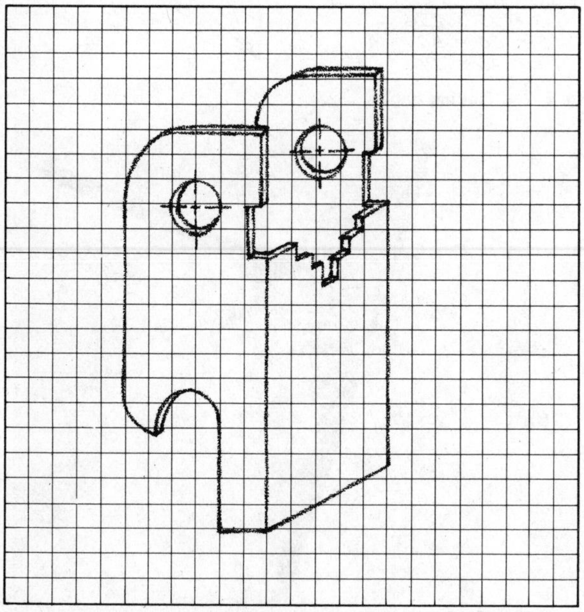

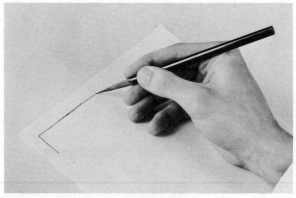

Fig. 6-4. Sketching a horizontal line.

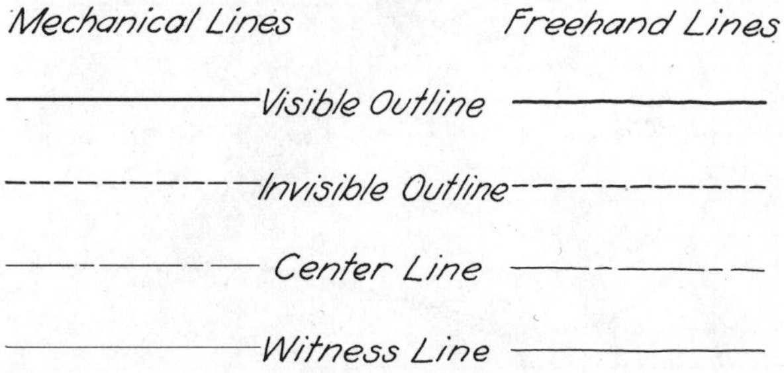

Mechanical Lines   Freehand Lines

—————————Visible Outline —————————

— — — — — — — —Invisible Outline— — — — — — —

——————— Center Line ———·———·———

—————————Witness Line —————————

Fig. 6-5. Comparison between ruled lines and sketched lines.

Fig. 6-3. Oblique sketch using rectangular coordinate paper.

or lines slanting up to the right and the finger or wrist movement for vertical lines or lines slanting down to the right.

d. Inclined lines. Inclined lines, whether on plain paper or on coordinate paper, are usually drawn between two previously located points or at some specified angle. Drawing between two points was discussed under horizontal lines. On coordinate paper, angles of 15, 30, 45, 60, and 75 degrees can be estimated with sufficient accuracy as shown in Fig. 6-7. If difficulty is experienced in drawing inclined lines, the paper may be rotated until the lines are either horizontal or vertical—whichever best suits the skill of the engineer making the sketch.

e. Borderlines. Borderlines and other horizontal or vertical lines may be made easily by holding the edge of the sheet parallel to the edge of the board and then drawing the line with the third and fourth fingers of the hand sliding along the edge of the board as a guide. See Fig. 6-8.

f. Parallel lines. One phase of sketching that many draftsmen find difficult is the drawing of parallel lines. This is a very important part of pictorial sketching. Figure 6-9 shows one method that can be used in certain circumstances. This consists of holding the pencil with the fingers as far from the point as convenient and moving the hand so the little finger slides along a line already drawn.

If this is not possible or convenient, the method shown in Fig. 6-10 will give very good results. The pencil is held in the hand, as shown, directly above the line and then moved to a parallel position. The pencil is then moved lengthwise to draw the line, always keeping the pencil parallel to the original line.

6.6 Sketching circles. Because of the frequency with which circles and ellipses occur in drawing, it is necessary for the draftsman to draw them with facility. Several methods are in common use which will give results sufficiently accurate for sketch purposes. The selection of the method to be used for any particular case depends on the conditions of the problem.

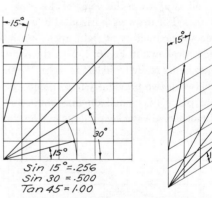

$Sin\ 15° = .256$
$Sin\ 30 = .500$
$Tan\ 45 = 1.00$

Fig. 6-7. Plotting angles.

Fig. 6-6. Sketching a vertical line.

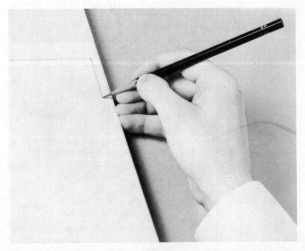

Fig. 6-8. Sketching border line along edge of drawing board.

a. Trammel method. On the edge of a piece of scrap paper, mark two points at a distance apart equal to the radius of the circle. With one point at the center, mark off as many points on the circumference as desired and sketch the circle through them as shown in Fig. 6–11.

b. Enclosing square method. On coordinate paper, a circle may readily be sketched in its enclosing square as shown in Fig. 6–12(*a*). On plain paper, the square can be sketched very lightly, the center lines drawn, and then the circle can be sketched in, making the arcs tangent to the sides of the square at the midpoints.

An additional point on the circle can be obtained as shown in Fig. 6–12(*b*). This is geometrically correct. See Fig. 4–30 under Geometrical Construction.

c. Semimechanical method. A semimechanical method for drawing circles is to hold in the fingers two pencils intersecting each other and having the distance between the points equal to the desired radius. By holding one pencil perpendicular to the paper with its point at the center of the circle, the paper may be revolved about

that point while the other pencil describes the circle. Some draftsmen prefer to use only one pencil, in which case one finger is used for the center. This method is illustrated in Fig. 6–13.

d. Free arm movement. The most useful method and the one that every draftsman should master is that of drawing circles and ellipses with a free arm movement. This method may be used to sketch a circle or ellipse so that it will go through certain points, be tangent to one or more straight lines or one or more circles or ellipses. The forearm should be held approximately perpendicular to the major axis of the ellipse with the fourth and fifth fingers riding lightly on the paper. In this position move the arm freely so that the point of

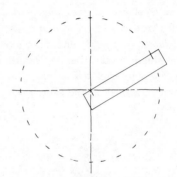

Fig. 6–11.   Sketching circles by trammel.

Fig. 6–9.   Drawing parallel lines.

(*a*)

Sketching a circle in a square.

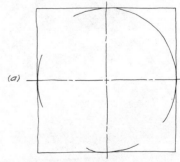

(*b*)

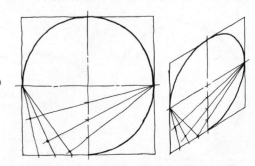

Fig. 6–10.   Drawing parallel lines.

Fig. 6–12.   Plotting points on a circle or an ellipse.

the pencil describes a circle or ellipse in space just above the desired position on the paper. After two or three complete circuits allow the pencil to touch the paper lightly and draw several ellipses, some of which will be inside the desired position and some outside. The number of circuits that will have to be made should decrease as the draftsman gains experience. This "finding line" can be used as the basis for a sketch-stroke circle or ellipse which will satisfy the desired conditions of position or tangency. After the finding lines and sketch stroke have been erased to the point where the circle or ellipse is faintly visible a smooth curve may be drawn as shown in Fig. 6–14. This method is the most rapid of all and with practice will produce a circle or ellipse that is practically perfect.

6.7   Sketching an ellipse. *a. Trammel method.* For the ellipse mark off three points, *m, n,* and *o,* as shown in Fig. 6–15, with *mo* equal to the semiminor axis and *mn* equal to the semimajor axis. Keeping points *n* and *o* always on the center lines of the ellipse, plot as many positions of point *m* as desired and sketch the ellipse.

b. Rectangle method. An ellipse may be sketched in a rectangle by drawing the center lines in the rectangle and making the arcs tangent at the midpoints of the sides in the same manner as for a square. The additional point may also be obtained in the same way. See Fig. 6–16.

6.8   Circles in pictorial sketches. Except for circles in the front face of an oblique sketch, all circles show as ellipses in pictorial drawings. These may be drawn by the enclosing pictorial square or parallelogram method as shown in Fig. 6–17. Again the extra point may be plotted upon the same geometric principle as in the case of a circle in true shape. Arcs are always tangent at the midpoint of the sides of the parallelogram.

6.9   Proportioning. Since the engineer must describe an object which he is creating in his mind, it is necessary that his sketches show the relative proportions of the part he wishes to have the draftsman represent. In other cases where a part is sketched for repair or replacement, or where observations are made in the field, it is desirable to have the sketch made first, before

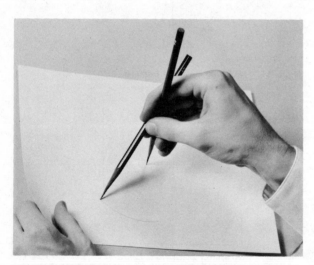

Fig. 6–13.   Method of drawing circle with two pencils.

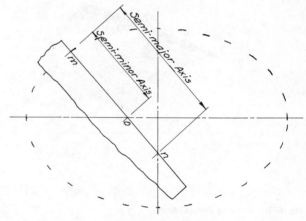

Fig. 6–15.   Ellipse by the trammel method.

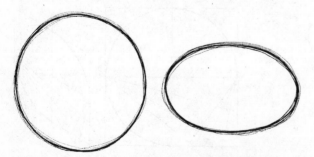

Fig. 6–14.   Sketching circle or ellipse by use of the finding line.

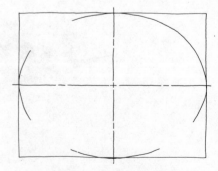

Fig. 6–16.   Sketching an ellipse in a rectangle.

measurements are taken since this gives a place to record dimensions properly. It is therefore necessary that the engineer have a good sense of relative distances so that he may show the width, depth, and height of an object in their proper proportion to each other. The problem of proportioning a sketch, therefore, naturally divides itself into two parts: first, the ability to recognize the relative lengths of lines on an object and second, the ability to layout these comparative lengths on paper. These are the two most difficult and at the same time the most essential steps in making a good sketch. From this point on in this chapter, the matter of proportioning will automatically be involved in the discussion of making various kinds of sketches. There are, however, certain aids which can be employed in obtaining good proportions in a sketch, once the proper estimates have been made of the actual sizes, either existing or to be embodied in a new design.

One convenient method for obtaining relative proportions when drawing in perspective is illustrated in Fig. 6–18. With the sketch board held almost perpendicular to the line of sight, the arm is extended full length with the pencil held in the fingers. By holding the pencil between the eye and the object, one end of the pencil can be made to coincide with one end of a line and the thumb moved along the pencil until it coincides with the other end of the line. This line may then be compared with other lines on the object to get the relative proportions of the object. It is also possible to hold the pencil parallel to any line of the object and then move it to a parallel position on the drawing.

6.10   Aids in proportioning. *a. Practice.* No matter what aids one may use, good sketching requires that one be able to divide a line in half, quite accurately by eye. These halves can then be again divided to give fourths. The best method to accomplish this on plain paper is to practice the art and then check it. The converse of this operation is to draw one line twice as long as another, first parallel and then at right angles to each other. Practice is the best teacher.

b. Scrap paper. Scales are assumed not to be available in sketching and such accuracy is not required. The straight edge of a piece of scrap paper, however, may be marked with a given dimension and then used to give a line two, three, or more times as long. To get one-half the length, the piece of paper may be folded in the middle of the space.

c. Geometric devices. For multiview sketching, the first problem is to draw a rectangle which will just enclose the view. Suppose the desired rectangle were found to be one-third as wide as long, then either the short side or the long side can be assumed and the other dimension determined from the first as shown in Fig. 6–19. When the short distance is assumed as *AB* in Fig. 6–19(*a*), a square can be drawn by erecting perpendiculars to *AB* at *A* and *B*. An easy way to complete the square is to bisect the two right angles visually at *A* and *B* and continue the bisectors to locate *C* and *D*. The center line *MN* can then be drawn and the diagonals *AN* and *BN*. The intersections *E* and *F* with *BC* and *AD* will locate the sides of another square of the same size as *ABCD*. By repeating this process a third square can

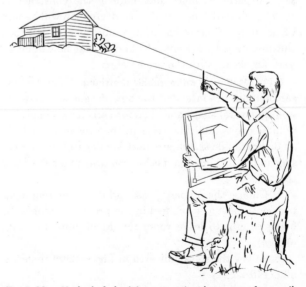

Fig. 6–18.   Method of obtaining proportions by means of a pencil.

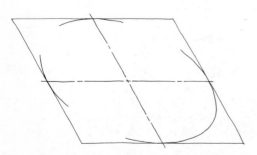

Fig. 6–17.   Sketching an ellipse in a parallelogram.

be formed, thus making a parallelogram three times as long as wide.

A method that is probably a little more accurate is to assume a line equal in length to the long side as *AB* in Fig. 6–19(*b*). If a square *ABCD* is constructed on this line, the square can be subdivided quite accurately by construction lines. The main center lines can be drawn through the intersection of the diagonals, thus dividing the line *BC* in two equal parts. By drawing the line *EA* to intersect *BD,* the point *F* is determined through which a line *GK* may be drawn making the rectangle *ABKG* three times as long as wide.

In Figs. 6–19(*c*) and (*d*) the same construction has been used to locate the ⅓ point of one side of the rectangle. In each case the ¼ point can be located by drawing a line from the ⅓ point to the corner of the rectangle to intersect the main diagonal. This intersecting point can then be projected to the side of the figure to locate the ¼ point. Starting from the ¼ point the same procedure may be used to locate the ⅕ point. This procedure can be carried as far as desired, but, for sketching, the ⅕ point is probably fine enough. This method, illustrated in Figs. 6–19(*c*) and (*d*), can be used to locate the position for details within the outline as well as to proportion the main outline. Any parallelogram may be subdivided in this manner, thus making this method applicable in orthographic as shown in Fig. 6–19(*c*), and axonometric or oblique as in Fig. 6–19(*d*), or in perspective as in Fig. 6–19(*e*).

For beginners these methods may be used to insure correct proportions to the sketch, but, as the draftsman gains experience, more and more of the construction may be omitted. The experienced draftsman will be sure of the proportions of his original outline and will then put in details by eye since he knows that he cannot go very far astray with the proper start.

6.11   Multiview orthographic sketching. Many technical sketches are intended to show details and sizes as well as general shape and therefore are drawn in orthographic projection. The steps in the process of making an orthographic sketch are quite similar to those necessary in the making of a mechanical drawing. See Chapter 7.

a. Choose the proper views, and draw the rectangle to inclose each as explained in the previous paragraph, being careful to leave room for dimensions. See Fig. 6–20(*b*).

b. Follow the steps indicated in Fig. 6–20(*c*) to locate all details.

c. Add all necessary dimensions, notes, and a title.

No scale should be indicated because the drawing has been proportioned by eye.

For a quick sketch, there are numerous short cuts that

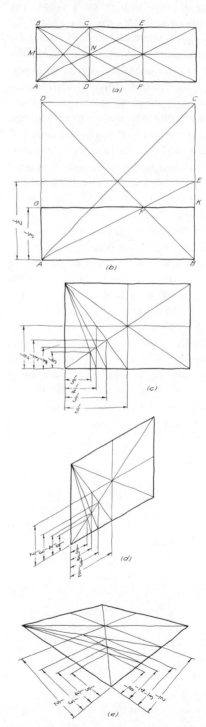

Fig. 6–19.   Method of proportioning a parallelogram.

may be used to save time; thus, symmetrical objects may be shown by drawing only one-half. By a generous use of notes and sections, details may sometimes be omitted on the drawing; or standard parts may be listed by number to avoid drawing them. When coordinate paper is available, proportions may be quickly established by counting squares.

6.12 Pictorial sketching. The pictorial sketch is used to clarify or explain an orthographic drawing, to explain ideas to other people, and as an aid in design and computation. Pictorial sketches may be made in axonometric, oblique, or perspective, depending on the purpose of the sketch, the kind of object being drawn, and the time available for completion.

6.13 Axonometric sketching. The first step in making an axonometric sketch is to choose the direction of the

three axes. These axes represent three mutually perpendicular lines which are the edges of a rectangular box inclosing the entire object. Thus, each of the three principal dimensions of an object may be laid off along one of the axes. The simplest form is isometric, in which the axes are equally spaced making the angles of 120° with each other, and the distances along each of these axes may be laid off in the same proportion to the true length. If other axes are chosen, distances along those axes may be foreshortened to suit, by keeping in mind the general principle that foreshortening increases as the angle that the axis makes with the picture plane increases.

6.13.1 *Geometric principles.* A few geometric principles should be remembered in making axonometric sketches.

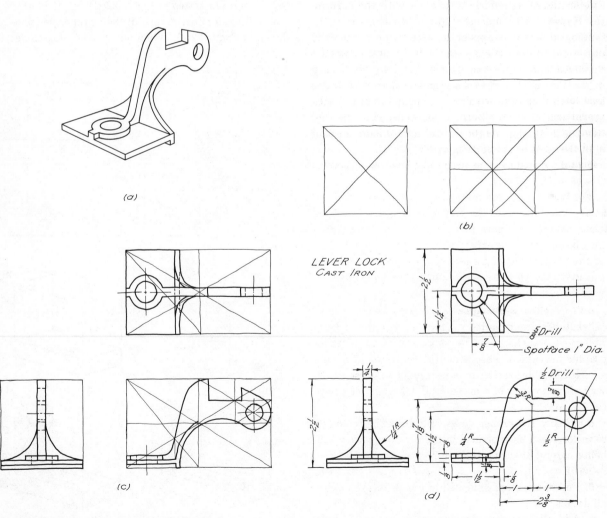

(a)

(b)

(c)

LEVER LOCK
CAST IRON

(d)

Fig. 6–20. Steps in making an orthographic sketch.

a. Parallel lines always show parallel. See Fig. 6–21.

b. Perpendicular lines very seldom show perpendicular. See lines indicated in Fig. 6–21.

c. The axis of a right circular cylinder is always perpendicular to the major axis of the ellipse representing the base. This is illustrated in Fig. 6–21.

d. No two of the axes should be at right angles to each other.

6.13.2   *Choice of axes.* The direction of the three axes to be used in the sketch depends on the desired view. One vertical axis is usually desirable but not absolutely necessary. The other two should be chosen in such a direction that the best view of the object will be obtained. If one face is more important than the other, the horizontal lines in that face should be plotted along an axis which is more nearly horizontal than the other. If the top is most important, one or both horizontal axes should make a fairly large angle with the horizontal. However, this angle should not be too great or the horizontal faces will appear distorted. One of the chief objections to isometric is that the horizontal planes are distorted and symmetrical parts tend to cover each other. For most purposes a dimetric sketch with one axis vertical and the other two at about 15° to the horizontal will give a well-proportioned drawing. In that case the dimensions on the two 15° axes should be about ¾ of the scale of the vertical axis.

6.13.3   *Procedure.* The steps to be followed in making an axonometric sketch are shown in Fig. 6–22 and listed below.

a. Study the object or its orthographic projections, Fig. 6–22(*a*), to determine the best direction of axes. Sketch these axes as shown in Fig. 6–22(*b*).

b. Proportion the object by drawing the inclosing box. When one is sketching from an orthographic working drawing, the methods of proportioning previously described may be used, or for fairly rough work, any desired distance may be chosen to represent 1 inch and the proper number of these marked off by eye on each axis. When one is sketching from the object, the distances may be estimated by careful observation or by using the pencil method previously described. See Fig. 6–22(*c*).

c. Locate the most important parts in the same manner as for orthographic sketches, the only difference being that three dimensions must be considered instead of two. This is illustrated in Fig. 6–22(*d*).

d. Fill in all minor details in their proper positions as shown in Fig. 6–22(*e*). When one is sketching circles, it

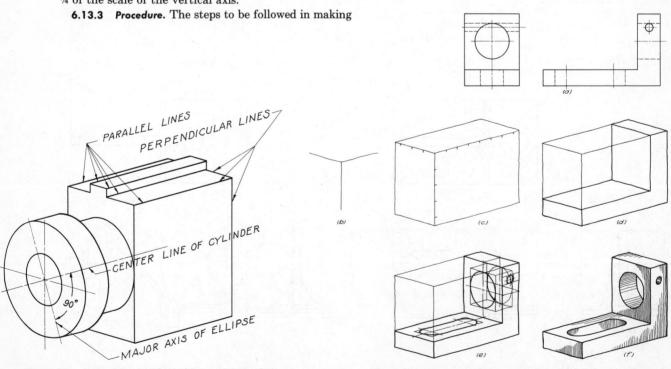

Fig. 6-21.   Geometric principles in axonometric sketching.

Fig. 6-22.   Steps in making an axonometric sketch.

is usually advisable to draw the parallelogram that represents the square circumscribing the circle before drawing the ellipse.

e. Clean up the drawing, and add a small amount of shading if desired as in Fig. 6–22(*f*).

6.14 Basic cube method in isometric sketching. When using plain paper, the most difficult parts of isometric sketching are: (1) getting the proper direction of the axes; (2) the shape of ellipses; and (3) proportioning. All of these can be readily determined by the basic cube method. Figure 6–23 illustrates the construction. The steps are as follows:

a. Construct a freehand circle by the arm movement method.

b. Draw the horizontal and vertical center lines.

c. Bisect the upper and lower half of the vertical center line to get points *A* and *B*.

d. Draw horizontal lines through *A* and *B* until they intersect the circle at points *C, D, E,* and *F*.

e. Connect these four points with the center of the circle and the end of the vertical centerline. This gives an isometric drawing of a cube.

f. Construct an ellipse in each of the faces of the cube to get the proper proportions for the projection of a circle.

6.15 Use of the basic cube method. To make an isometric sketch of the object shown in Fig. 6–24(*a*), construct a cube in isometric as discussed in the previous

paragraph and as shown in Fig. 6–24(*b*). The method of dividing the cube to get the proper proportion for the box is shown in Fig. 6–24(*c*). The details may be drawn in by eye or by means of further construction as illustrated in Fig. 6–24(*d*).

6.16 Dimetric sketching. When two of the angles between the axes are equal and the third different, a dimetric drawing results. The most convenient dimetric is when one axis is vertical and the other two make angles of 15° with the horizontal. In this case, the horizontal axes are laid out to a scale that is ¾ of that used for the vertical axis. Therefore the method illustrated in Fig. 6–22 may be used if the small unit divisions on the horizontal axes are ¾ of those on the vertical axis.

6.17 Basic cube method for dimetric. To obtain the direction of axes, proportions, and shape of ellipses in dimetric, the construction of the basic cube is shown in Fig. 6–25 and the steps are listed below.

a. Construct a freehand circle.

b. Draw the horizontal and vertical center lines.

c. Divide the vertical radii into four equal parts by eye. The points are marked *A, B, C,* and *D* for the upper radius and *1, 2, 3,* and *4* for the lower radius.

d. Through *A* draw a horizontal line till it intersects the circle at *E* and *F*.

e. Draw the top of the solid by joining *E* and *F* to *B* and the center point of the circle.

f. Through *3*, draw a horizontal line till it intersects

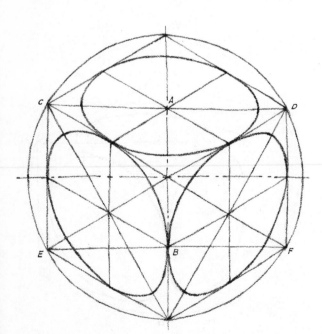

Fig. 6–23. Basic cube in isometric.

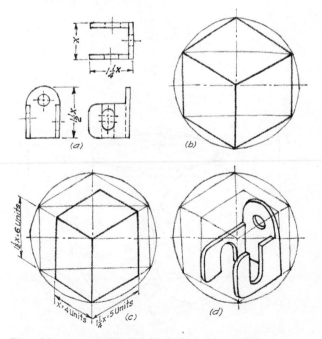

Fig. 6–24. Isometric sketching by the basic cube method.

the vertical lines through E and F to obtain points G and H.

g. Connect G and H with 4 to finish the solid.

h. By diagonals, subdivide the top face twice to obtain the ¾ point of the receding lines. This gives the projection of a cube in dimetric.

i. Inscribe ellipses in each face to determine the proper proportions for the projections of circles.

j. From there, the construction is the same as shown in Fig. 6–24(c) and (d).

6.18   Trimetric sketching. There are an infinite number of combination for trimetric, but the most commonly used has one axis vertical, one at 15° with the horizontal and one at 30° with the horizontal, as shown in Fig. 6–26. In this case, the scale on the vertical axis OG may be taken as one unit, then the scale on the 15° axis OE will be approximately ¹⁵⁄₁₆ and the scale on the 30° axis OF will be approximately ⁷⁄₁₀. The construction of the basic cube is shown in Fig. 6–26, after which the procedure followed for isometric will be used.

6.19   Oblique sketching. In the theory of projection there is a great difference between axonometric and oblique projection. However, in sketching the only important difference is in the relative positions of the three axes. In axonometric no two axes should be perpendicular to each other, but in oblique two of the axes are always perpendicular to each other and the third can be chosen at any angle. For practical purposes one axis is

drawn vertical and one horizontal, which makes all faces in the plane of these axes similar to shape to their front view. By placing the most descriptive face in this plane, the direction of the third axis can be chosen to give the proper emphasis to the other two faces. Thus, if the third axis is drawn at a small angle to the horizontal the side face will show more clearly, whereas if the third axis is nearer the vertical the top will become more important. The third or receding axis may be laid out in the same proportion as the front axis, or it may be foreshortened by any amount up to one-half. A foreshortening to about three-quarter size will be very effective in reducing distortion.

One of the chief advantages of oblique is, namely, that circles in the front face may be drawn as circles is not as important in sketching as in mechanical drawing since it is probably easier to sketch an ellipse than a circle. The principal disadvantage to oblique is that cylinders whose axes are parallel to the front face appear distorted as shown in Fig. 6–27(a). This is because the major axis of the ellipse of the base is not perpendicular to the axis of the cylinder. In sketching, this may be improved by arbitrarily drawing the ellipse so that its major axis is perpendicular to the axis of the cylinder as shown in Fig. 6–27(b). Although not a correct projection, this change is favored by many draftsmen. When one is drawing long objects in oblique, the receding lines are sometimes made to converge slightly, thus

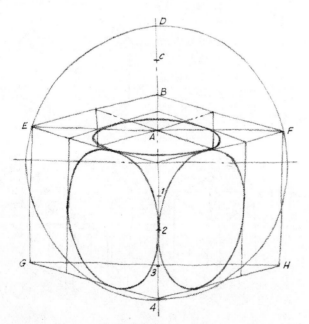

Fig. 6-25.   Basic cube in dimetric.

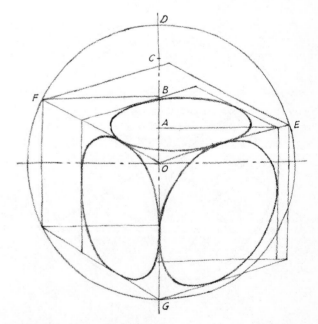

Fig. 6-26.   Basic cube in trimetric.

tending to eliminate distortion. This is shown in Fig. 6–28 and is sometimes called pseudoperspective. A study of Fig. 6–29 will show that the steps in making an oblique sketch are practically the same as those for axonometric.

6.20 Center-line construction. When an object having circular or cylindrical parts is sketched, it is frequently desirable to build up the drawing by locating the main center lines first instead of constructing a box enclosing the entire object. This method of approach is applicable to either axonometric or oblique sketching. The steps in making a sketch by the center-line layout method follow very closely those given for the enclosing-box method, as may be seen by a careful study of Fig. 6–30. In the center-line method, the best approach is to assume a unit distance and duplicate that distance by eye until the centers of all circles have been located. These unit distances can be foreshortened by a different

amount on each axis to produce a good axonometric or oblique sketch.

6.21 Perspective sketching. A perspective of an object is approximately the view as seen by the observer if he

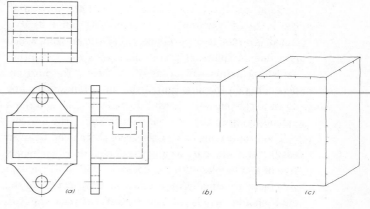

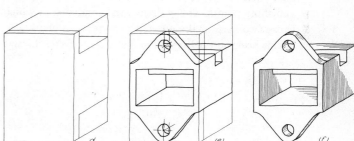

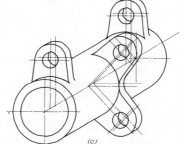

Fig. 6–29. Steps in making an oblique sketch.

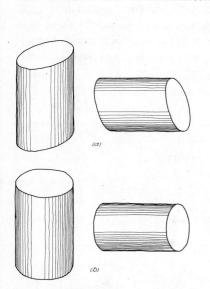

Fig. 6–27. Distorted cylinders in oblique.

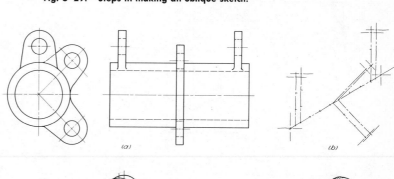

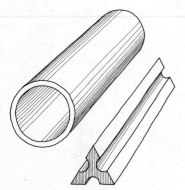

Fig. 6–28. Pseudoperspective.

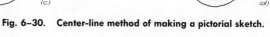

Fig. 6–30. Center-line method of making a pictorial sketch.

were to look at it with one eye. The most important difference between perspective and other forms of pictorial is that receding lines appear to converge instead of remaining parallel. In perspective, lines which are parallel to the picture plane will show parallel on the drawing but all parallel receding lines are drawn to converge at a point. If these receding lines are horizontal, the point of convergence, or vanishing point as it is called, is on the horizontal line, called the horizon, which is a line at the level of the observer's eye. All other vanishing points will be above or below the horizon, depending on the direction of the lines. Lines extending down to the rear will vanish below the horizon and those extending up to the rear will vanish above the horizon.

The proportions of a perspective sketch can be most easily determined by basing the sketch on the perspective of a cube placed in the desired position. If the two side faces are equally important the front corner of the cube should be placed equidistant between the two vanishing points. This will give the condition in which those two faces make 45° with the picture plane, and in this position the horizontal distance between the two

vertical lines of the sides of the cube will be about one-half the height of the front edge as shown in Fig. 6–31 (*a*). If it is desired to have the faces of the cube make angles of 60° and 30° to the picture plane the front edge of the cube should be placed at one-quarter of the distance from one vanishing point to the other. In this position the horizontal width of the broad face will be about ¾ of the height of the front edge while the width of the narrow face will be about ⅓ of the height of the front edge as shown in Fig. 6–31(*b*).

After the cube has been established, any desired proportions can be obtained by duplicating the cube in perspective by means of diagonals or subdividing it by the methods indicated in Fig. 6–19. When sufficient space is available, it is usually best to draw a cube having one side equal to the largest dimension of the object and subdivide it rather than build it up from a small cube, although by careful work either method will give good results. In Fig. 6–32, the basic proportions in the ratio 1:2:3 were determined by building the figure from a basic cube, one unit in size, by the method shown in Fig. 6–19(*a*). In Fig. 6-33 the basic cube was considered

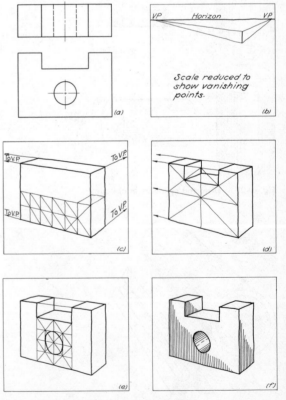

Fig. 6–32. **Steps in making a perspective sketch.**

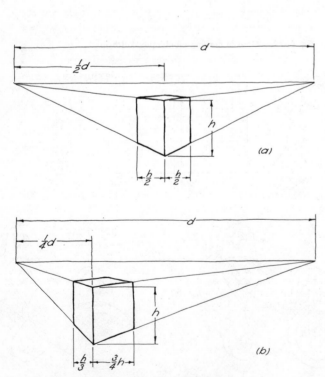

Fig. 6–31. **Proportioning a cube in perspective.**

to be three units on a side and the final proportions determined by subdividing.

In making a perspective sketch it is advisable to follow an orderly procedure such as that listed below.

a. Assume a horizontal line at the level of the eye as the horizon, and choose two points on it as far apart as possible for vanishing points. See Fig. 6–32(*b*).

b. Locate the front corner of the object in such a position that the desired view of the object will be obtained. By placing it near the right vanishing point the left side of the object will be made more prominent and vice versa. By placing this line near the horizon the top becomes relatively unimportant but, as the line is lowered, the top becomes more prominent. The relative scale of the entire drawing will be determined by the length of the line assumed for this front corner as in Fig. 6–32(*b*).

c. Connect the ends of the vertical line to both vanishing points as shown in Fig. 6–32(*b*), which has been drawn to a greatly reduced scale to show the location of the vanishing points.

d. Complete the box enclosing the entire figure. The ability to judge distances in perspective may be acquired by practice. As an aid in developing this ability, the student should practice sketching squares and cubes in various positions. Thus in Fig. 6–32(*c*), the enclosing box has been proportioned so that the three edges are in the ratio of 1:2:3. This has been done by drawing approximately 1-inch squares in the two vertical faces and repeating them by graphical construction of drawing successive diagonals. A better method is shown in Fig.

6–33, where a cube three units on a side was drawn first and subdivided by the methods shown in Fig. 6–19.

e. Sketch all details, beginning with the more important and ending with the minor parts. The location and size of the details may be determined by subdividing squares or rectangles. Thus, in Fig. 6–32(*d*), the width of the notch is one-half the length of the entire object and its depth is one-quarter of the total height of the object. Therefore, by subdividing the front face twice, the corners of the notch can be located. After some practice these distances may be estimated directly without construction lines, although it is much more difficult to do this in perspective than in axonometric.

f. When circles are sketched in perspective, the square circumscribing the circle should always be drawn first, after which the center of the circle may be found by drawing the diagonals. The center point of each side may be found by drawing the center lines of the square in perspective. The ellipse representing the circle can then be drawn within the square and tangent at the center point of each side as shown in Fig. 6–32(*e*).The completed perspective sketch in Fig. 6–32(*f*) may be improved by a small amount of shading.

When a circle occurs in a horizontal plane perpendicular to the picture plane, it will appear as a straight line when it is at the level of the eye. As the circle is moved either above or below the horizon it becomes a narrow ellipse, which broadens as it moves away from the horizon. This is illustrated in Fig. 6–34.

6.22 Use of perspective grid. Prepared grids may be purchased for a variety of setups for making perspective

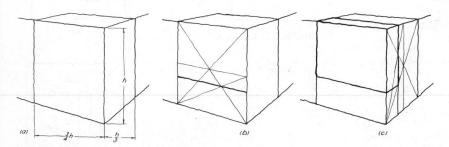

Fig. 6–33.   Proportioning a box in the ratio of 1:2:3.

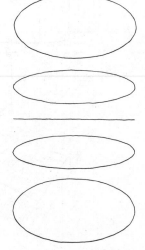

Fig. 6–34.   Circles in perspective.

drawings. Each set has definite points of sight and corresponding vanishing points, and if another relationship between the object and the picture plane is desired, it is necessary to select a different grid. These grids, such as the one shown in Figure 6–35, are very useful for freehand perspective, but are accurately drawn so that they can be used for instrumental drawing. The one shown in Fig. 6–35 has the object so placed that one face makes 30° with the picture plane and the other 60°.

Figure 6–35 gives the procedure for sketching the little building shown in the upper right-hand corner of the figure.

6.23   Line quality. For many purposes a very rough sketch is satisfactory and speed is more important than appearance. For this kind of a sketch, it is not necessary to erase any construction lines or smooth up the outlines. These outlines may be very rough and broad consisting of several overlapping sketch strokes. These sketches are usually made with a very soft pencil and frequently the desired outline is made very black right over the construction lines.

PROBLEMS

The problems in freehand sketching are to be done without instruments of any kind except pencil and eraser. Rectangular coordinate paper or isometric paper may be used if so directed by the instructor, but is recommended that the student acquire skill in sketching on plain unruled paper. The problems are to be done on 8½ × 11 or 9 × 12-inch paper as directed.

Orthographic Sketches

The figures for the following problems will be found in Chapter 8. The parts shown removed in these illustrations are to show the shape of the object but are not to be shown in your sketches.

1. Make a two-view orthographic sketch of the gland shown in Fig. 8–32.

2. Make a two-view sketch of the face-plate blank shown in Fig. 8–33.

3. Make a sketch of the pulley shown in Fig. 8–34.

4. Make a sketch showing the views necessary to describe the shape of the stuffing box of Fig. 8–35.

5. Make a two-view sketch of the pulley shown in Fig. 8–36.

6. Make a sketch showing the views necessary to describe

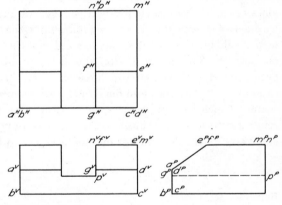

Fig. 6–36.   Cut block.

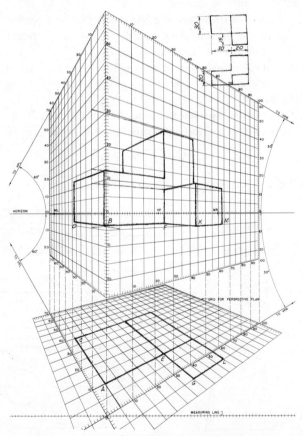

Fig. 6–35.   Perspective grid. (Courtesy of Professor Grace Wilson.)

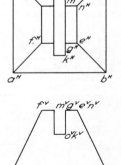

Fig. 6–37.   Cut block.

the shape of the eccentric sheave of Fig. 8–37.

7. Make a two-view orthographic sketch of the end plate shown in Fig. 8–38.

8. Make a two-view orthographic sketch of the conveyor box end shown in Fig. 8–39.

9. Make a sketch showing the views necessary to describe the shape of the tool rest holder of Fig. 8–40.

10. Make the necessary freehand views to show the shape of the tool box holder in Fig .8–41.

11. Make a two-view orthographic sketch of the pipe support shown in Fig. 8–42.

12. Make a sketch having the necessary views to describe the shape of the bracket in Fig. 8–43.

Pictorial Sketches

The making of pictorial sketches from orthographic drawings provides excellent practice in reading drawings. In all cases the object should be drawn to show its shape to best advantage.

13. Make an isometric sketch of the object shown in Fig. 6–36.

14. Make an isometric sketch of the object shown in Fig. 6–37. Sketch the complete pyramid first; then cut off the portion as shown in the figure.

15. Sketch the object shown in Fig. 6–38 or 6–39, in isometric form as assigned by the instructor.

16. Sketch in isometric form the block shown in Fig. 6–40.

17. Make an isometric sketch of the abutment shown in Fig. 6–41.

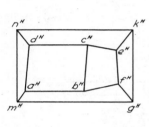

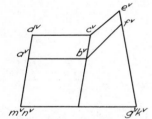

Fig. 6–38. Cut block.

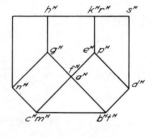

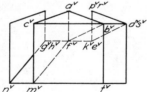

Fig. 6–40. Cut block.

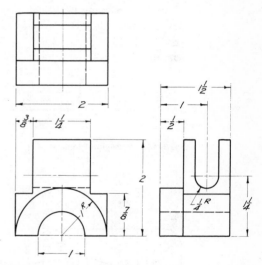

Fig. 6–42. Slide bearing.

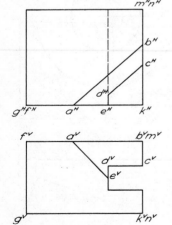

Fig. 6–39. Cut block.

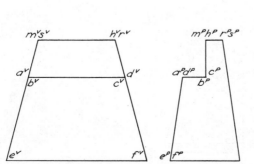

Fig. 6–41. Abutment.

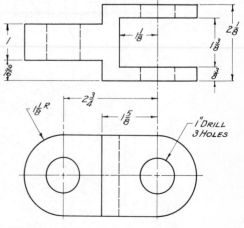

Fig. 6–43. Link.

18. Make an oblique sketch of the bearing cap shown in Fig. 6–42.

19. Make an oblique sketch of the link shown in Fig. 6–43.

20. Make an oblique sketch of the face-plate blank shown in Fig. 6–44.

21. Make an isometric sketch of the bracket shown in Fig. 6–45.

22. Make an isometric sketch of the lever shown in Fig. 6–46.

23. Make an oblique sketch of the bevel washer shown in Fig. 6–47.

24. Make a dimetric sketch of an object shown in Figs. 6–36 to 6–47 as assigned by the instructor.

25. Make a perspective sketch of an object shown in Figs. 6–36 to 6–47 according to specifications given by the instructor.

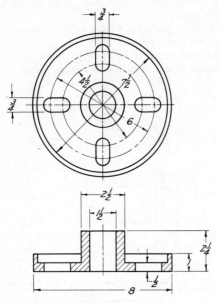

Fig. 6–44.   Face-plate blank.

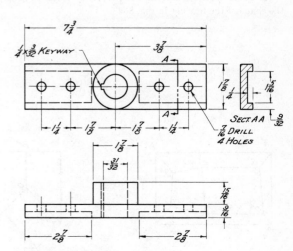

Fig. 6–46.   Lever arm.

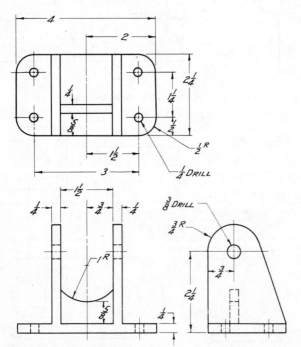

Fig. 6–45.   Hinge bracket.

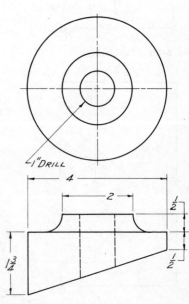

Fig. 6–47.   Beveled washer.

Two 16,000-KW single shaft, simple cycle gas turbine engines (General Electric Company).

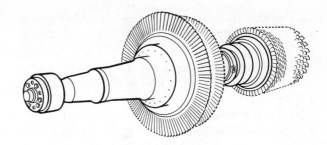

7

Orthographic Projection

7.1 Introduction. The fundamental geometric principles and relationships that constitute the bases of the several forms of projection underlying the art of drawing have been discussed in Chapter 5. It was noted that the various types of projection produce drawings that can be classified broadly as pictorial or multiview in character. Multiview drawings are always done in orthographic projection, which means that the lines of sight, or projecting lines, are perpendicular to the plane of projection. Such drawings constitute the major part of the drawing output of any engineering or industrial drafting office. They are often supplemented by pictorial drawings of one type or another to aid in the interpretation of the plans and specifications of the designer. This chapter deals with the basic principles of orthographic projection as they apply to the preparation of multiview drawings. These principles, as well as the numerous variations and conventional practices that have become approved through general usage, must be learned thoroughly by every engineer and draftsman.

7.2 Planes of projection. Pictorial drawings may be made upon any kind of surface, as, for example, the paintings upon the curved walls and domes of cathedrals and other public buildings. The engineer's drawings, however, are always conceived as projections upon plane surfaces, excepting, of course, maps and a few other special projections where curved surfaces may be used. As previously noted, such planes are called planes of projection. As these planes are set up in space, for projective purposes, they are imagined to be transparent, but in the making of actual drawings they are supplanted by the paper or other material upon which the draftsman works. In fact, *the drawing paper represents several planes of projection at one and the same time* as will be seen presently.

Since there is a different point of sight for each view in orthographic drawing, it follows that there must be a different plane of projection for each view. The projection planes most commonly used are shown in Fig. 7-1. One plane is set up in a vertical position, the second perpendicular to the first in a horizontal position, and the third is set perpendicular to the first two through any point in their line of intersection but preferably to the right or left of the object to be projected. These three planes, known as the coordinate or principal planes of projection, are named the vertical or *V*-plane, the horizontal or *H*-plane, and the profile or *P*-plane, respectively. The planes are considered infinite in extent and in a sense surround the object, thus making it possible to project the object upon each plane in turn.

The two primary or basic views are called the front and top views. To obtain the front view, the observer is assumed to be standing in front of and facing the vertical plane. *Relationships between parts of the object such as right and left, top and bottom, front and back are referred to this position of the observer.* To obtain the top view the observer is assumed to be above the horizontal plane, looking down on the object. See Fig. 7-1. All other positions that the observer must assume are determined by the complexity of the object which may require that it be viewed from the right side, left side, or some other direction.

7.3   Rotation of the coordinate planes. Drawings, whether composed of one, two, three, or even more views, are always shown in appropriate relation to each other on a single plane surface, namely, the sheet of drawing paper. The transformation from a series of projection planes in space, at right angles to each other, to a single plane may be accomplished readily by holding the vertical plane fixed while the others are revolved about their intersections with that plane into coincidence with it. Any projections that have been made on the planes will, of course, revolve with them into the *V*-plane (the drawing paper). In Fig. 7-2(*a*), *each plane with its projection is revolved away from the object* in the manner indicated by the direction arrows. The horizontal planes, both top and bottom, and the profile planes, both right and left, revolve about their respective intersections with the vertical plane, whereas the plane for the rear view revolves into either profile plane and with that plane into the vertical plane. When all six views are projected, the revolution of the various

planes, as described above, places the views on the vertical plane, which is the drawing paper, in the relative positions shown in Fig. 7-3(*b*). It should be noted that the several views have been spaced more compactly than in the perspective of Fig. 7-2(*a*) and that each view shows two dimensions on the object. The dash lines indicate invisible edge lines.

Seldom is it necessary to project more than three views; at least two are always required except with very simple objects, when one view will do. The front and top views or the front and profile views are usually chosen.

The arrows in Fig. 7-3(*a*) show the direction in which the observer looks to obtain the views shown in Fig. 7-3(*b*). *It should be noted that the observer is on the opposite side of the plane from the object.* The spatial concepts here emphasized are important, particularly in determining the visibility of lines and surfaces on the object and in fixing the point of sight for the various views.

It should be noted also that, if these arrows could be fastened to their respective planes in a perpendicular position so that they could revolve with the planes, they would all become parallel to and pointing in the same direction as the one fixed to the *V*-plane as shown in Fig. 7-2(*b*). This consideration will aid in determining the proper direction of revolution for the auxiliary planes to be discussed in Chapter 14.

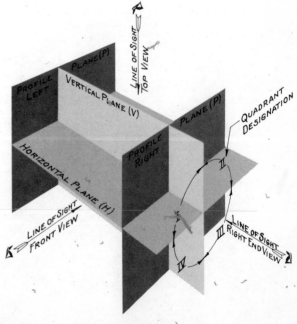

Fig. 7-1.   The principal coordinate planes.

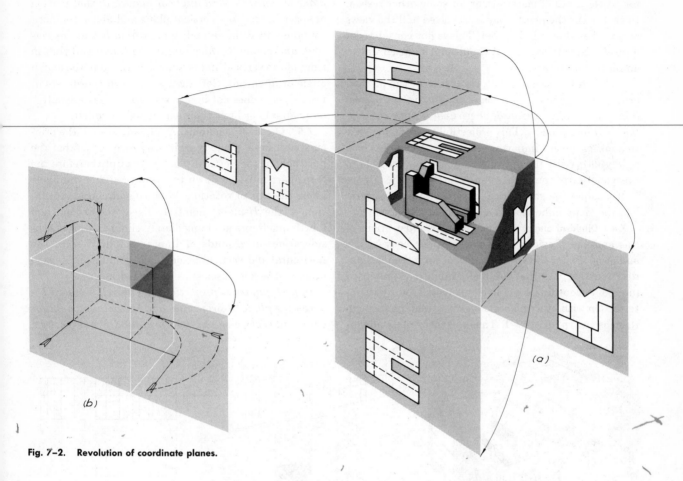

Fig. 7–2. Revolution of coordinate planes.

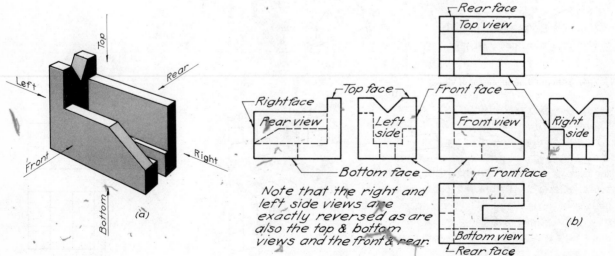

Fig. 7–3. Arrangement of views.

Note that the right and left side views are exactly reversed as are also the top & bottom views and the front & rear.

Occasionally, the standard arrangement of views shown in Fig. 7–3(*b*) is not satisfactory because of the necessity to clear a certain portion of the drawing sheet for a title, a bill of materials, or for some other reason. In that event the planes may be revolved and the views arranged as shown in Fig. 7–4. This is not considered a desirable arrangement and should not be used unless absolutely necessary.

It should be observed that, regardless of the method of revolution, *the various views are always "in projection," that is, in horizontal or vertical alignment with the front or top views.* This projectibility from one view to another is very important and must be maintained rigidly; otherwise the drawing becomes unintelligible to everyone save the draftsman who made it. Figure 7–4(*c*) shows the geometrical constructions used to relate the views in horizontal and vertical alignment.

7.4   Dihedral angles or quadrants. The illustrations of this and the previous chapters have, for convenience and of necessity, shown the planes of projection as limited in extent, but they are really infinite or unlimited in area. A coordinate plane is not restricted by its intersection with other planes but may extend on through them as shown in Fig. 7–1. Thus the horizontal and ver-

tical planes divide all space into four equal parts called dihedral angles or quadrants. That portion of space *in front of the vertical plane* and *above the horizontal plane is called the first angle or quadrant;* that portion of space behind the vertical plane and above the horizontal is called the second; *that portion behind the vertical and below the horizontal, the third;* and that in front of the vertical and below the horizontal, the fourth angle or quadrant. Setting up the third coordinate or profile plane does not in any way affect the designation of quadrants or limit their extent right and left.

7.5   Choice of quadrants. As already stated, the principal horizontal plane is arbitrarily revolved so that the part behind the vertical plane turns up; therefore the front part must go down to avoid breaking the plane along the axis of rotation. With this direction of rotation of the *H*-plane definitely fixed, the second and fourth quadrants are immediately eliminated from consideration on grounds of impracticability, since the horizontal and vertical projections would overlap each other and become useless as working drawings.

In *first quadrant projection, the object is placed between the plane of projection and the point of sight for each and every view;* in *the third quadrant projection,*

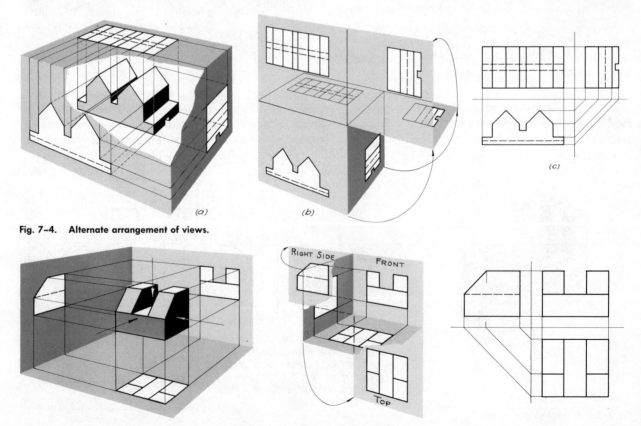

(a)   (b)   (c)

Fig. 7–4.   Alternate arrangement of views.

Fig. 7–5.   First angle projection.

the planes are placed between the object and the points of sight for the several views. Both of these quadrants are widely used since there is no overlapping of views in the rotation of the planes of projection and the rules of visibility are readily stated and applied in each case. In continental European countries, *first quadrant drawing* is the rule. However, this results in a somewhat unnatural arrangement of views (top below the front and end views reversed), which is not favored in the United States except for certain kinds of drawing such as architectural, ship drafting, and a few others. In the machine industries, third quadrant drawings are always used.

The method of projection and the arrangement of views for first quadrant projection is illustrated in Fig. 7–5. It is emphasized again that the top view appears *below* the front view and the right side view appears to the *left* of the front view. If the *left* side view were drawn, it would appear to the *right* of the front view.

If an object is placed in the third quadrant and the rules for revolving the planes are observed, a natural and logical arrangement of views follows, as may be seen from Fig. 7–3(*b*). In this quadrant, the top view of an object appears *above* the front view, and the *right* and *left* views appear at the *right* and *left* of the front view, respectively. This arrangement of views correlates with the successive positions of the observer in obtaining the views and does no violence to his imagination in representing most objects dealt with in engineering practice.

Beginning draftsmen often locate the views incorrectly, making the drawing partially in the first quadrant and partially in the third. Only careful checking of the arrangement of the views will avoid this error and insure that visible and invisible lines on the object are properly distinguished on the drawing.

From the foregoing discussion it is readily deduced that in multiview drawings the planes of projection are set up perpendicular to one another in a box arrangement around the object to obtain as many orthographic views of the object as are necessary to describe its shape and size completely. It may be seen also that *the revolution of the planes of projection, including auxiliary and section planes yet to be discussed, is always away from the object in the first and third quadrants;* and that the second and fourth quadrant drawings are never used.

7.6 Rules of placement of the object and the planes of projection. In the shop or factory and in nature everywhere, we are accustomed to see objects in certain definite positions, and when we see them upside down, or in other unusual placements, they are quite unfamiliar. What is true of the objects themselves in this respect is equally true of the drawings of the objects. Hence, it may be stated as a definite rule that objects should be *placed in their normal, natural, or functional position or as near thereto as possible.*

It is emphasized here that the theory of projection as developed in the preceding pages is entirely independent of the shape of the object. The object can be projected accurately whatever its placement with respect to the planes of projection, but, if useful drawings are desired, the relation of the object to the plane of projection is of great importance.

The object should be placed with its principal faces parallel to the planes of projection in order that the true sizes of faces and true lengths of lines may show on the drawing whenever possible. Figure 7–6 shows a cube correctly projected onto the plane but with the object

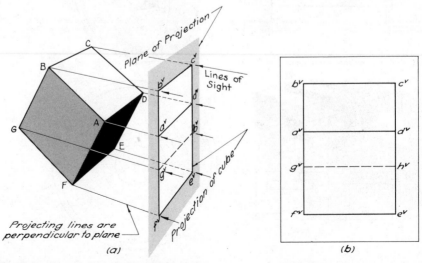

Fig. 7–6.   Poor position of object for projection.

poorly placed with respect to the plane since none of the faces show in true size.

It may be stated, therefore, as a second fundamental rule that, *in making multiview working drawings, the principal faces of the object should be placed parallel* or *perpendicular to the planes of projection.*

For ease in reading the drawing, the object should be turned so that as many of its contour and edge lines as possible will be visible; that is, the most descriptive faces should be parallel and nearest to the planes of projection. Figure 7–7 shows the front and two end

views of an object. Only one end view is necessary, and it should be the one seen from the right side of the object because too many lines are invisible to the left side view.

A third rule therefore requires that the views be chosen to show as few hidden lines as possible.

Since all other views are generally in alignment with the front view, it is usually considered the principal view. The object, therefore, is normally turned so that the most complicated view or the view having *the most descriptive contour becomes the front view.* Figure 7–8

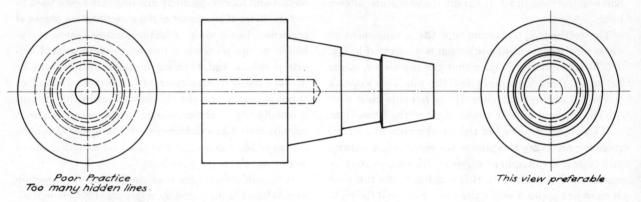

Poor Practice
Too many hidden lines

This view preferable

Fig. 7–7.   Selection of views to avoid hidden lines.

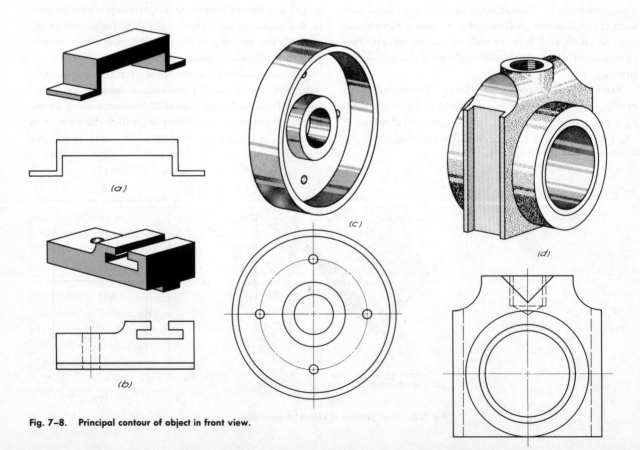

(a)

(b)

(c)

(d)

Fig. 7–8.   Principal contour of object in front view.

shows several objects in pictorial projection and the proper front view in each case.

In brief, the three most important rules to be observed in placing the object with respect to the planes of projection or, perhaps stated more logically, in setting up projection planes around an object, are:

a. Keep the object in its natural position, that is, as seen in its usual functioning position.

b. Place the faces of the object parallel to the planes of projection.

c. Select the views to be shown so that as few invisi-ble lines as possible will appear in the drawings.

It should be obvious at this point that the engineer-draftsman must use his powers of imagination and visualization to create a mental picture of what takes place geometrically in making a drawing of an object on a plane sheet of paper.

7.7 Determination of number of views to be drawn. The basic purpose of all multiview projection is, of course, to show the true size and shape of the object being represented. Other features such as hardness, roughness, and type of material are shown by symbols and notes that are added to the dimensioned drawings at appropriate places. Hence the draftsman must determine at the outset what the minimum number of views may be to show completely both the shape and size of the object for which he is requested to make drawings. He should *make no more than the minimum number required for clear understanding.*

It must be remembered also that each view of an orthographic drawing shows actual distances on the object in all directions that are parallel to the plane of projection on which the view appears. In three-view drawings many distances and dimensions show in true value on two planes of projection. *Front views show heights and also distances from left to right* (width); *top views show distances right and left* and *also distances from the front to the back of the object* (depth); *side or end views show both height and depth.* Other scalings may be made on each view, as indicated above, but dimensioning is primarily done in the three directions mentioned. With these facts in mind, it is comparatively easy for a draftsman to determine not only the necessary number of views but which ones are most advantageous in a given situation.

a. One-view drawings. A single orthographic view is often adequate in representing thin flat objects having uniform thickness or even in representing simple cylindrical parts. Such objects as shims, gaskets, steel springs, and a host of other thin parts cut from thin plate may be represented in a single view, provided the thickness is given in a note. The top view of the shim in Fig. 7–9 shows its true length and width and the cuttings that must be made, and the thickness and material used are shown in the note. The drawing completely specifies the size and shape of the shim, and no additional information is needed for its manufacture. Such a one-view drawing when executed to full scale is sometimes called a pattern or templet. Similarly, the one-view drawing of the cylindrical part shown in Fig. 7–10 is sufficient for all purposes of manufacture. The fact that the part is

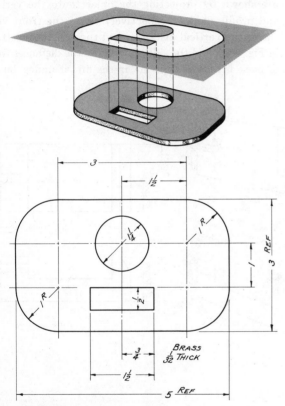

Fig. 7–9. One-view drawing of flat part.

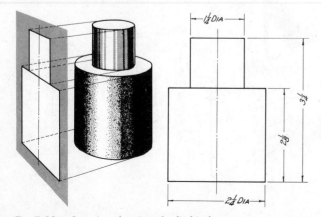

Fig. 7–10. One-view drawing of cylindrical part.

cylindrical is shown by the two dimensions with the notation Dia. added to indicate diameter measurements. Except for extremely simple objects of the kind just mentioned, one-view orthographic drawings are rarely used.

b. Two-view drawings. Most objects, even though quite simple, cannot be described adequately by a single orthographic view. The reason, of course, is that neither the shape nor the size of the object in the third coordinate direction is evident from such a view alone. It must be supplemented by notes and dimensional information that can be more readily shown on a two-view drawing.

The most common two-view drawing is obtained by projecting the object upon the vertical and horizontal planes. The method of obtaining the projections of an object on these two planes, the rotation of the horizon-

tal plane, and the resulting arrangement of views are shown in Fig. 7–11. The two views are called the *V-* and *H-*projections or, more commonly, the front and top views. From the pictorial view in the figure, it can readily be seen that vertical distances and those right and left are shown in the front view, and distances right or left and front or back are shown in the top view, thus giving a drawing in which all three major dimensions may be specified.

Another common arrangement in two-view drawing is shown in Fig. 7–12 in which the front and side views are shown by projecting the object onto the vertical and profile planes, respectively. Here the front view shows the vertical distances and those right or left, as in Fig. 7–11, and the side view shows the distances front or back as did the top view in the first instance, but as

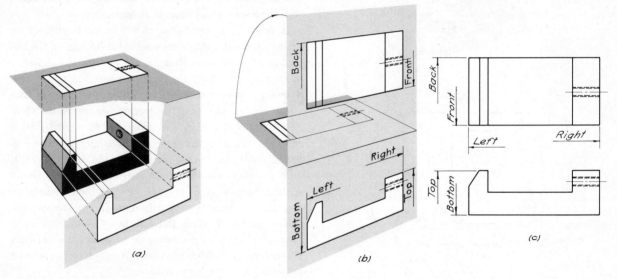

Fig. 7–11.   Third quadrant arrangement of views.

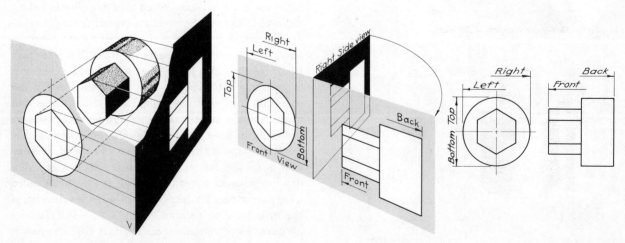

Fig. 7–12.   Arrangement of front and side views.

horizontal measurements on the drawing instead of vertical ones as in Fig. 7–11.

It should be noted again that when *top and front views* are used, they *are always in vertical alignment with the top view directly above the front view;* when the *front and side views* are drawn they *are in horizontal alignment*. On the other hand, in first quadrant drawing the top and front views are reversed in position, but the alignments remain the same. See Fig. 7–5.

The cylinder, cone, sphere, and simple sections of each, together with standard structural shapes of regular cross section, are geometrical forms that can be completely described by two views. Two-view drawings involving other shapes are frequently capable of more than one interpretation. For instance, Fig. 7–13(a) to (f) shows several side views of an object which are possible in conjunction with the given top and front views. With only two views shown, the assumption that the

object is a cube might be justified in such a simple case, but any other shape will require a third view. When there is any doubt as to meaning, the better practice is to draw a third view and give complete information about the shape of the object.

c. Three-view drawings. As noted in the preceding paragraph, many objects cannot be satisfactorily described with two-view drawings even with the addition of notes and symbols. In all such cases three principal planes—horizontal, vertical, and profile—are used, as shown in Fig. 7–14, thus giving three views arranged as in (c) of the figure. *If the right and left side views are equally effective in showing the shape of the object, the right side view is usually drawn.*

The student should observe that in a three-view drawing each measurement or distance on the object in the three principal or coordinate directions is shown in each of two views. The vertical distances (heights) are shown

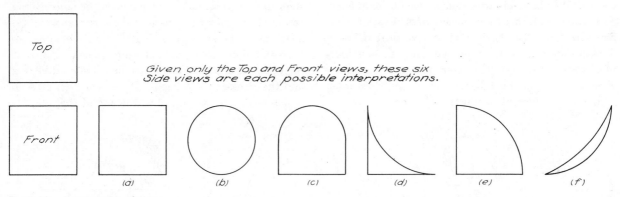

Fig. 7–13.   Interpretation of views.

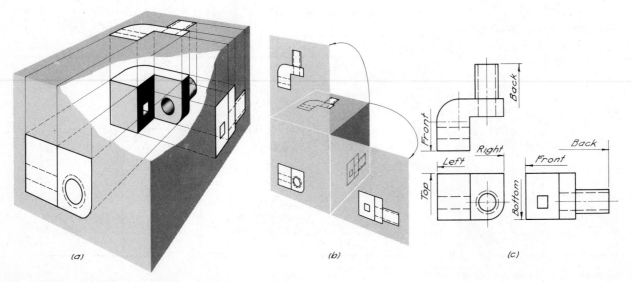

Fig. 7–14.   Third quadrant arrangement of three views.

in the front and side views; the right or left distances (widths) are shown in the top and front views; and the front or back distances (depth) are shown in the top and side views as illustrated in Fig. 7–15. This does not mean, of course, that the actual dimensions of any feature will be placed on each of two views. It means rather that a good deal of care must be exercised in selecting the view on which to place certain dimensions in order not to confuse the drawing.

7.8   Notation of planes, ground lines, and projections. As explained in Art. 7.2, the three primary planes of projection are called the *H-*, *V-*, and *P*-planes, respectively. Auxiliary planes of projection, on the other hand, are designated by numbers beginning with number 1. The use of auxiliary planes is discussed in Chapter 14.

The intersections of the planes of projections are commonly called ground or reference lines, but the student will do well to think of them also as the edgewise views of the planes of projection, as seen from different points of view, rather than as mere axes of rotation and reference lines. The horizontal and vertical reference lines are not ordinarily numbered but, when auxiliary planes are introduced, the reference lines formed are given the names and numbers of the planes whose intersection they represent, as illustrated in Chapter 14.

A point on an object is designated by a capital letter as shown in the pictorial sketch of Fig. 7–15, and the projections of the points are indicated by a corresponding small letter with superscripts representing the name or number of the plane on which the several projections lie. Thus the projection of the point R on the H-plane is r^H. The projection of R on the V-plane is r^V, and the projection of R on the P-plane is r^P. The first auxiliary projection of R would be r^1, the second would be r^2, and so on. This notation will be used throughout the book and is the one commonly employed in engineering drawing and geometry.

7.9   Determination of visibility. The draftsman must remember that *every corner or intersection line which actually exists on the object must appear in some form on every view of the object.* Double curved surfaces that have no actual lines on the object are represented by their outlines, and consequently a different outline will show in each view. Each visible line on the object is represented by a solid line having the heaviest weight of any line on the actual drawing. The invisible lines are represented by dashed lines of lighter weight. In executing either of these lines, a sharp pencil should be used and the stroke should begin with a firm even pressure which should be continued to the end of the line. The

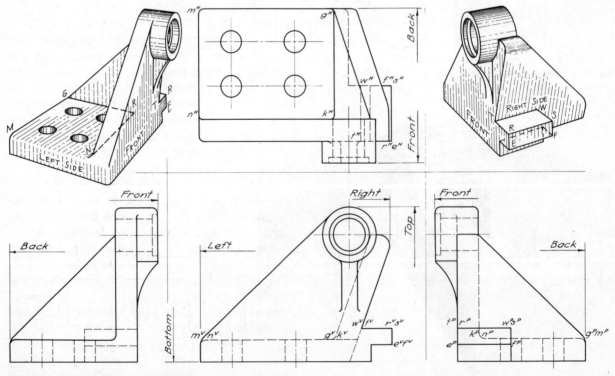

Fig. 7–15.   Determining visibility of lines.

pen or pencil should be lifted from the paper without dragging.

Whether a line is visible in any particular view depends entirely on the point of sight. *In making the top view, the point of sight must be above the object.* This is true regardless of the quadrant in which the object is placed.

It follows, then, that the highest parts of the object will be visible from that point of sight. *To determine which lines are the highest it is necessary to observe the front or side view.* In Fig. 7-15 the front view shows clearly that the cylindrical bearing is the highest part of the bracket, so that it is possible to outline that part in the top view, immediately, with visible outlines. The hole through the bearing will be obscured by the outer part, and consequently it must be shown with invisible outlines.

Although the visibility of many of the lines may be obvious, it is well to consider each line individually. Thus the line *RS* shows higher than *EF* on the front view and would therefore be visible in the top view unless something higher conceals it. Since the front view shows nothing above it, the line *RS* must be visible but the line *EF* is invisible in the top view. Since the two lines coincide in the top view, the visible line covers the invisible and no other indication of the line *EF* appears in the top view. The line *TW* although on top of the base lug is hidden by the bearing cylinder and its supporting brace and consequently shows invisible in the top view.

For the front view, those points which are nearest the front will be shown with visible outlines and those at the back will be shown with invisible outlines. *To determine which lines are in front, a study must be made of either the top or side view.* From these it can be seen that there is a face of the cylinder which is in front of all other parts, and so the circles representing that face can be drawn with visible outlines immediately. To determine the visibility of other lines, each one must be considered individually. Thus, from the top view it can be seen that *RT* is in front of *SW*. Consequently *RT* must be visible in the front view. The line *NK* is in front of *GM*, but both are behind the supporting web, and therefore both must be shown with invisible outlines in the front view.

Similar reasoning will determine the visibility of every line in any view.

7.10   Representation of invisible lines. Regardless of how the object is placed with reference to the point of sight and to the planes of projection, there will almost

certainly be, even on comparatively simple objects, certain edge and contour lines which cannot be seen except in the imagination of the observer. Nevertheless, such lines must be shown on the drawing in order to portray accurately the shape of the object. Moreover, they must be distinguished from the lines representing visible outlines in a very distinctive way. This is accomplished by using a broken line on the drawing composed of short dashes. The dashes should vary somewhat in length, depending on the size of the drawing, but for ordinary drawings a dash about 3/16 inch long with a space of 1/32 inch between dashes will give a good appearance. Uniformity of dashes and spaces should be maintained throughout any drawing except as limitations of space may dictate. The weight of the dash lines, particularly in ink work, should be slightly less than the solid outline. See Fig. 7-15 and also chart of weights of lines in Fig. 3-32.

To insure the highest degree of clarity on a drawing, the draftsman must religiously maintain certain mechanical techniques of representing invisible lines as stated in the following paragraphs and illustrated in Fig. 7-16.

7.10.1   When a dash line representing an invisible outline ends at its intersection with a line representing a visible outline, the last dash must terminate sharply on the full line and not with a space between them. See Fig. 7-16(*a*).

7.10.2   When a dash line ends at its intersection with another dash line, both representing invisible lines, the point of intersection must be definitely located by the intersection of two dashes. See Fig. 7-16(*b*).

7.10.3   When a corner is formed by the intersection of two dash lines representing invisible outlines, the corner must be definitely located by beginning each line with a dash starting at the point of intersection. See Fig. 7-16(*c*).

7.10.4   When three dash lines representing invisible outlines meet to form a corner, the corner should be definitely located by beginning each line with a dash starting at the point of intersection. See Fig. 7-16(*d*).

7.10.5   When a solid line continues beyond an intersection as a dash line representing an invisible outline, the dash portion should begin with a space. See Fig. 7-16(*e*).

7.10.6   When an arc of an invisible circle is tangent to a straight or curved line, and terminates thereon, the arc should begin at the point of tangency with a dash. See Fig. 7-16(*f*).

7.10.7   Arcs representing invisible lines of such small radius that the arc is not long enough to make two complete dashes may be drawn solid. See Fig. 7-16(*g*).

7.10.8 When a full line arc continues beyond an intersection as a dash line representing an invisible outline, the second portion should begin with a space rather than a dash. See Fig. 7-16(*h*).

7.10.9 When two dash lines representing invisible circles or other curves are tangent, the point of tangency should be definitely located by the tangency of two dashes. See Fig. 7-16(*i*).

7.10.10 In orthographic projection it is very common to find two or more lines on the object represented by one line (projection) on the drawing. In all such cases *a visible line projection takes precedence over the projections of invisible lines.* In other words, the solid or full line will cover up the dash lines that are coincident with it. Thus, in the front view of Fig. 7-15, the pro-

jections of object lines *TR* and *WS* coincide, but the line *TR,* being visible, is shown as a full line projection, $t^v r^v$. If the projections of two or more invisible lines coincide, only one dash line is drawn, as is shown in the front view of Fig. 7-15 where $n^v k^v$ is the edgewise view or projection of a flat surface and all the edge lines thereon, whereas the drawing might give the impression of a single invisible line.

7.11 Elimination of invisible lines. Sometimes there is an advantage in choosing a combination of views, such as is shown in Fig. 7-17, to reduce the number of invisible lines to be represented and thus clear the drawings of many dash lines. In this figure a front and two partial end views have been drawn. In each end view only the features on one side of the central or dividing drum are shown. The remainder of the object is omitted in each case. This method usually clarifies the drawing as

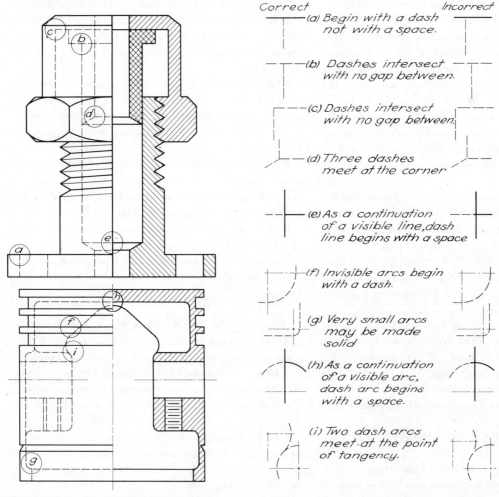

Fig. 7-16. Invisible line technique.

a whole by eliminating the need to represent many hidden lines on the object in a single view.

7.12 Projection of curved lines. Straight-line projections are always determined in one of two ways, either by means of two points or by one point and a specified direction. Similarly, circular projections are determined by a projected center and a known radius. Non-circular curves, however, cannot be so projected. A sufficient number of points on the curve must be projected in each view to enable the draftsman to draw a smooth line through them. The points must be close enough together to determine the direction of the curved projection at any place. This requires that the selected points be close together where the curvature is changing rapidly in the projection, whereas they may be farther apart in so-called flat curves. Figure 7-18 illustrates the method of representing a curved line where its top view has been worked out from the known front and profile views of the curve. The proper way to use the irregular curve in such problems is discussed in Art. 3.24.

7.13 Projection of curved surfaces. Many objects are bounded to a considerable extent by curved surfaces. These consist, for the most part, of portions of cones, cylinders, and spheres, which occur in various combinations with one another and with plane surfaces. A curved surface is represented by the projection of its enveloping or contour element in any view, that is, by the projection of the line on the surface along which the lines of sight are tangent to the surface. For example, on a sphere the great circle which is parallel to the *V*-plane is the enveloping or contour element for the front view.

When combinations of curved surfaces or curved and plane surfaces occur, difficulty is sometimes experienced in determining whether to represent their line of intersection in a particular view. In general it may be said that when two parts of a continuous surface are tangent to each other in a common tangent plane, the line of tangency will be shown when the tangent plane is perpendicular to the plane of projection upon which the view is being made, and when the line is an actual contour line. See Fig. 7-19(*a*).

When the tangent plane is at an angle to the plane of projection, theoretically no line is to be shown, as illustrated in Fig. 7-19(*b*). However, a line is frequently drawn to give meaning to the view as shown in Fig.

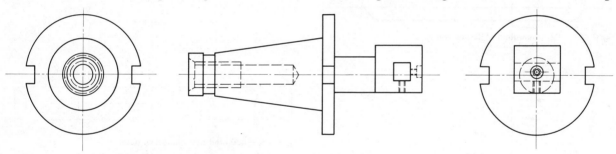

Fig. 7-17. Use of two end views to avoid hidden lines.

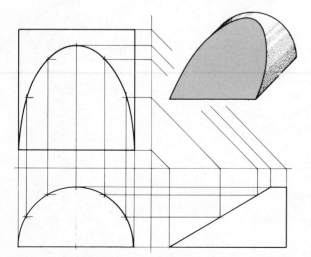

Fig. 7-18. Projection of a curved line.

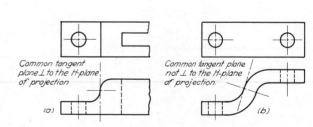

Fig. 7-19. Representation of curved contours.

7–20. In aircraft drafting certain rounded and beveled shapes are handled in this manner. The method of obtaining and representing curved lines of intersection of various kinds is treated in detail in Chapter 16. Two common intersections are encountered in dealing with fillets and small rounded corners. They and other special cases are give further consideration in the next article.

7.14   Projection of filleted angles and rounded corners. Most of the objects shown in the illustrations thus far have been represented as though they were bounded by plane and curved surfaces intersecting in clear-cut edge lines. In industrial production, however, only objects with machined or otherwise finished surfaces have sharp and distinct lines of intersection between the faces, and even these are often rounded to a small radius. The intersections of unfinished surfaces are always well rounded. External corners are spoken of as rounded, whereas internal corners or angles are filleted.

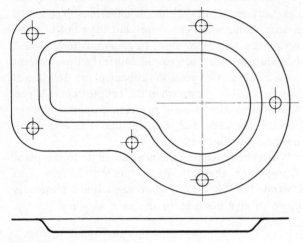

Fig. 7–20.   Representation of curved contours.

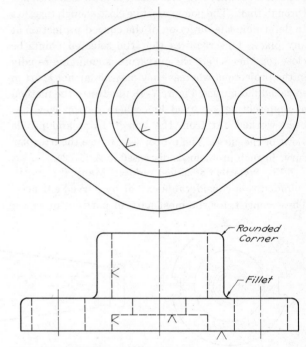

Fig. 7–21.   Rounded and filleted corners.

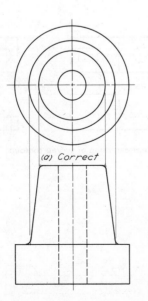
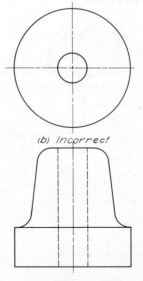
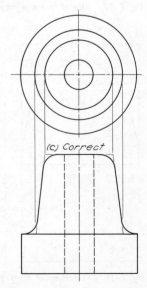

(a) Correct   (b) Incorrect   (c) Correct

Fig. 7–22.   Representing rounded corners.

In drawings of objects that are to have small rounded corners and filleted angles, it is customary to show these rounds and fillets on the drawing in the manner illustrated in Fig. 7-21. Notice that when either of the adjoining surfaces is to be finished the corners are shown square and sharp.

In drawing the top view of such objects as the tapering hub shown in Fig. 7-22, the question arises whether any circles, representing the tapering part of the hub, may properly be shown. As represented in Fig. 7-22(a), the rounding of the end of the hub and the filleting of the angle are done on very small radii, primarily to add strength to the casting and to make it easier to remove the pattern from the mold. In such cases the circles representing the actual corners before rounding are always drawn in the top view. Under the condition indicated in Figs. 7-22(b) and 7-22(c), where the radii of the rounding curves are larger to give a streamlined effect, the end view should not be represented without the circles as in Fig. 7-22(b) but with circles representing the imaginary corners as shown in Fig. 7-22(c) in keeping with the latest American Drafting Standards. Figure 7-23 illustrates good drafting practice when the object is generally rounded at all corners and surface intersections.

7.15   Run out lines. When the intersection between two surfaces is filleted, the question arises as to the best method of showing the intersection. Standard practice is to use a more or less conventional representation for these situations, a few of which are illustrated in Fig. 7-24. These curved extensions of true projections are commonly referred to as "run out" lines for rounded or filleted corners. They have no determinate radius of curvature but are drawn to suggest the general shape of the theoretical line of intersection as much as possible.

7.16   Partial views. When space is limited on the drawing sheet and the object is symmetrical about one or more center cutting planes, one-half of a view may be

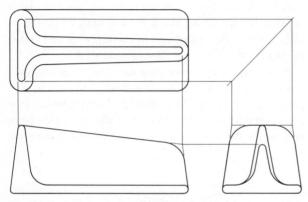

Fig. 7-23.   Representing streamlined object.

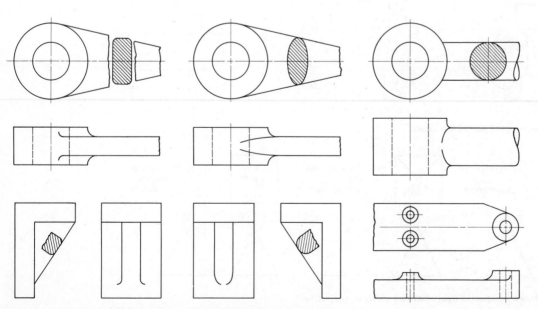

Fig. 7-24.   Standard run-outs. (Courtesy American Standards Association.)

omitted as has been done in Fig. 7–25. If the front view is a half or full section, it is customary to draw the back half of the top view as in (a) and (b) of the figure. If the front view is not sectioned and a half top view is shown, it should be of the front half of the object, as shown in Fig. 7–25(c).

7.17 Construction methods. In making the views of an object, it is customary to draw two lines, called reference lines, at right angles to each other, representing the intersections of the three principal planes. Since the top view of any point of an object is directly above its front view, this relation may be used to locate either projection from the other. This process is sometimes spoken of as projecting a point from one view to another. If two projections or views of a point are known, the third may be obtained by projection from these two. The three possible combinations are shown in Fig. 7–26. Thus the projection a^V can be located in the front view by projecting across from a^P and down from a^H. The projection b^P can be located by projecting across from b^V and around from b^H. Likewise, the projection c^H in the top view can be located by projecting

up from c^V and around from c^P. Note that, in going around from the side to the top view or vice versa, the distance of the horizontal projection from the horizontal reference line remains the same as the distance of the profile projection from the vertical reference line. Three methods of projecting from the top to the side view, or the reverse, are shown in Fig. 7–27. These are simply convenient methods for making the distance from the horizontal and vertical reference lines equal in the top and side views.

Sometimes it is more convenient to lay out the third view by transferring the distances with dividers instead of projecting them as in Fig. 7–26. This method is illustrated in Fig. 7–28, where the right side view has been constructed by taking the front and back distances on either side of the center line in the top view and transferring them to the side view as indicated.

7.18 Layout of a three-view drawing. After studying the preceding paragraphs, the student should have a good understanding of the theory of orthographic projection and a clear mental image of the views necessary to describe the object. In addition, however, it is neces-

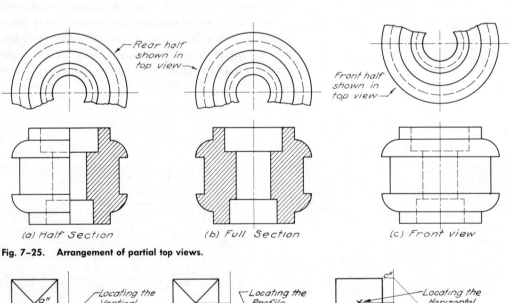

(a) Half Section   (b) Full Section   (c) Front view

Fig. 7–25. Arrangement of partial top views.

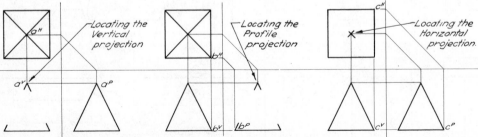

Fig. 7–26. Third view constructed from other two views by projection.

sary to develop a method of procedure that will enable the draftsman to proceed rapidly with the necessary steps and to arrive at the proper answer with a minimum of waste motion and lost time. The following paragraphs suggest a method of procedure for the beginner which he may vary to suit his own desire as he gains experience.

Before beginning his drawing, the draftsman must first determine the proper position of the object and the necessary number of views so that the drawing will fully describe the object in a clear manner. He must first visualize the object in its natural position with the faces parallel to the coordinate planes of projection and turned so that the desired views will have as few invisible lines as possible. The view that has the most descriptive contour usually should be chosen as the front view. Thus, the object shown in Fig. 7–29(a) should be turned so that the left face of the pictorial becomes the front view because it shows the shape of the standard and the clearance between the jaws.

In addition to the front view discussed above, it is necessary that two other views be drawn, the top view to show the shape of the base and the right side view to show the circle and the cross section of the standard. Another factor that will influence the choice of views, where other considerations are equal, is the overall size of the views. In general, the longer horizontal dimension will be better in the front view rather than in the side view because this gives a more compact arrangement of the three views.

Having decided which views are to be drawn, the next step is to select the scale of the drawing to fit the desired size of paper or the size of paper to fit the desired scale. A convenient method of approaching this problem is to make a freehand sketch of the views to be drawn and put down the known dimensions in the proper place. If the scale is known, the size of each view can be calculated from the overall dimensions, or, if the size of the sheet is known, the space available for the views can be calculated and the scale determined from that. All these calculations are affected by the amount of space to be left between views, which is a variable factor that may range from ½ inch to several inches, depending on the size and shape of the drawing and the number of dimensions that must be placed between the views. The experienced draftsman estimates the number of lines of dimensions to be placed between each pair of views and spaces his views accordingly, at the same time making proper allowance for the size of the drawing. Beginners are apt to go to extremes in spacing, making the views either too close together or too far apart. Until the draftsman has learned this detail by experience, it is well to use an average distance between views that will serve for a majority of drawings. A spacing of 1⅝ inches between views for drawings of average size will allow three lines of dimensions between the

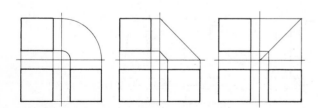

Fig. 7–27. Methods of transferring distances from top to side views.

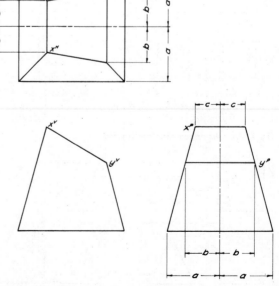

Fig. 7–28. Transferring distances by measurement.

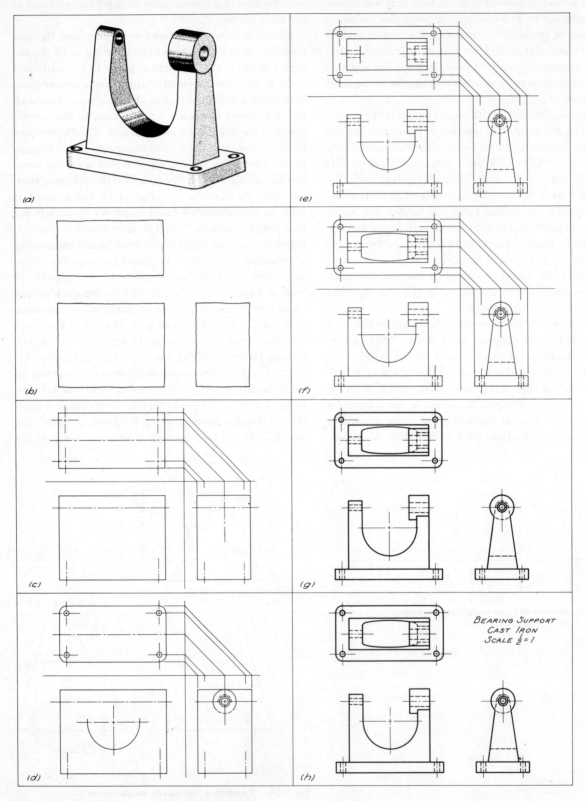

(a)

(b)

(c)

(d)

(e)

(f)

(g)

(h)

BEARING SUPPORT
CAST IRON
SCALE ½ = 1

Fig. 7-29. Development of an orthographic projection.

views, but more space will be necessary if additional lines of dimensions are needed. This spacing is therefore recommended for use until the student has acquired the ability by observation and experience to space them more accurately.

The complete layout of a three-view drawing may be divided into steps which are illustrated in Fig. 7–29.

a. Choose the number and arrangement of the views.

b. Make a freehand layout of the areas required for each view. From this, determine the scale of the drawing or the size of the paper, and the spacing of the views, Fig. 7–29(*b*).

c. Make an accurate mechanical layout of the area sketch, using reference lines. Then add the main center lines and center lines of details. Figure 7–29(*c*).

d. Draw circular parts. Figure 7–29(*d*).

e. Draw straight lines. Figure 7–29(*e*).

f. Locate intersections and irregular curves. Figure 7–29(*f*).

g. Clean up drawing with art gum or soft eraser. Take out excess lines, construction lines, and reference lines. Figure 7–29(*g*).

h. Go over all lines to make them heavier and to improve the technique. Figure 7–29(*h*).

i. Put in title and scale. Every drawing whether dimensioned or not must have a title and have the scale specified.

7.19   Calculation of weights. Whenever a new part has been designed or drawn it is usually necessary to calculate the weight in order to make an estimate of cost. In doing this the object must be divided into its component parts so that the weights of these may be computed individually.

All objects may be broken down into four groups as follows:

a. Those objects that are bounded by plane surfaces such as prisms and pyramids, as shown in Fig. 7–30.

b. Those objects bounded by single curved surfaces and planes such as cones and cylinders, as shown in Fig. 7–31.

c. Those objects bounded by double curved surfaces such as spheres, spheroids, and toruses, as shown in Fig. 7–32.

d. Those objects bounded by warped surfaces usually

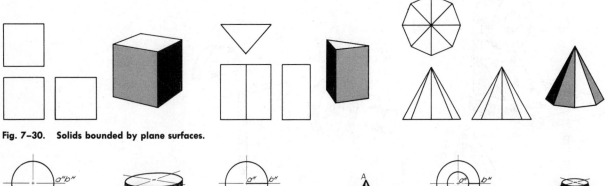

Fig. 7–30.   Solids bounded by plane surfaces.

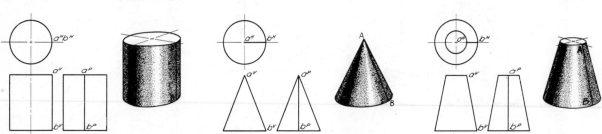

Fig. 7–31.   Solids bounded by plane and single curved surfaces.

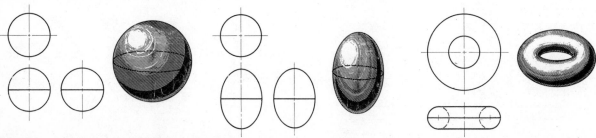

Fig. 7–32.   Solids bounded by double curved surfaces.

in combination with some other type of surface. Some of these are illustrated in Fig. 7–33.

For calculation purposes it is best to make an exploded sketch of these parts, as shown in Fig. 7–34. The volume of each part can then be computed individually, and all these results can be added together to give the complete result. Note that the holes have been taken out as solid cylinders so that it will be necessary to deduct their volume from the total of the other pieces.

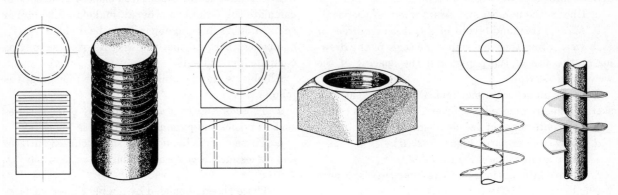

Fig. 7–33.   Solids involving warped surfaces.

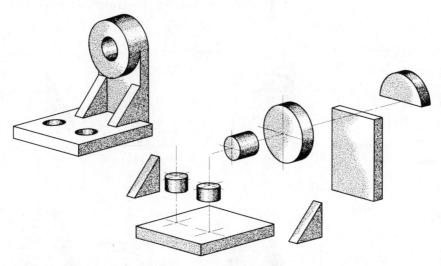

Fig. 7–34.   Breakdown of object into component parts.

PROBLEMS

In the following group of problems the student is to select and draw the minimum number of views which will unmistakably describe the shape of the object. The scale given is for an 8½ × 11-inch sheet. It is recommended that the student make a freehand sketch showing the views he proposes to make before beginning the instrumental layout.

The views should be well balanced on the sheet with ample space between views and around them for dimensions. The drawings, however, are not to be dimensioned unless the instructor so specifies.

For fillets and rounded corners not dimensioned on the fig-ures or for other missing dimensions, the student is to use his own judgment. The objects in Figs. 7–35 to 7–42 are assumed to be finished all over. On a shop drawing this is shown by the abbreviation F.A.O. In all cases the material is assumed to be cast iron.

1 to 22. Make the necessary number of orthographic views to describe adequately the shape of the object assigned from Figs. 7–35 to 7–56.

In a space below the views, or elsewhere, if necessary, to balance the sheet, place a well-balanced title giving the name of the object, the material of which it is made, and the scale.

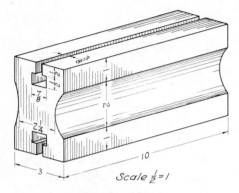

Fig. 7–35.   Indicator base.

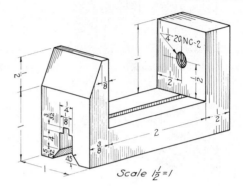

Fig. 7–38.   Vise base.

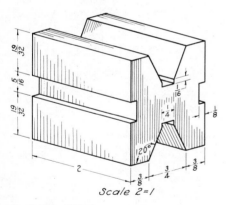

Fig. 7–36.   V-block.

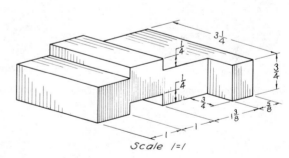

Fig. 7–39.   Guide block.

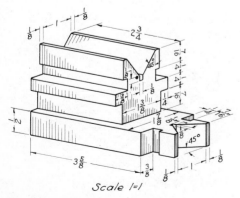

Fig. 7–37.   V-block.

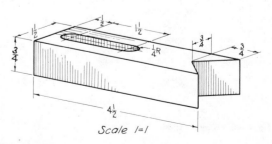

Fig. 7–40.   V-slide.

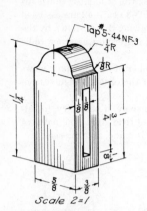

Scale 2=1

Fig. 7–41. Gage clamp.

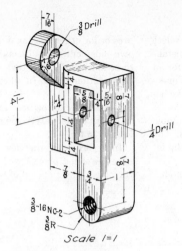

Scale 1=1

Fig. 7–44. Swing tool.

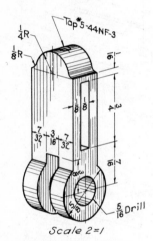

Scale 2=1

Fig. 7–42. Vernier clamp.

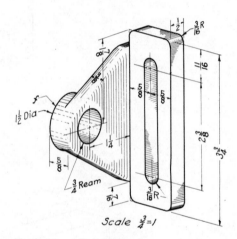

Scale ¾=1

Fig. 7–45. Adjustable bearing.

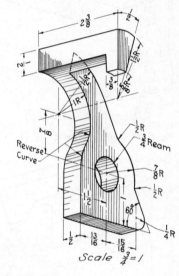

Scale ¾=1

Fig. 7–46. Clutch finger.

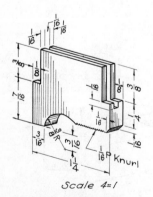

Scale 4=1

Fig. 7–43. Caliper slide.

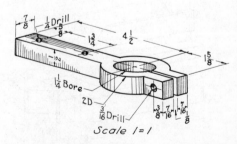

Scale 1=1

Fig. 7–47. Collar clamp.

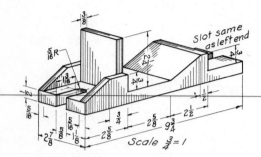

Fig. 7-48.   Fixture.

Slot same as left end

$\frac{5}{16}$R

Scale $\frac{3}{4}$=1

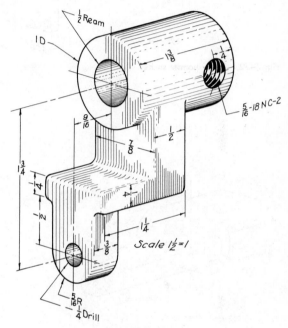

$\frac{1}{2}$Ream

ID

$\frac{5}{16}$-18NC-2

$\frac{9}{16}$

$\frac{7}{8}$

$1\frac{3}{4}$

$1\frac{1}{4}$

$\frac{3}{8}$

$\frac{5}{16}$R

$\frac{1}{4}$Drill

Scale $1\frac{1}{2}$=1

Fig. 7-50.   Adjustable bearing.

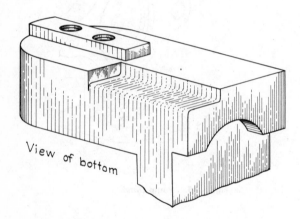

View of bottom

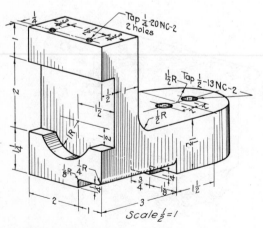

Tap $\frac{1}{4}$-20NC-2
2 holes

Tap $\frac{1}{2}$-13NC-2

$\frac{1}{2}$R

$\frac{1}{8}$R $\frac{1}{4}$R

Scale $\frac{1}{2}$=1

Fig. 7-49.   Turret tool post.

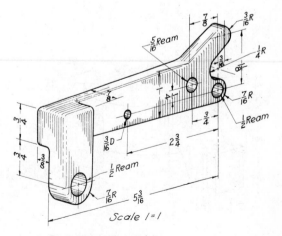

$\frac{7}{8}$

$\frac{3}{16}$R

$\frac{5}{16}$Ream

$\frac{1}{4}$R

$\frac{7}{16}$R

$\frac{1}{2}$Ream

$\frac{3}{4}$

$2\frac{3}{4}$

$\frac{3}{16}$D

$\frac{1}{2}$Ream

$3\frac{3}{4}$

$\frac{3}{8}$

$\frac{7}{16}$R

$5\frac{3}{16}$

Scale 1=1

Fig. 7-51.   Roller release.

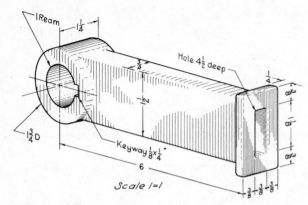

Fig. 7-52. Lever handle socket.

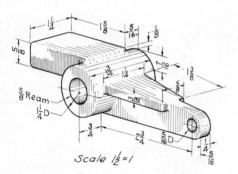

Fig. 7-53. Stripper bracket.

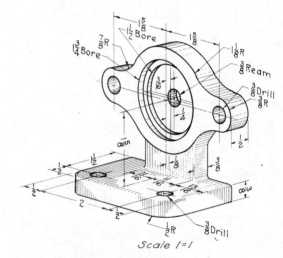

Fig. 7-55. Pump stand.

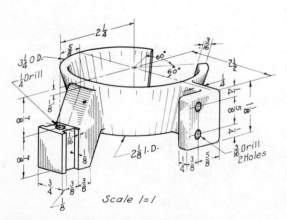

Fig. 7-54. Developer tank support.

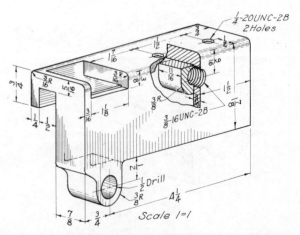

Fig. 7-56. Fence clamp.

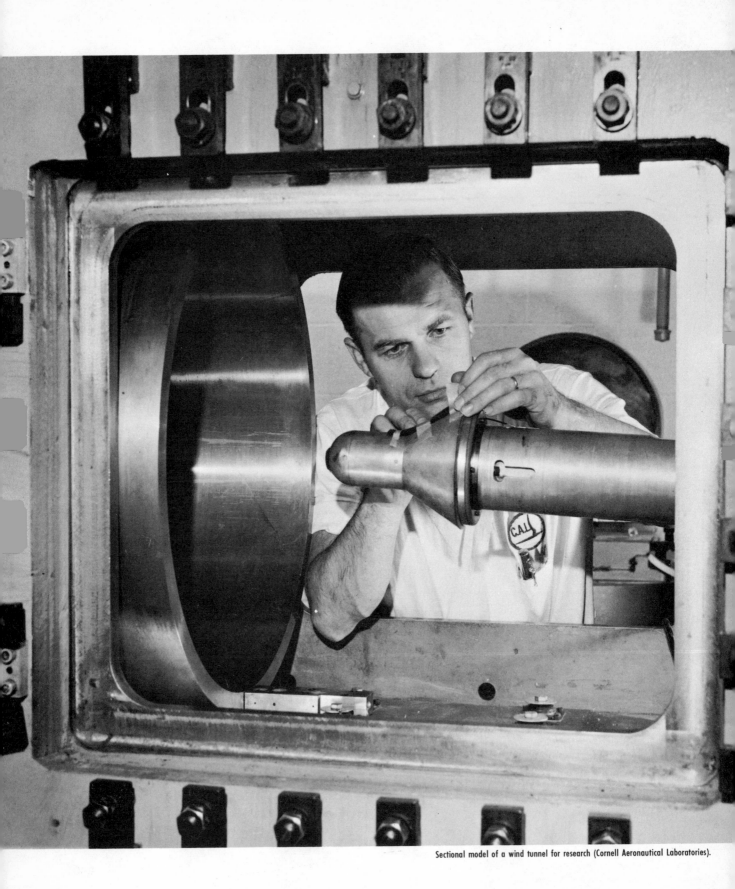

Sectional model of a wind tunnel for research (Cornell Aeronautical Laboratories).

8

Sectional Views

8.1 Purpose of sectional views. With the principles of projection thus far discussed the interior parts of an object which are hidden from view can only be represented by dash lines or hidden lines as they are called. When these dash lines become numerous the drawing is difficult to interpret. To overcome this difficulty the sectional view is used.

A sectional view is any view seen when a portion of the object nearest the observer has been imagined removed by means of cutting planes, thus revealing the interior construction.

A sectional view, or section as it is called, is also used to show the exact shape of exterior parts which are so curved or rounded that the usual two- or three-view drawings do not reveal their true form as, for example, fenders, housings for revolving parts, propellers, ships, airplane bodies, and wing contours.

8.2 Location of cutting or section planes. To show the interior construction of an object, the main cutting plane is passed through an axis of symmetry parallel to one of the principal planes, as shown in Fig. 8–1(b). Other cutting planes, if necessary, are passed parallel or perpendicular to the main cutting plane, as shown in Fig. 8–1(a) and (c).

The cutting plane need not be continuous but may be offset, as shown in Fig. 8–1(c), or turned through an angle, as shown in Fig. 8–13, thus giving rise to various types of sectional views as discussed later. To show the true shape of a part such as a spoke or a connecting arm, the plane may be passed perpendicular to the axis, as shown in Fig. 8–2.

When a cutting plane is passed on an axis of symmetry, as shown in Fig. 8–1(a) and (b), it is not necessary to indicate the location of the plane. When, however, the cutting plane is offset, as in Fig. 8–1(*c*) or Fig. 8–13, its location must be shown in the view where it appears edgewise. The symbol used for the cutting plane is a heavy dash-double-dot line, as shown in Fig. 8–3.

8.3   Drawing the views. *The view which is to be made in section is represented as though the portion of the object nearest the observer is actually cut away by the section planes and removed. It should be noted that the other views are not affected in any way and always represent the entire object.*

8.4   Section lining. In order that those parts of an object which have been cut by the section plane may stand out on the drawing, a conventional scheme called crosshatching, or section lining, is employed. This is done by drawing light, inclined lines on those parts of the view of the object which indicate where the plane actually cuts the material of which the object is made. The section lines may be drawn at any angle to the horizontal, *but 45° lines are usually employed.* The direction should, if possible, be so chosen that the *cross-hatch lines will not be parallel or perpendicular to any one of the main bounding lines of the area* being shaded. See Fig. 8–4. They should be spaced uniformly and approximately ⅟16 inch or more apart. For very large drawings the spacing may be as great as ³⁄16 inch. In weight, they should approximate a dimension line, and they should always be drawn completely up to the outlines of the object. Figure 8–5 shows examples of good and faulty section lining.

When several adjacent parts of a machine are of the same material and are cut by a section plane, each part should be distinguished from its neighbor by a change in slope of the section lining. The more nearly the crosshatch lines approximate 90° to each other, the better the effect will be. See Fig. 8–6(*a*). *If the section plane cuts the same part at different places in the object, the section lining should be given the same slope in the corresponding places on the drawing,* as shown in Fig. 8–6(*a*) and (*b*). When three parts of an assembly are cut, two of the parts can usually be crosshatched at 45° but some different angles such as 30° or 60° must be used

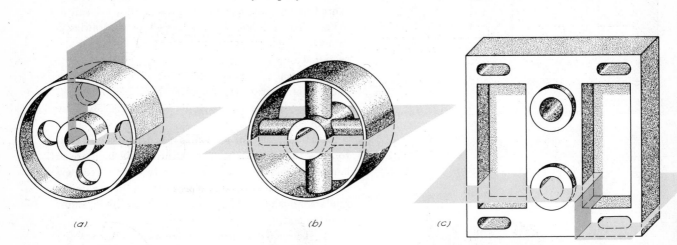

(a)   (b)   (c)

Fig. 8–1.   Location of cutting planes.

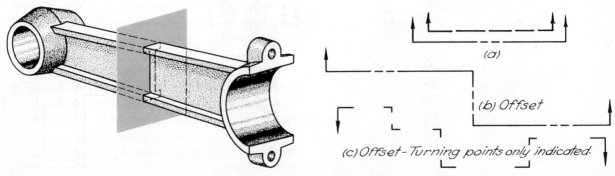

Fig. 8–2.   Position of cutting plane for a revolved section.

(a)

(b) Offset

(c) Offset—Turning points only indicated.

Fig. 8–3.   Cutting plane symbol.

for the third part. See Fig. 8–6(b).

8.5 Full sections. When the section plane passes completely through the object on the plane of symmetry, as shown in Fig. 8–7(a), one-half of the object is imagined to be removed in drawing the sectioned view. Figure 8–7(b) shows the object as it is imagined to appear in making the section view. From this it can be seen that the entire front view will be in section, which gives it the name "full section." The correct orthographic projections of the object with a full section in the front view are shown in Fig. 8–7(c). The following points should be observed in making a drawing with one view in full section:

a. In making the sectioned view, one-half of the object is imagined removed.

b. Invisible lines behind the section are omitted.

c. Visible lines behind the section are shown.

d. Only the parts actually cut by the section plane are crosshatched.

e. The position of the cutting plane is not shown on the final drawings, for full sections.

8.6 Half-section. When two perpendicular cutting

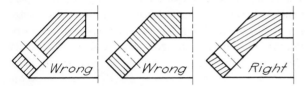

Fig. 8–4. Correct and incorrect section lining.

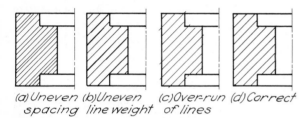

(a) Uneven spacing (b) Uneven line weight (c) Over-run of lines (d) Correct

Fig. 8–5. Common errors in section lining.

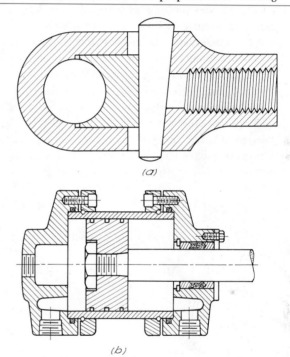

(a)

(b)

Fig. 8–6. Crosshatching adjacent parts.

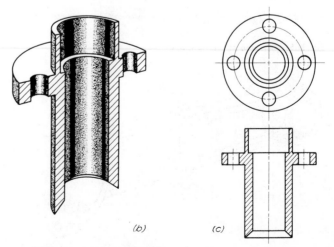

(a) (b) (c)

Fig. 8–7. A full-sectioned view.

planes are passed part way through the object on planes of symmetry, as shown in Fig. 8-8(*a*), one-quarter of the object is imagined to be removed in drawing the sectioned view. Figure 8-8(*b*) shows the casting as it would appear in making the sectioned view. From this it can be seen that only one-half of the front view will show in section and the other half will be an external view. From this, the name half-section is derived for such a view. All the rules that have been given for drawing a full section, except the first, also apply for the half of the front view that is in section. The other half may be considered as an external view only or as a complete orthographic projection in which all visible and invisible lines will show. In the interest of economy in drafting time the invisible lines may be omitted unless they are needed for

clarity or for dimensioning.

In a half-section the line separating the interior part from the exterior part may be either a solid line, as in Fig. 8-8(*c*), or a center line, as in Fig. 8-8(*d*). The ASA recognizes both systems, but the SAE uses only the solid line.

8.7   Hidden lines in sectioned views. *It is standard practice to omit all hidden lines in the sectioned part of a view.* In making a detail of a single part, the invisible lines may be shown on the unsectioned half if they are needed for dimensioning.

In making a half-sectioned assembly, the invisible outlines are usually omitted from the unsectioned half as well from the sectioned half so that one side shows internal construction and the other half the external

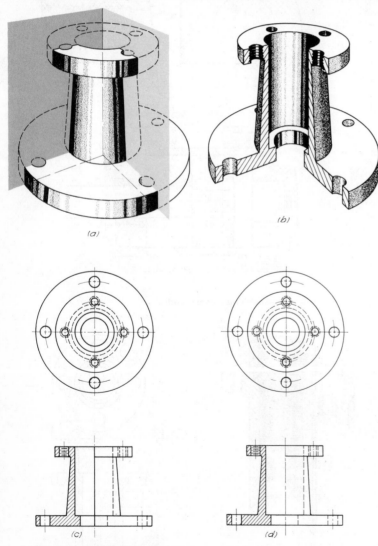

(a)

(b)

(c)

(d)

Fig. 8-8.   A half-sectioned view.

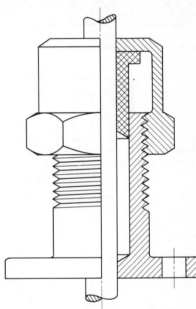

Fig. 8-9.   Hidden lines omitted in a sectioned drawing.

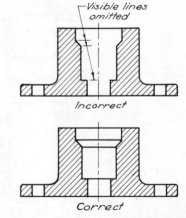

Visible lines omitted

Incorrect

Correct

Fig. 8-10.   Visible lines behind cutting plane shown.

appearance. This is illustrated in Fig. 8–9.

8.8   Visible lines behind the section plane. *Visible outlines appearing behind the cutting plane must always be shown in the sectioned view.* Beginners frequently omit them. Correct and incorrect practice is shown in Fig. 8–10. In objects with an odd number of axes of symmetry as, for example, a wheel with five spokes, the visible outline of spokes not lying in the cutting plane may be omitted as in Fig. 8–11.

8.9   Offset sections. The section cutting planes are almost always passed through axes of symmetry of the object. If several such axes of symmetry occur, not coinciding with a single central axis of the object, the cutting plane is offset, as in Fig. 8–12, to include two or more of these axes of symmetry. No particular difficulty is exper-

ienced in reading a drawing when this is done; yet it is always best to show the location of the offset cutting planes by the characteristic dash-and-two-dot line and the direction in which the view is taken by arrows on the end of the line. These arrows should always point away from the sectioned view. *No indication of the offsets in the cutting plane are shown on the sectioned view.*

8.10   Aligned sections. In sectioning certain objects, more information can be given if the section plane is bent or turned at an angle, as shown in Fig. 8–13. The various segments of the cutting plane are imagined to be revolved until they are parallel to the principal plane of projection. This shows all cut portions of the object in true size in the sectioned view. This is known as an

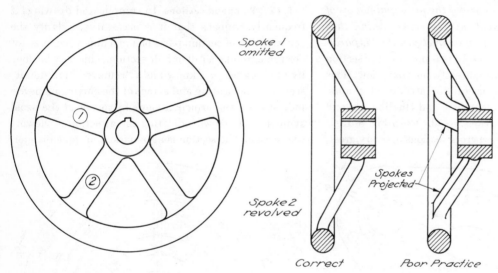

Fig. 8–11.   Spokes of wheel in sectional view.

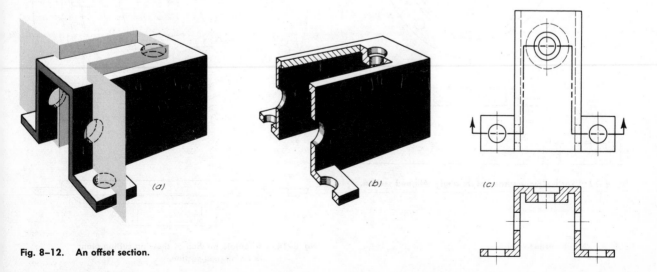

Fig. 8–12.   An offset section.

aligned section. No indication of the bends in the cutting plane is shown in the sectioned view. The position of the cutting plane is shown on the unsectioned view by the usual symbol to indicate the edgewise view of the cutting plane. Arrows pointing away from the sectioned view show the direction in which the section has been taken. The position of the cutting plane is sometimes shown by marking only the "points" of turning or bending, as shown in Fig. 8–14.

8.11 Revolved sections. In many cases the cross section of some part of a structure or machine is necessary for the purpose of shape or size description. Frequently the easiest way to obtain this without drawing an extra view is by means of a revolved section. *The revolved section is obtained by passing a cutting plane through the member perpendicular to one of the principal planes of projection and then revolving the cross section thus obtained about its own axis of symmetry until it is parallel to the plane of projection.* In this position the section will show the true shape directly on that view. This method is particularly useful for structural shapes, spokes of wheels, arms, handles, and the like. Several examples of revolved sections are shown in Fig. 8–15.

The advantages of these cross sections are very great,

inasmuch as they convey to the mind instantly the shapes of pieces used in the design of any structure, simply from an examination of one view of the object. Dimensions are frequently placed on such sections, thereby adding to their effectiveness. Many draftsmen make a break in the piece and place the revolved section in the opening between the broken ends. This convention may be used for any revolved section but is almost a necessity for sections such as the one in the front view of Fig. 8–16. It should be observed in this connection that the revolved section always shows the true cross section of the piece regardless of the direction of the axis or boundary lines of the part sectioned. Streamlined objects, such as car fenders and propeller blades, are sometimes shown by taking sections at regular intervals.

8.12 Removed sections. In complicated drawings it frequently happens that it is necessary to clarify the construction of certain parts of a machine when it is not desirable to take a full or half-section. This may be done by drawing what is known as a "removed" or "detail" section. The location and extent of the cutting plane are indicated on the principal views by means of the usual symbol with arrows indicating the direction of viewing the section. The section is also marked in some manner,

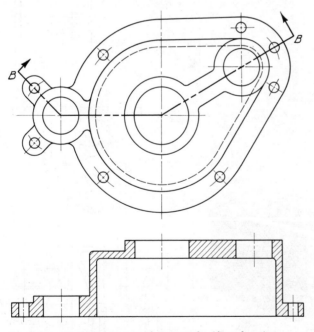

Fig. 8–13. Section plane turned at an angle. Aligned section.

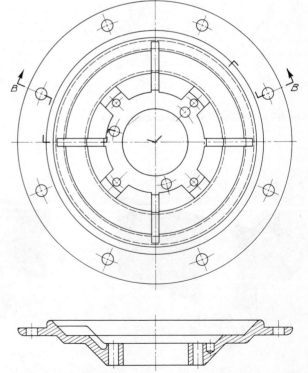

Fig. 8–14. Alternate method of showing cutting plane in an aligned section.

usually with a capital letter at each end of the cutting plane. See Fig. 8–17. The actual section may then be drawn at some other place on the sheet or even on some other sheet. If drawn on another sheet the section is marked with a letter placed over a number. The letter refers to the section and the number to the sheet on which the section is drawn. See Fig. 8–18(a). The sectional view is tied in with the original drawing by labeling it Section *AA* or Section *BB,* Sheet No. 3. Only the outlines actually formed from the parts cut by the plane are

shown, except where it may be desirable to show some of the outlines behind the section, for ease in interpretation. The draftsman must be careful to draw the removed section in approximately the same position in which it appears on the object. That is, it should not be drawn upside down or turned at an angle from its true position as indicated by the cutting plane. On a zoned drawing, the section may be tied in by letters on the arrows and also by reference to the zone where the section may be found, as illustrated in Fig. 8–18(b). The

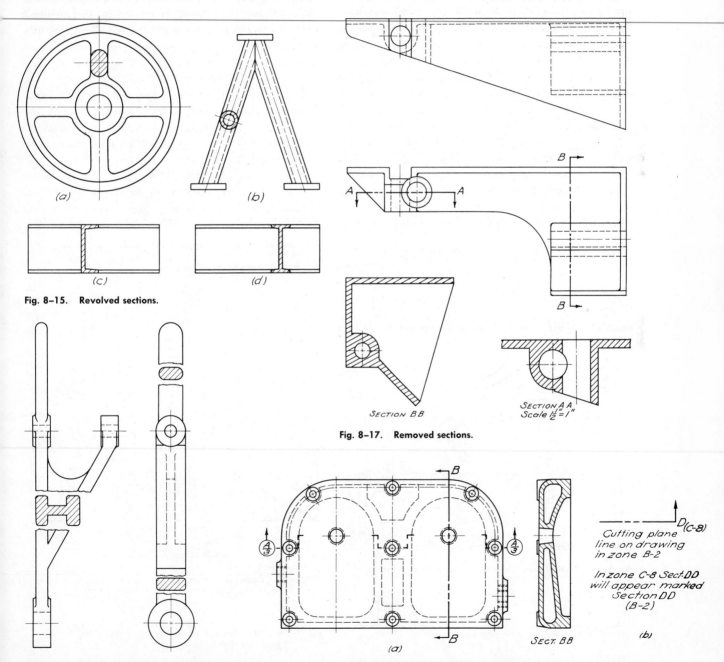

Fig. 8–15.   Revolved sections.

Fig. 8–16.   Alternate method of showing a revolved section.

Fig. 8–17.   Removed sections.

Fig. 8–18.   Marking removed sections.

section itself should then be lettered and referenced by zones to the position of the cutting plane. It is often convenient to extend the cutting plane to form the center line of the section, as shown in Fig. 8–19.

One of the first advantages of the removed section lies in the fact that the sectioned views may be drawn to a much larger scale than the main views, thus showing the detail more clearly. In such cases the scale must be clearly indicated with each section, as shown in Fig. 8–17. A second advantage is that the main views showing the general outlines of the object are not confused by a large number of broken lines or cross-section lines.

A third advantage may be found in the better balanced drawing sheets, since the cross-sectioned views may be moved to any open space on the sheet.

8.13   Auxiliary sections. One type of removed section that is very easily read, because it ties in with the principal views so well, is the auxiliary section, as shown in Fig. 8–20. The auxiliary plane is set parallel to the cutting plane and the auxiliary view drawn as though the object had actually been cut on the section plane. In fact, any principle of sectioning that can be applied to one of the main views is equally applicable to any auxiliary view. When the position of the section plane is shown,

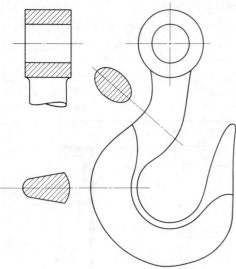

Fig. 8–19.   Removed section on extended center line.

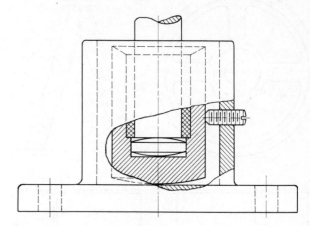

Fig. 8–21.   Broken-out section.

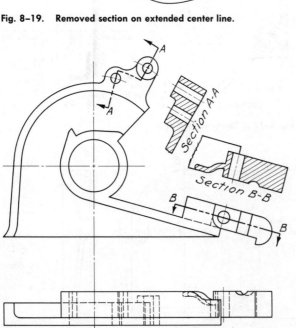

Fig. 8–20.   Auxiliary sections.

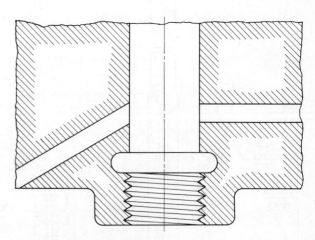

Fig. 8–22.   Partial section lining.

the arrows should point away from the sectional views.

8.14   Broken-out sections. In some instances it will be found that a single interior detail needs to be made clearer than any of the principal views are able to make it and yet it does not justify a full or a half-section. Or it may be possible that a full or half-section would eliminate some exterior detail that must be preserved. In a situation of this kind it is possible to break out a small portion of the outer part covering just the area desired. The broken part is outlined with an irregular freehand line to mark the break. See Fig. 8–21. This is called a broken-out section.

8.15   Partial or outline section lining. In many instances, the appearance of large areas which have to be sectioned can be improved by carrying the crosshatching only a short distance from the outlines and leaving the central portions blank, as in Fig. 8–22. Not only is time saved by this practice, but the appearance of the drawing is improved by eliminating large shaded areas. The blueprints of tracings made in this way are even more improved in their appearance.

8.16   Phantom section. One type of section that is seldom used is the invisible or phantom section illustrated in Fig. 8–23. This section is marked by dotted crosshatching and is used to emphasize some inner part while at the same time retaining all the exterior construction. It is also used occasionally to show the method of attaching or manner in which an adjacent part joins the part being drawn.

8.17   Thin sections. When thin members such as gaskets, plates, channels, angles, and other structural members are shown in section, they may be made solid black if the scale of the drawing is small. Adjacent pieces should then be separated by a space, as shown in Fig. 8–24.

8.18   Solid shafts and bars, bolts, pins, keys, and screws in sections. When the cutting plane passes through the longitudinal axes of solid cylinders such as shafts, bolts, and screws, it is the custom to consider that these parts are not cut by the section plane. Nothing would be gained by showing the solid interior of such parts, and a great deal of time is saved by eliminating large areas

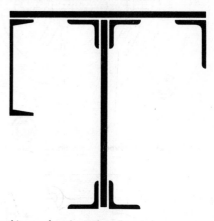

Fig. 8–24.   Showing thin members in section.

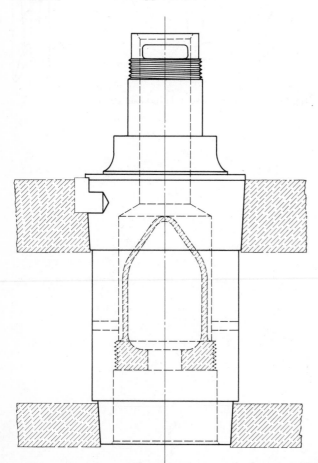

Fig. 8–23.   A phantom section.

of crosshatching. Figure 8–25 illustrates a safety valve, the stem, weight bar, and two bolts of which come under this rule.

8.19 Spokes of wheels and thin webs. *Spokes of wheels are not sectioned even though the cutting plane passes through them.* This not only saves time but also gives a method of distinguishing, in the sectioned view, between a wheel with spokes and a wheel with a solid web. Figure 8–26 illustrates the general practice in the arms of a sheave.

When the section plane passes through a thin web, parallel to its larger dimensions, as in Fig. 8–27, the most commonly accepted practice is to omit the section lining on the web and show a visible outline at the intersection of the web with the body of the piece. This is the preferred method and is illustrated in Fig. 8–27(*a*). Sometimes the line of intersection between the web and the body is drawn as an invisible outline and every other crosshatch line is extended through the web. This method is illustrated in Fig. 8–27(*b*). When a section plane cuts through a web perpendicular to its larger dimensions, the web is crosshatched.

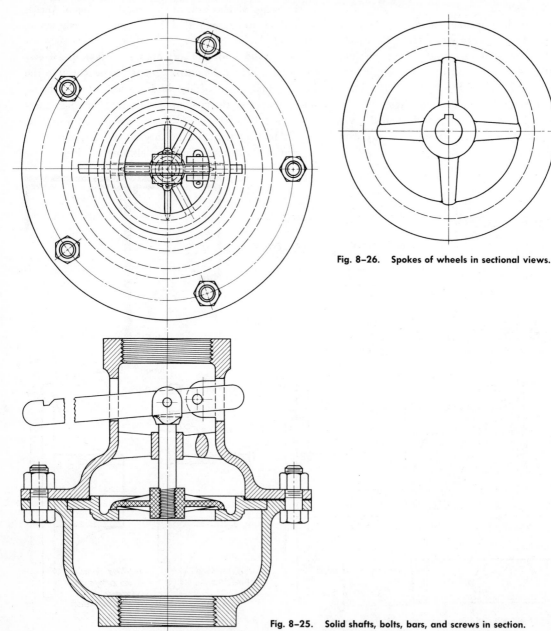

Fig. 8–26.   Spokes of wheels in sectional views.

Fig. 8–25.   Solid shafts, bolts, bars, and screws in section.

8.20 Conventional practice. In passing a section plane through such objects as a cover plate with three webs, as in Fig. 8–28, or through webs of couplings with an odd number of drilled holes, and similar objects, only one of the webs or holes will fall in the plane. To show the other webs or holes in their true positions by projecting them in the section view would usually require the use of a large number of hidden lines and difficult projections. This would make the object appear unsymmetrical. To avoid this confusion and to make the drawing easier to read, it is customary in representing the areas not on the section plane to consider them rotated into the section plane, as shown in Fig. 8–28(*b*). Certain features contiguous to these areas must also be considered revolved at the same time.

This rotation of parts, though not in strict accord with the theory of orthographic projection, is so commonly used that it has come to be recognized and accepted as standard practice. It is used on both sectioned and unsectioned drawings. See Figs. 8–11 and 8–28(*c*). *A part should not be revolved if its true relation to the rest of the object will be changed by the revolution;* that is,

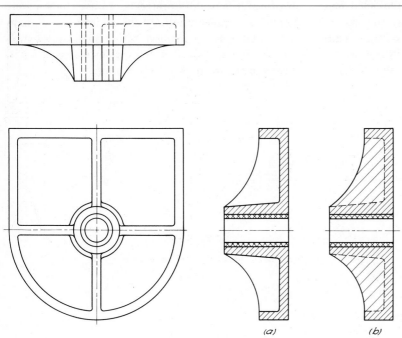

(a)   (b)

Fig. 8–27.   Thin webs in sectioned views.

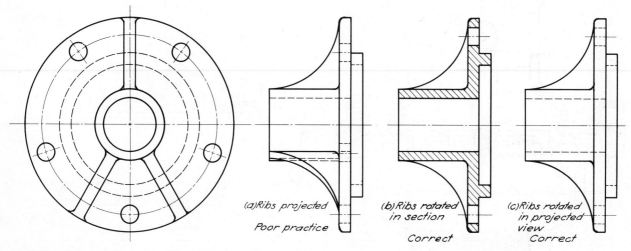

(a)Ribs projected

Poor practice

(b)Ribs rotated
in section

Correct

(c)Ribs rotated
in projected
view

Correct

Fig. 8–28.   Section of object with odd-numbered axes of symmetry.

only those areas that are on objects that fall in the class of cylindrical shapes can be treated in this manner.

8.21 Conventional breaks. Long members of uniform cross section are usually not drawn to scale lengthwise. This fact is brought out by showing a conventional break in the member, as illustrated in Fig. 8–29. The correct length of the member is shown by a dimension. A revolved section may or may not be interpolated in the break. However, the appearance of the break usually gives some indication of the shape of the cross section. Structural members when not to scale are not broken.

8.22 Threads and bolts in section. Threaded holes and bolts in section are represented by conventional symbols. A complete discussion of the methods of representing threads is given in Chapter 10. Typical sections involving threads, bolts, and screws are shown in Figs.

10–21 and 10–29 to aid the student in interpreting some of the drawings in this chapter. Notice that the bolts and screws are drawn as though the section plane did not pass through them.

8.23 Material symbols in sections. Many industries indicate the kind of material by using a different type of section lining. The American Drafting Standards Manual recommends the symbolic sections shown in Fig. 8–31. The use of these is particularly valuable in those assemblies where the drawing is complicated and several kinds of material are to be shown. For detail drawings it is usually preferable to use the standard symbol of parallel uniformly spaced lines for all materials and specify the material with a note. An assembly is shown in Fig. 8–30, in which various materials are indicated by characteristic section lining.

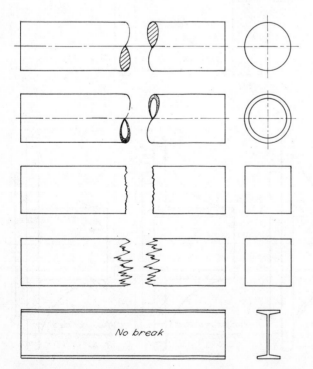

No break

Fig. 8–29. Conventional breaks.

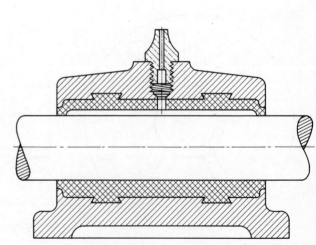

Fig. 8–30. Symbolic crosshatching in an assembly.

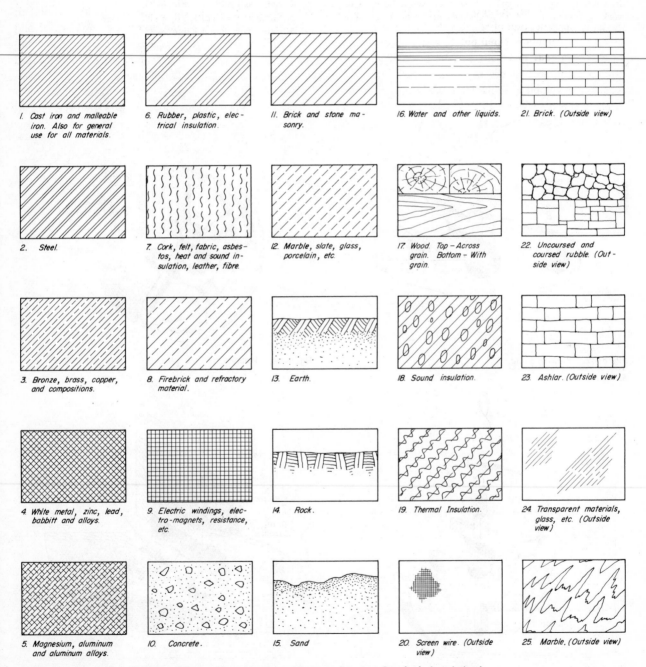

Fig. 8–31. Standard symbols for sections and outside views. (Courtesy American Standards Association.)

PROBLEMS

The following problems are designed for 8½ × 11 or 11 × 17 inch paper. The student should select his scale to suit the size of paper. Ample space should be allowed between views to place dimensions in later assignments.

Drawings are not to be dimensioned unless specified by the instructor.

It should be noted that the dimensions given on the pictorial drawings are not necessarily those that would be used on a working drawing nor are they always placed where they should be on a working drawing.

Half-Sections

1. Make the necessary views to describe the shape of the packing gland in Fig. 8–32. One view to be in half-section.

2. Same as Problem 1, Fig. 8–33.

3. Same as Problem 1, Fig. 8–34.

4. Same as Problem 1, Fig. 8–35.

5. Same as Problem 1, Fig. 8–36.

6. Same as Problem 1, Fig. 8–38.

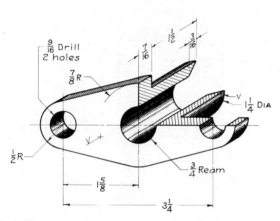

Fig. 8–32.   Packing gland.

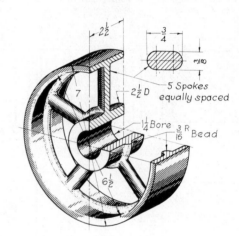

Fig. 8–34.   Pulley.

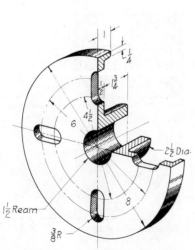

Fig. 8–33.   Face plate.

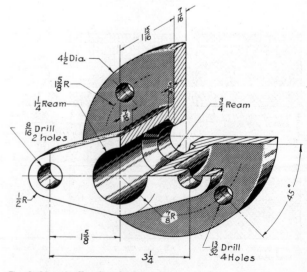

Fig. 8–35.   Stuffing box body.

Full Sections

7. Make the necessary views to describe the shape of the object shown in Fig. 8–33. Make one view in full section.

8. Same as Problem 7, Fig. 8–34.

9. Same as Problem 7, Fig. 8–36.

10. Same as Problem 7, Fig. 8–37.

11. Same as Problem 7, Fig. 8–38.

12. Same as Problem 7, Fig. 8–39.

(*Problems continued on next page.*)

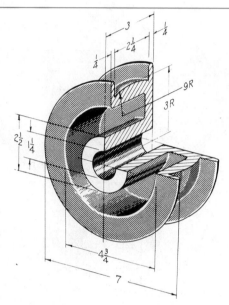

Fig. 8–36.   Flanged pulley.

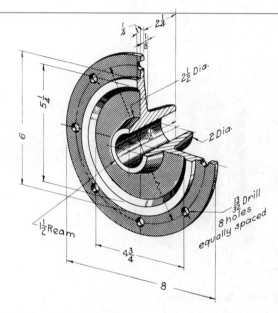

Fig. 8–38.   Motor end bearing.

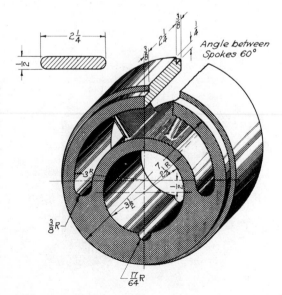

Fig. 8–37.   Eccentric sheave.

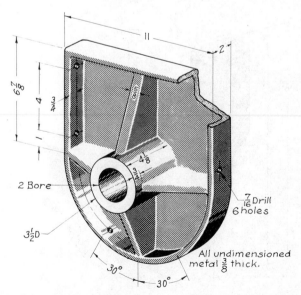

Fig. 8–39.   Conveyor box end.

Removed Sectional Views

13. Make the necessary views to describe the shape of the object shown in Fig. 8–40. Show a removed section.

14. Same as Problem 13, Fig. 8–41.

15. Same as Problem 13, Fig. 8–42.

16. Same as Problem 13, Fig. 8–43.

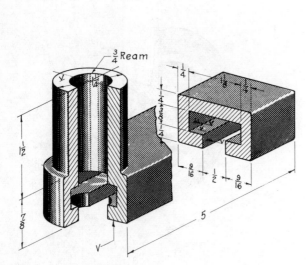

Fig. 8–40. Tool rest holder.

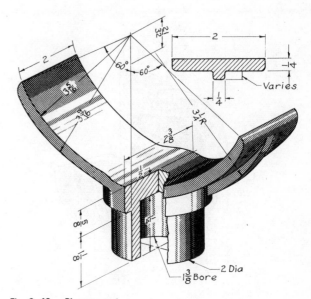

Fig. 8–42. Pipe support.

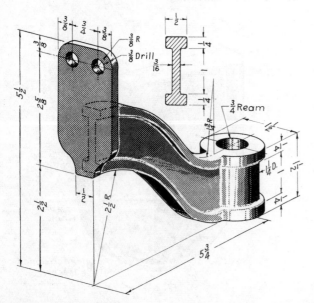

Fig. 8–41. Tool box holder.

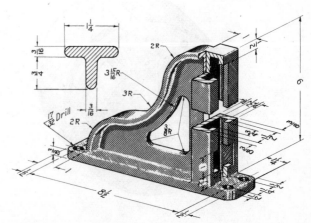

Fig. 8–43. Wall bracket.

Caliper measurement of a shaft (Ben Schnall).

9

Basic Dimensioning

9.1 Introduction. The fundamentals of dimensioning are the same in all fields of engineering practice, whether the projects are civil, mechanical, or electrical engineering. It is always necessary to define accurately the size of all the parts of any structure or machine and to locate the various parts with reference to each other and sometimes to locate them with reference to other structures, machines, or property lines in the vicinity.

In this chapter we shall endeavor to give those general principles which apply in all fields and then to elaborate more in detail upon those refinements which apply particularly in the mass-production machine industry. Limit dimensioning is discussed in Chapter 13. Dimensioning as it applies to architectural working drawings is treated in Chapter 26. The rules for dimensioning structural steel are found in Chapter 27.

The problem of dimensioning in the machine industry has become more exacting in the drafting room as mass production and the demands for precision have increased and made obsolete the methods whereby the skilled mechanic in the shop could decide how closely parts of a machine were to fit together. With the advent of mass production, however, parts of a machine may be made in widely separated places. Mass production calls for interchangeable assembly; that is to say, in assembling a machine any outside part will fit any inside part selected at random. Hence it now becomes the duty of the engineering staff in the drafting office to specify all dimensions and to decide just how much variation can be tolerated in those parts that must fit into other parts. Mass production also requires very exact drawings for production tools such as jigs and fixtures. Hundreds of such drawings are required for new auto models.

In all industry the workman must be able to find quickly every dimension he needs for construction without having to do any arithmetical computation himself, and there must be no ambiguity in the dimensions. This means that the draftsman, before he can become very useful in an office, must understand the methods of manufacture that are to be used so that he can give all necessary dimensions and yet omit those that would serve no useful purpose. The beginning draftsman can best learn dimensioning by considering it under the three major subdivisions as discussed in the following paragraphs.

a. Technique of dimensioning. This phase is very much the same in all engineering practice and includes among other things such items as the kind and weight of lines to use for dimensioning, size and shape of arrowheads, size and position of the numerals and the proper placing of these on or in the dimension lines, and designation of feet, inches, degrees, etc. Technique is fully treated in Art. 9.2.

b. Where to place dimensions. It is not enough that a dimension appear somewhere on the sheet. It must appear in a place where the workman will naturally look for it and where it is easily found. The methods of placing dimensions on a drawing have been rather well stand-ardized, and this phase of the subject is thoroughly treated in Art. 9.3.

c. What dimensions to give. This involves first, consideration of the functioning of the part, then methods of construction or manufacture and methods of gaging. It must include: the size of all parts, holes, bosses, lugs, and the like and the location of these parts with respect to each other. In dimensioning any object the engineer must have constantly in mind the fundamental requirements: (1) the part must be dimensioned to function properly, (2) it must be possible to manufacture economically, and (3) it must be dimensioned so that gaging is both practical and economical. It is clearly impossible to discuss all the phases of manufacturing which may affect the dimensioning of a part, but there are certain fundamental principles which are universal in application. With these the draftsman should be thoroughly familiar, and they are discussed in detail in Art. 9.4.

When parts are to be made by contract with other shops, many companies are very cautious about specifying methods of manufacturing on their drawings. The drawing specifies only the finished product; thus, for example, a hole will be marked ½ Dia. rather than ½ Drill. Illustrations in this book show both methods.

9.2 Technique or how to dimension. Before beginning

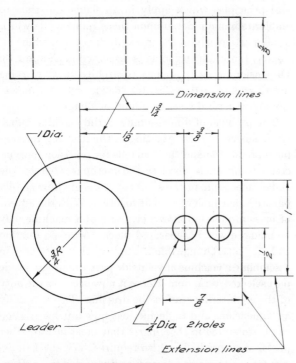

Fig. 9-1. Definition of dimensioning terms.

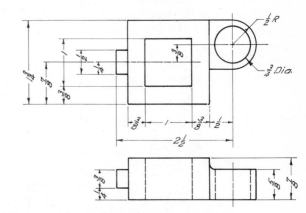

Fig. 9-2. Extension lines cross outlines and each other.

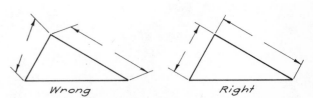

Fig. 9-3. Dimensioning inclined lines.

the discussion of technique, it will be necessary to define a few terms. Dimension lines are the lines, terminated by arrows at each end, which show the length of a dimension. See Fig. 9–1. Extension lines are the lines which extend out from an object to indicate the limits or extent of a dimension. See Fig. 9–1. Leaders are lines which run from some point on a drawing indicated by an arrow to a note which concerns that part of the drawing. See Fig. 9–1.

a. Dimension lines, extension lines, and leaders. These lines should be thin black lines. Along with center lines they should be the thinnest black lines on a drawing in distinct contrast to the visible and invisible outlines of the object. See Fig. 9–1. The dimension line is always parallel to the line it dimensions. Dimension lines should never coincide with a center line or any object line, nor with an extension of either. See Figs. 9–16 and 9–17.

b. Extension lines. Extension lines should not touch the outline of the object dimensioned. A gap of ¹⁄₁₆ inch is recommended. The purpose is to show clearly the limits or boundaries of the object. See Fig. 9–2. The extension lines should extend about ⅛ inch beyond the dimension line. They should normally be perpendicular to the line being dimensioned. See Fig. 9–3.

c. Crossing extension lines. When extension lines must cross the boundaries or outlines of the object, they may be drawn across solidly, as shown in Fig. 9–2. Occasionally it is necessary to cross extension lines. They should be crossed solidly without interruption in either set, as shown in Fig. 9–2. However, if an extension line crosses a dimension line at an arrow head, a break in

the extension line is recommended. See Fig. 9–21.

d. Break in dimension line. In machine drawing open spaces are left near the center of dimension lines for the numerals. Inserting the numeral in a gap in the dimension line is the standard practice for machine drawing and is illustrated in all the machine drawing figures in this chapter.

In the case where limit dimensions or tolerances are used, the dimension line may be continuous when decimals occur in two lines as shown in Fig. 9–4.

e. Staggered dimensions. When a series of dimension lines occur in close proximity to one another, the dimensions should be offset or staggered, as shown in Fig. 9–5, rather than have all of them in line at the center.

f. Arrowheads. Arrowheads should be made as shown in the enlarged illustration in Fig. 9–6. Some companies prefer the open form shown on the left, others prefer the closed form on the right. Since the spaces which must be dimensioned are sometimes quite narrow, the size of the arrow must be reduced somewhat in keeping with the space, but the length of the arrow should still be three times its width. When there is ample room, however, they should be of uniform size, approximately ⅛ to ³⁄₁₆ inch long.

g. Leaders. Leaders should be made mechanically with a straight edge. Notes should always be placed on the drawing horizontally if possible, and hence the end of the leader adjacent to the note should terminate in a short horizontal line at the mid-height of the letters of the first line of the note, as shown in Fig. 9–7. The horizontal direction is assumed to be parallel to the side of the drawing from which the title reads. When a leader

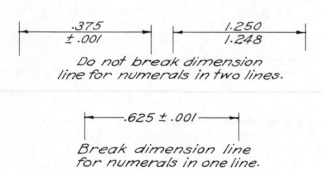

Fig. 9–4.   Dimension lines.

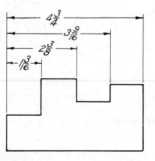

Fig. 9–5.   Staggering dimensions.

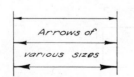
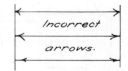

Fig. 9–6.   Arrowheads.

points toward a line of the figure it should end with an arrow, but if it points to an area, it should end with a dot. See Fig. 9–9.

h. Parallel leaders. When two or more leaders are close together, the appearance of the drawing will be improved if they are made parallel. See Fig. 9–8. When possible they should be made 60° with the horizontal, but other angles may be used except the vertical and horizontal. When leaders point to a straight line, the leader should make an angle of more than 30° with that line. See Fig. 9–9.

i. Leaders to circles. A leader referring to a circle or hole should have the arrow touching the circle, not the center. The direction of the leader, however, should be radial, so that, if it were extended, it would pass through the center of the circle. See Fig. 9–7. In giving the size of a hole it is more common to give the diameter rather than to specify a drill size. Some shops, however, use the drill size. Both methods are illustrated in this book.

j. Length of leaders. Leaders should not cross nor be too long.

k. Fractions. Fractions should always have a line between the numerator and denominator. This should be in line with, but not a part of, the dimension line. See Fig. 9–10. The numerals in fractions should be not less than two-thirds the height of the integer as recommended in the chapter on lettering. This makes the overall height of the fraction about two times that of the corresponding whole number, as shown in Fig. 9–10.

This is much better than making the fractions too small, which is a common error of beginners. The inclined bar or the omission of the bar is not to be countenanced. Neither numerator nor denominator should touch the bar.

l. Feet and inches. When dimensions include both feet and inches, the single accent is used to designate feet and the inches are unmarked, as shown in Fig. 9–11.

Majority practice and the American Standards approve separating the feet and inches by a dash. If the dimension is in even feet, it should be followed by a dash and zero inches. Failure to observe this point is a common error of inexperienced draftsmen.

When the dimension is in feet and a fraction of an inch, a zero should precede the fraction. See Fig. 9–11.

m. All dimensions in inches. If all dimensions of a drawing are in inches, the inch marks may be omitted. In this event, however, it is well to note on the drawing that "all dimensions are in inches." Practice varies widely upon this point throughout the country, but the

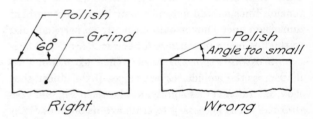

Fig. 9–9. Leaders steeply inclined to surface.

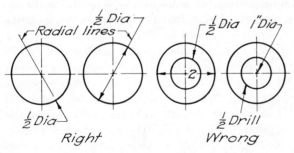

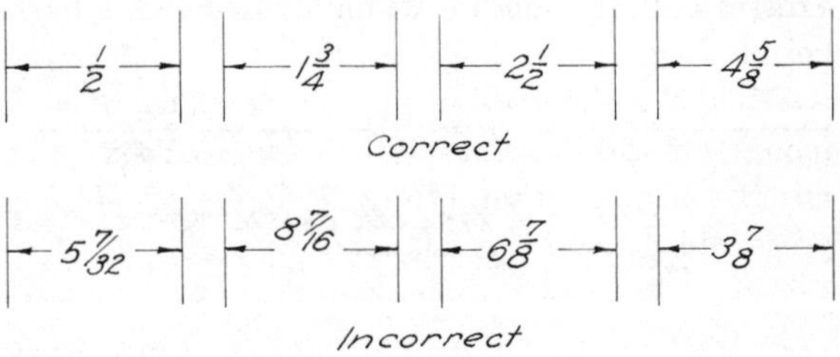

Fig. 9–7. Correct and incorrect leaders.

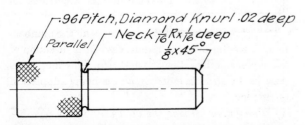

Fig. 9–8. Leaders parallel when close together.

Fig. 9–10. Method of lettering fractions.

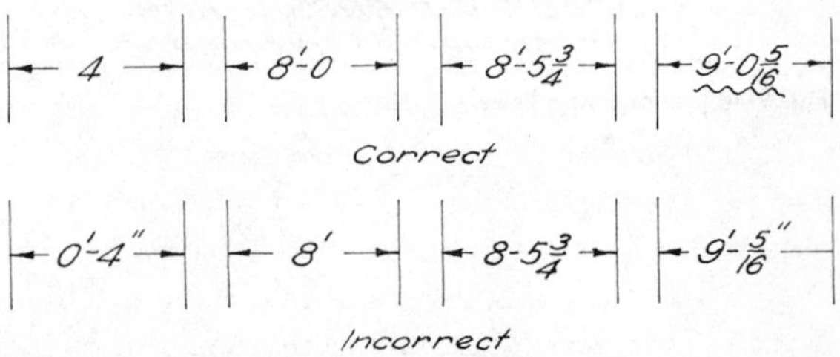

Fig. 9–11. Dimensioning in feet and inches.

omission of such marks is recommended, except where a dimension is likely to be misunderstood. For instance 1 BORE should read 1″ BORE.

The point of change-over for expressing a dimension all in inches or in feet and inches is not well standardized. Two general practices seem to be in effect. One is to change at or below 2 feet; the other to make no limit at all. A few companies change over at 3, 4, 5, or 6 feet.

n. Dimensions not to scale. When a dimension is not to scale, this fact may be indicated by placing a wavy line under the dimension or by the letters NTS as shown in Fig. 9–11.

o. Abbreviation. Avoid the use of abbreviations on drawings unless they are universally understood. Only those abbreviations recommended as American Standards should be used.

p. Dimensioning angles. For degrees use °, for minutes one accent ′, and for seconds ″. These may be written thus 15° 30′ 15″; when only degrees are given the abbreviation DEG. may be used.

q. Decimal dimensions. In many industries there is a definite trend toward complete decimal dimensioning instead of the combination of common fractions and decimals. The fundamental basis of the complete decimal system is the use of a two-place decimal, that is, a decimal consisting of two figures after the decimal point. In all dimensions where a fraction would ordinarily be used, a two-place decimal can be applied. The figures after the decimal point should be in fiftieths where possible so that when the dimensions are halved (diameters to radii), even two-place decimals will result. Some exceptions will have to be made but these should be kept to a minimum.

When a decimal value obtained by converting common fractions to decimals is to be rounded off to a lesser number of places than the total number available, the procedure should be as follows:

When the number in the place next after the last one to be retained is greater than 5, add 1 in the last place retained. Thus 1.627 becomes 1.63. When it is less than 5, do not change the number in the last place. Thus 1.623 becomes 1.62. When the number in the next place after the last one to be retained is exactly 5, do not change the last number retained if it is even, but add 1 to it if it is odd. Thus 1.625 becomes 1.62, and 1.615 also becomes 1.62. Figures 9–38, 9–39, and 9–40 show objects dimensioned completely with decimals.

The use of decimal dimensioning in the machine industries is increasing rapidly as more and more industries are convinced of its advantages. A few of those advantages are:

1. Simplifies arithmetical computations.
2. Greatly reduces mistakes.
3. Decreases time required for calculations.
4. Easier to learn and understand.
5. Simplifies conversion to metric system.
6. Decimals can be used in data processing and numerically controlled equipment.

This last item alone is enough to make fractions undesirable since decimals can be used in numerical positioning control of automatic systems.

9.3   Where to place dimensions on a drawing. Location or placing of dimensions on a drawing is quite important from the viewpoint of clearness of meaning and ease of finding them. There are certain places where a workman will quite naturally look for a dimension, and, if it is not there, he must lose time hunting for it. Long experience has indicated that the following rules are almost universally observed, and they are in conformity with American Standard recommendations.

There are certain phases of dimensioning which concern both what and where to dimension. Such borderline cases as, for example, the dimensioning of circular arcs have been discussed under the more important phase of construction dimensioning. See paragraphs 9.4.1(*d*) and (*e*).

a. Placing dimension numerals. There are two systems in general use for placing the dimension numerals on a drawing, either of which is acceptable, depending on the practice of the industry under consideration.

1. The *aligned* method is that in which the dimensions may be read from the bottom and right side of the drawing, except for radii and diameters. In other words, when the dimension line is horizontal the figures are read from the bottom of the sheet, and when the dimension lines are vertical the figures should read from the right side of the sheet. Radii and diameters are placed so that the guide lines for the numbers are parallel to the dimension line. Dimensions that give an unnatural position for lettering, such as slightly left of vertical, should be avoided if possible. This method is illustrated in Fig. 9–12(*a*).

2. The *unidirectional* system places all the numbers in a horizontal position, regardless of the direction of the dimension line. See Fig. 9–12(*b*). This method is used in the aircraft industry and is being adopted in other places.

b. Dimensions outside the views. As far as possible, and practicable, dimensions should be placed outside

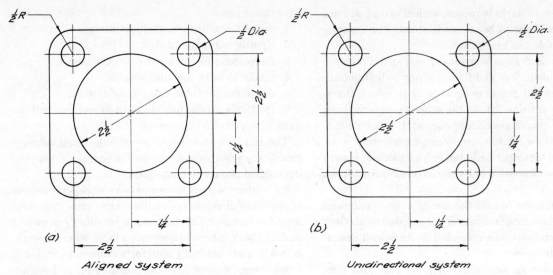

Fig. 9–12.   Two systems of placing dimension numerals.

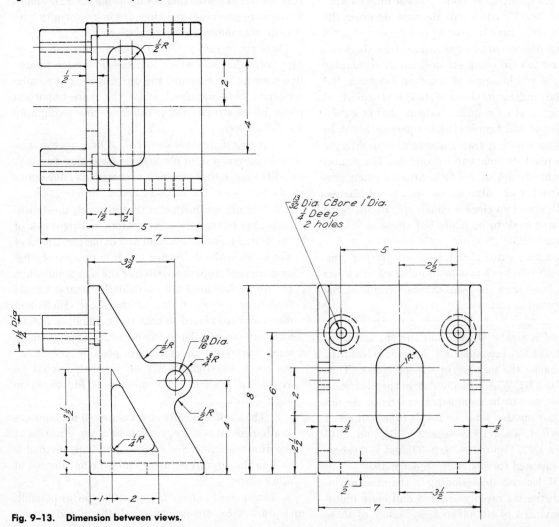

Fig. 9–13.   Dimension between views.

the views. Again diameters and radii are excepted. See Fig. 9–13. If it becomes necessary to carry a dimension across many lines to get it outside the view and if its meaning would be clearer if placed on the view, that should be done. Clearness of meaning is the test of any rule.

c. Dimensions between views. So far as possible, dimensions should be placed between views, always, of course, closest to the appropriate view. See Fig. 9–14. This serves to tie the views together and helps to interpret the drawing since the dimension lines act in lieu of projecting lines and aid visual projection between corresponding parts in adjacent views. Extension lines and center lines, however, should not be carried from one view to another.

d. Dimension the proper view. Always place dimensions on the view showing the *contour* of the object to best advantage. Thus hole patterns will be dimensioned where the circles show and not on hidden lines. See Fig. 9–14. Cylinders will usually be dimensioned on the view that shows as a rectangle rather than the view that shows as a circle. See Figs. 9–20 and 9–27(*e*).

e. Spacing dimension lines. The first line of dimensions should not be closer to the view than ⅜ inch. One failing of the beginner is to crowd dimensions too close to the views. A good drawing should permit the view to stand out clearly so that the workman can see the shape and contour, after which he can find the dimensions that he needs. Second and third lines of dimensions should not be closer than ¼ inch to each other, and preferably ⅜ inch apart. See Fig. 9–15.

f. Placing dimension lines. Dimensions should never be put on or along center lines, nor should they be placed on any line of the object or on an extension of such a line. See Figs. 9–16 and 9–17. If they are placed on a center line, the center line and its meaning are obliter-

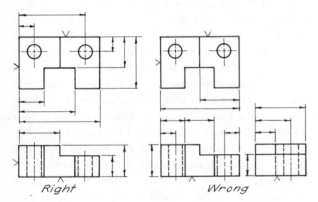

Fig. 9–14. Contour dimensioning.

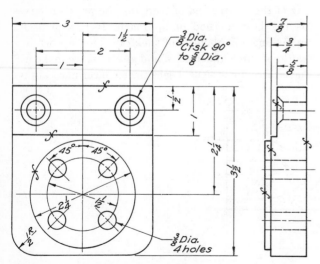

Fig. 9–15. Spacing dimensions.

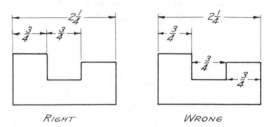

Fig. 9–16. Right and wrong placement of dimensions.

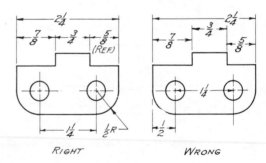

Fig. 9–17. Right and wrong placement of dimensions.

ated. If the dimension line is an extension of a line of the object, this placement makes for confusion in reading the view; hence this practice should be avoided. A permissible exception to this rule is shown in Fig. 9–18.

g. Dimensions in one line. A series of related dimensions should be placed in the same straight line and not offset. An overall dimension should accompany each series, but it need not be repeated on the same view if there happens to be more than one series of dimensions. See Fig. 9–19.

h. Dimensions not in line. Unrelated dimensions should not be placed in the same series. The workman cannot use them, and hence they are a cause of confusion. The inside dimensions of Fig. 9–19 are needed by the core maker, whereas the outside dimensions are needed by the machinist. Neither craftsman has any need to use for the other set of dimensions.

i. Avoid duplicate dimensioning. In machine drawing when an overall dimension is given, one dimension of the series should be omitted, as in Fig. 9–16, or, if it is put in for reference, it should be so marked, as in Fig.

9–17. This insures that a detail will be located in only one way, which is always good practice.

j. Dimension visible outlines. Hidden lines should not be dimensioned unless absolutely necessary. Dimensioning to the center line of a hidden hole is the equivalent of dimensioning to a hidden line. There are usually better places to put the dimension. Occasionally it may be better to make a section to avoid the hidden lines and clarify the dimensioning.

On half-sectioned views, it is permissible to dimension to a hidden line on the external half of the view if the other end of the dimension line is based on a visible line in the sectioned half of the view. See Fig. 9–20.

k. Dimensioning narrow spaces. It is sometimes necessary to dimension spaces which are quite narrow. The recommended practice is shown in Fig. 9–21. The actual space available on the paper will determine which of these forms to use.

l. Placing dimensions by size. Avoid crossing extension and dimension lines whenever possible. The small dimensions should be placed nearest the object or view and the larger ones farther out. In all cases the overall should be the last dimension, and it should be farthest from the view. See Figs. 9–19 and 9–20.

9.4   What to dimension. *Size and location.* The workman, in building a machine or structure, needs information on two points regarding dimensions, and these should always be kept in mind by the draftsman. They are: first, the *size of the object* and each of its several parts; and second, the *location of the parts relative to each other and to the whole.* These two phases of dimensioning cannot always be separated from each other in actual dimensions, but this method of thinking of the matter and of studying the problem serves as the best method of approach. It is also useful in making a final check of the drawing. We work in a world of three dimensions, and anything we make will have three dimensions; hence the engineer must always

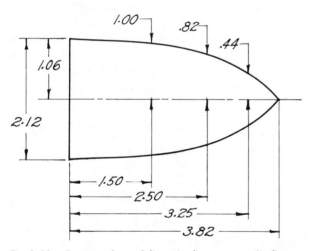

Fig. 9–18.   Exceptional use of dimension lines as extension lines.

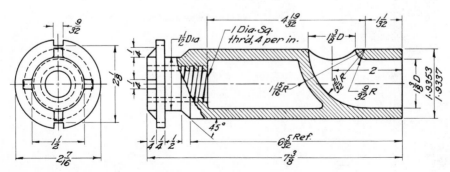

Fig. 9–19.   Related dimensions in line.

think of size in three dimensions: width, depth, and height. Location must also be determined in three directions but only two can be shown in any one view. Therefore, it is usually necessary to dimension two views.

Again it cannot be too strongly emphasized that dimensioning is entirely conditioned by *function of the part, the methods of measurement, construction, manufacture, checking or gaging, and the quantity to be produced.* In this book, only those fundamental principles which apply in all industries and those detailed practices which have become standardized and accepted throughout a wide range of industry will be given. The young engineer will always have to learn those practices peculiar to the shop in which he is employed. Differences in methods of presenting dimensions have been illustrated where practicable.

A satisfactory drawing accomplishes two things: first, it gives sufficient information from which the object can be made; and second, it provides a permanent record of the construction, on which changes can be made if necessary. A complete record of changes is always made on the drawing. Through a period of years in manufacturing, drawings undergo an average of approximately seven changes.

It is also important to avoid duplicate dimensions. In other words a component part should be dimensioned in only one manner and one place. This is important for

two reasons: first, in case of a change there will be only one place to revise with less danger of missing one; and second, if a component part is dimensioned in two ways, there is a probability that one method will allow an accumulation of tolerances that might impair the usefulness of the part. *Every dimension will have a tolerance, either specified with the dimension or by means of a general note or referenced specification.* This does not apply to reference dimensions which are for general information only.

9.4.1 *Size dimensioning.* Any object is described by the engineer by means of two, three, or more views which are severally simple plane figures upon which the dimensions of the object must be placed. The problem of dimensioning resolves itself into dimensioning a series of related plane areas. These are usually composed of simple geometric figures, such as the triangle, rectangle, and circle or combinations thereof. Examples of the dimensioning of these figures are shown in Figs. 9–22 to 9–24. Any one of them could be cut from cardboard or sheet metal from the dimensions indicated without further information. Note that in all cases dimensions are given in two directions at right angles to each other. Occasionally, as in Fig. 9–3, the draftsman may need to place dimensions on an inclined line; in which case *the extension lines should be perpendicular to the line being dimensioned and the dimension line parallel to it.*

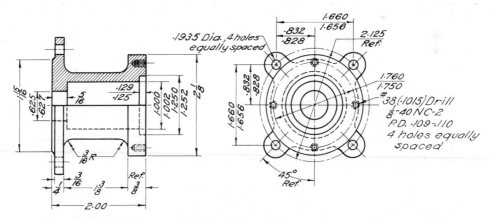

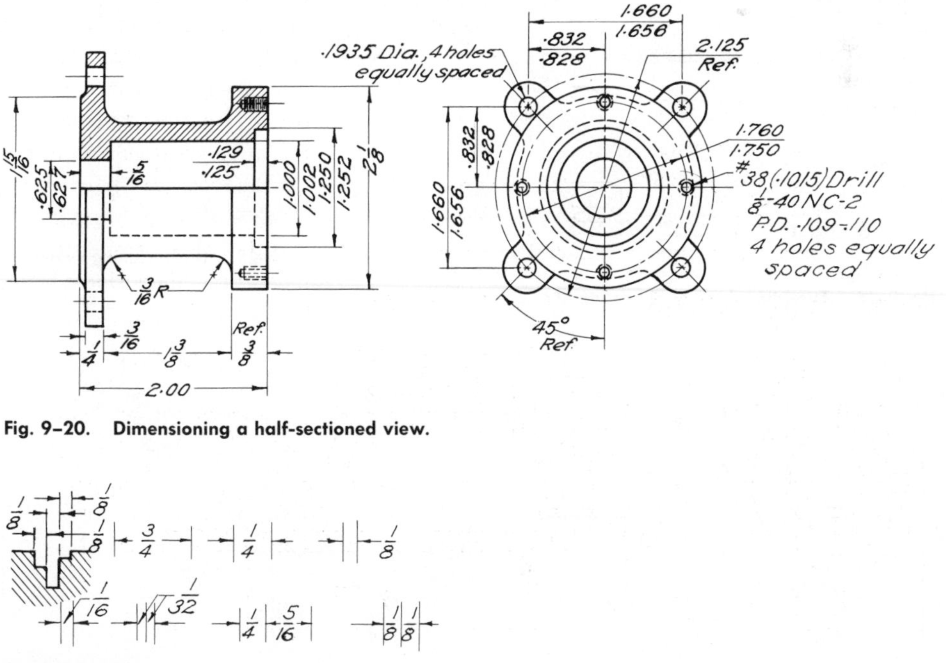

Fig. 9–20.   Dimensioning a half-sectioned view.

Fig. 9–21.   Dimensioning narrow spaces.

In planning the dimensions of an object, it is necessary to realize that all the dimensions must be laid out in the shop and therefore they must be measured from some definite line or plane. These are known as reference or datum lines or planes. For each object there will be three reference lines or planes so chosen that any part or element can be located in three directions in such a manner that the shop man can conveniently make the measurement. Choosing the location of these three datum planes is the first step in dimensioning any object. They should be either *(1) functional surfaces; that is, surfaces that are to be in contact with some other part; (2) finished surfaces; or (3) center lines or planes of symmetry.*

a. Definitions. In engineering practice, the term "size" has several meanings. A.S.A. Y14.5 gives the following definitions:

> *Nominal size.* The nominal size is the designation which is used for the purpose of general identification. Example: ½-inch pipe.
>
> *Basic size.* The basic size is that size from which the limits of size are derived by the application of allowances and tolerances.

b. Dimensioning simple objects. The dimensioning of the right rectangular prism becomes simply the problem of dimensioning two rectangles as shown in Fig. 9-23. Note that the correct method places the dimensions outside the views and between them. Several methods of dimensioning a wedge are shown in Fig. 9-24. *Note that dimensions are on the contour view.* The method of dimensioning a cylinder is shown in Fig. 9-25. Only one view and a diameter are necessary to dimension a sphere. See Fig. 9-26(*a*). The torus shown in Fig. 9-26 gives a good illustration of the connection between the drafting room and the shop. If the torus were to be made by bending a rod around a cylindrical mandrel, the method of dimensioning shown in Fig. 9-26(*b*) could be used. If the torus were to be made by bending a rod to fit inside a cylindrical die, the method shown in Fig. 9-26(*c*) would probably be preferable. However, if the torus is to be turned on a lathe, the method shown in Fig. 9-26(*d*) might be more desirable.

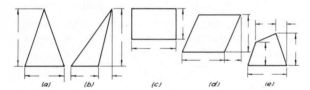

Fig. 9-22.   Dimensioning plane figures.

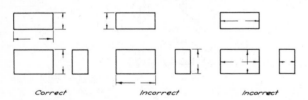

Fig. 9-23.   Dimensioning a prism.

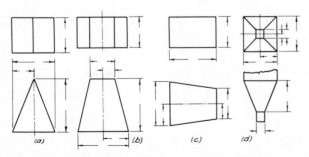

Fig. 9-24.   Dimensioning wedges and pyramids.

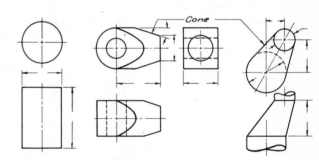

Fig. 9-25.   Dimensioning cylinders and cones.

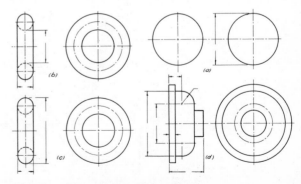

Fig. 9-26.   Dimensioning sphere and torus.

c. Dimensioning circles and cylinders. For a circle the diameter is the only essential dimension. The diameter, not the radius, should always be given for a circle, since this is the dimension the workman will use whether he is turning a cylinder on a lathe or drilling a hole. The correct method for various situations is shown in Fig. 9–27. In cylindrical objects, it is usually better to show the diameter of the circle on the view in which the plane of the circle shows edgewise, as indicated for the cylinders in Fig. 9–27(e). If there is any doubt about such a dimension being a diameter, the letters Dia. should be placed after the number.

d. Dimensioning circular arcs. For circular arcs, the radius is usually specified for the simple reason that this is the dimension the workman will use. The center of the arc is usually marked with a small cross. The leader, which indicates the radius in the case of small arcs, must always be a radial line, as shown in Fig. 9–28. This is also true for very large arcs where a leader may again be used. When the center of the arc is inaccessible or

off the paper, the radius and center are shown as in Fig. 9–29.

e. Dimensioning concentric circles. Where a series of concentric circles must be dimensioned on the circular view, the methods of Fig. 9–30 may be used. The dimension number should always read from the bottom or right-hand side unless the unidirectional system is being used. For this reason the shaded area of the figure should be avoided. Whenever possible the method of Fig. 9–27(e) should be used.

f. Compound curves. Curves composed of a series of circular arcs are dimensioned by giving the radii and locating the centers in two directions. The two directions may be at right angles to each other, or they may consist of an angle and a direction, as shown in Fig. 9–29(b), or the two distances acting as radii from two known centers may be used, as in Fig. 9–31.

g. Non-circular curves. Curves which are not circular are almost invariably dimensioned by giving coordinates to a series of points on a curve. This can be done in a

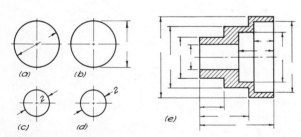

Fig. 9–27. Dimensioning circles.

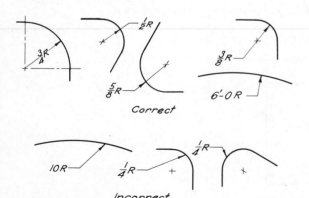

Fig. 9–28. Dimensioning arcs.

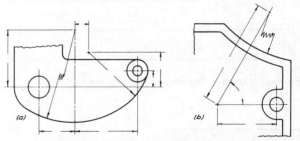

Fig. 9–29. Dimensioning long-radius arcs.

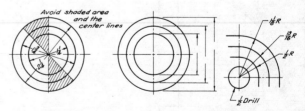

Fig. 9–30. Dimensioning concentric circles and arcs.

variety of ways, as illustrated in Fig. 9–32. The highway or railroad engineer, in laying out a parabola, has a series of horizontal stations at each of which he gives the vertical ordinate to the curve in terms of elevation above some datum plane, usually sea level. See Fig. 25–35.

In the spillway of a dam, Fig. 9–32(b), elevations would be the basic coordinates, and abscissae to the curve would be specified at each elevation. For the curve in Fig. 9–32(a), which might be the contour of a fender, coordinates from two datum lines can be given. When necessary for accuracy, some points may be located by three place decimals. The intersection of the datum lines is the zero point of coordinates.

h. Dimensioning angles. Frequently angles must be specified on drawings or in data from which drawings

are made. In machine drawing, an angle is specified by drawing an arc between the legs of the angle, as shown in Fig. 9–33. The number should be made to read from the horizontal. An exception is made in the case of large arcs when the dimension may be placed along the arc.

The angle may also be specified by giving the two legs of the right-angle triangle which form the angle. In structural work the slope or angle which a member makes with the horizontal is given by the run and rise. This is always expressed as the ratio of 12 inches to some other number in inches, as shown in Fig. 9–34(a). The smaller number is given to the nearest 1/32 inch. In civil engineering, retaining walls and some other structures have sloping faces in which the departure from the vertical is very slight. These slopes are specified by giving the "batter," which is the ratio of the run or hori-

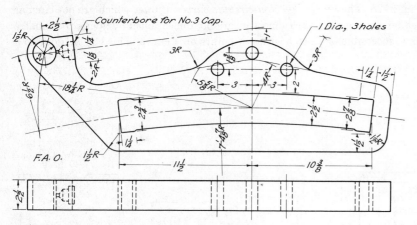

Fig. 9–31.   Location dimensioning with arcs and radii.

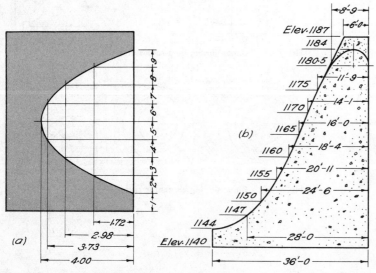

Fig. 9–32.   Dimensioning curves.

zontal distance to the rise or vertical distance between two points. See Fig. 9–34(b). The same system is used in earthwork but the slopes are usually not so steep. Thus the ratio in Fig. 9–34(c) means a measurement of 1½ units horizontally to 1 unit vertically. In architectural work, the slope of a roof is defined by its "pitch," which is the ratio of the *rise to the total span of a gabled roof.* This is illustrated in Fig. 9–34(c).

i. Dimensioning tapers. Slopes on shafts in machine drawing are called tapers. Tapers are used for a number of purposes, depending upon the design requirements. Three standard tapers are in use, namely, the Brown and Sharpe which has a taper of ½ inch per foot, the Morse, which has two types, ⅝ inch per foot, and ¾ inch per foot. *A taper means a change of diameter (not radius) in an axial length of 1 foot.*

When the taper serves no other purpose than to provide a gradual reduction in the diameter between two functional surfaces, the part may be dimensioned, as in Fig. 9–35(a), by giving the end diameters with reasonable tolerances and the length with a generous tolerance.

When an external and internal taper must fit permanently or intermittently, closer tolerances must be set

and controlled. In this case the taper can be specified with a tolerance, and a diameter given without tolerance, located by an axial dimension with a tolerance as shown in Fig. 9–35(c).

9.4.2 *Location dimensioning.* A detail or component part of an object must be located by dimensions in three directions at right angles to each other, and the measurements must be made from some base planes or lines. In choosing these base or datum planes, the draftsman must consider the purpose and function of the part, the method of manufacture, and the ease with which the dimensions may be laid out and inspected in the shop or field.

a. Choice of datum. These datum planes should be chosen so that each principal view gives an edgewise view of two of the planes, and they will usually coincide with some surface of the object or with a main center line. Care should be taken to see that they are chosen in such a way that they can be located on the object, if possible. When a center line is used, it is desirable, but not always possible, to have two holes or some other identifying feature on that center line. In the choice of surfaces for datum planes, the draftsman must consider

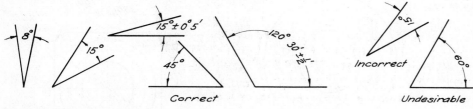

Fig. 9–33. Dimensioning angles.

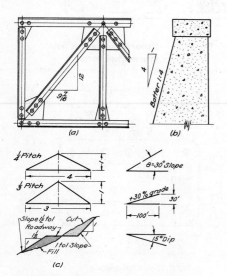

Fig. 9–34. Dimensioning angles or slopes.

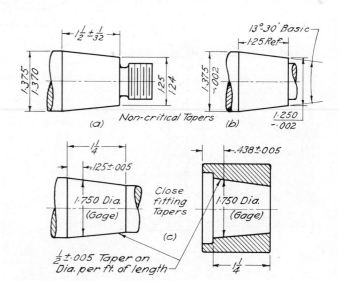

Fig. 9–35. Dimensioning tapers.

the character of that surface. External surfaces which touch no other part are frequently rough and should seldom be used except for very rough objects. *Surfaces of a part that are to be in actual contact with other parts or which control the operation of the part are called functional surfaces and make good datum planes for dimensioning.* Frequently a center plane must be used for symmetrical objects to insure the proper tolerances and clearances for all parts.

b. Location of holes. A point on an object such as the center of a hole must be located in two directions in the contour view. Three schemes for locating such a point are possible, as shown in Figs. 9–29 and 9–31. In Fig. 9–29(*a*), the center of the hole has been located by two dimensions at right angles to each other from two known or established datum planes. In Fig. 9–29(*b*), the center of the arc has been located by giving an angle and a distance, and, in Fig. 9–31, it has been located by distances from two known points by describing arcs of known radii with these base points as centers. Any one of these

methods locates the center, but the choice of method will depend on the situation.

It is frequently necessary to locate holes in a circular pattern, as indicated in Figs. 9–36, 9–37, and 9–38. Two methods of dimensioning such holes are shown in Fig. 9–36. For more exacting conditions, location may be made by specifying an upper and lower limit on each dimension in a rectangular coordinate system with the diameter of the circle given for reference, as shown in Figs. 9–37 and 9–38, or by true position dimensioning, as explained in Art. 13.20.

c. Location of holes by base-line or datum dimensioning. When it is necessary to locate holes or any features with great accuracy, base-line dimensioning must be used to avoid excessive cumulative tolerance. In Fig. 9–39, the center lines are used as base lines; in Fig. 9–40, the center lines of two sets of holes are used. By making all dimensions read from these base or datum planes, it is possible to locate each hole within the tolerance of one dimension. This allows a larger tolerance than would be

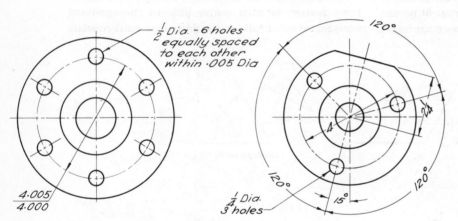

Fig. 9–36.   Dimensioning holes in circular pattern.

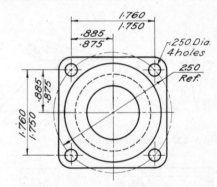

Fig. 9–38.   Dimensioning a four-hole symmetrical flange.

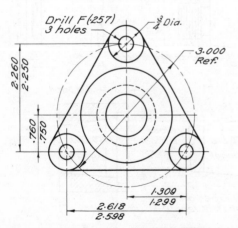

Fig. 9–37.   Dimensioning a three-hole flange.

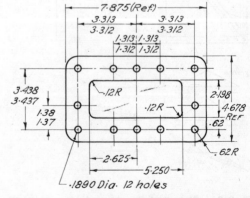

Fig. 9–39.   Dimensioning with center lines.

possible with other systems of dimensioning, assuming the same degree of accuracy in each case.

The use of datum dimensioning does not mean that all dimensions can be held to a single tolerance. Usually the distance between the individual adjacent holes will be subject to two tolerances. Thus if the smallest allowable distance from the datum to the first hole happened to occur and at the same time the largest allowable distance from the datum to the second hole occurred, then the distance between the first and second holes will be subject to two tolerances. However, the probability of the part ever being made so that this maximum of two tolerances will happen is very small.

d. Symmetrical parts. Symmetrical parts are commonly dimensioned from the axis of symmetry, unless the method of manufacture requires the use of some other datum plane. Two methods are commonly employed, as shown in Fig. 9-41, but the first method is usually considered the better.

When there are two or more points to be located on each side of a center line or from a base line, each of these points may be dimensioned directly from the base line or one from the base line and then the second from the first, as illustrated in Fig. 9-41(*a*). This second system can be useful when the tolerance between the two items

of a group must be held relatively close.

The system called chain dimensioning, as in Fig. 9-41(*c*), in which each unit is dimensioned from the preceding, involves cumulative tolerances and should be used only when the error thus caused is not important in the functioning of the part.

On parts where the location of the last point is as important as the first and cumulative errors cannot be permitted, the method by which each point is dimensioned individually from the base or datum plane is the only satisfactory method whether that datum be a finished surface or a center line. See Figs. 9-39 and 9-40.

e. Progressive or consecutive dimensioning. Where space limitations do not permit giving a separate line for each dimension, the numbers may be placed in one line as shown in Figs. 9-32(*a*) and 9-42. In this method, called progressive dimensioning, there is only one arrow for each dimension after the first, thus indicating that each dimension goes back to the original base line. This is used extensively in structural and aircraft drawing.

f. Dimensioning partial circular parts with polar coordinates. Some objects of a partial circular character can be dimensioned by giving the radius or diameter of the circular center line and the range or extent of it by an angle, as shown in Fig. 9-43.

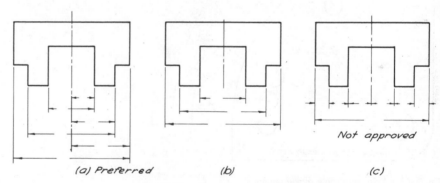

(a) Preferred   (b)   (c)

Fig. 9-41. Dimensioning symmetrical parts.

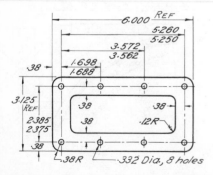

Fig. 9-40. Dimensioning from two data lines.

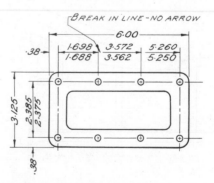

Fig. 9-42. Progressive dimensioning.

Other objects, such as those shown in Figs. 9–44 and 9–45, cannot be dimensioned in this way. Although the center lines of the holes and the extension lines from the ends are radial, it is understood that the dimensions given are on the surface and not at the location of the dimension line. The mating portion of an object like this will frequently be drilled to match in assembly.

g. Coordinate dimensioning. The coordinate system is used where there are a great many dimensions to be placed in a small area, as for example, in watch and clock plates. Here two coordinate axes are drawn through one of the holes. The other holes are lettered or numbered, and then a table of coordinates, usually reading to thousandths of an inch, is prepared giving the location of each hole and its size, as shown in Fig. 9–46.

The coordinates are sometimes placed on the drawing instead of in a table, in which case the coordinate axes,

which become datum lines, will be marked zero. Datum lines or surfaces may be on finished surfaces which have a functional relationship to other parts. The center line or surface of a hole may be a datum. See Fig. 9–47.

h. Dimensioning parts with circular ends. When an object with cylindrical ends is to be dimensioned, the extreme overall dimension should be omitted, as shown in Fig. 9–48. In these instances, the dimension between the center lines takes the place of the overall dimension. In simple cases, the method shown in Fig. 9–49 may be used. It is important for these to avoid duplicate dimensioning.

i. Dimensioning with polar coordinates. In certain cases it may be desirable to specify the radius and angular distances to holes, slots, or other features of a part. These can be dimensioned as shown in Fig. 9–43. See also Fig. 9–36.

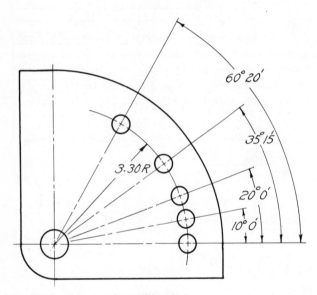

Fig. 9–43. Polar coordinate dimensioning.

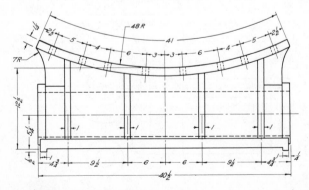

Fig. 9–44. Circumferential dimensioning.

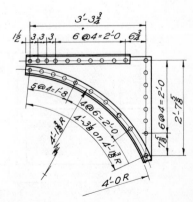

Fig. 9–45. Circumferential dimensioning.

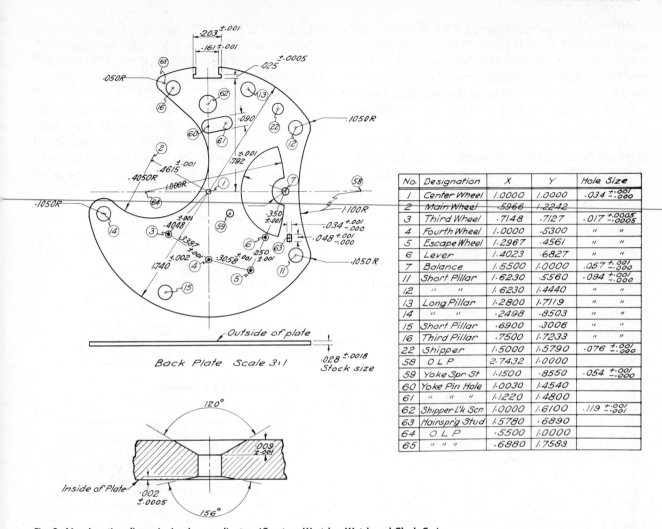

No.	Designation	X	Y	Hole Size
1	Center Wheel	1.0000	1.0000	.034 +.001 -.000
2	Main Wheel	.5966	1.2242	
3	Third Wheel	.7148	.7127	.017 +.0005 -.0005
4	Fourth Wheel	1.0000	.5300	" "
5	Escape Wheel	1.2967	.4561	" "
6	Lever	1.4023	.6827	" "
7	Balance	1.5500	1.0000	.057 +.001 -.000
11	Short Pillar	1.6230	.5560	.094 +.001 -.000
12	" "	1.6230	1.4440	" "
13	Long Pillar	1.2800	1.7119	" "
14	" "	.2498	.8503	" "
15	Short Pillar	.6900	.3006	" "
16	Third Pillar	.7500	1.7233	" "
22	Shipper	1.5000	1.5790	.076 +.001 -.000
58	O L P	2.7432	1.0000	
59	Yoke Spr St	1.1500	.8550	.054 +.001 -.000
60	Yoke Pin Hole	1.0030	1.4540	
61	" " "	1.1220	1.4800	
62	Shipper L'k Scr	1.0000	1.6100	.119 +.001 -.001
63	Hairspr'g Stud	1.5780	.6890	
64	O L P	.5500	1.0000	
65	" "	.6880	1.7583	

Fig. 9-46. Location dimensioning by coordinates. (Courtesy Westclox Watch and Clock Co.)

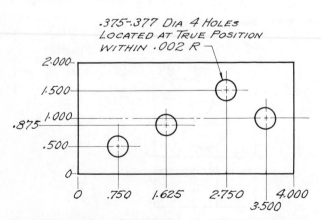

Fig. 9-47. Coordinate dimensioning.

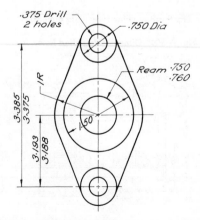

Fig. 9-48. Location of holes with limit dimensions.

9.5   Dimensioning parts produced by standard shop operations. Many machine parts involve certain standard shapes produced by common shop operations. The methods in dimensioning and noting these procedures are discussed and illustrated in the following paragraphs.

a. Blind holes. A hole that does not go all the way through a part is called a blind hole. It is specified by giving the diameter and depth, as shown in Fig. 9–50. Such holes are usually drilled. *The depth is indicated to the shoulder, not to the drill point.* When the terms Dia. or

Drill are used in notes, it is customary to place the size number first, as illustrated in Fig. 9–48. Some companies, however, prefer to place the word "drill" before the numerical value, as shown in Fig. 9–51, when tolerances are specified.

b. Tapped or threaded holes. Practice varies in the specification of tapped holes. For accurate work or for work that is to be the subject of legal contract, complete specifications, as shown in Fig. 9–51(a), should be used. For ordinary work or work done in the company shop

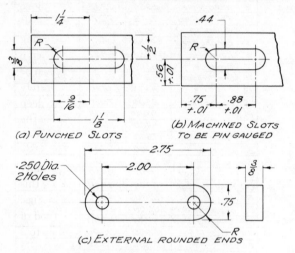

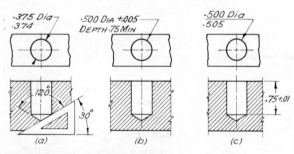

Fig. 9–49.   Dimensioning objects with rounded ends.

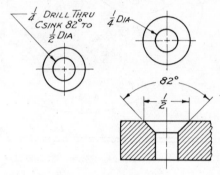

Fig. 9–52.   Dimensioning a countersink.

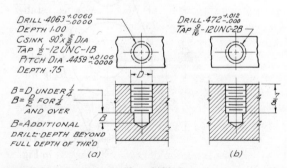

Fig. 9–50.   Dimensioning blind holes.

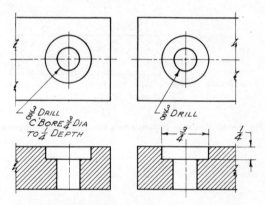

Fig. 9–53.   Dimensioning a counterbore.

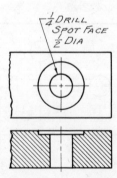

Fig. 9–51.   Dimensioning threaded holes.

Fig. 9–54.   Dimensioning a spotface.

where operating procedures are understood, the shorter form of Fig. 9-51(b) may be used.

It should be noted that for blind holes the drill depth must be greater than the threaded depth. The usual practice is shown at the bottom of Fig. 9-51(a). Where this is impossible, bottoming taps may be used, but this requires an extra operation and is more expensive.

c. Countersinking. To accommodate beveled screw heads so that the head may come flush with the surface of the part, holes are countersunk. Two methods of speci-

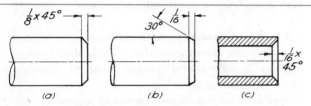

Fig. 9-55. Dimensioning a chamfer.

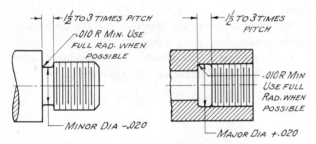

Fig. 9-56. Threading against a shoulder.

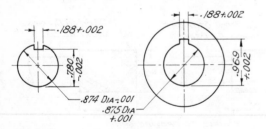

Fig. 9-57. Dimensioning a keyway.

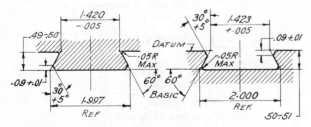

Fig. 9-58. Dimensioning a dovetail tongue and slot.

fying countersunk holes are shown in Fig. 9-52. Although the shape of the countersink is normally 82°, the drawing may be made at 90°, using the 45° triangle. The countersink should be wide enough to permit the head of the screw to come slightly below the surface.

d. Counterbore. Holes are counterbored to accommodate fillister head screws. Two methods of specifying such holes are shown in Fig. 9-53. The method of performing this operation is described in the chapter on Shop Operations. *Clearance for screws or bolts must be provided in both drilled holes and counterbore.* The amount of clearance varies, but an allowance of 1/32 above the screw or bolt size is common practice.

e. Spotface. In order to provide a smooth-bearing surface for a bolt head or nut, the process of spotfacing is used. The method of specifying this operation is shown in Fig. 9-54. The depth of spotfacing is rarely given since it is understood that it is to be just deep enough to provide a smooth surface. The diameter of the spotface must be large enough to accommodate the cross-corner dimension of a nut.

f. Chamfer. The ends of rods, bolts, etc., are usually cut off on a bevel. Two correct methods of showing this cut, which is called a chamfer, are illustrated in Figs. 9-55(a) and (b). When applied to a hole, the method of Fig. 9-55(c) may be used. Although this is similar to a countersink, the depth is usually smaller.

g. Threading against a shoulder. When threading a part, either external or internal, against a shoulder it is necessary to provide clearance for the thread-cutting tool. This is referred to as thread relief. The usual practice in providing and dimensioning this relief is shown in Fig. 9-56.

h. Keyways. Keyways in shafts and hubs should be dimensioned as indicated in Fig. 9-57. This is most convenient both for manufacture and gaging.

i. Dovetail tongue and slot. The dimensioning of a dovetail tongue and slot is shown in Fig. 9-58. Note that the 60° angle is marked "basic." This simply means that the angle must fall within the tolerance zones established by the other toleranced dimensions. This avoids cumulative tolerances.

The selection of the functional datum surface is also important. In this case it was assumed that bearing was to be maintained on the shoulder.

j. Oblique extension lines. In dimensioning flat curves, as for example on car fenders, when there is not enough room to place extension lines and dimensions in the usual way, oblique extension lines may be used as in Fig. 9-59. Note that the dimension is given in the usual direction, in which it is to be measured and not perpendicular to the oblique extension lines.

k. Knurls. Knurling consists in producing ridges or depressions in surfaces for the purpose of providing a better grip or for joining two parts together in a press fit. The method of dimensioning both types is illustrated in Fig. 9–60.

9.6   Notes. Notes on drawing fall into two general classes, namely, general notes, applying to the entire drawing, and local or specific notes applying to a particular part of the drawing.

9.6.1   *Local notes.* Local notes are connected to the part to which they apply by leaders, as illustrated in many of the drawings of this chapter. Leaders from local notes should not be parallel or perpendicular to extension or dimension lines. So far as possible they should not cross these lines, but it must be recognized that this cannot always be avoided. If a local note applies in three or four places and leaders are required to indicate the places, it is better to repeat the note rather than have many leaders crossing the drawing to one note.

9.6.2   *General notes.* General notes should be placed in a prominent place near the title block. Typical of general notes, which apply to the entire drawing, are the following:

All dimensions in inches.

Finish all over, or FAO.

Break sharp edges .01 to .03 R unless otherwise specified.

All small fillets ⅛ R.

All dimensions to be met after plating.

Remove burrs.

All draft angles 7° unless otherwise specified.

Paint one coat of red lead.

Rivets ¾ Dia. unless otherwise noted.

9.7   Limit dimensions. Limit dimensions, tolerances, both geometric and positional, are discussed in Chapter 13.

9.8   Use of standard parts. In dimensioning a drawing it is advisable, almost mandatory, for the draftsman or engineer to make use of available standard materials, parts, tools, and gages.

Specifications and dimensions should require:

a. Use of standard stock sizes and gauges for specification of materials such as bar stock, sheet metal, and wire.

b. Use of commercially standard and available parts such as bolts, nuts, keys, washers.

c. Use of part sizes which can be produced with standard tools and inspected with standard gages.

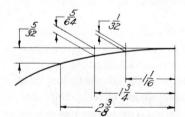

Fig. 9–59.   Oblique extension lines.

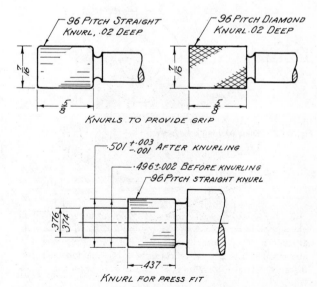

KNURLS TO PROVIDE GRIP

KNURL FOR PRESS FIT

Fig. 9–60.   Dimensioning a knurled part. (Courtesy ASA.)

PROBLEMS

The problems given in this chapter have most of their dimensions given in the form of verbal size specifications. A few dimensions, principally radii, are shown on the figures. The student should read the specifications under each problem very carefully while referring to the pictorial figure. Some dimensions must be worked out from others. Thus a radius may give the diameter of a part and the width of a straight part tangent to the circular part.

In all problems, draw the views necessary to adequately de-scribe the shape of the object. Allow ample space between and around views for dimensions.

1 to 12. Make the necessary views of the object assigned from Figs. 9–61 to 9–72, dimension the drawing, indicate finished surfaces, and add any necessary notes so that no further information is needed to manufacture the object. Place name of object, material specification, and scale under the views or in a title block if one is provided on the sheet.

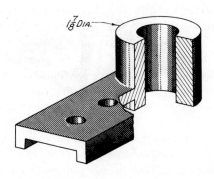

Rectangular groove ¼ × 1⅜ sliding fit; surrounding material ¼″ thick; nominal size of shaft ¹⁵⁄₁₆, class 2 fit; overall length 5″; height 1½″; ⁷⁄₁₆″ holes spread 1½″ center-to-center; ³⁄₃₂″ × ¼″ keyway; cast steel; finish as needed; scale 1″ = 1″.

Fig. 9–61. Connecting-rod end.

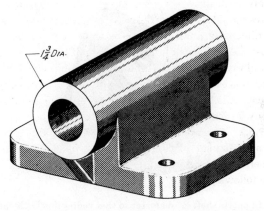

Shaft ¹⁵⁄₁₆″ nominal diameter, class 2 fit; center of shaft 1⅝″ above base plane; bearing 5″ long; base 3½″ × 4¾″; four ¹³⁄₃₂″ holes in base, ¾″ from each edge; brace on each end ⅜″ thick; base ½″ thick; cast iron; finish as needed; scale ½″ = 1″.

Fig. 9–63. Pillow block.

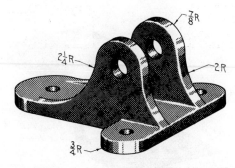

All material ⅜″ thick, three ⁷⁄₁₆″ holes in base, located on corners of an isosceles triangle having a base of 3¾″ and an altitude of 3⅞″; center line of ⁹⁄₁₆″ holes in uprights is 1½″ above top of base and ¾″ left of base of the hole triangle; clear distance between uprights is 1½″; cast iron; unfinished; scale ½″ = 1″.

Fig. 9–62. Bracket.

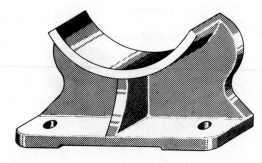

Supports 9″ pipe so that center line is 7⅞″ above support under base surface; saddle has 120° bearing 2″ long; all material ½″ thick; base 2¾″ × 12″; holes in base ¹³⁄₁₆″ diameter, 1½″ from ends and 1¼″ from front of base; ⅛″ pads on base, 3″ on each end; design back and center brace to suit; cast iron; finish as needed; scale ⅜″ = 1″.

Fig. 9–64. Saddle.

Supports shaft ½″ diameter so that center line is 2⅜″ above base plane; use class 2 fit; bearing 1½″ long; base 2¼″ × 3¼″; two 5/16″ holes in base with their center lines ¾″ from ends and front of base; base and supports ¼″ thick; design shape of back and center brace to suit; cast iron; finish as necessary; scale ¾″ = 1″.

Fig. 9-65. Bearing bracket.

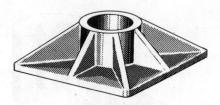

Size of base 12″ × 12″; designed for 4″ OD column; all material ⅜″ thick; height of collar 3″; cast iron; unfinished; scale ¼″ = 1″.

Fig. 9-67. Column base.

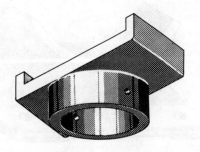

Beam seat 6″ × 12″; all material ¾″ thick; post collar 2″ deep; designed for 4½″ OD post; drill two ½″ holes in collar; cast iron; unfinished; scale ½″ = 1″.

Fig. 9-66. Post cap.

Blank ⅜″ × 2″ × ?; offset 1 3/16″; two 5/16″ holes 3¾″ center-to-center; interior radius of bend ⅜″; wrought iron; unfinished; scale 1″ = 1″.

Fig. 9-68. Offset strap.

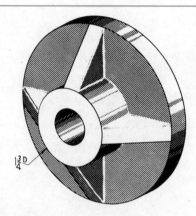

Maximum diameter 4″; hole ¹³⁄₁₆″; total height 1½″; height of base ½″; thickness of braces ⅜″; cast iron; finish as necessary; scale ¾″ = 1″.

Fig. 9–69.   Washer.

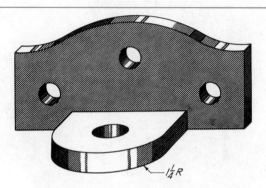

Overall dimensions of back 2¼″ × 5″; overall dimensions of base 1¼″ × 2½″; all material ⅜″ thick; three ⁷⁄₁₆″ holes in back located on corners of isosceles triangle, base of triangle 3½″; height ¾″; base of triangle ¾″ from bottom of bracket; hole in base ¹³⁄₁₆″; center line of hole 1¼″ from back of bracket; design shape of back and base to suit; cast iron; unfinished; scale ¾″ = 1″.

Fig. 9–71.   Bracket.

Holes 1″ diameter, 2¾″ center-to-center; external radius of ends 1⅛″; material in clevis end ⅜″ thick; clear opening of clevis 1⅜″; clearance center line of holes to back of clevis 1⅛″; single end 1″ thick; steel; finish as needed; scale 1″ = 1″.

Fig. 9–70.   Link.

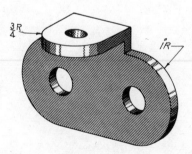

All material ¼″ thick; drill 2 holes in back ⅝″ diameter, 2″ center-to-center; drill one hole in top ½″ diameter; clearance between center line of holes in back and the top of bracket, 1¼″; clearance between center line of hole in top and the back of bracket ¾″; wrought iron; unfinished; scale 1″ = 1″.

Fig. 9–72.   Chain-link attachment.

Exterior and interior views of a wind tunnel showing fasteners (Robert M. Mottar).

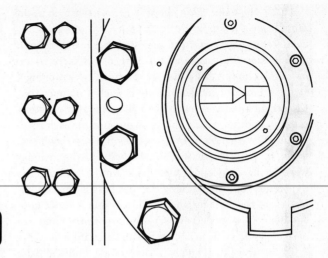

10

Fasteners

10.1 In all kinds of structures designed by engineers, the various parts are held together by devices known as fasteners. These fasteners vary in kind and use from ordinary nails and glue for wood structures to bolts, machine screws, keys, splines, and rivets for machines varying in size from locomotives to watches.

On working drawings, the engineer may specify some fasteners by means of notes without actually showing the fasteners themselves. Other fasteners may be shown in actual projected outline or in some common conventionalized form. Such fasteners as brads, nails, spikes, cotterpins, dowelpins, and other simple devices are included in the first group and are seldom shown on the drawings. Standard bolts, screws, rivets, keys, and pins are sometimes shown, particularly on assembly drawings. Special threaded fasteners and other types of special design are usually detailed on drawings.

Little study of the fasteners listed in the first class is necessary from a purely drafting standpoint, and they are, therefore, omitted from further consideration in this book. But it must not be assumed from this omission that the engineer does not know when and how to use these fasteners and how to specify them by names and notes on his drawings. Fasteners in the second class need careful study from the standpoint of the drafting-room methods and conventions employed in representing or specifying them, in addition to a knowledge of their use in the field and shop.

Since the most important fasteners in the second group are those which involve screw threads, it is logical to begin with a study of the generation and true projections of a helix, which is the curve of the thread elements.

10.2 **The helix.** *This curve is generated by a point moving on the surface of a cylinder or cone in a circumferential direction, at a constant angular speed, and with a simultaneous uniform rate of advance in an axial direction.* A helix may be obtained by wrapping a string around a cylinder or cone in such a manner that the string advances parallel to the axis at a constant rate, or, in other words, the same amount for each revolution. *The amount of this advance for one revolution is called the pitch, or lead, of the helix.* If the cylinder were to be developed, the helix would become the hypotenuse of a right triangle whose base is the circumference of the cylinder and whose altitude is the lead of the helix. The angle between the hypotenuse and the base of the triangle is known as the helix angle.

To construct the two projections of a cylindrical helix of one turn, it is first necessary to draw two views of the cylinder, making the length of the front view equal to the pitch or lead of the helix. Then the top view must be divided into a given number of equal parts, 12 for convenience, and the pitch on the front view into the same number of equal parts. Since the motion of the generating point is uniform in both angular and axial directions when the projection of the point has moved from 1 to 2 on the circle, in the top view it will have moved parallel to the axis from 1 to 2 in the front view. Points on the front view of the helix may there-

fore be obtained by projecting as indicated in Fig. 10–1(*a*).

A conical helix may be generated in a similar manner, as shown in Fig. 10–1(*b*). The principal difference between the projections of the two helices is that the top view of the conical helix is a spiral of Archimedes instead of a circle.

10.3 **Threads.** In a study of threads and the representation of them on a drawing, it is advisable to define a few terms. These definitions (abbreviated from ASA B1.2—1951 Screw Thread Gages and Gaging Standard) are illustrated in Fig. 10–2 and Fig. 10–3.

Screw thread. A ridge of uniform cross section in the form of a helix on the surface of a cylinder, Fig. 10–2.
External thread. A thread on the outside of a member, such as a bolt, Fig. 10–2.

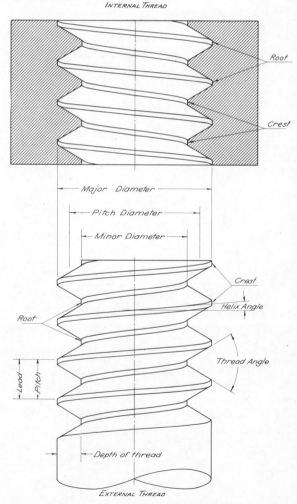

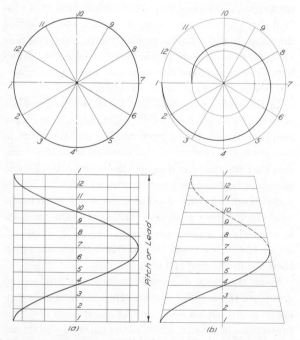

Fig. 10–1. **The helix.**

Fig. 10–2. **Illustration of thread terms. (Courtesy ASA.)**

Internal thread. A thread on the inside of a member, such as a threaded hole or nut, Fig. 10–2.

Major diameter. The largest diameter of a screw thread, Fig. 10–2.

Minor diameter. The smallest diameter of a screw thread, Fig. 10–2.

Pitch diameter. On a cylindrical screw thread, the diameter of an imaginary cylinder, the surface of which would pass through the threads at such points as to make equal the width of the threads and the width of the spaces between the threads, Figs. 10–2 and 10–3.

Pitch. The distance from a point on a screw thread to a corresponding point on the next thread measured parallel to the axis, Fig. 10–2.

Lead. The distance a screw thread advances axially in one turn, Fig. 10–2 and Fig. 10–4.

Angle of thread. The angle between the sides of a thread measured in an axial plane, Fig. 10–2.

Crest. The top surface joining the two sides of a thread, Fig. 10–2.

Root. The bottom surface joining the sides of two adjacent threads, Fig. 10–2.

Base. Bottom section of thread. Greatest section between two adjacent roots, Fig. 10–3.

Depth of thread. The distance between the crest and root of a thread measured perpendicular to the axis, Fig. 10–2.

Single thread. All the threads on a member are built on a single helix. On a single thread the pitch is equal to the lead, Fig. 10–4.

Double thread. Two threads are wrapped around the cylinder on two parallel helices. The lead is twice the pitch, Fig. 10–4.

Multiple thread. Two or more separate threads on as many parallel helices are wrapped around the cylinder, Fig. 10–4.

Helix angle. Angle the helix makes at any point with a plane perpendicular to the axis. The tangent of this angle is equal to the lead divided by the circumference of the helix cylinder.

Fit. The relative size of the pitch diameter of external and internal mating threads. Allowance and tolerance are shown in Fig. 10–20.

Clearance. An intentional difference between the major and minor diameters of the external and internal mating threads. Clearance is provided on the major and minor diameters of the nut as shown in Figs. 10–3. and 10–20.

Profile. The shape of the thread on a section plane containing the axis of the thread, Fig. 10–6.

Right-hand thread. A thread that advances into engagement in a direction away from the observer when turned in a clockwise direction, Fig. 10–5.

Left-hand thread. A thread that advances into engagement in a direction away from the observer when turned in a counterclockwise direction, Fig. 10–5.

10.4   Thread profiles. The purpose for which the screw is to be used will frequently determine the shape or profile of the thread. In the United States, general-purpose threads will usually be the Unified or American National thread form. The profile of the Unified thread is shown in Fig. 10–7. Various other forms in common use are shown in Fig. 10–6.

The American National thread as a modification of the Sharp-V thread is still used to some extent. The Whitworth thread is used in England for the same purpose

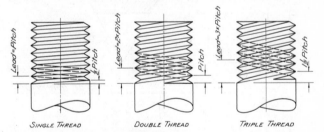

Fig. 10–4.   Single and multiple threads.

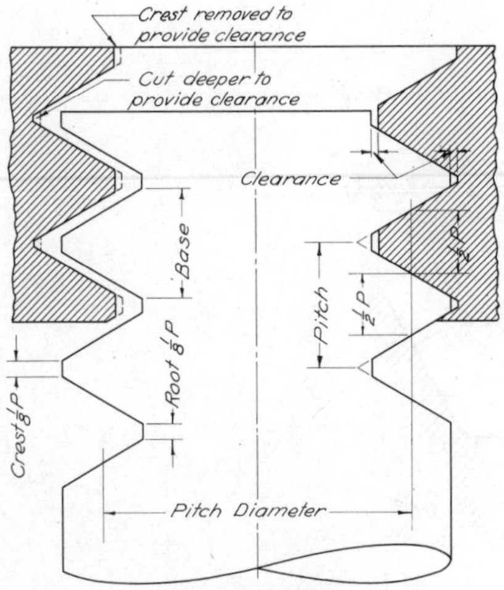

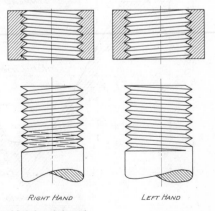

Fig. 10–5.   Right- and left-hand threads.

Fig. 10–3.   Clearance on threads.

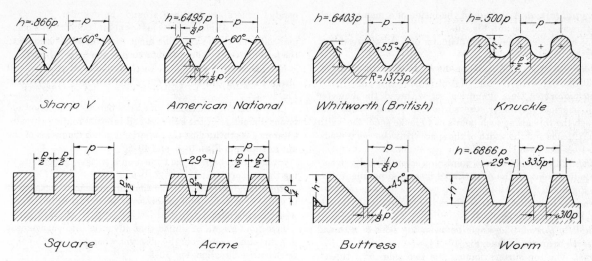

Fig. 10–6.   **Types of threads.**

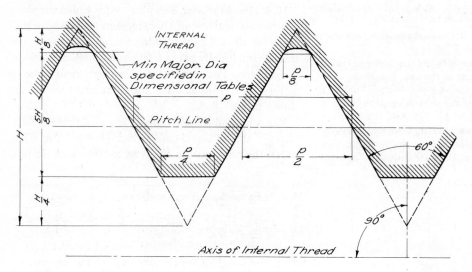

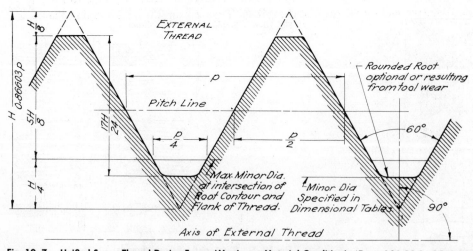

Fig. 10–7.   **Unified Screw Thread Design Forms (Maximum Material Condition). (From ASA B1.1—1960.)**

as the American National is used in the United States. The knuckle thread has a rounded profile which is convenient because it can be cast or rolled easily. The thread on the base of light bulbs is a form of the knuckle thread. The American National thread is not suitable for transmitting power since a large component of the force will be radial and tend to burst the nut. This is avoided by use of a Square, Acme, or Buttress thread. The Square thread has a profile composed of a series of squares. This thread transmits the force almost parallel to the axis, but is only about half as strong as the American National thread because it has such a small base dimension. The Acme is a modification of the Square thread; it has a 29° thread angle but is much stronger than the Square thread. The Buttress thread is used for transmitting power in one direction only, but the force is transmitted almost parallel to the axis and the thread is as strong as the American National. The standard worm gear thread is similar to the Acme thread, but has a greater depth of thread.

Translating threads which must move freely for such things as steering gears sometimes have ball bearings between the internal and external thread. Thus the entire load is transmitted through the ball bearings which roll in the threads as one part moves in relation to the other. A tube is provided to carry the balls from one end to the other, thus keeping the same balls in continual motion.

The Standards Associations of the United States, Canada, and Great Britain have agreed on the unification of screw thread standards in the industries of the three countries. The form of this thread is shown in Fig. 10–7.

10.5   Representation of Sharp-V Unified and American National threads, large size. Since the crest and root lines

of a thread are always helices, it is a slow and difficult job to show a thread in its true projection. For this reason, the thread is seldom drawn in correct projection. Occasionally very large threads on display drawings may be drawn accurately, in which case one thread would be drawn carefully and the other threads reproduced by means of templates cut from the first thread.

On most working drawings, the large threads would be drawn as shown in Fig. 10–8. This is a conventionalized form in which the profile for the Unified and American National thread is made the same as for the Sharp-V thread. The crest and root lines are drawn as straight lines instead of helices. The slope of these lines indicates the lead of the thread and shows the difference between right-hand and left-hand threads. For a right-hand single thread these lines on the bolt slant down to the right, in the position shown in Fig. 10–8, and advance parallel to the axis one-half of the lead in going across the width of the bolt.

In a section view of a nut or internal thread the lines slope up to the right because these threads must fit the threads on the back of the bolt. The end view of the bolt or threaded hole is represented by two circles of the proper visibility, as shown in Fig. 10–8. The nominal size of the thread is always the size of the larger circle regardless of its visibility. This convention should be used when the diameter of the bolt projects on the drawing as 1″ or larger.

10.6   Construction of conventional threads, large size. The steps to be followed in laying out this conventional thread are given below and illustrated in Fig. 10–9.

a. Draw two light parallel lines so that the distance between them is equal to the diameter of the bolt. On one of these lines mark off distances equal to the pitch of the thread. If convenient, the pitch should be laid out

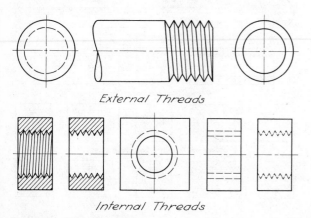

External Threads

Internal Threads

Fig. 10–8.   V-thread symbols.

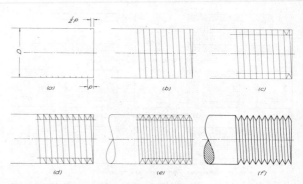

Fig. 10–9.   Construction of thread symbols.

accurately, but if not convenient the nearest even number can be used. At the first point erect a perpendicular to the lines, and on the other line mark off from this perpendicular a distance equal to one-half the lead. See Fig. 10–9(*a*). In a single thread this distance will be one-half the pitch since pitch and lead are equal.

b. Draw a line joining the two end points on the parallel lines. Draw lines parallel to this first line through the points previously marked off on the lower lines. These lines represent the crest lines of the thread, Fig. 10–9(*b*).

c. With the 60° triangle, draw the V in the first space on each side of the bolt. Through the point of the V thus formed, draw light guide lines parallel to the sides of the bolt, Fig. 10–9(*c*).

d. For the sake of speed, draw one side of each V from the ends of the crest lines to the guide lines drawn in step *c,* Fig. 10–9(*d*).

e. Complete the other side of the 60° Vs, and then draw the lines joining the bottoms of the V notches. These lines form the root lines of the thread, Fig. 10–9(*e*).

f. Erase all construction lines; work over all lines to give good clean lines. Make the root lines and outlines heavier than the crest lines, Fig. 10–9(*f*).

10.7 Representation of Unified and American National threads, small size. For threads which project smaller than 1″ diameter the convention is still further simplified. The thread profile along the edge is replaced by a straight line at the edge of the bolt. The root and crest lines are drawn perpendicular to the edges instead of slanting. The lines should be spaced at approximately the correct pitch. However, for convenience the pitch may be changed slightly. A minimum distance between crests should be set at approximately ¹⁄₁₆ inch,

even though the threads may be actually much finer. An invisible threaded hole is represented by two sets of parallel lines, one representing the major diameter and the other the minor diameter. The end view remains the same as for large-size threads. Figure 10–10 shows the conventional representation of threads under various conditions. When the thread does not go completely through a member, the drill point is always shown, sometimes with the tap drill and sometimes without. Normally the tap drill would be deeper than the desired depth of thread because it takes an extra operation to thread a hole to the bottom. The internal angle for the point of the drill is 118° but it is always drawn 120°. This conventional representation merely indicates the location of the thread and must always be accompanied by a thread specification.

When speed is essential another convention, known as the simplified thread symbol, may be used. This symbol is illustrated in Fig. 10–11. It is much faster since it avoids the necessity of drawing the root and crest lines. However, it should be used with discretion on drawings having a large number of invisible outlines.

Further simplification of these symbols has been proposed by the American British Canadian Conference and accepted by many in the United States.

10.8 Construction of conventional threads, small size. The steps to be followed in laying out this conventional symbol are listed below and illustrated in Fig. 10–12.

a. Draw two parallel lines at a distance apart equal to the diameter of the thread. Using the pitch of the thread (actual or assumed) as a base, draw a 60° triangle to determine the depth of thread on each side. Project the vertices of the triangles to the end of the bolt, and from these points draw the 45° chamfer. This locates

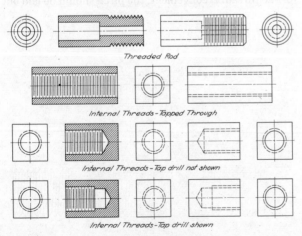

Fig. 10–10. Conventional thread symbols.

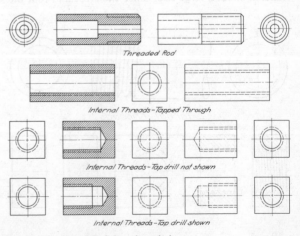

Fig. 10–11. Simplified thread symbols.

the first crest line. From this line, mark off distances equal to the pitch of the thread. This spacing does not have to be exactly equal to the pitch, and the minimum spacing should be not less than ⅟₁₆ inch, Fig. 10–12(a).

b. Through each of these points, draw lines perpendicular to the axis of the thread. These represent the crest lines of the thread. Through the points of the V's previously constructed, draw light guide lines parallel to the axis, Fig. 10–12(b).

c. Draw the root lines midway between the crest lines, and ending on the guide lines, Fig. 10–12(c).

d. Clean up the drawing, and go over all lines, making light lines for crest lines and heavy lines for outline and root lines, Fig. 10–12(d).

In making this symbol, the standards formerly required the crest and root lines to be drawn at an angle with the axis to show the pitch. Many industries still

use this form. The method of constructing this symbol is illustrated in Fig. 10–13 with steps corresponding to those shown in Fig. 10–12.

10.9 Representation of Square threads. The drawing of Square threads has been conventionalized as shown in Fig. 10–14. When the diameter of the thread shows 1 inch or over, the form shown in Fig. 10–14(a) should be used. When the diameter shows less than 1 inch, the simplified form shown in Fig. 10–14(b) may be used. In a long screw, ditto marks may be used to avoid the necessity of drawing all the threads, as illustrated in Fig. 10–14(c). The method of representing internal Square threads is shown in Figs. 10–14(d), (e), (f), and (g).

10.10 Construction of Square-thread symbol. The steps for making a right-hand, single, external thread are listed below and illustrated in Fig. 10–15.

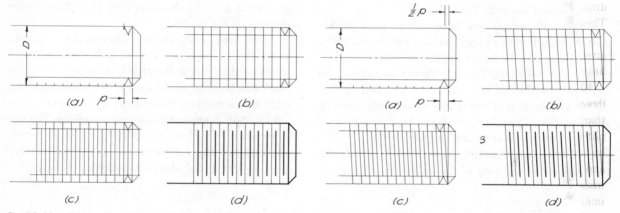

Fig. 10–12. Construction of conventional symbol.

Fig. 10–13. Construction of old form of thread symbol.

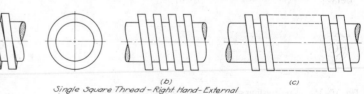

Single Square Thread – Right Hand – External

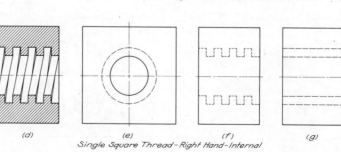

Single Square Thread – Right Hand – Internal

Fig. 10–14. Square-thread symbols.

a. Lay out four parallel lines spaced as shown in Fig. 10–15(*a*). Mark off from a right section distances equal to ½ the pitch on the two outside lines. Draw the indicated inclined lines to follow one edge of a thread for one complete revolution.

b. Lay out the squares shown in Fig. 10–15(*b*) lightly, for the sides will be erased later. For a single or triple thread, the opposite squares will be laid out in the same direction. For double or quadruple threads, the opposite squares will be laid out in opposite directions. From the external corners of the squares, draw lines parallel to the visible inclined line in Fig. 10–15(*a*). These are the crest lines of the threads.

c. The root lines will be drawn to join the interior corners of the squares. Only the half of this line which lies outside the crest lines should be drawn, as the other half will be invisible, as in Fig. 10–15(*c*).

d. From the external corners of the squares, draw lines as indicated in Fig. 10–15(*d*), which are parallel to the dotted line shown in Fig. 10–15(*a*).

e. Erase all unnecessary lines, and go over the remaining lines to make them heavier. The drawing will now be complete, as shown in Fig. 10–15(*e*).

To make the internal Square thread in section, the steps will be slightly different, as illustrated in Fig. 10–16. The squares of the profile become the outlines of the section. The root lines should be drawn first, as they are the lines that remain entirely visible.

Another system of making the external Square thread that avoids the necessity of erasing so many lines and is therefore a little faster is shown in Fig. 10–17.

10.11   Construction of the symbol for Acme thread. Although the Acme thread is used for approximately the same purpose as the Square thread, the layout of this thread on the drawing is somewhat different. The following paragraphs give a description of the steps shown in Fig. 10–18.

a. Lay out three sets of parallel lines with the spacing shown in Fig. 10–18(*a*). The two outside lines represent the major diameter of the thread, the two inside lines represent the minor diameter, and the intermediate lines represent the pitch diameter. Starting from a right section, measure off distances equal to ½ *p* on the two pitch lines.

b. From these points on the pitch lines, draw lines making 15° with a perpendicular to the axis, as shown in Fig. 10–18(*b*). If a single thread is being drawn, a ridge on one side is opposite a groove on the other side, but, with a double thread, the ridge on one side is made opposite the ridge on the other side. Draw lines joining the crests on the profile.

c. Draw lines joining the root lines on the profile. See Fig. 10–18(*c*).

d. Draw that part of the crest line on the back of the thread which is visible. As none of the single thread is visible, the single thread is actually finished in (*c*).

10.12   Specification of threads on a drawing. The representation of threads on a drawing has been so conventionalized that the drawing itself gives little information about the thread except its location. However, it is

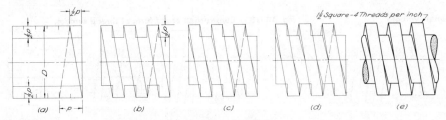

Fig. 10–15.   Construction of external Square-thread symbol.

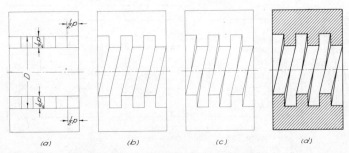

Fig. 10–16.   Construction of internal Square-thread symbol.

necessary to give the man in the shop complete information about the thread. For this reason a standard form of note is used to specify threads.

a. Unified or American National thread. Under the Unified or American Standard, the classes of straight screw threads are distinguished from each other by the amount of tolerance or tolerance and allowance. Classes 1A, 2A, and 3A refer to external threads only, whereas 1B, 2B, and 3B refer to internal threads. Classes 2 and 3 from the former American Standard refer to both external and internal threads.

For these threads, the standard note takes the general form 5/16-18 UNC-2A or 5/16-18 NC-2. The first number gives the major diameter of the thread; the second specifies the number of threads per inch; the letters UNC, Unified National Coarse; and 2A refers to the fit of an external thread. When the letters NF are used instead of NC, it means that the fine thread series is being used, and the letter *N* by itself means that a thread of the same shape as the American National thread is being used but that a special pitch is required.

The manner of placing the thread note on the drawing is shown in Fig. 10-19 for external and internal threads. Although many drawings may be found where the internal thread is specified merely by the thread note as in Fig. 10-19(b), it is generally considered better practice to give the tap drill size also as in Fig. 10-19(c). Many companies require complete information concerning the thread even to the tolerance on the pitch diameter. This is shown in Fig. 10-19(d).

Unless otherwise noted, the thread is considered to be right hand and single. For a left-hand double thread, the note L.H. Double is added to the thread note as in Fig. 10-19(a).

The old-style thread notes, such as Tap ½ USS, #6 ASME or ¾ SAE, are still found on drawings, and refer to the thread series commonly used before the American National series was standardized.

The length of thread on a bolt or in a hole is taken to mean the length of full form threads and does not include the imperfect threads that are always found at the beginning of a thread. For bolts under 6″ in length, the minimum length of threading is 2D + ¼″. Bolts that are too short, should be threaded as near the head as possible.

b. Sharp-V threads may be specified by using the same form of thread note by substituting "Sharp V" for the letters NC thus: ½-13 Sharp V-2.

c. For Square or Acme threads, the standard note gives the major diameter and the number of threads per inch, as shown in Figs. 10-15 and 10-18.

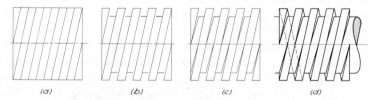

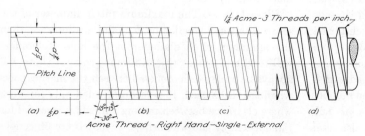

Fig. 10-17. **Alternate method of constructing Square-thread symbol.**

Fig. 10-18. **Construction of Acme thread symbol.**

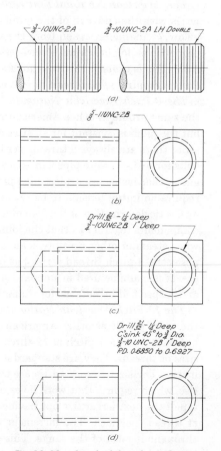

Fig. 10-19. **Standard thread specifications.**

10.13   Thread series. Before the standardization of the American National thread, there were two main groups of threads in use in the United States. For most work the United States Standard or Sellers thread was specified, but, for automotive work, a special thread was devised by the Society of Automotive Engineers. This thread had a smaller pitch than the United States Standard to give better resistance to vibration. These two groups were taken over almost entirely as the American National Coarse and American National Fine series. Three other constant-pitch series were also added, namely, the 8-pitch, 12-pitch, and the 16-pitch series. Threads in the National series that are common with the British and Canadian practice are known as the Unified Standards.

The American National Coarse series is the old U. S. Standard with the addition of numbered sizes 1 to 12 below ¼″ diameter taken from the table of standard proportions for machine screws established by ASME. *This group is recommended for the great majority of thread applications.* It is specified thus: ⅜-11 NC-2.

The American National Fine series is the old SAE series with the addition of the numbered sizes 0 to 12 below ¼″ diameter, taken from the table of standard proportions for machine screws established by the ASME. *This group is recommended where special conditions require a fine thread.* It is specified ⅜-18 NF-2.

The 8-Pitch American National Thread series has the same profile as other American National threads, but the pitch is constant for all sizes of threads. In this series there are always 8 threads per inch. It is used on bolts for high-pressure pipe flanges, cylinder head studs, and similar fastenings against high pressure. Such bolts require an initial tension to be set up in the fastening by elastic deformation of the fastening, thus holding the components together so that the joint will not open up when steam or other pressure is applied. For such purposes the 8-pitch thread series has come into general use. It is manufactured in standard sizes from 1″ to 6″, and is specified by note as, for example, 2½-8N-2.

The 12-Pitch American National Thread series has the same profile as other American National threads but has a constant pitch of 12 threads per inch for all sizes of threads. They are standard in sizes from ½ to 6 inches. The sizes from ½ to 1¾ are used in boiler practice, which requires that worn holes be retapped with a tap of the next larger size but having the same number of threads per inch. The increment of size is 1/16 inch throughout most of the range. This series is also used in machine construction for thin nuts on shafts and sleeves. It is specified by a note of the form ¾-12N-2.

The 16-Pitch American National Thread series is a uniform-pitch series for such application as requires a very fine thread. It is intended primarily for threaded adjusting collars and bearing retaining nuts. It has 16 threads per inch for all sizes and is made in standard sizes from ¾″ to 6″. To specify this thread a note like the following is used, 1½-16N-2.

The SAE Extra Fine Series has more threads per inch than any of the other series for the smaller threads. The sizes above 1¾ are the same as the 16-thread series. This extra fine series is used in thin sections and where vibration is great.

10.14   Classes of thread fit. In a study of thread fit, it is necessary to understand the meaning of a few terms. Fit is the relation between the size of two mating parts with reference to ease of assembly. In a thread, the fit determines the pitch diameter of the screw. The quality of the fit is dependent on relative size, and quality of the finish, of mating parts.

Basic diameter is the theoretical or nominal standard size from which all variations are made.

Tolerance is the amount of variation allowed in manufacture.

Allowance is the intentional difference in size between mating parts.

Crest clearance is the space between the crest of a thread and the root of its mating thread.

The thread standards provide for four classes of fits for various purposes. These classes are distinguished by numbers from 1 to 4, number 1 being the loosest and number 4 the closest fit. The four fits are obtained by the application of specific tolerances, or tolerances together with allowances to the basic pitch diameter of the thread. This basic pitch diameter is the same for both internal and external threads of like size and pitch. The tolerances throughout are applied plus to the hole and minus to the screw, as shown in Fig. 10–20. The allowances when used are applied to the bolt only. For this reason the external threads have been designated A and the internal B so that pitch diameters can be more easily specified.

Class 1, loose. The maximum pitch diameter of the screw is always smaller by a definite allowance than the minimum pitch diameter of the hole. Tolerances will tend to increase this difference so that there will always be a play or looseness between the mating parts when this fit is used. It is recommended only for work where clearance between mating threads is essential for rapid assembly and when shake or play is not objectionable.

Class 2, free. In this class there is no allowance. There is a variation from the tightest fit, where the pitch diameters of both internal and external threads are at the nominal pitch diameter, to the loosest fit, in which there is some play due to the fact that total class 2 pitch diameter tolerance has been applied to both parts.

This fit gives a high quality commercial screw thread product. It is recommended for the great bulk of interchangeable screw thread work.

Class 3, medium. There is no allowance in this class of fit. There is a variation from the tightest fit when both pitch diameters are at basic value to the loosest fit when class 3 tolerance has been applied to both parts. The maximum play will be about 70% of that found in class 2 fit.

This class of fit is used for an exceptionally high grade of commercial product and is recommended only where the high cost of precision tools and continual checking of tools and product are warranted.

Class 4, close. There is a negative allowance in this class of fit. This results in a selective assembly, because there is an actual interference between the maximum screw and the minimum hole. The pitch diameter of the maximum screw is greater than the basic value by a definite allowance, whereas the pitch diameter of the minimum hole is basic. With minimum screw and maximum hole, when total class 4 pitch diameter tolerance has been applied to both parts, there is a slight amount of play.

This fit is intended for very unusual requirements, and is not as yet adaptable to quantity production. It requires selective fit if initial assembly by hand is required.

10.15 Methods of cutting threads. Standard threads are cut with special automatic machines when bolts, nuts, and screws are being manufactured on a production basis. Threads may also be cut on a lathe, by hand, ground, or rolled. The automatic machine forms the entire bolt including the head from a plain rod, by means of a series of operations including upsetting, shearing, and threading. In handwork threads are cut by means of taps and dies. For internal threads, it is first necessary to drill a hole and ream it if fine threads are to be cut. The size of the tap drill for any given thread may be found in Table 2 in the Appendix. The tap is then used to cut the threads, as illustrated in Fig. 11–35. External threads are cut by a die either by hand or on a lathe, as shown in Fig. 11–36. They may also be rolled or ground. The method of cutting them will depend somewhat on the desired fit.

10.16 Bolts. One of the most common applications of the use of threads is on bolts. Two pieces of solid material may be held together by a bolt which holds by means of a head on one end and a nut which screws on the other end. Both pieces of material must first be drilled to a diameter larger than the diameter of the bolt. For a close fit the hole should be 1/64″ larger than the bolt, and for a free fit it should be 1/32″ larger; for rough work still greater allowance may be used to permit assembly when two or more bolts hold parts together. For a bolt in a hole this clearance may or may not be shown on the drawing, depending somewhat on the scale. See Fig. 10–21.

Although the primary purpose of a bolt is to hold two pieces of material together, the exact conditions under which the bolt is used have brought into use a wide variety of shapes, each of which is designed for a special purpose. Some of the most commonly used bolts and screws are shown in Fig. 10–22. A short discussion of these follows.

The square-head and the hexagonal-head bolt are general-purpose bolts. Of these two the hexagonal head is preferred when space for a wrench is limited because it can be tightened with a wrench movement of one-sixth of a turn, whereas the square head requires a full

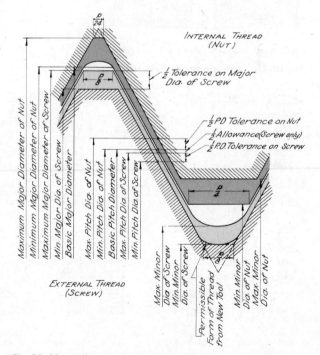

Fig. 10–20. Tolerances on screw threads. (ASAB 1.1–1960.)

one-quarter turn. The hexagonal head is frequently preferred on high-grade machinery because of its better appearance.

The stud bolt has threads on both ends so that one of the pieces being held together must be threaded to replace the head. The stud bolt is turned into the threaded hole by means of a pipe wrench or a special lock-nut device until the threads jam. The bolts then become an assembly guide by means of which the other part, which is drilled but not threaded, is properly placed. A nut screwed on the other end of the bolt holds the two parts together.

The carriage bolt is used principally for wood work. It has a smooth oval head for a finished appearance and a square shank which prevents the bolt from turning as

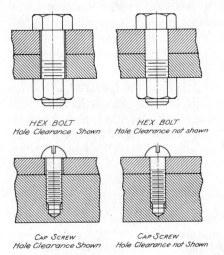

HEX BOLT
Hole Clearance Shown

HEX BOLT
Hole Clearance not shown

CAP SCREW
Hole Clearance Shown

CAP SCREW
Hole Clearance not Shown

Fig. 10–21.   Bolts and screws in sectional assemblies.

the nut is tightened.

The stove bolt. The standard stove bolt is peculiar in that it has a round flat head which is beveled on the under side to fit a countersunk hole. It is provided with a screw-driver slot for turning the threaded end into the nut. This bolt is used where it is desirable to have the head of the bolt flush with the surface of the metal held in place. A second kind of stove bolt has a button-shaped head with a slot for a screw driver but is not beveled on the under side.

The plow bolt is similar to the first-mentioned stove bolt except that it does not have the screw-driver slot. The head has a projecting lug or square shank to keep the bolt from turning as the nut is being tightened.

10.17   Finish of bolts. The square- and hexagonal-head bolts are made in three grades of finish which are listed as unfinished, semifinished, and finished. See Fig. 10–23.

Unfinished bolt heads or nuts are not machined or treated on any surface except in the threads.

Semifinished bolt heads or nuts are machined or otherwise formed or treated on the bearing surface so as to provide for nuts, either a washer face or a circular bearing surface. For bolt heads a washer face is used.

Finished bolt heads and nuts are the same as semifinished except that the surfaces other than the bearing surface have been machined or so treated as to provide

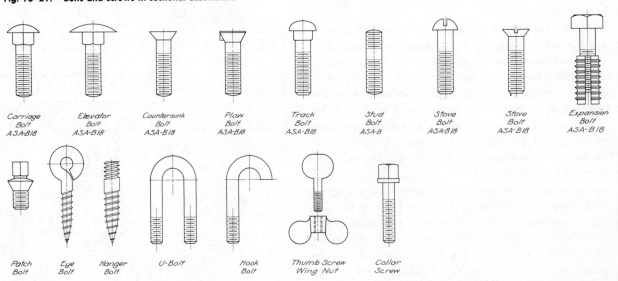

Carriage Bolt
ASA-B18

Elevator Bolt
ASA-B18

Countersunk Bolt
ASA-B18

Plow Bolt
ASA-B18

Track Bolt
ASA-B18

Stud Bolt
ASA-B

Stove Bolt
ASA-B18

Stove Bolt
ASA-B18

Expansion Bolt
ASA-B18

Patch Bolt

Eye Bolt

Hanger Bolt

U-Bolt

Hook Bolt

Thumb Screw
Wing Nut

Collar Screw

Fig. 10–22.   Special types of bolts and screws.

a special appearance. The finish desired on all non-bearing surfaces of finished bolt heads should be specified by the purchaser.

10.18 Representation of bolts and nuts. The three classes of bolt heads and nuts are listed here; dimensions may be obtained in American Standard-Wrench Head Bolts and Nuts and Wrench Openings, listed in ASA B18.2—1955.

Regular series bolt heads and nuts. Regular bolt heads and nuts are for general use. The dimensions and resulting strength are based on theoretical analysis of stresses and on results of numerous tests.

Heavy series bolt heads and nuts. Heavy bolt heads and nuts are for use where greater bearing surface is necessary, that is, where a large clearance between the bolt and hole or a greater wrench-bearing surface is considered essential.

Light series nuts. Light nuts have smaller dimensions across flats than regular series nuts.

Dimensions for regular square- and hexagonal-head unfinished and semifinished bolt heads and nuts are given in Tables 6 to 13 in the Appendix.

On regular unfinished and semifinished bolt heads the distance across flats (W) as indicated in Fig. 10–23 is one and one-half times the diameter, with adjustments to sixteenths to eliminate $\frac{1}{32}$-inch-size wrench openings. Regular nuts follow the same rule except that $\frac{1}{16}$ inch is added in sizes from $\frac{1}{4}$ to $\frac{5}{8}$ inch.

The nominal height of the regular unfinished head is $\frac{2}{3}D$ and of the semifinished head is $\frac{2}{3}D$ minus $\frac{1}{64}$ to $\frac{1}{8}$, depending on the size. The height of the semifinished and finished bolt head includes the height of the washer face, which is usually $\frac{1}{64}$ inch.

The nominal thickness of the regular unfinished nut is $\frac{7}{8}D$ and of the unfinished nut is $\frac{7}{8}D$ minus $\frac{1}{64}$ to $\frac{3}{64}$, depending on the size.

Bolt heads and nuts may be laid out on the drawing by means of dimensions taken from the tables, but for speed and convenience the method illustrated in Figs. 10–24, 10–25, and 10–26, known as the Jorgensen method, is preferred. Although the dimensions obtained by this method are not exactly accurate, they are as close as would be required, except when clearances are involved. To lay out a hexagonal bolt head by this method, the following steps are necessary.

a. Draw the outline of the bolt and the base of the head and nut. With a 30-60 triangle, draw the sides of the triangle with the hypotenuse equal to the diameter of the bolt. See Fig. 10–24(a).

b. The altitude of the triangle is equal to $c/4$ as indicated in Fig. 10–24(a). This distance should be laid off twice on each side of the center line of the bolt to give the vertical lines of the bolt head and nut.

c. The long leg of the triangle marked H_2 gives the thickness of the nut, which may be laid off as shown in Fig. 10–24(a).

d. By projecting the apex of the triangle horizontally

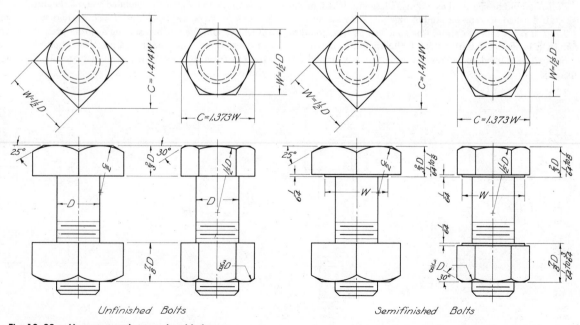

Unfinished Bolts   Semifinished Bolts

Fig. 10–23. Hexagon- and square-head bolts.

to the center line, the distance H_1 is obtained, which is the height of the head, and is laid off as shown in Fig. 10–24(a).

e. By using a radius $R_1 = D$, the curve on the front face of head and nut may be drawn as in Fig. 10–24(b).

f. The distance R_2 is taken from the point where the long leg of the triangle crosses the center line of the bolt and is used as a radius for the curves on the side faces of head and nut. The center point is on the center line of the face as shown in Fig. 10–24(c). The corners may be chamfered to finish the drawing if desired.

Similar steps for the square head and nut are illustrated in Figs. 10–25 and 10–26.

10.19   Bolt specifications. In many instances the fasteners are not drawn in projection but are listed in the bill of material. All the information necessary for ordering the bolt must therefore be included. This will require specifying the diameter, length, material, finish, kind of head and nut, bolt series, length of thread, and thread specification. Normally several of these would be omitted because they are assumed to be standard unless otherwise specified.

Diameter is the diameter of the rod from which the bolt is made and is usually the same as the thread diameter. It is always in the specification.

Length is the distance from the under side of the head to the tip of the bolt. When a countersunk head is used the length is to the top of the head. This dimension must be given in the specification.

Material is assumed to be steel unless otherwise specified.

Finish should be specified as unfinished, semifinished, or finished. If finished, the special kind of finish must be specified.

Kind of head and nut should be specified as hexagonal or square. If head and nut are different, this should be noted.

Series is assumed to be regular unless heavy or light is specified.

Length of thread is assumed to be normal unless otherwise noted.

Thread specification consists of the four items previously mentioned. A typical specification would be ¾–10NC–2.

Therefore the complete specification for a bolt would usually read: ⅝ × 3–Brass–Hex head and nut, semifinished–⅝–11NC–2.

Length of engagement. When a steel bolt is assembled into a steel part, the minimum length of engagement is equal to the diameter of the bolt; when assembled into cast iron, brass, or bronze, the length of engagement is equal to $1\frac{1}{2}D$; and when assembled into aluminum, zinc, or plastic, the length is $2D$.

10.20   Locking devices. It is frequently necessary to provide some method of preventing the nut from unscrewing and thus leaving a loose connection. This is particularly true when the fastening is subject to vibration.

Jam nuts. There are many different devices that have been designed for this purpose, the most common of which is the lock nut or jam nut. The American National jam nut has the same dimensions as the regular nut except for thickness, which is smaller because it is not designed to develop the full strength of the bolt, but merely to hold the regular nut in place; Table 11 in the Appendix gives dimensions of regular jam nuts such as that illustrated in Fig. 10–27(a). Jam nuts may be obtained in the regular, heavy, and light series and also in unfinished, semifinished, and finished design.

A patented lock nut known as Palnut, shown in Fig. 10–27(i), is used principally in electrical work and holds by tightening sufficiently to deform the rounded web of the nut.

Lock washers. Various kinds of lock washers are in use, some of which hold the nut by exerting a spring pressure on one side of the nut and others hold by a positive action which prevents the nut from turning. These are illustrated in Figs. 10–27(b) and 10–27(c).

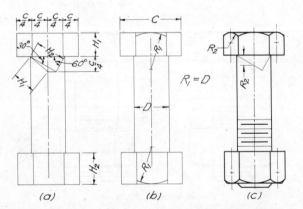

Fig. 10–24.   Conventional construction of hexagon head and nut.

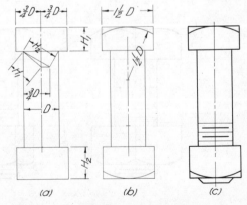

Fig. 10–25.   Conventional construction of square head and nut.

Cotter pins. The bolt may be drilled, and a cotter pin or wire may be placed through the bolt and above the nut, as in Fig. 10–27(*d*). This will prevent the nut from coming off, but does not avoid a certain amount of loosening. A more definite lock is obtained by using a slotted nut so that the cotter pin may be placed in the slot and through the bolt, as shown in Fig. 10–27(*e*).

Split nuts. The nut may be split and deformed in various ways before it is in place. The deformation exerts a pressure on the threads that holds the nut in place by its friction. One method of doing this is shown in Fig. 10–27(*f*).

Elastic stop nut. This is a patented fastener which has an elastic collar built into the nut, which grips the threads of the bolt when screwed on. This gripping action prevents the nut from backing off even when subjected to vibration. It has been used frequently in the airplane industry. Figure 10–27(*g*) shows a section of an elastic stop nut. Another form in which the elastic stop nut is used is shown in Fig. 10–27(*h*). In aircraft work it is frequently used to fasten a bolt to a thin web, in which case a flanged nut is riveted to the web to provide a suitable length of penetration.

Various other methods of locking a nut are in use, some of which are as simple as the use of a set screw in a nut and others as complicated as the use of a specially designed thread which is cut on a taper so that the friction is increased when the load is applied.

10.21 Cap screws. Cap screws are similar to bolts in that they have a head on one end and threads on the other. But, in the method of holding two pieces together, they differ widely. The bolt clamps two pieces between the head and the nut, and the cap screw is threaded into one of the pieces, thus clamping one piece between the head and the other piece. The bolt requires a smooth hole in both pieces slightly larger than the bolt, whereas

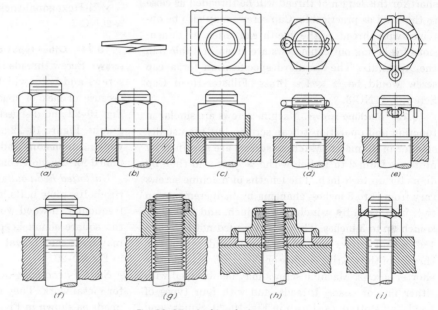

Fig. 10–27. Locking devices.

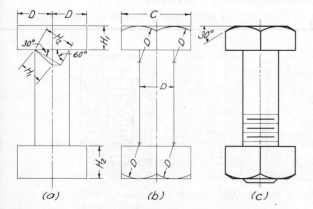

Fig. 10–26. Alternate construction for square head and nut.

the cap screw requires a smooth hole in one piece and a threaded hole in the other. Cap screws are manufactured with several styles of heads, as shown in Fig. 10–28, and in diameters varying from ¼″ to 1¼″. They may be obtained in lengths from ¼ inch to 6 inches, varying by ⅛-inch increments up to 1 inch, then by ¼-inch up to 4 inches, and finally by ½-inch up to 6 inches. The length of a cap screw is measured from the largest diameter of the bearing surface of the head to the extreme point, in a line parallel to the axis of the screw. The point of all cap screws is flat and chamfered 35° to the flat surface and to a depth equal to the depth of the thread.

Slotted-head cap screws are regularly threaded with American National coarse threads with a usable length of thread equal to $2D + ¼$ inch. Screws that are too short for this length of thread will be threaded as close to the head as practicable. Cap screws may also be obtained with threads of the fine-thread series. All dimensions for laying out cap screws are given in Table 5 in the Appendix. The standard specification for a cap screw would be ⅝ × 1⅝ Brass, Fillister-Head Cap Screw, ⅝-11NC-3.

10.22 Machine screws. Machine screws are similar in function and operation to cap screws, but are usually smaller in diameter. Machine screws are specified by numbers from 2 to 12 below the ¼″ size and then by diameter up to ⅜ inch. The lengths of machine screws vary from ⅛ to 3 inches, changing by ¹⁄₁₆-increments up to ½ inch, then by ⅛-inch up to 1 inch, and finally by ¼-inch up to 3 inches. They are threaded not less than 1¾″ for all screws over 2″ in length, and within two threads of the bearing surface or closer if practicable for shorter screws. Machine screws may be obtained with either fine or coarse threads, and with four types of heads, all slotted, as shown in Fig. 10–29. Square and hexagonal nuts may be obtained for all sizes of machine screws. The usual method of specifying machine screws

is: No. 10 × ¹⁵⁄₁₆-Flat-Head Machine Screw-10-24NC-3. The material should also be specified if other than steel. Dimensions for drawing machine screws are given in Table 4 in the Appendix.

10.23 Set screws. The purpose of a set screw is to prevent rotation or sliding between two parts. It is screwed into one part so that its point presses against the other, thus resisting relative motion between the two parts by means of the friction between the point of the set screw and one of the parts. The standard square-head set screw and several kinds of headless set screws are shown in Fig. 10–30. Information necessary for drawing set screws is given in Tables 14 and 15 in the Appendix. They are specified on the drawing by giving the diameter, length, type of head, type of point, and thread specification. Thus the specification could read ¼ × ¾-Hexagonal socket head, cone point, set screw, ¼-20NC-2.

10.24 Other types of standard and special bolts and screws. Screw threads have been used on many kinds of screws and bolts which cannot be discussed in detail because of lack of space. Some of these are shown in Fig. 10–22 and discussed briefly in the following paragraphs. Figure 10–22 also gives the ASA number from which dimensions and other information may be obtained for the more commonly used bolts.

Unslotted-head bolts such as carriage bolts, step bolts, tire bolts, plow bolts, track bolts, and others are used frequently in wood work as well as metal work where the square shank keeps the bolt from turning. They may have round, oval, or countersunk heads as shown in Fig. 10–22.

Slotted-head bolts such as stove bolts are used chiefly for metal work. They may have round or countersunk heads as shown in Fig. 10–22. The slot allows them to be tightened with a screw driver.

Special-purpose bolts having threads on one end only

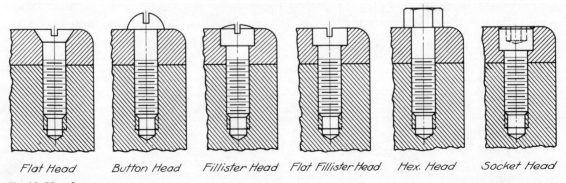

Flat Head   *Button Head*   *Fillister Head*   *Flat Fillister Head*   *Hex. Head*   *Socket Head*

Fig. 10–28. Cap screws.

such as eye bolts, U bolts, hook bolts, thumb screws, and patch bolts, are also illustrated in Fig. 10–22. They are used in many places where ordinary bolts would not be satisfactory.

Wood screws are usually designed with the thread forming a conical helix although they sometimes continue long threads on a cylindrical helix, as on the lag screw. They are designed in this manner so that they will cut their own threads in the wood as they are driven. The heads are usually slotted for a screw driver and may be either round, elliptical, or countersunk. They are specified by number. Various types of screws are illustrated in Fig. 10–31. A special type head known as the Phillips recessed head is used frequently for production work.

Self-tapping screws which have a special hardened thread which cuts its own internal thread when they are driven are used for many purposes. Since these screws eliminate the necessity of tapping the hole, the time thus saved frequently makes their use desirable when conditions are satisfactory. After being driven, the screw may be removed and then replaced without affecting its holding power.

Hardened drive screws are used to make permanent fastenings to various kinds of thin metal, wood, or masonry. A hole of the proper size is first drilled and the fastener driven with a hammer. With the proper equipment they may be driven without drilling the holes in softer materials.

Rivnut is the patented name of a fastener that may be used to fasten two plates together and at the same time provide a nut plate to which other parts may be fastened. One of the important features of this fastener is that the entire operation can be completed from one side of the plate. Figure 10–32 shows the Rivnut being used as a rivet to hold two plates together and also as a nut plate by means of which the clip is fastened to the plate.

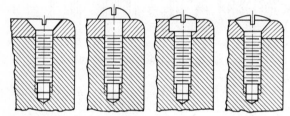

Fig. 10–29.   Machine screws.

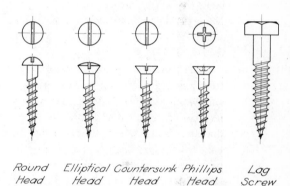

Round Head   Elliptical Head   Countersunk Head   Phillips Head   Lag Screw

Fig. 10–31.   Wood screws.

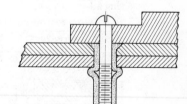

Fig. 10–32.   Rivnut.

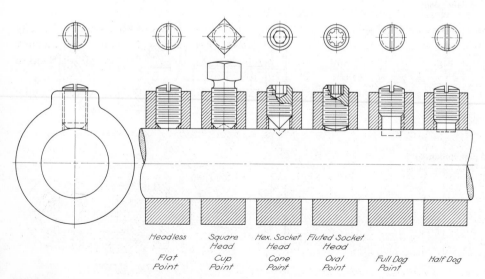

Headless   Square Head   Hex. Socket Head   Fluted Socket Head

Flat Point   Cup Point   Cone Point   Oval Point   Full Dog Point   Half Dog

Fig. 10–30.   Set-screw heads and points.

10.25   Pipe threads. The pipe thread used in this country is known as the American, formerly the Briggs, standard. It differs from the British pipe thread in that the sides of the thread form an angle of 60°, whereas the British thread, which is built on the Whitworth system, shows an angle of 55°. The crest and root of the Standard American thread are slightly flattened, as shown in Fig. 10-33.

Pipe threads are cut on a taper of 1 in 16 measured on the diameter. Both internal and external threads are tapered. This taper allows the first few turns to be made by hand and insures a tight joint when the threads are well engaged. A few of the threads on the pipe are slightly imperfect owing to the axial taper of the thread, but they

are counted as fully effective in holding the fitting to the pipe. Figure 10-34 shows the American Standard pipe thread.

The pitch of pipe threads has been standardized for the various sizes of pipes, as shown in Table 42 in the Appendix.

For certain purposes, as, for example, when a pipe must pass through the walls of a tank, for hose couplings, and free-fitting couplings, straight pipe threads are used. These threads have the same form as the standard pipe thread, but do not have any taper.

In representing pipe threads on a drawing, the taper may or may not be shown as desired. When shown it should be exaggerated to call attention to the taper.

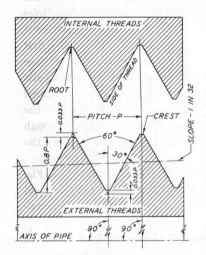

Fig. 10-33.   American pipe thread dimensions.

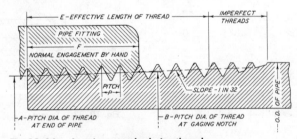

Fig. 10-34.   American standard pipe thread.

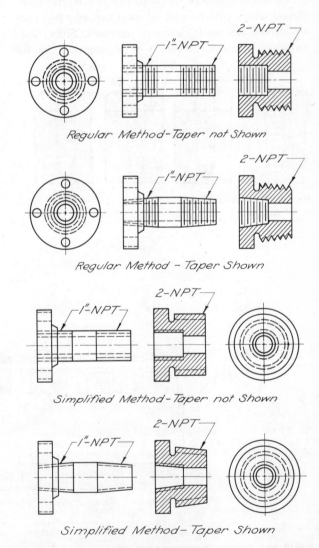

Regular Method-Taper not Shown

Regular Method – Taper Shown

Simplified Method-Taper not Shown

Simplified Method-Taper Shown

Fig. 10-35.   Pipe thread symbols and notes.

The pipe thread is specified on the drawing by a standard note as shown in Fig. 10–35. In the top view of the threaded hole, the dotted circle should be equal to the outside diameter of the pipe.

10.26 Measuring and gaging threads. To measure the pitch of a thread, a gage on which various thread profiles have been constructed may be used to match the thread. Each leaf of the gage is marked with the number of threads per inch so that the pitch of the thread is found when the proper gage is determined.

To measure the pitch diameter of a thread, the three-wire method is frequently used. This method is illustrated in Fig. 10–36. By measuring the distance L, the

pitch diameter may be obtained from the formula $D = L + .866p - 3W$ for any 60° thread. Any size wire that will come in contact with both sides of the thread may be used, but the best size is the one that is tangent to the sides of the thread at the pitch diameter. Tables are available which give the best size for various thread pitches.

To secure interchangeability of parts and to insure that the part meets the desired specifications of fit and tolerance, threads are gaged by means of "go" and "not go" gages.

10.27 Rivets. The chief purpose of rivets is to make a permanent fastening between plates or rolled sections. Rivets are made with various shapes of heads, but all function alike in their method of holding the parts together. They are manufactured with a head on one end only, the other head being formed in the driving. Holes for the rivets are punched slightly larger than the rivet so that they may be put in place easily. They are first heated and then inserted in the hole, after which the other head is formed by hammering with a pneumatic hammer or by pressure. The length of a rivet is figured from the area of greatest bearing on the head to the point. This length is specified so as to allow only enough material to form the head and fill the hole around the rivet.

The various shapes of rivet heads are shown in Fig. 10–37. Rivets are sometimes shown on the drawing and sometimes omitted entirely. When shown they are rep-

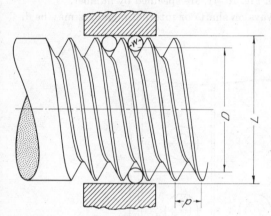

Fig. 10–36. Gaging a thread.

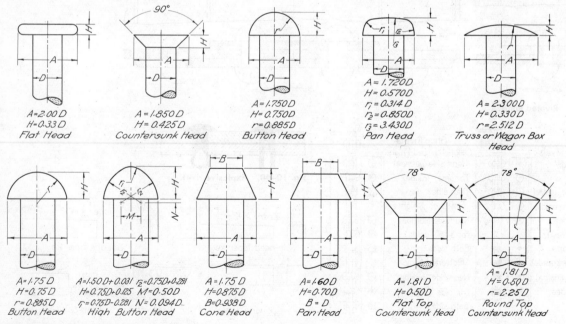

Fig. 10–37. Rivet heads. (Courtesy ASA.)

resented by a circle as indicated in Fig. 10–38 or simply by center lines.

Since the pieces held together by rivets may be joined in the field or in the shop, it is necessary to have other symbols to indicate which way the riveting is to be done. Also rivet heads may be countersunk and/or chipped to provide clearances, and symbols have been devised to show these things. These symbols are shown in Fig. 10–39.

In boiler and tank work, considerable pains may be taken to show the actual shape of the rivet head and the type of joint desired. Such a drawing for a lap joint and a butt joint is shown in Fig. 10–38. In structural work the shape of the rivet head is seldom shown.

Explosive rivets are used in aircraft work where it is not convenient to work on both sides of the plate. These are aluminum rivets that have been hollowed out at the end to allow space for the explosive charge. When exploded the rivet is expanded to grip the plates as shown in Fig. 10–40.

10.28   Keys. Those fasteners called keys are chiefly used to hold pulleys, gears, and rocker arms on rotating shafts. There are several standard types.

Figure 10–41 shows five common types. Square, flat, taper, and gib-head taper keys are dimensioned by notes giving the width, height, and length. Whenever possible, sizes should conform to standards. The keys need not be drawn except for special keys or when limits other than those of the standard are necessary. Patented keys such as the Woodruff and Pratt and Whitney, shown in Fig. 10–41, are specified by number.

Keyways on shafts or internal members may be di-

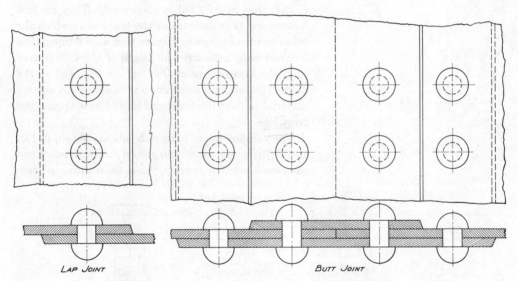

LAP JOINT   BUTT JOINT

Fig. 10–38.   Riveted joints.

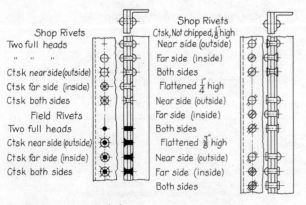

Fig. 10–39.   Rivet symbols.

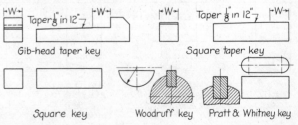

Fig. 10–40.   Explosive rivet.

Fig. 10–41.   Types of keys.

mensioned as shown in Fig. 10–42(a). On the hub or external member the keyway may be dimensioned as shown in Fig. 10–42(b). The key seat for patented varieties may be specified by the key number.

Tables may be found in the Appendix giving dimensions for several standard keys. More complete information may be found in any mechanical engineer's handbook.

When heavy loads are to be transmitted from the shaft to the pulley or vice versa, two or more keys may be used or the Kennedy or Lewis systems may be practicable. See Fig. 10–43.

10.29   Involute splines. In many cases where heavy loads are to be transmitted, keys have been eliminated by the use of multiple spline shafts as illustrated in Figs. 10–44 and 10–45. Involute splines and serrations are commonly used.

10.30   Taper pins. In light work taper pins are sometimes used as fasteners in place of keys or as dowels. They taper ¼ inch in diameter per foot of length. Dimensions of standard taper pins may be obtained from Table 19 in the Appendix.

10.31   Springs. Although springs are not considered as fasteners, the method of representing them is closely related to the drawing of screw threads. Springs are formed by winding the wire in the form of a cylindrical or conical helix. In actual practice, the projections of the spring are conventionalized in a manner similar to threads by using straight lines instead of helices. Figure 10–46 shows by steps the method of drawing a spring. Compression springs are usually ground on the ends to provide a flat bearing. Tension springs must have a loop of some kind on each end. In long springs a few turns may be shown on each end with ditto marks between, rather

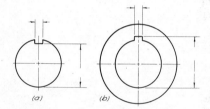

Fig. 10–42.   Dimensioning keyways.

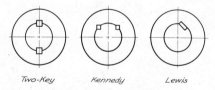

Two-Key   Kennedy   Lewis

Fig. 10–43.   Heavy-duty keys.

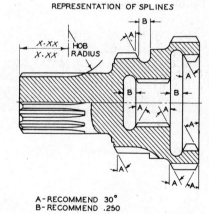

REPRESENTATION OF SPLINES

A–RECOMMEND 30°
B–RECOMMEND .250

Fig. 10–45.   Representation of splines. (Courtesy ASA.)

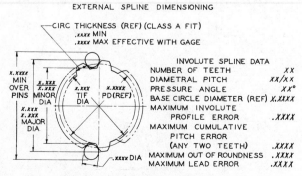

EXTERNAL SPLINE DIMENSIONING

Fig. 10–44.   External spline dimensioning. (Courtesy ASA.)

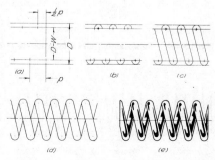

Fig. 10–46.   Construction of a spring symbol.

than drawing the entire spring. These things are illustrated in Figs. 10-47, 10-48, and 10-49. For further information on springs see Mil. std. 29—1958.

In specifying a spring, the following information should be given: diameter and kind of wire, free length of spring, number of turns, and controlling diameter.

Springs are frequently represented by single lines as in Fig. 10-50 instead of the more complicated double line.

10.32   Welding. Welding is a very valuable method of making permanent connections. Because of its increasing importance in both mechanical and structural design an entire system of nomenclature and symbols has been developed to transmit the desired information. So many methods and techniques have been developed that welding has been discussed separately in Chapter 29.

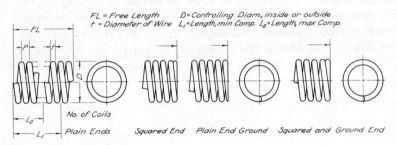

FL = Free Length   D = Controlling Diam, inside or outside
t = Diameter of Wire   L₁ = Length, min Comp. L₂ = Length, max Comp.

No. of Coils

Plain Ends   Squared End   Plain End Ground   Squared and Ground End

Fig. 10-47.   Compression springs.

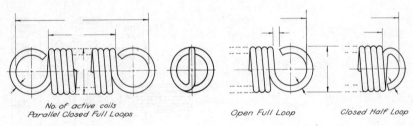

No. of active coils
Parallel Closed Full Loops   Open Full Loop   Closed Half Loop

Fig. 10-48.   Tension springs.

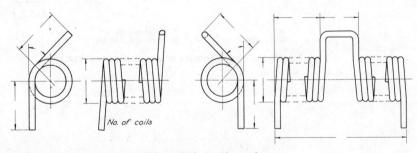

No. of coils

Fig. 10-49.   Representing and dimensioning torsion springs.

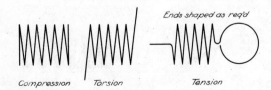

Ends shaped as req'd

Compression   Torsion   Tension

Fig. 10-50.   Single-line spring symbols.

PROBLEMS

Standard bolts and screws are not ordinarily shown upon working drawings, except in assemblies, but it is necessary to make drawings of all bolts and screws which depart from the standard forms. This is a common occurrence.

The problems below, however, have been confined to standard forms since they provide the necessary practice and are completely specified as to form and dimensions without the use of text figures. The student is referred to tables of standard dimensions in the Appendix. The bolts and screws should be shown holding two parts together as they would function in an assembly drawing.

The problems are to be made in ink or pencil as directed by the instructor. In either case show the necessary construction lines for bolt heads and nuts in light pencil lines. The scale will be full size unless otherwise specified. Specify the threads by means of a note of standard form, but in other respects leave the drawings undimensioned.

When the bolt or screw is under 1 inch actual diameter on the paper, use the straight-line convention for threads; when 1 inch or more in diameter, use the V symbol for threads.

1. Make a two-view drawing of an American Standard bolt as described: Square head unfinished bolt and nut 2″ in diameter and 4″ long. Show the nut on the bolt.

2. Same as Problem 1: Square-head semifinished bolt and nut, 1¾″ × 5″.

3. Same as Problem 1: Hex-head unfinished bolt and nut, 2¼″ × 4½″.

4. Same as Problem 1: Hex-head semifinished bolt and nut, 1½″ × 5″.

5. Make a two-view drawing of an American Standard machine, cap, or set, screw as described: Flat-head machine screw, ¼″ × 1½″. Scale 2″ = 1″. Use the straight-line symbol for threads.

6. Same as Problem 5: Flat-head machine screw, ³⁄₁₆″ × 2″. Show in a blind tapped hole.

7. Same as Problem 5: Round-head machine screw, ⁵⁄₁₆″ × 1¾″.

8. Same as Problem 5: Fillister-head machine screw, ⁵⁄₁₆″ × 1¾″. Show in a blind tapped hole.

9. Same as Problem 5: Oval-head machine screw, ⅜″ × 2¼″.

10. Same as Problem 5: Flat-head cap screw, ⁵⁄₁₆″ × 2″. Show in a blind tapped hole.

11. Same as Problem 5: Button-head cap screw, ⅜″ × 2½″.

12. Same as Problem 5: Fillister-head cap screw, ⁹⁄₁₆″ × 2¼″.

13. Same as Problem 5: Hex-head cap screw, ⅝″ × 2½″.

14. Same as Problem 5: Square-head set screw, ¾″ × 2″. Point as assigned: (a) Cup, (b) Flat, (c) Cone, (d) Dog, (e) Round.

15. Make a one-view drawing of the thread specified. Use straight lines to represent the helix curve. Show one turn of the invisible part of the thread. Make the thread 3″ long, and show ½″ of shaft beyond the thread on each end, equal to the minor diameter of the thread. Show the conventional break on each end. The thread to be: single, right-hand, Square thread, 2½″ diameter, ½″ pitch.

16. Same as Problem 15: Double, left-hand, Square thread, 3″ in diameter, and ¾″ pitch.

17. Same as Problem 15: Double, right-hand, Square thread, 2¾″ diameter, ⅝″ pitch.

18. Same as Problem 15: Triple, right-hand, Square thread, 3″ diameter, ¾″ pitch.

19. Same as Problem 15: Single, right-hand, Acme thread, 2″ diameter, ½″ pitch.

20. Same as Problem 15: Single, left-hand, Acme thread, 2½″ diameter, ⅝″ pitch.

21. Same as Problem 15: Double, right-hand, Acme thread, 3″ diameter, ¾″ pitch.

22. Same as Problem 15: Double, left-hand, Acme thread, 3″ diameter, ¾″ pitch.

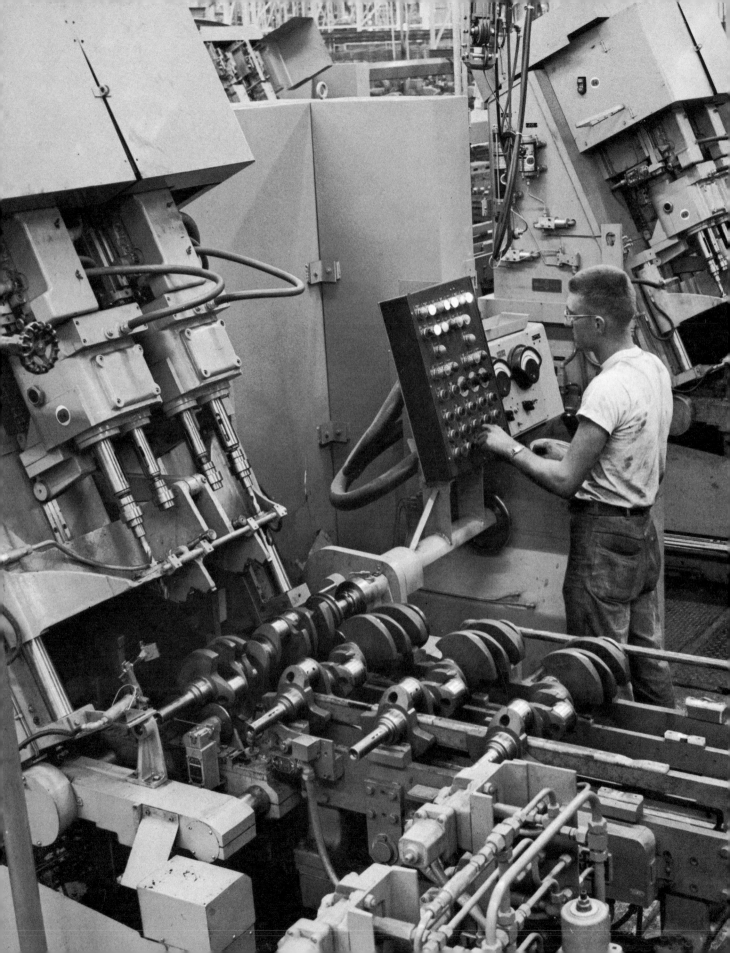

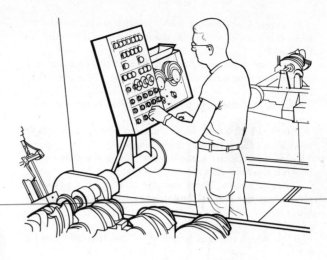

11

Shop Terms and Processes

11.1   The relation of the drafting room to the various shops is often underestimated in teaching the draftsman the techniques of his profession. No design has commercial value unless the thing designed can be made in the shops, and at a cost that will allow it to compete with similar products in the markets. Odd-size tools, impractical methods, and even impossible operations are often specified on drawings of the uninformed. The draftsman must know the capabilities and limitations of the shops. His drawings must "talk" in the shopman's language.

11.2   Castings. The genesis of all cast metal work is found in the pattern shop. All drawings specifying castings must first go to the patternmaker who constructs a wood or plaster model of the object to be cast. This model, called a pattern, is then sent to the foundry where the actual casting is made. Castings are made from various kinds of iron and steel and also from nonferrous metals, such as aluminum, magnesium, zinc, copper, bronze, and brass. To understand the processes that are carried on in the pattern shop and foundry, it will be necessary to have a general knowledge of the terms employed therein.

11.3   Definition of pattern and foundry terms. The following terms are used in the pattern shop, core shop, and foundry.

Boss. A projection on an object whose height is usually less than its diameter, placed there for the purpose of providing a bearing surface or to enable the shop to drill a hole to better advantage. See Fig. 11–9.

Core. A sand model of the hollow interior of a casting. See Fig. 11–11.

◄ Electronic balancing machines which determine correct crankshaft balance of automobile engines (Ford Motor Company).

Core box. A wooden box whose internal shape is such that, when it is packed with sand, the desired core is formed. See Fig. 11–11.

Core print. A projecting part of the pattern which makes an impression in the sand mold into which the core is placed. See Fig. 11–3.

Cupola. A furnace in which the metal is melted in the foundry.

Draw or draft. The taper on a pattern which makes it easier to withdraw the pattern from the mold.

Fillet. The concave surface which fills in the sharp angles between two faces on a pattern. See Fig. 11–5.

Finish allowance. Extra material allowed on a pattern to provide additional metal for finishing a face on the casting. See Fig. 11–1.

Flask. Two or more boxlike parts having the same cross section into which the sand is packed to form the mold. See Fig. 11–12.

Cope. The upper part of the flask. See Fig. 11–12(*b*).

Drag. The lower part of the flask. See Fig. 11–12(*a*).

Gate. The opening in the sand through which the metal flows to the casting. See Fig. 11–13.

Parting plane. A plane on which the pattern can be divided so that both parts can be removed from the sand. See Fig. 11–1.

Pattern. A slightly oversize model of the object to be cast, usually made of wood. See Fig. 11–3.

Shrinkage allowance. The oversized measurement of the pattern to allow for the shrinkage of the metal when cooling.

Shrink rule. A rule used by the patternmaker which is made sufficiently oversize to allow for the shrinkage of the metal being used.

11.4   Pattern drawing or layout. The source from which the patternmaker obtains his information is the working drawing made in the drafting room. Since this working drawing contains information to be used in other shops but not needed by the patternmaker, he sometimes makes a new drawing called a pattern drawing or layout which omits all unnecessary information and adds such items as parting plane, finish allowance, draft, and core prints. This drawing is made full scale with the shrink rule. On the drawings many curves and intersections must be carefully constructed since dimensions are taken directly from the pattern drawing. Sections may also be taken at different places on the pattern drawing for the purpose of cutting sheet metal templates with which to check the pattern. Figure 11–1 shows the working drawing of a simple object and also the pattern drawing for the same object.

11.5   Patternmaker's shrink rule. When the metal in a casting is cooling, it continues to get smaller until room temperature is reached. The amount of this shrinkage varies with different metals, but in any case the patternmaker must allow for it by making the layout and the pattern oversize. *This is done by using a shrink rule on which the divisions are all slightly larger than a normal rule.* The amount of allowance made for the shrinkage of various metals is given below in inches per foot.

Cast iron	⅛
Cast steel	¼
Aluminum alloys	⁵⁄₃₂
Magnesium alloys	1¹⁄₁₆

Thus a 12-inch shrink rule for cast iron would actually measure 12⅛ inches.

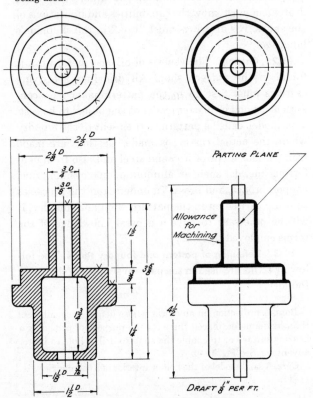

Fig. 11–1.   Machine drawing and pattern drawing.

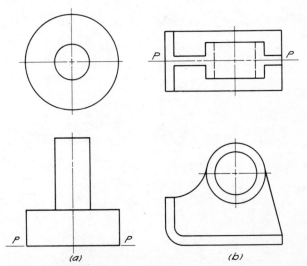

Fig. 11–2.   Parting plane.

11.6 Finish allowances. Before the pattern drawing is complete, the patternmaker must add the "finish," which may be indicated by means of a heavy line. *The term "finish" as applied to pattern drawings means the amount of material added to the pattern to provide metal on the casting that is to be cut away in the finishing process.* The amount of this allowance varies from ⅛" to ¾", depending on the size of the casting and the metal from which it is made. The finish allowance on the drawing in Fig. 11-3 has been indicated by dotted lines which show the outline of the finished piece. On the engineer's working drawing the finished surfaces must always be indicated by one of the standard methods explained in Chapter 13.

11.7 Parting plane. Before the pattern drawing can be carried any further, the location of the parting line or plane must be determined. This is not indicated on the engineer's working drawing, but the designer must have considered the matter to avoid a design that is unusually hard to cast and therefore expensive. *The purpose of the parting plane is to enable the pattern to be removed from the mold without breaking the walls of the sand.* The parting plane should be at the largest part of the object and so arranged that there will be no undercut faces or projections. In casting the object, the parting plane is made to coincide with the plane between the two parts of the mold or flask. In simple objects such as that shown in Fig. 11-2(a), it is sometimes possible to use one face of the object as the parting plane, thus making the work of casting easier and less expensive. Usually one parting plane is necessary as in Fig. 11-2(b). Occasionally more than one plane is necessary, but this should be avoided if possible. The line on the drawing which shows the position of the parting plane is called the parting line. This line is marked on the patternmaker's layout.

11.8 Core prints. As soon as the position of the parting plane has been determined, the core prints should be added to the full-size drawing. *Core prints are projections from the pattern whose purpose is to make an impression in the sand mold into which the core will be placed.* Since the core will completely fill the impression made by the core print, the function of the core print is merely to hold the core in the proper position until the metal has cooled. Figure 11-3 shows the core prints added to the pattern layout and to the pattern. Core prints are not shown on the working drawing.

11.9 Draft. *To make the removal of the pattern from the mold easier, the pattern is tapered away from the parting plane. This taper is called "draft" or "draw."* The draft can be added to the pattern by increasing the size at the parting plane, thus making the piece stronger and heavier, or by allowing the material to remain the same at the parting plane and decreasing it at the top or bottom. This latter method decreases the strength and weight. When a wood pattern is used, a draft of ⅛" per foot is used, but with a metal pattern ¹⁄₁₆" per foot is sufficient. Draft may be specified by degrees and will usually be from ½° to 3°. The draft is shown on the full-size patternmaker's layout. It is not indicated in any way on the engineer's working drawing.

11.10 Design details. *a. Fillets and rounds.* When the metal in a casting cools, the crystals tend to arrange themselves so that their lines of strength are perpendicular to the cooling surface as indicated in Fig. 11-4. Therefore sharp angles tend to become planes of weak-

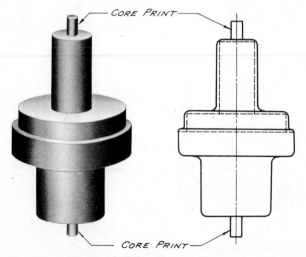

Fig. 11-3. Core prints on pattern.

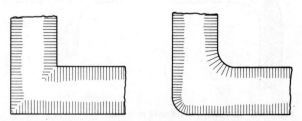

Fig. 11-4. Corners rounded and filleted to relieve stress.

ness where holes or cracks may occur during cooling. *For this reason the sharp internal angles on a pattern are filled with wood, leather, or wax, as illustrated in Fig. 11–5. This process is called filleting. Sharp external corners on a casting should also be rounded.* Careful attention to these details makes it easier to remove the pattern from the mold, allows the metal to flow more freely through the casting, and helps to avoid cracks and planes of weakness.

Each company will usually have its own rules concerning size of fillets. Some require the fillets to have a radius equal to the thickness of the section, as shown in Fig. 11–6; others give the radii for fillets in tabular form. The following design data for minimum webs and fillet radii on aluminum alloy castings are being used by a large industrial company.

Material No.	43	356	195	220	AM 265
t Min. web thickness	5/32	5/32	5/32	5/16	5/32
r Min. fillet radii	5/32	3/16	3/16	3/8	3/16

Although it is essential that all angles be filleted and corners rounded, it is also important to avoid using too large a radius for fillets with thin web sections. Too large fillets may cause cooling stresses in thin webs, owing to the heavy concentration of material at the intersections and consequent unequal cooling.

The engineer's working drawing should always show all fillets and carry a note such as: All fillets are (x) radius and rounds (x) radius unless otherwise specified.

b. Section thickness in castings. As the casting is be-

ing poured the metal flows in various directions into the parts of the mold, and gradually cools as it flows. *If sections are too thin, the metal may cool so much that it will not be hot enough to join properly when metal flowing in two directions comes together.* This forms a plane of weakness, called a "cold shut." The minimum thickness of webs varies with the kind of material and with company practice. For instance, one company recommends the following minimum thickness in inches: iron, 5/32; brass and bronze, 3/32; aluminum, 1/8 to 3/16.

A thin web intersecting a heavier member may develop cracks, owing to unequal cooling of the two parts. For this reason it is well to avoid too abrupt a change in cross section of the members. When such a change cannot be avoided, the thin member should be tapered to reduce the shrinkage stresses. It is recommended that

LENGTH OF TAPER L—WALL THICKNESS W

T	t—Aluminum and magnesium alloys										Max. R
	5/32		3/16		7/32		1/4		5/16		
	L	W	L	W	L	W	L	W	L	W	
5/32											3/16
3/16											3/16
7/32			Values in this area under								7/32
1/4			critical 2 to 1 ratio								1/4
5/16											5/16
3/8	1⅛	⅜									3/8
7/16	1¼	⅜	1¼	13/32							3/8
1/2	1¼	⅜	1¼	13/32	1¼	7/16					7/16
3/4	1¼	⅜	1¼	13/32	1¼	7/16	1¼	½	1¼	17/32	

Courtesy Douglas Aircraft Co.

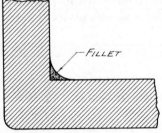

Fig. 11–5. Filleted corner.

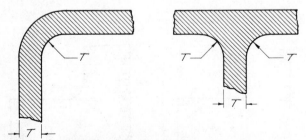

Fig. 11–6. Relation of fillet radii to thickness. (Courtesy Douglas Aircraft Co.)

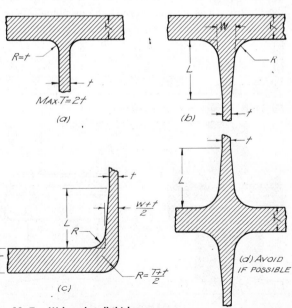

Fig. 11–7. Web and wall thickness. (Courtesy Douglas Aircraft Co.)

the heavy section be not more than twice the thickness of the thin section, as shown in Fig. 11–7(a). When the minimum 2 to 1 ratio cannot be maintained, the thin section shall be tapered as shown in Fig. 11–7(b) and (c), according to the dimensions given in the accompanying table.

Intersecting webs may tend to cause cooling cracks because of the heavy concentration of material at the intersection. See Fig. 11–7(d). This may be avoided or improved by alternating the webs as in Fig. 11–8, whenever possible.

c. *Bosses. Projections on a casting to allow for drilling holes or to provide bearing for a bolt head are called bosses.* When bosses occur they must be filleted to provide as gradual a change in cross section as possible, as shown in Fig. 11–9(a). When bosses must be placed in webs, the web must be tapered, as in Fig. 11–9(b), to provide the proper thickness.

d. *Pads*. Pads as illustrated in Fig. 11–10 will save in the cost of the part by eliminating large areas which must be machined.

e. *Ribs*. On a casting, ribs perform two functions: one to strengthen and stiffen the part and the other to prevent cooling cracks by acting as heat conductors, thus promoting the cooling of a section.

11.11   Color. For ease of interpretation, the complete pattern is stained in various colors. The parts that are to be unfinished are made black, those that are to be finished are red, and the core prints are yellow. Other color symbols are in use, but these are the more important.

11.12   Core box. Since the pattern forms only the outer surface of a casting, it is necessary to have some method of forming the interior surfaces. The shape of these interior surfaces is determined by the shape of the core which is molded in the core box. It is part of the patternmaker's job to build up the core box, which is merely a hollow box whose interior shape conforms to the shape of the interior surfaces of the object to be cast. Since the core is usually made in two parts, which

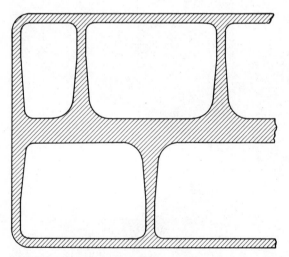

Fig. 11–8.   Arrangement of interior webs. (Courtesy Douglas Aircraft Co.)

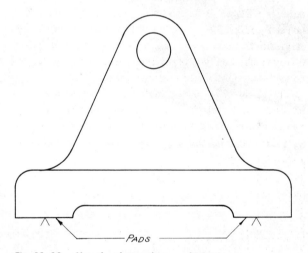

Fig. 11–10.   Use of pads to reduce machining.

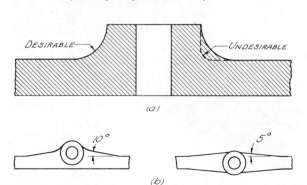

Fig. 11–9.   Filleting bosses.

are later glued together, the construction of the core box will involve consideration of parting plane, shrinkage, draft, and finish, just as was done in the construction of the pattern itself. Figure 11–11(*a*) shows a core box.

11.13   Cores. After the patternmaker has completed the core box, it is sent to the core shop where the core itself is made. *The purpose of the core is to occupy the space in the mold where an opening is desired.* The engineer must design interior spaces so that it is possible to remove the core after the metal has been cast.

11.14   Foundry. The draftsman has little immediate connection with the foundry, since the patternmaker acts as an intermediary between him and the molder.

Shop drawings do not, as a rule, include any reference to foundry operation. However, there probably is no place where the item of cost is of more vital importance than in the foundry. Excessive metal and difficult shapes to cast make the manufactured product costly, and the designer must always be on guard against these expensive items.

11.15   Permanent molds. When a large number of castings are to be made, a metal or permanent mold will decrease the cost and improve the quality of the casting. The metal mold must be thick and heavy enough to have a large heat-absorbing capacity and have enough cooling capacity so that the temperature of the mold does not get too high.

11.16   Centrifugal castings. In this type of casting the mold is rotated while the metal is being poured. There

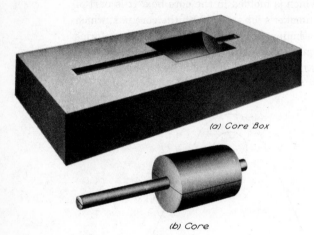

(a) Core Box

(b) Core

Fig. 11–11.   Core box and core.

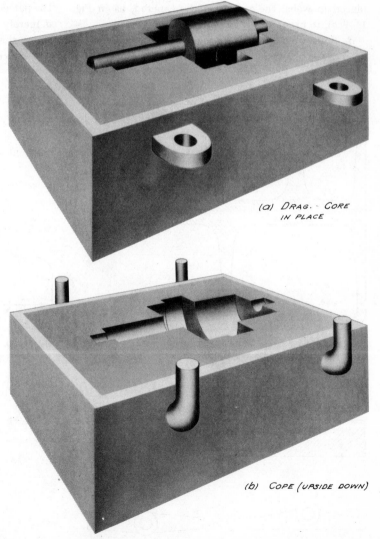

(a) DRAG - CORE IN PLACE

(b) COPE (UPSIDE DOWN)

Fig. 11–12.   Foundry flask.

are three types of centrifugal castings: (1) die molds; (2) semicentrifugal or center pour; and (3) true centrifugal for cylindrical shapes where the inner diameter is controlled by the volume of metal poured.

Centrifugal casting is occasionally used as a substitute for forging, since it seems to give a product that has characteristics somewhat similar to a forging. It requires a rigid control of temperature and speed, but when it can be used it is sometimes cheaper than sand casting, because it is possible to hold the casting closer to finished specifications, thus saving in machining.

11.17   Die casting. When a large number of castings of the softer metals are desired on which considerable machining would be necessary if sand castings were used, the cheapest and best method is die casting. This

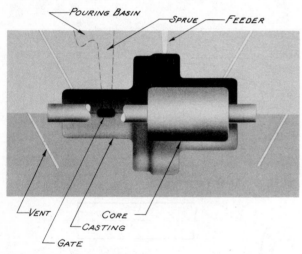

Fig. 11-13.   Section through flask.

requires the construction of very accurate dies from high-grade steel. *The molten metal is forced into the dies under pressure, forming a casting that is as accurate as would be obtained by ordinary machine work, and harder than a sand casting made from the same metal.* Much machine work can thus be eliminated. Die castings are made from various alloys of zinc, aluminum, magnesium, and copper. This process is used for any small object which does not have undercut parts.

11.18   Powder metallurgy. A process which is being used extensively at the present time and which shows promise of still further usefulness is that of forming objects from metal powder. *The powder is placed in accurately cut dies and formed under heavy pressure varying from 5 tons to 100 tons per square inch.* The object is then turned out of the die and heated or sintered at temperatures below the melting point until the grains of powder unite to form a solid piece.

11.19   Forging. Many parts of a machine or structure must be designed to withstand shock or sudden stress, a characteristic for which castings are not recommended.

Hand forging is forming a piece to specified size by hammering or pressing with flat surfaces. *The hot metal is moved around on the anvil as desired and pounded into the desired shape either by hand or machine.* Considerable machining may be necessary to produce a finished piece from a hand forging, and the waste is apt to be large. This method is not used in mass production.

Drop forging is a process in which the hot metal is forced into dies by means of drop hammers. The dies are similar in principle to those used in die casting or powder metallurgy; the metal, very hot but not in a molten condition, is forced into the die by pounding.

Because of the hammering that the metal receives in the forging process, it is much less porous than a casting and the consistency is more uniform. Another important characteristic of a forging that affects its physical properties is the fiber direction or grain of the metal.

11.20   Design details for forging. For this type of work a special forging drawing is made which differs from the engineer's working drawing in that it shows the piece as it will be forged rather than the finished part after the machining has been completed. Figure 11-14 shows a forging drawing. Some of the practical considerations that must be kept in mind when making a forging drawing are given below.

a. Scale. All forging drawings should be made full scale.

b. Draft. The draft angle is usually shown in degrees

on the forging drawing. The slope begins at the parting line but must be measured from the direction of stroke of the forging press. For exterior surfaces the draft varies from 5° to 7°, depending on the shape of the piece, but for internal surfaces it should be about 10°, as shown in Fig. 11–15(*a*) and (*b*). Bathtub-type fittings such as that in Fig. 11–15(*d*) should have approximately 5° draft for both interior and exterior surfaces.

c. Parting plane. The parting plane should be indicated on the forging drawing and when possible it should be located so that one die half contains all the impression. When both die halves contain part of the impression, the parting line will usually be placed on the center of a web, if there is a web in the object, but it need not be one continuous plane surface. See Fig. 11–16.

d. Forging plane. The forging plane which is perpendicular to the direction of stroke, on which the dies come together, must be arranged to avoid unbalanced die load. Care should be exercised to avoid interference between die and piece, and to take advantage of natural draft. Notice that the forging plane in Fig. 11–16(*g*) has been located to give a better balanced die load than would have occurred if the forging plane had been made to coincide with the main parting line. Figure 11–16(*d*) shows a forging plane located to take advantage of the natural draft angle of the piece.

e. Minimum fillets. To facilitate the flow of metal through the die, the angles should be filleted. No fillet should be less than 1/8″ radius. The chart shown in Fig. 11–17 gives recommended fillet radii.

f. Rounded corners. To avoid excessive hammering and consequent breakage of dies, the corners should be rounded to allow the metal to fill the die more easily.

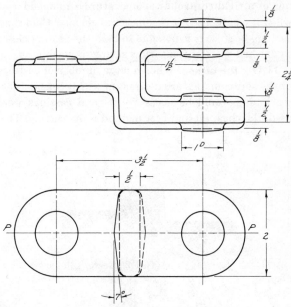

Fig. 11–14.   Forging drawing.

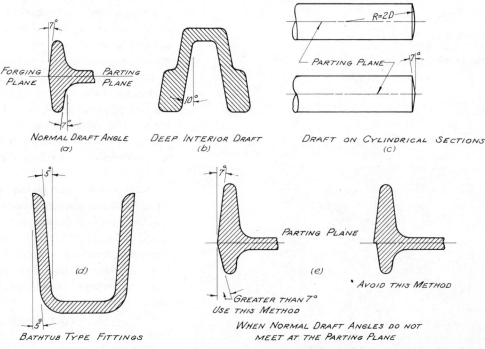

NORMAL DRAFT ANGLE
(*a*)

DEEP INTERIOR DRAFT
(*b*)

DRAFT ON CYLINDRICAL SECTIONS
(*c*)

BATHTUB TYPE FITTINGS
(*d*)

PARTING PLANE

GREATER THAN 7°
USE THIS METHOD

(*e*)

AVOID THIS METHOD

WHEN NORMAL DRAFT ANGLES DO NOT
MEET AT THE PARTING PLANE

Fig. 11–15.   Recommended draft angles.
(Courtesy Product Engineering and O. A. Wheelon.)

Figure 11–18 gives recommended edge radii.

g. *Thin webs on I-beam sections.* In I-beam sections the web has a tendency to cool rapidly, owing to the large area of contact with the die, thus making it hard to forge. At the same time the flange tends to fill first, leaving no place for the metal to flow as the web is brought down to size. This sometimes causes the shearing of the flange, as indicated in Fig. 11–19(a). The de-

sign suggestions given in Fig. 11–19(b) and (c) are recommended.

h. *Tolerances.* Dimensional tolerances should be as large as possible on all forgings to avoid excessive cost. The variations which must be allowed for are: (1) shrinkage and warping as forging cools; (2) mismatching of dies; (3) failure to bring finish dies together; (4) die wear. The following minimum dimensional toler-

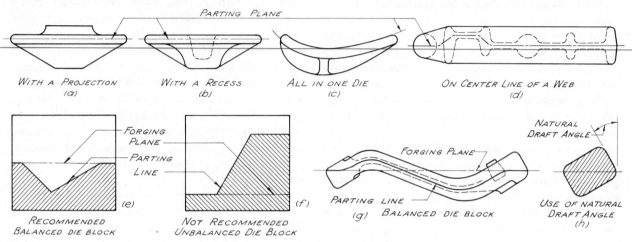

Fig. 11–16.   Parting lines and forging planes. (Courtesy Product Engineering and O. A. Wheelon.)

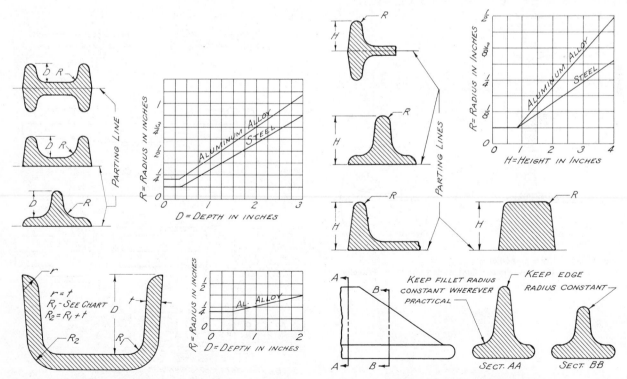

Fig. 11–17.   Recommended fillet radii for forgings.
(Courtesy Product Engineering and O. A. Wheelon.)

Fig. 11–18.   Recommended edge radii for forgings.
(Courtesy Product Engineering and O. A. Wheelon.)

ances, in inches, illustrated in Fig. 11–20 may be held without excessive cost:

(1) Width for small forgings, $\pm \frac{1}{32}$.

(2) Length for large forgings, $\pm \frac{1}{32}$ per foot of length.

(3) Thickness across parting plane, $+\frac{1}{32}$, -0 for small forgings.

(4) Thickness across parting plane, $+\frac{1}{16}$ $-\frac{1}{32}$ for large forgings.

(5) Location of punched holes, at least $\pm \frac{1}{32}$, preferably $\pm \frac{1}{16}$.

(6) When bosses which are to be bored out are located far apart one should be made circular and the other elongated by an amount equal to twice the tolerance on the dimension between bosses, as shown in Fig. 11–21.

(7) Tolerances for warping and mismatching of dies, shown in Fig. 11–20(b) and (c), must be added to the above tolerance.

(8) Allowance for machining. The amount of material to be allowed for finishing operations should include the dimensional tolerances plus an allowance for warping and mismatching of dies, which may vary from 0 to $\frac{1}{8}$ inch, depending on the size of the piece. If the corner radius is to be cut away, that radius or a portion of it

must also be added to the allowance for machining. See Fig. 11–22.

11.21   Stamping. *The term "stamping" is applied to a variety of processes used in the forming of thin metal parts.* It often includes cutting of the metal as well as shaping. A series of definitions with appropriate illustrations will give the best idea of some of the processes.

a. Blanking means cutting of the metal to the desired shape with one stroke of the press. See Fig. 11–23.

b. Nesting of blanks means that they should be designed so that they can be cut from the metal sheet with as little waste as possible. See Fig. 11–24.

c. Punching is a method of producing a hole in a part by one stroke of the press. A cylindrical punch produces a hole with practically smooth sides, as in Fig. 11–25(a). A conical punch produces a flanged hole with ragged edges, as in Fig. 11–25(b). A combination of the two punches having a cylindrical shape with a shoulder, as in Fig. 11–25(c), produces a flanged hole with a fairly smooth edge.

d. Trimming is the process of removing excess metal from a stamping. Sometimes trimming is recommended rather than developing a blank.

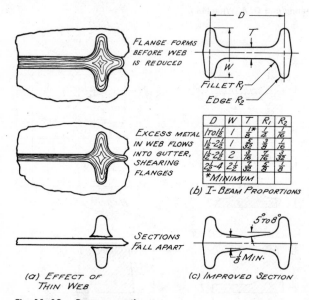

Fig. 11–19.   Beam proportions.
(Courtesy Product Engineering and O. A. Wheelon.)

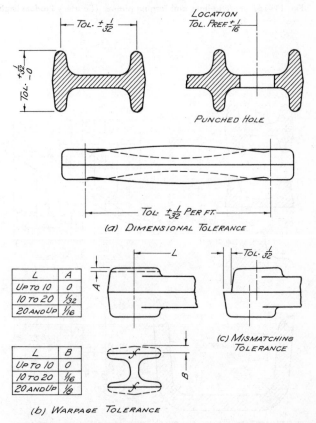

Fig. 11–20.   Forging tolerances.
(Courtesy Product Engineering and O. A. Wheelon.)

e. Shaving or burnishing is a process which removes a very small amount of metal to produce a surface with a very close tolerance.

f. Cutting off is a process of cutting a blank to length from a strip of metal that has been slit or sheared to correct width.

g. Notching is done for the purpose of providing clearance, for attachment, or for locating elements, or to facilitate forming.

h. Bending, forming, and embossing are names applied to shaping a blank without materially changing the thickness of the metal.

i. Drawing is a process of forcing a metal blank to assume the shape of a die by stretching the metal. The depth of draw should be as shallow as practicable to keep down the number of operations.

j. Coining is a process by which great pressure forces the metal to flow in the die, thus making it thicker in some places and thinner in others.

k. Swaging is a cold forging operation in which the metal is squeezed to reduce the thickness in certain places. The metal flows outward and must be trimmed off.

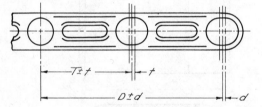

Fig. 11-21. Tolerance on location of bosses.
(Courtesy Product Engineering and O. A. Wheelon.)

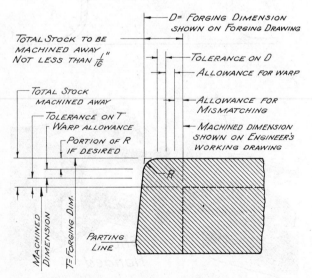

Fig. 11-22. Summary of tolerances and allowances needed on a forging.
(Courtesy Product Engineering and O. A. Wheelon.)

l. Extrusion is a process whereby the metal is made to flow in a die either by pressure or impact.

m. Necking, bulging, and curling are processes for reducing, enlarging, or forming a rounded edge on drawn shells. Curling may be done on flat blanks for such purposes as hinge manufacture.

11.21.1 *Design limitations for stamping.* Certain limi-

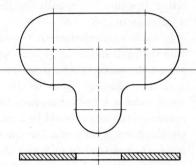

Fig. 11-23. Stamped blank.

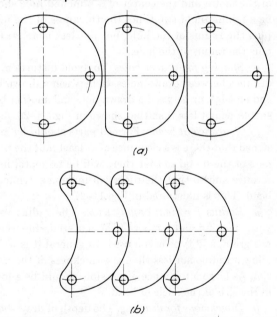

(a)

(b)

Fig. 11-24. Redesign for economy of material.

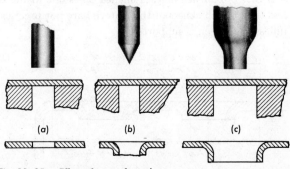

(a)　　　(b)　　　(c)

Fig. 11-25. Effect of type of punch.

tations on the design of blanked parts must be considered for economical and efficient operation. A few of these will be mentioned.

a. Grain. Sometimes the functioning of a part requires that the grain of the metal run in a certain direction. This direction may be marked on the blank, but, as it can usually be allowed to vary by as much as 45° in either direction, it is usually specified by an arrow with a tolerance of ±45°.

b. Radii of blanked parts. To facilitate tool construction the radii should be as large as possible. The ends are usually made as semicircles, as shown in Fig. 11-23.

c. Hole spacing. To avoid distortion of the metal when holes are to be punched, the distance between centers of the holes should be a minimum of two times the thickness of the metal plus the sum of the two radii, but never less than 1/32 inch plus the sum of the radii.

d. Edge distance. The clear distance between the edge of the metal and the center of a punched hole should be a minimum of two times the thickness of the metal plus the radius of the hole, but not less than 1/32 inch plus the radius of the hole.

e. Spacing for drawn holes. To avoid distortion, the distance between drawn holes, or between a drawn hole and an edge, or between a drawn hole and another bend should be not less than that shown in Fig. 11-26.

f. Clearance at bends. Formed parts should be so designed that there is a clearance of at least half the thickness of the metal so that there will be no metal interference and so that the tools can make a satisfactory bend. This is illustrated in Fig. 11-27.

g. Radius for right-angle bends. The radius varies with the kind and temper of the material, direction of the grain, and type of die used. In general it is well to allow a radius not less than the thickness of the material. As large a tolerance as possible should be allowed in the size of the angle of bend.

h. Dimensions for drawing. The depth of draw should be as small as possible. Figure 11-28 shows acceptable dimensions for single-operation draws.

i. Size of punched holes. Punched holes of a diameter less than the thickness of the material are not practical unless the punch is supported.

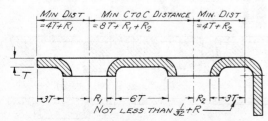

Fig. 11-26.   Minimum material between drawn holes.

11.22   Machine shop. The draftsman must be most familiar with the machine-shop processes. Dimensions on the drawing must be arranged so that they can be conveniently used in the shop. Machine-shop processes such as drill, ream, bore, mill, and others are sometimes indicated on the drawing. The degree and method of finish, and sometimes even the direction of the cutting strokes, are specified on the drawing. The draftsman must therefore be familiar with the shop tools, the machines in which they are used, and the limitations and possibilities of each, even though some companies do not specify shop operations on their drawings. In the following paragraphs, a brief explanation of the important ma-

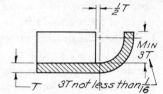

Fig. 11-27.   Clearance for bending.

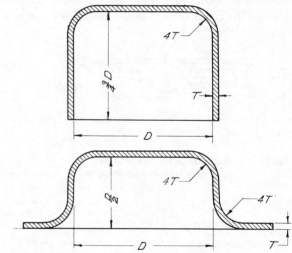

Fig. 11-28.   Depth of draw.

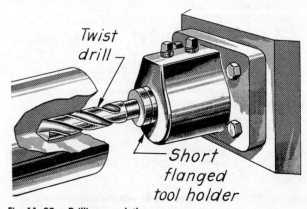

Fig. 11-29.   Drilling on a lathe.
(Courtesy Warner and Swasey Co.)

chines and tools will be given as well as the method of indicating on the drawing what processes are to be used.

11.23 Machine tools. Many of the tools in common use in the machine shop may be used in more than one machine. The following tools may be used on either the drill press or the lathe.

a. Twist drill. When a hole is to be drilled in a piece, it is marked on the drawing by giving the diameter followed by the word "drill," thus ⅝ Drill. Metal drills, such as that shown in Fig. 11–29, are obtainable in sizes varying from ¹⁄₆₄ to 3 inches in diameter, and in length up to 14 inches. The smaller drills are not rigid enough to prevent a slight deflection; consequently the tolerances indicated in Drill Table 1 in the Appendix will have to be allowed. When used to precede a threading operation the tool is called a tap drill. Sizes of tap drills are given by numbers, letters, and fractional dimensions as listed in Table 2 in the Appendix. Figure 11–30 gives some suggestions concerning design details for drilling operations.

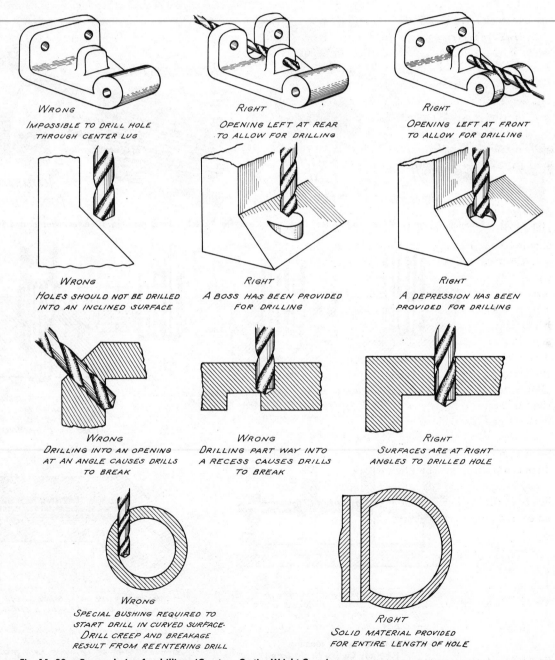

Fig. 11–30. **Proper design for drilling. (Courtesy Curtiss-Wright Corp.)**

b. Reamer. A hole that has been drilled is left with a rough and slightly scarred surface, which is not suitable for close fits or for tapping if fine thread crests are desired. A reamer similar to the one illustrated in Fig. 11–31 is used to finish this rough surface. Reamers may be either straight or tapered for cylindrical or conical holes. See Fig. 11–32. The drawing should indicate the diameter of the drill as well as the reamer; thus $^{3}\%_{4}$ drill, ⅝ ream. Reamers up to 3″ in diameter and 17″ in length can be secured. For holes up to ¾″ in diameter,

¹⁄₆₄″ should be left for reaming; for holes over ¾″ in diameter, ¹⁄₃₂″ may be left.

A few suggestions about the proper use of a reamer are given in Fig. 11–33.

c. Countersink. When a flat-headed screw is used the hole must be enlarged in a conical manner to allow the top of the head to come flush with the surface of the piece. This enlarging is called countersinking. The note on the drawing should be similar to the following: "Countersink 82° to ⅞″ Diameter." For details of

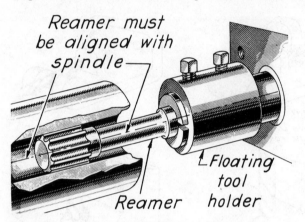

Fig. 11–31. Reaming. (Courtesy Warner and Swasey Co.)

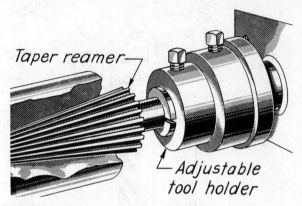

Fig. 11–32. Taper reaming. (Courtesy Warner and Swasey Co.)

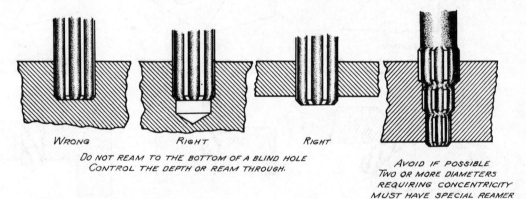

WRONG RIGHT RIGHT

DO NOT REAM TO THE BOTTOM OF A BLIND HOLE
CONTROL THE DEPTH OR REAM THROUGH.

AVOID IF POSSIBLE
TWO OR MORE DIAMETERS
REQUIRING CONCENTRICITY
MUST HAVE SPECIAL REAMER

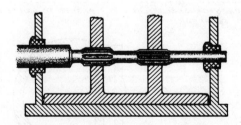

LINE REAM FOR CONCENTRICITY AND
ALIGNMENT OF HOLES. HOLES MUST BE
THE SAME SIZE OR PROGRESSIVELY
SMALLER FOR LINE REAMING.

Fig. 11–33. Proper design for reaming.
(Courtesy Curtiss-Wright Corp.)

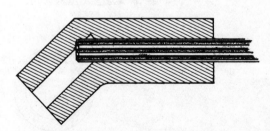

HOLES REAMED AT AN ANGLE SLOW DOWN
PRODUCTION. ALL TEETH SHOULD ENGAGE FOR
A GOOD START.
DEPTH CONTROL IS DIFFICULT. THERE IS
DANGER OF HAVING SHOULDERS AT THE
CORNERS AND OF LEAVING THIN WALLS.

dimensioning a countersink, see Chapter 9.

d. Counterbore. Heads of bolts and screws may be brought level with the surface of the part by enlarging the hole to a depth equal to the height of the head. This operation is called counterboring and is done with a tool similar to the one illustrated in Fig. 11-34(c). The pilot on the tool fits into a drilled hole and insures concentricity. The note on the drawing should be similar to the following: ⅜" Drill, ¾" Counterbore, ½" Deep.

e. Spotface. Sometimes it is desired to make a smooth-bearing surface for the head of a bolt or a nut. This sit-

uation frequently occurs on a projection, called a boss. Spotfacing is accomplished by using a counterboring tool, as illustrated in Fig. 11-34. The note on the drawing should read "Spotface ¾" Diameter." Figure 11-34 gives a few design suggestions for pieces on which spotfacing is specified.

f. Taps and dies. These tools are used for cutting internal and external threads. For more detailed information, see Chapter 10. The use of a tap is shown in Fig. 11-35 and a die in Fig. 11-36.

11.24 The drill press. The single-spindle drill press

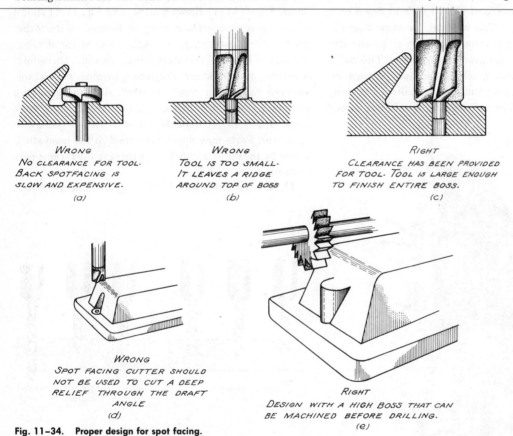

WRONG
NO CLEARANCE FOR TOOL. BACK SPOTFACING IS SLOW AND EXPENSIVE.
(a)

WRONG
TOOL IS TOO SMALL. IT LEAVES A RIDGE AROUND TOP OF BOSS
(b)

RIGHT
CLEARANCE HAS BEEN PROVIDED FOR TOOL. TOOL IS LARGE ENOUGH TO FINISH ENTIRE BOSS.
(c)

WRONG
SPOT FACING CUTTER SHOULD NOT BE USED TO CUT A DEEP RELIEF THROUGH THE DRAFT ANGLE
(d)

RIGHT
DESIGN WITH A HIGH BOSS THAT CAN BE MACHINED BEFORE DRILLING.
(e)

Fig. 11-34.   Proper design for spot facing.
(Courtesy Curtiss-Wright Corp.)

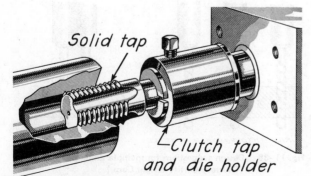

Fig. 11-35.   Tapping internal threads.
(Courtesy Warner and Swasey Co.)

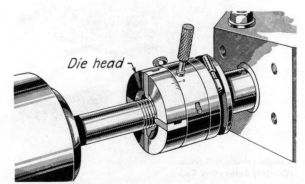

Fig. 11-36.   Cutting external threads.
(Courtesy Warner and Swasey Co.)

shown in Fig. 11–37 is found in practically every machine shop. It may be used for drilling, reaming, countersinking, and counterboring. For special purposes where more than one hole is to be drilled at one time, multiple-spindle drill presses are used. Several design suggestions for efficient use of multiple-spindle drills are shown in Fig. 11–38. The radial drill press shown in Fig. 11–39 is a very useful type of machine because holes can be drilled in almost any part of a rather large piece without reclamping or moving it. This is accomplished by having the chuck mounted on an arm which can be revolved around and moved up and down on a vertical axis of the machine while at the same time the chuck may be given a horizontal motion along the arm by means of a screw and gear arrangement. The radial drill is a very versatile machine and can be used for such purposes as tapping and hollow milling. For practical purposes, the depth of the hole should not exceed 5 diameters.

11.25   The lathe. The lathe is one of the most useful machines in the shop because of the many different operations that may be performed on it. The piece to be machined is supported between two centers, one in the tail stock and the other in the head stock, and then revolved by power supplied through the head stock. A tool post, which may be moved longitudinally along the lathe, carries the cutting tool. This tool removes a thin layer of metal each time it traverses the length of the surface being machined. This process is called turning and is used for machining practically all cylindrical surfaces. Figure 11–40 shows a lathe, and Fig. 11–41 shows a closeup of an operation being performed on the lathe. In addition to turning, the lathe is used for drilling, reaming, boring, counterboring, facing, threading, knurling, and polishing. For rough turning, normal tolerances vary from .005″ to .015″, depending on the diameter. For the finish cut the tolerance may vary from .002″ for a ¼″ diameter to .007″ for a 4″ on larger diameter. Parts may also be clamped to the head stock alone by means of a chuck, and turning operations performed on the end face.

11.26   The boring mill. The boring machine does prac-

Fig. 11–37.   A single-spindle drill press.
(Courtesy Barnes Drill Co.)

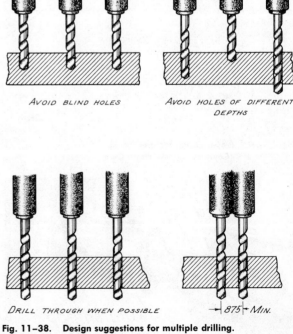

AVOID BLIND HOLES   *AVOID HOLES OF DIFFERENT DEPTHS*

DRILL THROUGH WHEN POSSIBLE   *.875 MIN.*

Fig. 11–38.   Design suggestions for multiple drilling.
(Courtesy Curtiss-Wright Corp.)

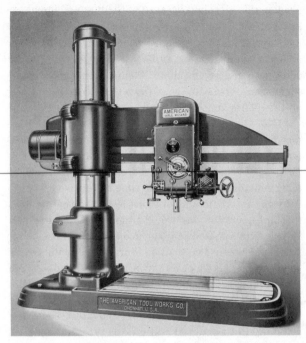

Fig. 11–39. Radial drill.
(Courtesy The American Tool Works Co.)

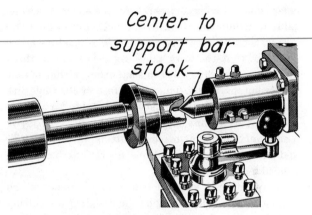

Center to
support bar
stock

Fig. 11–41. Turning operation on a lathe.
(Courtesy Warner and Swasey Co.)

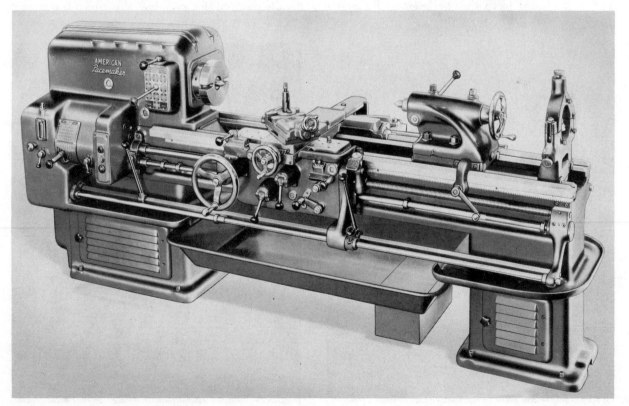

Fig. 11–40. A lathe. (Courtesy The American Tool Works Co.)

tically the same work as the lathe but is used for larger pieces. In the vertical boring machine, the table holding the work revolves while the cutting tool moves horizontally or vertically on the cross rail. A horizontal boring machine is also available on which an almost unlimited number of operations may be performed. Production tolerances of .003″ for a 1″ diameter to .01″ for 54″ diameter may be used.

11.27   The milling machine. A machine, in which circular-type revolving cutters remove the metal, as a work table to which the piece is clamped moves under the cutter, is called a milling machine. The machine is designed so that the work table can be moved in three directions at right angles to each other, either manually or automatically. The rate of feed of the table and the speed of the cutter must be adjustable for various kinds of material and depth of cuts. Figure 11–42 shows a close-up of a milling machine cutting flutes on a drill, and Fig. 11–43 shows multiple operations being performed.

Many different kinds of cuts may be made on the milling machine, depending on the design of the cutting tool. These tools may have straight teeth or helical teeth, and the cutting edge may be ground on the tool itself or a cutting tooth may be inserted. Either the cylindrical surface of the tool or the end face may be used as the cutting surface. The milling machine may be used for cutting plane or irregular surfaces, slots, keyways, gears, and similar surfaces. Production tolerances of about .005″ may be specified for work to be done on a milling machine. Figure 11–44 gives a few suggestions for the design of parts that are to be finished on the milling machine.

11.28   The grinding machine. The wheel on a grinding machine may vary from the ordinary fine and coarse emery wheels to high-speed carborundum wheels. The purpose of grinding is to leave a finely finished surface on the metal and at the same time to remove economically the small amount of stock left after the previous finishing operation has brought the piece almost to size. In grinding a cylindrical surface the piece may be revolved between two centers during the grinding, as shown in Fig. 11–45, or it may be allowed to roll between the grinding wheel and a regulating wheel, as shown in Fig. 11–46. A work rest is used to help hold the work in place. The latter method is known as centerless grinding. Both external and internal grinders are used for cylindrical surfaces where fine finish and close tolerances are desired. For surface grinding, the piece is usually clamped to a movable table which is traversed

Fig. 11–42.   Milling flutes on a drill.
(Courtesy Cincinnati Milling Machine Co.)

Fig. 11–43.   Multiple operations on a milling machine.
(Courtesy Kearney-Trecker Co.)

to bring the work under the grinding wheel. A surface grinder is shown in Fig. 11–47. The grinding machine is also used for grinding threads when close fits are desired and for making and sharpening tools for other machines. The draftsman indicates the grinding operation on his drawing by means of a note when the limits and finish require its use. A tolerance of .0005″ may be obtained by grinding.

11.29   Polishing. Polishing must not be confused with grinding. Although a ground surface is very smooth, it is not said to be a polished surface until it has been gone over carefully with a rapidly revolving disk of ma-

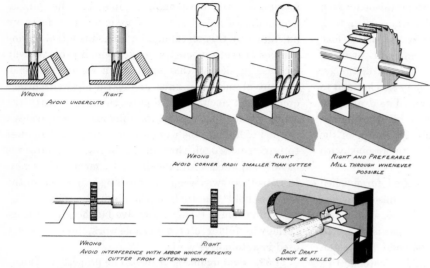

Fig. 11–44.   Design for milling operations. (Courtesy Curtiss-Wright Corp.)

Fig. 11–45.   Cylindrical grinding. Center type.
(Courtesy The Carborundum Co.)

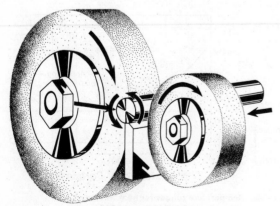

Fig. 11–46.   Cylindrical grinding. Centerless type.
(Courtesy The Carborundum Co.)

Fig. 11–47.   Surface grinding.
(Courtesy The Carborundum Co.)

terial like muslin or leather, containing a fine abrasive, which gives it a luster impossible to attain with the finest grinders. The draftsman indicates such an operation by the note "grind and polish."

11.30   The planer. When large flat surfaces are to be finished, a machine called a planer is used. The piece to be planed is mounted on a long horizontal bed which moves forward and backward under the cutting tool. The tool advances a small amount across the surface with each run of the bed, the width of each cut being determined by the distance that the tool advances. Numerous pieces of the same kind may be clamped to the bed and planed at the same time. The draftsman makes no reference to this machine on his drawing but simply marks the surface to be finished by one of the standard symbols. Tolerances of .005″ are obtained with this machine.

11.31   The shaper. The shaper is used for finished surfaces on pieces that are smaller than those for which a planer is required or where the surfaces are curved. For pieces within the capacity, the shaper is preferred to the planer because it is less cumbersome and faster. In the shaper, the piece to be finished is fastened to a table while the cutting tool moves backward and forward. The table advances the piece a small amount with each stroke of the cutting tool until the entire surface has been machined. Figure 11–48 shows a standard shaper. The shaper is particularly useful for cutting

slots, keyways, and small flat or curved surfaces. Tolerances of .004″ may be obtained with this machine. However, the draftsman does not refer to this machine on the drawing.

11.32   The broaching machine. Originally the broach was used for cutting keyways and internal work such as forming square, hexagonal, or holes of other shapes from a drilled hole, but now many external surfaces are machined by this method. The broach is a tool having a series of teeth or cutting edges which progressively increase in size so that each tooth removes a small amount of material, thus giving the desired surface quickly and accurately. Figure 11–49 illustrates the action of the broach. The broaching machine provides a method of holding the work and of supplying the power to force the broach through the work. This power is usually supplied hydraulically or by means of a screw. In cutting keyways, a guide bushing is inserted in the hole to hold the tool in the desired position. The broaching tool is rather expensive but because it is especially useful for interchangeable work, it is extensively used in automotive work.

11.33   Heat treatment of steel. The properties of steel, such as tensile strength, ductility, and hardness, depend on two items, namely, the chemical composition of the metal and the heat treatment to which it has been subjected. The principal heat treatments used in the production of steel products are annealing, normalizing,

Fig. 11–49.   Action of a broaching tool.

Fig. 11–48.   A shaper. (Courtesy South Bend Lathe Works.)

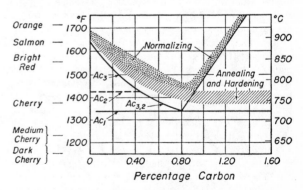

Fig. 11–50.   Temperature ranges for heat treatment.
(Courtesy ASM Handbook, 1948.)

hardening, tempering, and case hardening. These processes involve the heating and cooling of the metal for the purpose of altering the grain structure and the amount of carbon or other substances dissolved in the steel.

11.34 Annealing. The steel is heated to a temperature close to the lower limit of the critical range, as shown in Fig. 11–50, and then cooled very slowly. Of the many purposes for annealing, the principal ones are probably to remove stresses and induce softness or increase ductility.

11.35 Normalizing. This involves heating the steel to the temperature indicated in Fig. 11–50 and cooling in air. This gives faster cooling than annealing. The treatment increases the tensile and yield strength over annealed steel while still retaining sufficient ductility for many purposes.

11.36 Hardening. When steel is heated and cooled quickly, by quenching in water, oil, or some other cooling substance, the metal becomes hard and brittle. The temperature range for hardening is shown in Fig. 11–50.

11.37 Tempering. As hardened steels are too brittle for most uses, they must be tempered. This is done by heating the hardened steel to some point below the lower critical temperature, holding for a sufficient period of time and cooling as desired. Quenching is sometimes used.

11.38 Case hardening. For high surface hardness and resistance to abrasion, case hardening is used. This is done by raising the temperature to 1700 to 1800° Fahrenheit and packing the steel in some carburizing compound. Carbon is absorbed to a certain depth, forming a hard case on the outside of the metal.

11.39 Heat treatment of non-ferrous alloys. When the percentage of one metal dissolved in the other metal can be changed by varying the temperature, the properties of the alloy can usually be changed by heat treatment. For further information on this subject, see any good book on metallography.

PROBLEMS

The problems on the following pages are designed so that the student must apply the principles that have been explained in this chapter. These figures are intended to represent a preliminary drawing of the part to be built. In each case only the major dimensions have been given, thus making it necessary for the student to scale or proportion other parts. *In many cases corners should be rounded to save excess metal.* It is always assumed that necessary changes can be made in adjacent parts. *Each problem also has some features that would be difficult or impossible to manufacture in the shop.* These points should be apparent to anyone who has studied the chapter carefully, and *it is expected that the student will use his ingenuity to correct these errors.* It is quite probable that there will be several answers equally correct for these problems.

To illustrate the purpose and use of these problems, consider the crank support in Fig. 11–51.

The size of the base is given as ¾ × 3 ×5⅛, the center line of the bearing is 3″ above the base, and the right bearing is ¾ Dia. The whole part is to be fastened down by means of 4-¾″ cap screws. Other dimensions must be scaled or estimated on the basis of the information given. In this particular problem,

the student should make several corrections and adjustments. First the center supporting web is too thin; second, the larger bearing in the center cannot be reamed; third, the corners of the base should be rounded to make casting easier and to save metal; fourth, to save time in machining there should be pads on each end of the base; fifth, *all unfinished corners and angles should be rounded or filleted; sixth, the surfaces where finish and limits are necessary must be recognized.* When the student has recognized these problems, he can begin the drawing and make all necessary corrections.

All problems in this group contain situations similar to this one, and in each case the errors must be recognized before drawing is begun.

The scale given under each problem is the scale at which the student's drawing is to be made and not the scale of the pictorial drawing.

Read general instructions before solving any problems.

1 to 13. Make a complete working drawing of an object assigned from Figs. 11–51 to 11–63. In each case change the design of the part so that it can be made economically.

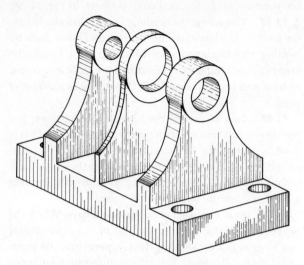

Size of base 5⅛″ × ¾″; center line of bearing 3″ above bottom of base; bearing on the right ¾″ diameter; base to be fastened down by four ⅜″ hex-head cap screws; scale ¾″ = 1″.

Fig. 11–51.   Crank support.

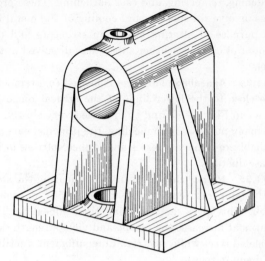

Center line of a ¾″ shaft to be supported 2″ ± .005 above bottom of base; bracket to be held down by two ½″ bolts or the equivalent; bosses are to be spot faced; oil hole to be threaded for standard oil cup; base is 3⅜″ × 2″ × ¼″; scale 1″ = 1″.

Fig. 11–53.   Bearing bracket.

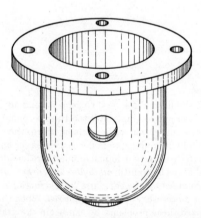

Problem (a). Interior diameter 2⅜″ × 3″ high; material 3⁄16″ thick, base 5⁄16″ thick; flange drilled for four ¼″ cap screws; ¼″ pipe tap through side ¾″ from center line and 1¼″ from base; scale 1″ = 1″.

Problem (b). Change the cover to a pressed-steel part, and show holes as punched. Use same general dimensions. Include proper data for pressed-steel part. Use SAE 1010 Sheet Metal −16 gage. Inside radius of bends must be equal to the thickness of the stock. Extrude the pipe center hole for pipe tap before threading. The four cap-screw holes must allow head clearance for the screw.

Fig. 11–52.   Cover.

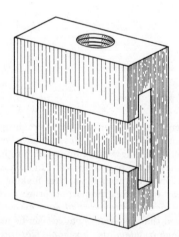

The clamp is to slide on a ¼″ × 1¼″ rod; the threaded hole is tapped for a ⅜″ cap screw which locks the clamp in place; scale 1″ = 1″.

Fig. 11–54.   Clamp.

Read general instructions before solving problems

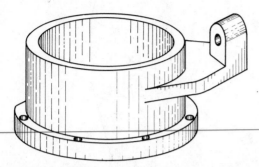

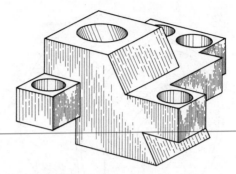

The internal diameter is 3″. The total depth of the hole and housing is 1⅛″; flat side on the left is tangent to outside of housing; center line of the hole in the bracket is parallel to the flat side of base, is 1¹⁵⁄₁₆″ from the main center line and level with the top of the housing; it must clear the main hub by ¾″; the housing is held down by seven #12 fillister-head machine screws; scale 1″ = 1″.

Fig. 11-55.   Gear housing.

Bearing is 2½″ long and 1″ bore; support lugs are ¾″ thick; center line of bearing makes an angle of 60° with the plane of the supports. Held down by four ½″ fillister-head cap screws with heads flush; scale 1″ = 1″.

Fig. 11-57.   Angle bearing bracket.

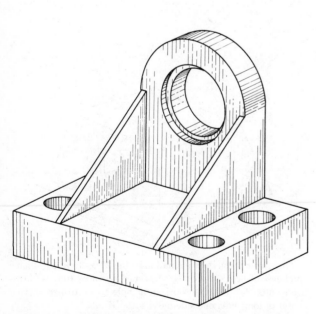

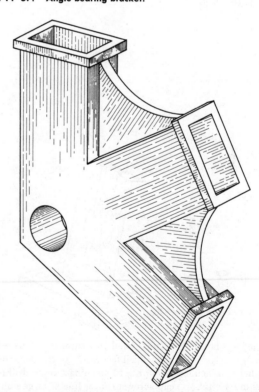

Center line of 1½″ bronze bushing is 3″ above base; counterbore is 1¾″ diameter, ³⁄₁₆″ deep; the back of bracket is ¾″ thick; base is 5¼″ × 3″ × 1″; counterbore base for four ¾″ fillister-head cap screws; bracket rests on steel plates; scale ½″ = 1″.

Fig. 11-56.   Bearing bracket.

Cross section of lever is ¾″ × 1½″; it must slide in easily to a depth of 3 inches. Purpose of lever is to turn the shaft; lever positions are 60° apart; shaft is 1″ diameter; length of bearing 1½″; scale ¾″ = 1″.

Fig. 11-58.   Lever fulcrum.

Read general instructions before solving problems

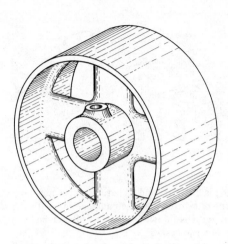

The 4" pulley has a 2" face; the hole is to be tapped for standard ⅜" set screw; scale 1" = 1".

Fig. 11-59.   Pulley.

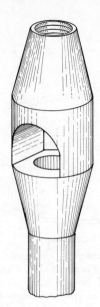

Total length 14"; length of enlarged tip 2⅝"; drilled hole in handle ¼" diameter, 1" deep; it is desired to make ¼" threads in threaded hole; scale 2" = 1".

Fig. 11-61.   Handle.

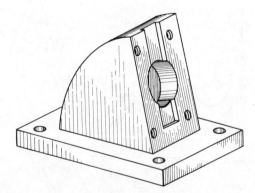

The large hole is 1" diameter and goes through ½" material; the slot is ⅛" × ⅝". The inclined face is 75° to the horizontal; four holes in inclined face for #10 machine screws; drill four holes in base for ⁵⁄₁₆" cap screws; center line of large hole at front face is 1⁹⁄₁₆" above base; scale 1" = 1".

Fig. 11-60.   Bracket.

Read general instructions before solving problems

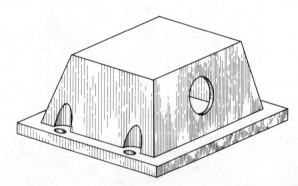

This cover must clear a small machine 2" × 3" × 1⅝" high; thickness of box ⅛", base ¼"; fastened down by four ¼" hex-head bolts; ¾"-diameter horizontal hole to be drilled in the center of long side, one side only; scale ¾" = 1".

Fig. 11-62.   Cover.

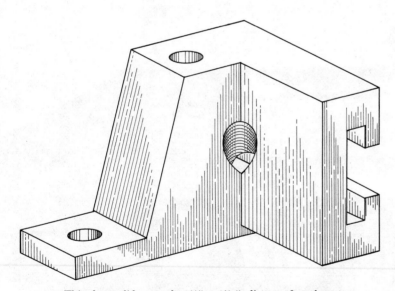

This clamp slides on a bar ¼″ × 1¹⁄₁₆″; distance from base to center of slot, 1⁵⁄₃₂″; the two drilled holes are for ⁵⁄₁₆″ cap screws; the threaded hole is for a ⅜″ cap screw which should bear against the center of the bar; this threaded hole makes 45° angle with the horizontal and equal angles with the two faces of the clamp; if desired this hole can be placed in a plane perpendicular to the slide and 45° with the horizontal; scale 1″ = 1″.

Fig. 11–63.   Saw fence clamp.

Steel yard (Bethlehem Steel Company).

12

Material Specification

12.1 Introduction. Material specification is of increasing importance in engineering, manufacture, and all construction. The ability on the part of the engineer to tell the shop or outside contractor exactly what he desires is of great importance. Much has been done and much remains to be done along this line.

Many organizations are carrying on standardization activities with regard to material specification. Among these are the following:

American Iron and Steel Institute (AISI)

American Railway Engineering Association (AREA)

American Society of Mechanical Engineers (ASME)

American Society for Testing Materials (ASTM)

Society of Automotive Engineers (SAE)

Space does not permit discussion concerning specifications for many materials or from several organizations. Specifications for wrought or rolled steel, automotive gray iron castings, aluminum casting alloys, and copper-base alloys from the Society of Automotive Engineers standard are used to illustrate some details of material specification.

12.2 General information for carbon and alloy steels. The conception that all steels are the same except for chemical constituents is false. Carbon steels may be produced with chemical composition (carbon, manganese, phosphorus, sulfur, and silicon) within the specified limits of a given grade and still have characteristics that are widely different.

In all phases of steel production, various practices are employed which determine the quality and type of the finished material. The diversity of steel requirements necessitates a differentation in grades and qualities, and governs the practices and precautions in steelmaking.

Quality, as the term relates to steel products, may indicate many conditions such as the degree of internal soundness, relative uniformity of composition, relative freedom from injurious surface imperfections, and finish. When sheet steel is to have a good painted surface for exposed parts, it should be broadly identified by the suffix "E," and when the surface is unexposed and the surface finish is unimportant the suffix "U" is used.

For complete descriptions of the qualities and supplementary requirements for carbon and alloy steels, reference should be made to the latest applicable *AISI Steel Products Manual*.

12.2.1   *Types of steel.* In most steelmaking processes, the primary reaction is the combination of carbon and oxygen to form a gas. If the oxygen necessary for this reaction is not removed prior to or during casting (by the addition of silicon or some other deoxidizer) the gaseous products continue to evolve during solidification. The amount of gas evolved determines the type of steel. If no gas is evolved, the steel is termed "killed" because it lies quietly in the molds. Increasing degrees of gas evolution results in semikilled, capped, or rimmed steel.

Killed steels are recommended for forging, piercing, carburizing, and heat treating applications.

Semikilled steels are produced for structural parts and noncritical forgings or heat-treated parts.

Capped steels may be used to advantage when the material is to withstand cold bending, cold forming, or cold heading.

Rimmed steels may be used advantageously for finished articles involving cold bending, cold forming, deep drawing, and, in some cases, cold heading.

12.2.2   *Commonly specified elements.* The effect of any single commonly specified element (carbon, manganese, phosphorous, sulphur, silicon, or copper) on steelmaking practice and carbon-steel properties is dependent upon the effect of other elements. As the number of elements specified increases, and as restrictive requirements increase, availability decreases, to the end that special heats are necessary and material must be ordered in heat lots.

The amount of carbon required in the steel limits the type of steel that can be made. Carbon is the principal hardening element of all steel. Tensile strength in the as-rolled condition increases as the carbon increases up to about 0.85% carbon. Ductility and weldability decrease with an increase in carbon.

Manganese contributes to the strength and hardness of steel but to a lesser degree than carbon, the amount of increase being dependent upon the carbon content. Increasing the manganese content decreases ductility and weldability but to a lesser degree than does carbon.

Phosphorus in appreciable amounts increases strength and hardness, but at the sacrifice of ductility and toughness. Since ductility and toughness are desirable for most applications, phosphorous is usually maintained below a specified maximum.

Increased sulfur content has little effect on longitudinal mechanical properties, but lowers transverse ductility. Notched impact toughness, which is a measure of the energy a notched specimen will absorb, is also lowered. Weldability decreases with increasing sulfur content. To avoid these undesirable qualities a maximum sulfur content is specified for most steels.

The silicon content of steel is related to the type of steel, because silicon is one of the principal deoxidizers used in steelmaking. Rimmed and capped steels contain no significant amounts of silicon. Semikilled steels may contain moderate amounts of silicon. Killed carbon steels may contain any amount of silicon up to 0.60%. Silicon is somewhat less effective than manganese in increasing as-rolled strength and hardness.

Copper in appreciable amounts is detrimental to hot-working operations. It adversely affects forge welding but does not seriously affect arc or acetylene welding. It is detrimental to surface quality. However, it is beneficial to atmospheric corrosion resistance when present in amounts exceeding 0.20%.

12.3   SAE numbering system for wrought or rolled steel. A numerical index system is used to identify the compositions of the SAE steels, which system makes possible the use of numerals on shop drawings to specify partially the composition of the material.

In the original conception, the first digit indicated the type to which the steel belonged; thus "1-" indicated carbon steel; "2-" nickel steel; and "3-" nickel-chromium steel. In the case of simple alloy steels, the second digit generally indicated the approximate percentage of the predominant alloying element. Usually the last two or three digits indicated the approximate average carbon content in "points" or hundredths of 1%. Thus, "2317" indicated a nickel steel of approximately 3% nickel and 0.17% carbon.

In some cases, in order to avoid confusion, it has been necessary to depart from this system of identifying the approximate alloy composition of a steel by varying the second and third digits of the number.

This is done for steel numbers selected for several corrosion and heat-resisting alloys. For instance, corrosion and heat-resisting nickel-chromium steels have a five digit number in which the first three digits are "303".

12.4   Use of the SAE numbering system in the selection of materials. Table 1 lists the grade numbers, characteristics, and uses of several grades of plain carbon steels. By the use of this table one can select steels within a certain range of numbers for certain uses, but he should refer to more detailed information for selecting individual steel numbers. The grade number should be placed in the title block or at some other appropriate place on the detailed drawing of the part. See Fig. 13–2.

Table 2 gives the characteristics of free-cutting carbon steels. This class of steels is intended for uses where easy machining is of primary importance, at some sacrifice of cold-forming properties, weldability, and forging characteristics.

12.5   Automotive gray iron castings. These specifications cover gray iron castings used in automotive and allied industries. The castings shall represent good foundry practice, shall be smooth and clean, and shall be free from injurious flaws and defects. Castings shall machine satisfactorily. Hardness, transverse, and tension tests shall be made on arbitration bars cast separ-

TABLE 1

SAE	Characteristics and uses of plain carbon steels
1006 1008 1009 1010 1012 1015	These steels are the lowest carbon steels of the plain carbon type and are selected where cold formability is the primary requisite. They have relatively low tensile values, but may have excellent surface finish and good drawing qualities. These steels are nearly pure iron or ferritic in structure and do not machine freely; rimmed steel is used for cold-heading wire for tacks and rivets, for body and fender stock, hoods, lamps, oil pans, and other deep-drawn products.
1016 through 1027	Steels in this group, because of the carbon range covered, have increased strength and hardness and reduced cold formability. These steels are used for numerous forged parts. SAE 1020 is used for fan blades and some frame members. SAE 1024 may be used for such parts as transmission and rear axle gears.
1030 1033 1035 through 1043 1045 1046 1049 1050 1052	These steels, of the medium carbon type, are selected where their higher mechanical properties are needed. All steels in this class are used for forgings. As a class they are considered good for normal machining operations. SAE 1030 and 1035 are used for shifter forks and many small forgings. SAE 1038 is used for bolts and studs.
1055 1060 1064 1065 1070 1074 1078 1080 1084 1086 1090 1095	Steels in this group are of the high carbon type. They are used principally for applications where the higher carbon is needed to improve wear characteristics for cutting edges, to make springs of various types, and for special purposes, such as valve-spring wire and music wire. These steels find wide usage in the farm implement industry.

TABLE 2

SAE	Characteristics and uses of free-cutting carbon steels
1111 1112 1113	These steels have excellent machining characteristics and are used for a wide variety of machined parts. They are not commonly used for vital parts owing to an unfavorable property of cold shortness.
1108 1109 1115 1117 through 1120 1126	Steels in this group are used where a combination of good machinability and uniform response to heat treatment is needed. These steels are used for small parts that are to be case-hardened.
1132 1137 1138 1140 1141 1144 1145 1146 1151	These steels are widely used for parts where a large amount of machining is necessary, or where threads, splines, or other operations offer special tooling problems. SAE 1137 is widely used for nuts, bolts, and studs with machined threads.

ately according to ASTM A48.

Table 3 gives the physical properties of automotive-type cast iron.

Table 4 gives the suggested uses for automotive gray iron castings.

12.6 General information for aluminum alloys. The alloying elements commonly used with aluminum in this country are copper, silicon, magnesium, zinc, and nickel, with the three first named the most common. Aluminum and its commercial alloys, being rather ductile materials, can be hot- or cold-worked into most of the common manufactured forms. Aluminum and most of its alloys can be welded by the common fusion and electrical-resistance methods, can be formed hot or cold, and can generally be machined easily. They can also be given a wide variety of mechanical, chemical, electrochemical, or paint finishes.

12.7 Temper designation system for aluminum. Temper designation, which is used for all forms of aluminum and aluminum alloy except ingot, follows the alloy designation, and is separated therefrom by a dash. The following Basic Temper Designations and Subdivisions are contained in table form in the SAE Handbook:

-F As fabricated.

-O Annealed, recrystallized (wrought products only).

-H Strain hardened (wrought products only).

Subdivisions of the -H Temper:
-H1 Strain hardened only.
-H2 Strain hardened and then partially annealed.
-H3 Strain hardened and then stabilized.

-W Solution heat treated. Unstable temper.

-T Treated to produce stable tempers other than -F, -O, or -H.

Sub-divisions of the -T temper:
-T2 Annealed (castings only).
-T3 Solution heat treated and then cold-worked.
-T4 Solution heat treated.
-T5 Artificially aged only.
-T6 Solution heat treated and then artificially aged.
-T7 Solution heat treated and then stabilized.
-T8 Solution heat treated, cold worked, and then artificially aged.
-T9 Solution heat treated, artificially aged, and then cold worked.
-T10 Artificially aged and then cold worked.

The -H designation is always followed by two or more digits. The first digit, 1, 2, or 3, indicates the specific combination of basic operations, and the following digit or digits the final degree of strain hardening.

H16 indicates a temper midway in strength between H14 and H18. A third digit may be used to identify a specified set of physical properties. For example, H161 represents a temper with similar physical properties to H16, but having specified maximum and minimum values developed for a specific application.

The -T designation is always followed by one or more digits. The numerals 2 through 10 each indicate a spe-

TABLE 3

SAE	Brinell hardness no.	Minimum transverse load, lb.	Minimum deflection, in.	Minimum tensile strength, psi
110	187 max.	1800	0.15	20,000
111	170–223	2200	0.20	30,000
120	187–241	2400	0.24	35,000
121	202–255	2600	0.27	40,000
122	217–269	2800	0.30	45,000

TABLE 4

SAE	Suggested uses for automotive gray iron castings
110	Miscellaneous soft iron castings in which strength is not of primary importance. Exhaust manifolds.
111	Small cylinder blocks, cylinder heads, air-cooled cylinders, pistons, clutch plates, oil-pump bodies, transmission cases, gear boxes, clutch housings, and lightweight brake drums.
120	Automobile cylinder blocks, cylinder heads, flywheels, cylinder liners, and pistons.
121	Truck and tractor cylinder blocks and heads, heavy flywheels, tractor transmission cases, differential carrier castings, and heavy gear boxes.
122	Diesel-engine castings, liners, cylinders, pistons, and heavy parts in general.

cific sequence of basic operations outlined above. Multi-digit symbols are used for some castings. As an example, in SAE 38 sand castings the T6 and T62 tempers are both designations for castings, solution heat treated and artificially aged, but varied to develop different specified physical properties.

12.8   General data on SAE aluminum casting alloys. The SAE Standard on Aluminum Casting Alloys covers a wide range of castings for general and special applica-tions but does not include all of the alloys in commercial use. Table 5 gives typical uses of SAE aluminum casting alloys.

12.9   General information for copper-base alloys. The two principal copper-base alloys are brass and bronze. Metallurgically they have zinc and tin, respectively, as their other major constituent, and classification of the wrought alloys as one or the other is usually not difficult. However, the nomenclature used in the nonferrous-

TABLE 5

SAE	ASTM designation	Usual form	General data
300	CS66A	Permanent mold castings	Pistons primarily
304	S5C	Die castings	Good to excellent casting characteristics and good to high corrosion resistance. Suited for use in thin-walled or intricate castings.
305	S12A		
306	SC84A		
308	SC84B		
309	SG100A		
310	ZG61A	Sand castings	General-purpose structural castings.
320	G4A	Sand castings	Moderate strength, high corrosion re-sistance.
321	SN122A	Permanent-mold castings	Pistons, low expansion.
322	SC51A	Sand and permanent mold castings	High strength and pressure for general use, such as pump bodies and liquid-cooled cylinder heads.
324	G10A	Sand castings	High strength and ductility, requires special foundry practice.
326	SC64B	Sand and permanent mold castings	General-purpose alloy.
328	SC122A	Permanent-mold castings	Pistons.
330	SC64A	Permanent-mold castings	Moderate strength, general-purpose alloy.
332		Permanent-mold castings	Automotive pistons.
34	CG100A	Sand and permanent mold castings	Pistons, air-cooled cylinder heads, and valve tappet guides.
35	S5B	Sand and permanent mold castings	Intricate castings having thin section.
38	C4A	Sand castings	General structural castings. High strength and shock resistance.
39	CN42A	Sand and permanent mold castings	Air-cooled cylinder heads, and high strength pistons.

metals trade may be confusing to those not accustomed to handling these metals since it does not always follow the above definition.

When the term "brass" is used without qualification, it is usually understood to refer to alloys of about two parts copper and one part zinc. Other widely used names for this composition are "yellow brass," "2 and 1 brass," and "high brass." "High brass" indicates a brass of high zinc content, "low brass" one of low zinc content.

True bronzes are the copper-tin alloys, and they are sometimes called "tin bronzes" or "phosphor bronzes." Today it is common practice to use a further qualifying adjective with so-called bronzes to designate the particular alloying element used, for instance, aluminum bronze or manganese bronze.

A number of copper-base alloys, both cast and wrought, are capable of being heat treated with considerable resultant increase in physical properties. Copper-base alloys can be joined by welding, soldering, and brazing, and lend themselves to a large variety of surface finishes and coatings. The preparation of copper and copper-base alloys for electroplating is comparatively simple, and such metals as gold, silver, nickel, and chromium can be readily plated for decorative and tarnish-resistant purposes.

Table 6 shows the effect of the alloying elements on copper-base alloys.

12.10   Classification and uses of commercial cast copper-base alloys. Table 7 shows the characteristics and uses of commercial cast copper-base alloys.

TABLE 6

Alloying element	Effect of alloying element
Zinc	Added to copper as a predominating alloying constituent, in amounts of 5 to 40% to form alloys known as brasses. Imparts a better strength and corrosion resistance to the copper.
Tin	Added to copper in amounts of 5 to 20% to form a series of alloys known as tin bronzes and leaded tin bronzes. Strengthens and hardens copper, making it tough and resistant to wear and increases its corrosion resistance.
Lead	Added alone to copper in large amounts of around 35% for automotive bearings. Increases machinability.
Aluminum	Added to copper as a predominating alloying constituent to form a series of high strength alloys known as aluminum bronzes. As an impurity it is detrimental to high leaded bronzes and non-leaded tin bronzes.
Iron	Added to copper-base alloys as a strengthening constituent for silicon, aluminum, and manganese bronzes. When present as an impurity, iron is detrimental to machining.
Phosphorus	Added to copper and copper-base alloys principally as a deoxidizer.
Nickel	Added to bronzes as an alloying constituent for refining the grain and toughening the alloy. It promotes strength and corrosion resistance, and is not detrimental as an impurity.
Silicon	Added to copper as an alloying constituent to form copper-silicon alloys. These alloys have high strength, toughness, and corrosion resistance. Small amounts of silicon are used as deoxidizing elements.
Beryllium	Added to copper as an alloying constituent to form a series of age-hardenable beryllium-copper alloys. These heat-treated alloys are the strongest of the known copper-base alloys.
Manganese	Used primarily as an alloying constituent for high strength alloy brasses.
Chromium	Added to copper as an alloying constituent to form a number of compositions used for resistance-welding electrodes.

TABLE 7

Alloy	SAE	Characteristics	Typical Application

Tin Bronzes
  Phosphor gear bronze
  Nickel phosphor gear bronze
  Nickel phosphor bronze
  Gun metal
  Leaded gun metal
  Navy "G"
  Leaded navy "G"
  Navy "M"
	
	65
	65 + Ni
	640
	62
	63
	620
	621
	622
		Hard, strong, tough resistant to wear, (especially with phosphorus), fine-grained, (especially with nickel), good machinability (with lead), and corrosion resistant to sea water.	Worm wheels and gears (nickel-bearing and zinc-free for heavy sections). Bushings for heavy loads and low speeds. Zinc-containing allows for pressure castings.

High lead tin bronzes
  Phosphor bronze
  Bronze bearing
  Bronze bearing
  Semiplastic bronze
  High lead bronze
	
	64
	660
	66
	67
	. . .
		Excellent antifrictional qualities and casting and machining properties. Strength and resistance to wear increase with tin-content. Antifriction qualities increase with lead content.	64-High speeds and heavy loads.
			660-General bushing applications, medium requirements.
			66-High speeds and light loads on bearing backs.

Leaded red brasses
  Leaded red brass
  (ounce metal)
  Leaded semi-red brass
	
	40
		General utility alloys with reasonable strength and corrosion resistance, good casting and machining properties. Hydrostatic tightness increases with zinc content.	Water pump fittings and valve bodies. Ounce metal also used for bearing backs.

High strength yellow brasses
  Manganese bronze
  High tensile manganese bronze
	
	43
	430 A and B
		Excellent strength, corrosion resistance, and casting properties.	Brackets, shafts, gears, and structural applications.

Leaded yellow brass Yellow brass	 41	Inexpensive, good corrosion resistance, and casting properties.	Radiator parts, fittings for water cooling systems, and battery terminals.

Aluminum bronzes
  Aluminum bronze
  Aluminum bronze
	
	68A
	68B
		Good strength, good corrosion resistance, and low coefficient of friction against steel.	Gears, worm wheels, bearings, valve guides and seats, and miscellaneous structural applications.

Copper silicons
  Silicon bronze
  Silicon brass
	
	. . .
	. . .
		Good strength, toughness, and corrosion resistance. Casting qualities increase with zinc content.	Pump parts, gears, shafts, and other engineering applications.

13

Dimensioning for Interchangeable Assembly

13.1 Assembly drawings. Since even the simplest machines involve several parts, it is necessary, both for purposes of design and production, to know how the various parts fit together. Drawings made to show these relationships are called assembly drawings. As the name clearly implies an assembly drawing shows the parts of a machine put together in their proper working position relative to each other. Drawings of this kind may serve a number of purposes as indicated in the following paragraphs. The use for which a drawing is intended will determine the character of the drawing and the dimensioning placed upon it.

13.2 Layout drawings. Most of the machines which an engineer is called upon to design have their beginning as an idea in someone's imagination. This idea is first explained by a sketch which the engineer elaborates as a mechanical drawing showing the complete machine and how its parts are to function. See Fig. 13–1. In this first design assembly or layout, the size and shape of parts are determined by judgment based on past experience. Many times these drawings are schematic in character.

From these layout drawings the various parts may now be designed, first, to give the movement and speed of the various parts which will insure the performance of the function of the machine, and, second, to design the parts so that they have the necessary strength with minimum weight. The detail of a part made from the layout of Fig. 13–1 is shown in Fig. 13–2.

13.3 Final or check assemblies. In some cases the original layout is sufficiently accurate so that no further work need be done. In other cases the actual design of

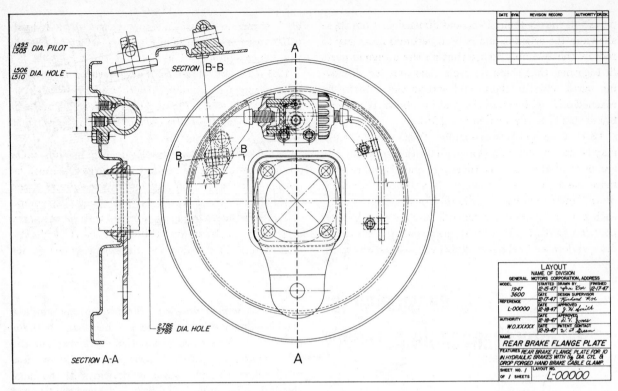

Fig. 13-1. Layout drawing.

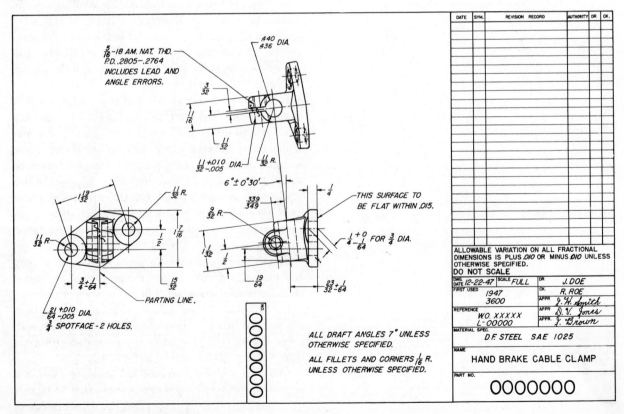

Fig. 13-2. Detail from layout of Fig. 13-1.

parts will change their shape and dimensions from those shown in the original, and it then becomes necessary to redraw the assembly to see that all the designed parts fit together, that there is ample clearance for all moving parts, and that bolts and screws can actually be reached and tightened in the position shown. An assembly of this type is shown in Fig. 13–3.

13.4 Shop and field assemblies. Assembly drawings may be used in the shop as a guide for the workmen who are putting the machine together, and they are even more useful where a machine is shipped "knocked-down" and assembled elsewhere. These drawings show each part numbered or marked in such a way that the part can be readily identified on the job and the detail drawing located in the files if necessary. Such an assem-

bly is shown in Fig. 13–3. In some cases exploded pictorial views are made as in Fig. 13–4, which represents the same assembly as Fig. 13–7.

13.5 Erection diagrams. Large structures such as bridges and steel buildings also require a type of drawing which will enable the workmen to assemble properly the parts. Such drawings are commonly referred to as erection diagrams. See Fig. 27–7.

13.6 Installation drawings. Frequently machine units are fitted into larger machines, and large machines require foundations or footings designed to support them. Assemblies are made showing principally the fastenings, anchor bolts, and clearances required with all necessary dimensions to show these things but omitting the details both in the drawing and dimensions which do not

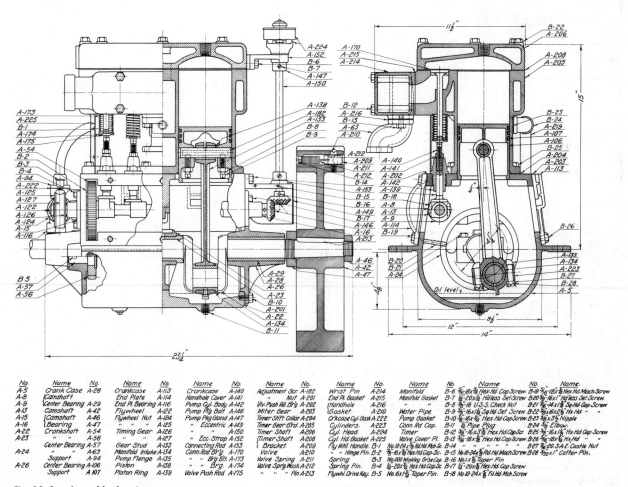

Fig. 13–3. Assembly drawing.

WATER PUMP

NO.	REQ.	DESCRIPTION	NO.	REQ.	DESCRIPTION
1	4	15/16"×1" HEX-HEAD BOLTS	9	1	PUNGER BOLT
2	1	OUTLET FLANGE	10	1	ECCENTRIC STRAP
3	2	STEEL BALLS	11	1	ECCENTRIC (INSIDE)
4	1	PUMP BODY	12	1	ECCENTRIC (OUTSIDE)
5	1	PACKING RING	13	1	FLAT HEAD SCREW
6	1	PUMP PACKING GLAND	14	1	CAM SHAFT REAR BEARING
7	1	PUMP PLUNGER	15	2	NO. 9 WOODRUFF KEYS
8	1	COTTER PIN	16	1	INTAKE FLANGE

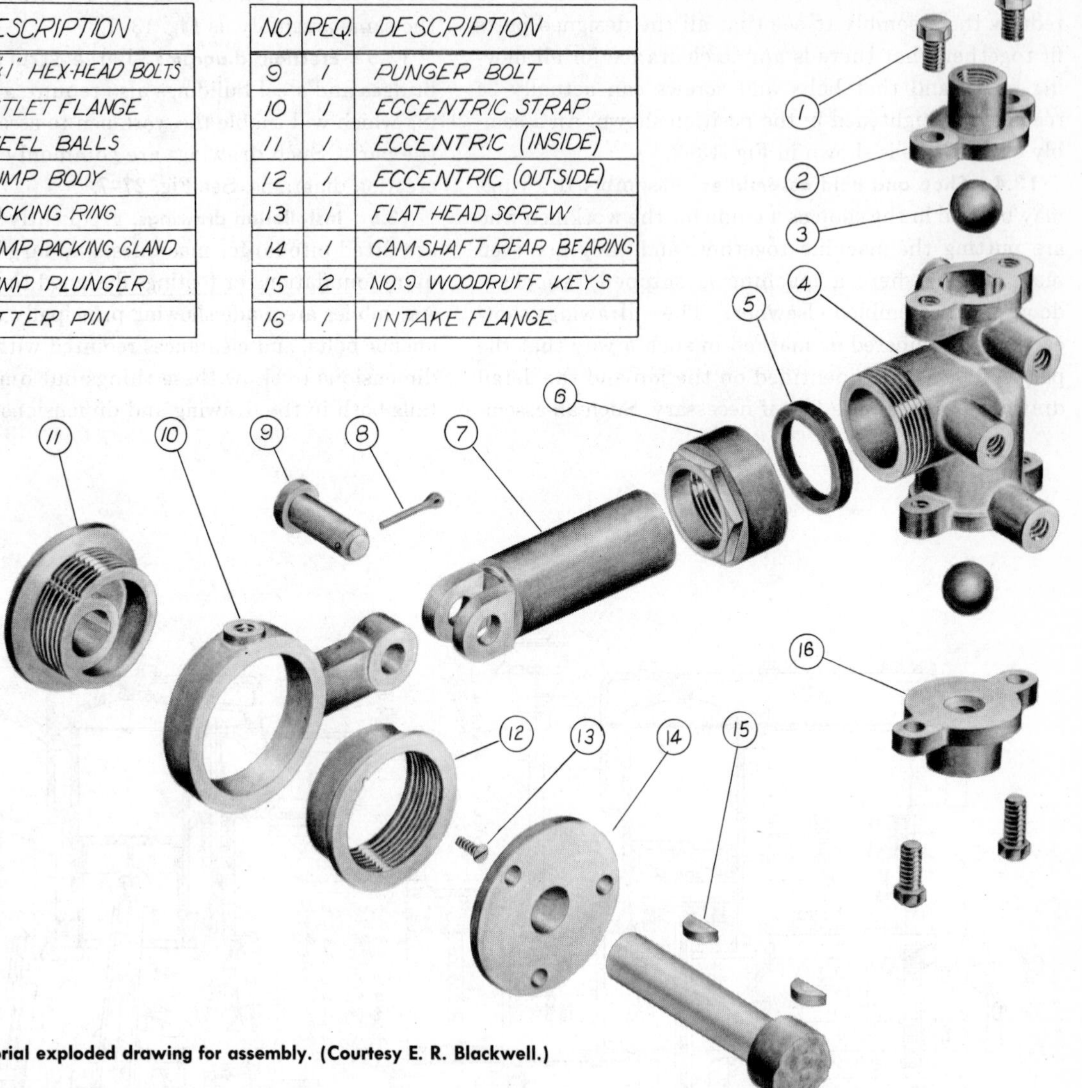

Fig. 13–4. Pictorial exploded drawing for assembly. (Courtesy E. R. Blackwell.)

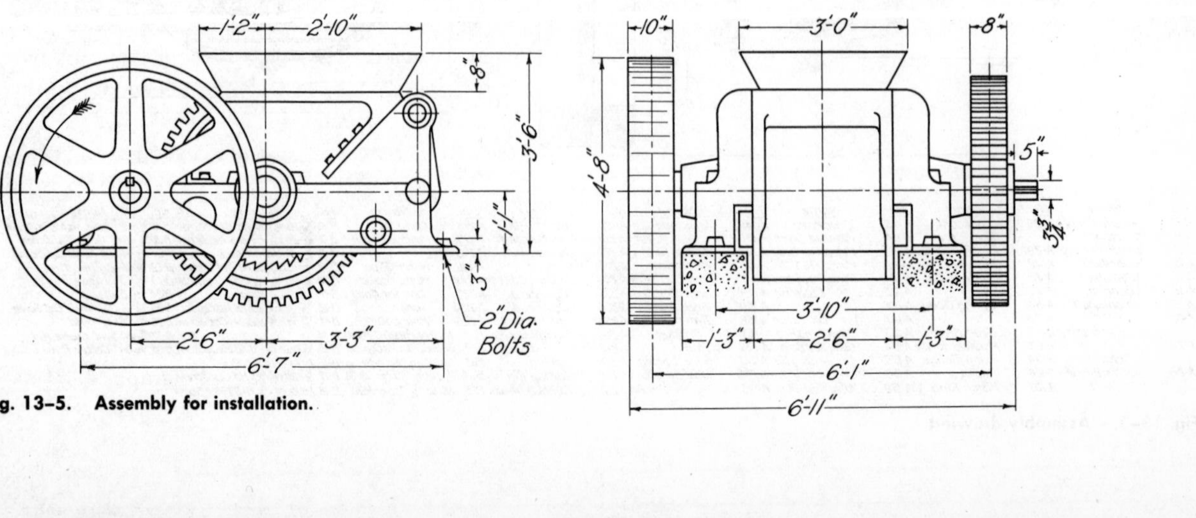

Fig. 13–5. Assembly for installation.

concern the persons making the installation. Figures 13–5 and 13–6 are illustrations of this type of drawing.

13.7 Dimensioning assemblies. As has been indicated in the preceding paragraph, the dimensioning of assembly drawings will depend upon the use for which they are intended. In general, however, it may be said that only the controlling dimensions, distance of travel of moving parts, and the like are shown on assemblies as illustrated in Figs. 13–5 and 13–7.

13.8 Crosshatching in assemblies. The system of using only one type of crosshatching is a common one on detail drawings; the use of different types of crosshatching to represent different materials seems to be the more common practice on assembly drawings. This is quite desirable since it calls attention in an unmistakable way to the difference in materials. Figure 13–7 illustrates the use of symbolic crosshatching as approved by the American Standards Association and illustrated

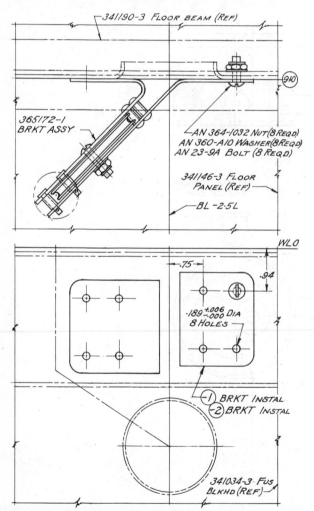

Fig. 13–6. Aircraft installation assembly.

in Figs. 8–30 and 8–31.

13.9 Hidden lines in assemblies. Since assembly drawings are frequently elaborately sectioned, it is the usual practice to omit hidden lines entirely unless it is necessary to show them for clearness. Then it is usual to show only the principal outlines of the object which may be needed.

13.10 Reference or part numbers. On assembly drawings for the shop, or for sales and service organizations, all the parts are identified by numbers or letters or combinations of letters and numbers. Each manufacturer has his own system of identification. In some shops the drawing number of the part is commonly used as a part number. See Figs. 13–3 and 13–7.

13.11 Standard details. Standard parts such as bolts, springs, and threaded parts are shown in conventional form. Hexagonal heads of bolts are shown as hexagons in both front and side views rather than as true projections since this identifies the bolt in either view. For economy in manufacturing, standard commerical parts should be used whenever possible in design.

13.12 Subassemblies. In larger and more complicated machines, it is impossible to show all parts in one assembly. The usual practice in such cases is to take groups of related parts which form a unit and make what is called a subassembly. See Fig. 13–7.

13.13 Selective assembly. To make parts completely interchangeable there must be clearance between the parts at their maximum material condition (M.M.C.). That is, when the allowance is positive, the largest shaft must be smaller than the smallest hole. When not at M.M.C. the hole is larger and the shaft smaller so that there is more clearance and it is equal to the allowance plus both measured tolerances on the actual parts. There are two methods of reducing this clearance to get a closer fit. One method is by reducing the tolerance, and the other is by selective assembly. The first method involves increased manufacturing costs, and the second calls for increased costs in assembling.

When selective assembly has been chosen, the parts are gaged and placed in various bins, depending on their actual size. In this manner the larger internal parts can be fitted to the external parts having the larger hole, and the smaller internal parts can be fitted to the mating part with the smaller holes. In this manner the excess clearance due to parts not being at maximum material condition can be made smaller because the actual measured tolerances on the parts are reduced.

13.14 Interchangeable assembly. The assembly drawings as discussed in the preceding paragraphs show how the parts of an object fit together. Before any part can be manufactured it must be detailed in a separate drawing. Usually each part is drawn on a sheet by itself, but occasionally the several parts of small assemblies may be detailed on one sheet.

Experience has shown that parts cannot be manufactured economically to exact dimensions. Hence when two or more parts must fit together some latitude in the size of each part must be allowed the workman producing the parts. It is therefore necessary to dimension parts in such a manner that the workman knows exactly how much leeway he has in producing them. This leads to the use of some new terms in production dimensioning which must be thoroughly understood.

13.15   Definition of terms. In order to comprehend a discussion of methods of tolerancing dimensions, it is necessary to have a clear understanding of the following terms which are used in the discussion.

*a. Nominal size.** The nominal size is the designation which is used for the purpose of general identification. It is most often used to designate a commercial product. It is not in any sense the numerical size of the part. An example of a nominal size is, ½ pipe, which actually has an outside diameter of .675″ and an inside diameter of .493″. Another is a piece of lumber called a 2 × 4 which is actually 1⅝″ × 3⅝″.

b. Basic size. This is the size of a part determined by design computations, from which the limits of size are determined by the application of allowances and tolerances. Thus, the requirements of strength and stiffness may require a 2″ diameter shaft. This is the basic size. It may also be the basic size of the hole into which the

*All definitions of terms, classes of fits, and some sentences or phrases in this chapter and drawings, when so indicated, have been taken from ASA Y14.5 and ASA B4.1—1955 with the permission of the publisher, The American Society of Mechanical Engineers, 29 West 39th St., New York 18, New York.

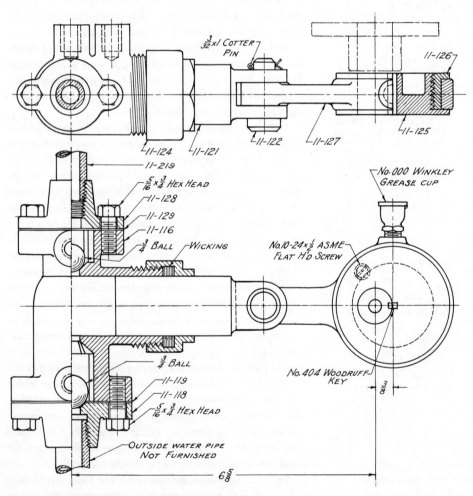

Fig. 13-7.   Subassembly of parts from Fig. 13-4.

shaft must fit, since the allowance is usually applied to the shaft. When necessary for special reasons the allowance may be applied to the hole.

c. Design size. Design size is that size from which limits of size are derived by the application of tolerances. When there is no allowance, the design size is the same as the basic size. Thus, the application of an allowance to the basic size is considered a part of the design process. In the previous illustration, if 2″ is the basic size of the hole, then this is also the design size for the hole. If an allowance of .003 for clearance is applied to the shaft, then the design size of the shaft is 1.997″. A tolerance is then applied to this dimension.

d. Actual size. The actual size is a measured size.

e. Limits. The term "limits" may be defined as the extreme permissible dimensions of a part. Two limit dimensions are always involved, a larger and a smaller or a maximum size and a minimum size.

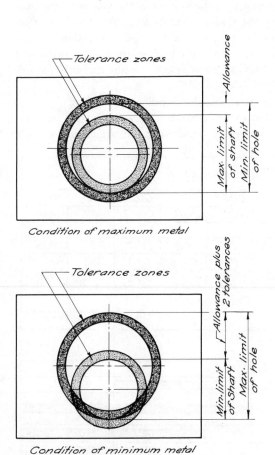

Condition of maximum metal

Condition of minimum metal

Fig. 13-8. Relation of tolerance and allowance to limits.

f. Tolerance. Tolerance is defined as the total amount of variation permitted in the size of a part. It is the difference between the two limits of the same dimension. The variation permitted in the dimensions for locating holes or other parts is also called a tolerance. Again it should be emphasized that the tolerance on a dimension is the total variation permitted.

g. Allowance. Another important term used in production dimensioning is allowance, which is defined as the intentional difference in the dimensions of mating parts to provide the minimum clearance or the maximum interference which is intended between the parts. It represents the condition of the tightest permissible fit or the largest internal member mated with the smallest external member. This is sometimes referred to as the maximum material condition since both parts have the maximum material in them. Allowance may be neutral or negative, thus providing interference fits for permanent assembly.

The student should note that the term "allowance" refers to the difference in size between two different parts. Thus the distinction between the three terms, limits, tolerance, and allowance, should be quite clear and unequivocal. They are illustrated in exaggerated form in Fig. 13-8. The purpose of an allowance is to provide for different classes of fits.

13.15.1 *Selecting tolerances.* Great care and good judgment must be exercised in deciding upon tolerances which may be permitted on a part. The greater the demand for accuracy the higher will be the cost of production. Since the specified tolerances will govern the method of manufacture, it is very important that tolerances be made as large as possible. When tolerances are reduced, the cost of manufacture rises very rapidly. The chart in Fig. 13-9 shows the accuracy that may be obtained economically in various common machine-shop operations, assuming the machines to be in good condition. This information, together with that shown in the chapter on shop terms and processes, will provide some basis for evaluating the effect of tolerances on manufacturing costs.

In working out limit dimensions the draftsman makes use of tables. Many companies have their own tables; others use the ASA Standards. In either case the method of computation is the same. Two systems are in use, namely, the basic hole method and the basic shaft method. The choice of the one to use depends upon the method of manufacture, but in most cases the basic hole method is preferred, because standard tools can be used to produce the hole, whereas it is comparatively easy to turn or grind a shaft to any desired size. The method of making computations for both methods are illustrated in Art. 13.18.

13.16   Classes of fits. Designation of standard fits. Standard fits are designated by means of the following symbols and used in the tables in the Appendix. They are for educational purposes to facilitate reference to various classes of fits. They are not to be shown on manufacturing drawings. Actual dimensions, as worked out from the tables, are used on drawings. The letter symbols have the following meanings:

RC   Running or sliding fit
LC   Location clearance fit
LT   Location transition fit
LN   Location interference fit
FN   Force or shrink fit

13.16.1   *Running and sliding fits.* Running and sliding fits, for which limits of clearance are given in Table 20 in the Appendix, are intended to provide an equivalent running performance, with suitable lubrication allowance, throughout the range of sizes.

RC 1. Close sliding fits are intended for the accurate location of parts which must assemble without perceptible play.

RC 2. Sliding fits are intended for accurate location, but with greater maximum clearance than class RC 1. Parts made to this fit move and turn easily but are not intended to run freely, and in the larger sizes may seize with small temperature changes.

RC 3. Precision running fits are the closest fits which can be expected to run freely, and are intended for precision work at slow speeds and light journal pressures, but are not suitable where appreciable temperature differences are likely to be encountered.

RC 4. Close running fits are intended chiefly for running fits on accurate machinery with moderate surface speeds and journal pressures, where accurate location and minimum play is desired.

RC 5–RC 6. Medium running fits are intended for higher running speeds, or heavy journal pressures, or both.

RC 7. Free running fits are intended for use where accuracy is not essential, or where large temperature variations are likely to be encountered, or under both these conditions.

RC 8–RC 9. Loose running fits are intended for use where materials such as cold-rolled shafting and tubing, made to commercial tolerances, are involved.

13.16.2   *Locational fits.* Locational fits are fits intended to determine only the location of the mating parts; they may provide rigid or accurate location, as with interference fits, or provide some freedom of location, as with clearance fits. Accordingly they are divided into three groups: clearance fits, transition fits, and interference fits.

These are more fully described as follows:

LC. Locational clearance fits are intended for parts which are normally stationary, but which can be freely

RANGE OF SIZES		TOLERANCES								
FROM	TO & INCL									
.000	.599	.00015	.0002	.0003	.0005	.0008	.0012	.002	.003	.005
.600	.999	.00015	.00025	.0004	.0006	.001	.0015	.0025	.004	.006
1.000	1.499	.0002	.0003	.0005	.0008	.0012	.002	.003	.005	.008
1.500	2.799	.00025	.0004	.0006	.001	.0015	.0025	.004	.006	.010
2.800	4.499	.0003	.0005	.0008	.0012	.002	.003	.005	.008	.012

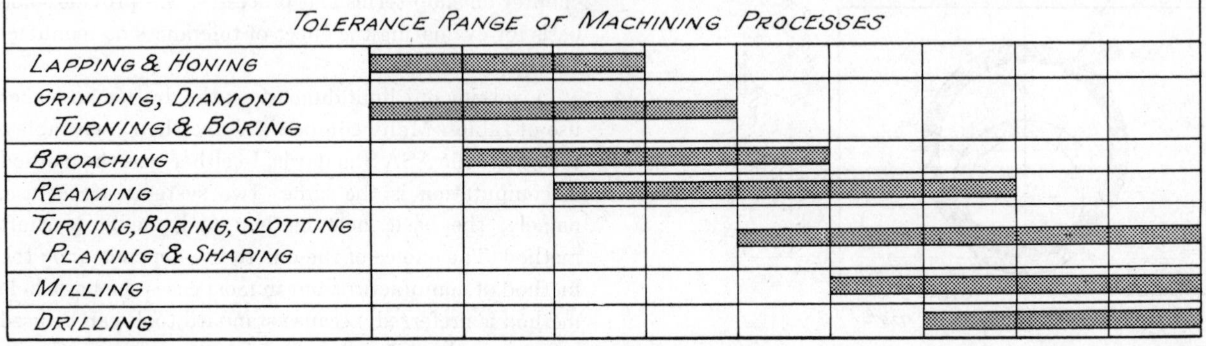

TOLERANCE RANGE OF MACHINING PROCESSES

Process	1	2	3	4	5	6	7	8	9
LAPPING & HONING	▓	▓	▓						
GRINDING, DIAMOND TURNING & BORING	▓	▓	▓	▓					
BROACHING		▓	▓	▓					
REAMING			▓	▓	▓				
TURNING, BORING, SLOTTING PLANING & SHAPING					▓	▓	▓	▓	▓
MILLING						▓	▓	▓	▓
DRILLING							▓	▓	▓

Fig. 13-9.   Tolerance range for machining processes. (Courtesy Mil Std No 8B—1959.)

assembled or disassembled. They run from snug fits for parts requiring accuracy of location, through the medium clearance fits for parts such as spigots, to the looser fastener fits where freedom of assembly is of prime importance.

LT. Transition fits are a compromise between clearance and interference fits, for application where accuracy of location is important, but either a small amount of clearance or interference is permissible.

LN. Locational interference fits are used where accuracy of location is of prime importance, and for parts requiring rigidity and alignment with no special requirements for bore pressure. Such fits are not intended for parts designed to transmit frictional loads from one part to another by virtue of the tightness of fit, as these conditions are covered by force fits.

13.16.3 *Force fits.* Force or shrink fits constitute a special type of interference fit, normally characterized by maintenance of constant bore pressures throughout the range of sizes. The interference therefore varies almost directly with diameter, and the difference between its minimum and maximum value is small in order to maintain the resulting pressures within reasonable limits.

These fits may be described briefly as follows:

FN 1. Light drive fits are those requiring light assembly pressures, and produce more or less permanent assemblies. They are suitable for thin sections or long fits, or in cast iron external members.

FN 2. Medium drive fits are suitable for ordinary steel parts, or for shrink fits on light sections. They are about the tightest fits that can be used with high grade cast iron external members.

FN 3. Heavy drive fits are suitable for heavier steel parts or for shrink fits in medium sections.

FN 4—FN 5. Force fits are suitable for parts which can be highly stressed, or for shrink fits where the heavy pressing forces required are impractical.

13.17 Tolerancing systems. There are three systems, in common use, of expressing tolerances on drawings in addition to the specification of general tolerances by note. The note form usually applies to all dimensions not specifically toleranced and is placed in or near the title block. The three systems are known as the unilateral, bilateral, and limit systems.

13.17.1 *Note form.* For dimensions which need not be held to close tolerances the variation permitted is frequently specified by a general note in the form illustrated by the following examples.

Unless otherwise specified tolerances are as follows:
Fractional dimensions $\pm\frac{1}{32}$
Decimals dimensions $\pm.01$
Angular dimensions $\pm0°\ 30'$
All diameters concentric within .001 FIR.

13.17.2 *Unilateral system.* In the unilateral system the tolerance is shown in one direction only, either plus or minus as illustrated in Fig. 13–10(*a*). It may also be expressed by giving the basic dimension and a plus or minus tolerance without indicating that the other is zero. This is shown in Fig. 13–10(*b*).

13.17.3 *Bilateral system.* In the bilateral system the tolerance is divided into two parts, thus permitting a variation on either side of the basic dimension. The tolerance is usually divided equally as shown in Fig. 13–11(*a*), but it is not mandatory that it should be. The tolerance of Fig. 13–11(*b*) is expressed in this manner. These deviations from the basic or design dimension are sometimes loosely called bilateral tolerances, but it should be noted that the tolerance is the total variation. Thus in Fig. 13–11(*a*) the tolerance is .002 and not .001. In no case may the two deviations be in the same direction, that is, both plus or both minus.

13.17.4 *Limit system.* In the limit system the extreme permissible dimensions are given on the drawing as shown in Fig. 13–12. Note that in this case the tolerance is the

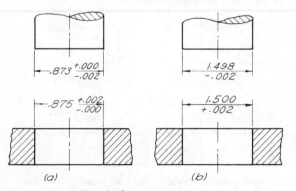

Fig. 13–10. Unilateral tolerance system.

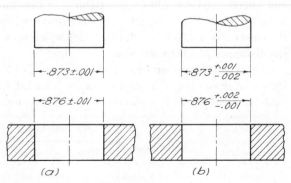

Fig. 13–11. Bilateral tolerance system.

difference between the limits. Two methods for placing limit dimensions on a drawing are approved in the American Standard.

1. *Maximum material method.* In this method the number giving the maximum material size is placed above the line, that is, the largest dimension for a shaft and the smallest for a hole. This system lends itself well where individual parts, perhaps only one, are produced and measured by the machinist. This method is shown in Fig. 13–13(*a*).

2. *Maximum number method.* This second method is more commonly used on mass production drawings, and in this scheme the largest number is always placed above the line as shown in Fig. 13–13(*b*). This is simpler for the draftsman and seems to be preferred by quality control departments. Both methods should not be used on the same drawing in any event.

13.18   Computing tolerance dimensions. *a. Basic hole method.* In this method the computed size of the hole is considered as the basic size, and the size of the shaft is determined by subtracting the allowance from the hole size, thus giving the design size for the shaft. Tolerances are then applied to each part.

Standard tolerances are obtained from ASA B4.1–1955 "Preferred Limits and Fits for Cylindrical Parts," or from similar company standards. For example, if the basic diameter of a hole is to be 3.000 inches and a class RC 7 fit is desired, the table shows the following data (limits are in thousandths of an inch):

Nominal size range, inches	Limits of clearance	Standard limits	
		Hole	Shaft
1.97–3.15	4.0 8.8	+3.0 0	−4.0 −5.8

For the hole the limits are 3.000 as the basic size and 3.000 + .003 = 3.003 as the upper limit.

For the shaft the limits are 3.0000 − .0040 = 2.9960 and 3.0000 − .0058 = 2.9942. The tightest fit therefore is 3.0000 − 2.9960 = .004, which is the allowance, and the loosest fits is 3.0030 − 2.9942 = .0088 which equals the allowance plus both tolerances.

As a second illustration let us consider a force fit FN3 for a 3″ diameter hole. The data below are from Table 5 ASA B4.1–1955. Limits are in thousandths of an inch.

Nominal size range, inches	Limits of interference	Standard limits	
		Hole	Shaft
2.56–3.15	1.8 3.7	+1.2 0	+3.7 +3.0

For the hole the limits are:

$$3.0000 + .0012 = 3.0012 \qquad \text{and}$$
$$3.0000 + .0000 = 3.0000$$

For the shaft the limits are:

$$3.0000 + .0037 = 3.0037 \qquad \text{and}$$
$$3.0000 + .0030 = 3.0030$$

Other types of fits are handled in the same manner. Although the tables in ASA B4.1–1955 do not specifically show allowance and tolerances as such, it may be noted that the upper figure in the shaft column for each size is the allowance and the difference between this figure, and the lower one is the shaft tolerance.

b. Basic shaft method. The tables in ASA B4.1–1955 are designed specifically for tolerances by the basic hole method, which is usually preferred unless there is a compelling reason for using the basic shaft system since this latter method results in non-standard shafts and holes.

The simplest way for computing the limits for the basic shaft method *in the case of clearance fits is to add the allowance* (upper figure in the shaft column) *to each of the limits obtained by the basic hole method.* Thus, using the same illustration as given for the basic hole method, add .0040

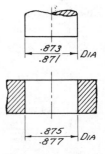

Fig. 13–12.   Limit tolerancing system.

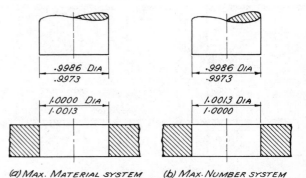

(*a*) MAX. MATERIAL SYSTEM   (*b*) MAX. NUMBER SYSTEM

Fig. 13–13.   Two methods of placing limit dimensions.

BASIC HOLE METHOD		BASIC SHAFT METHOD	
Hole	Shaft	Hole	Shaft
3.0000	2.9960	3.0040	3.0000
3.0030	2.9942	3.0070	2.9982

The limits of clearance will be the same in both cases. See Fig. 13–14(*b*).

For interference fits the allowance (upper number in the shaft column) *is subtracted from the basic hole limits.* Using the same illustration as before for an FN3 fit subtract .0037

BASIC HOLE METHOD		BASE SHAFT METHOD	
Hole	Shaft	Hole	Shaft
3.0000	3.0037	2.9963	3.0000
3.0012	3.0030	2.9975	2.9993

The loosest fit is −.0018 and the tightest fit is −.0037, which agrees with the data in the table under limits of interference.

13.19 Positional dimensioning. *a. Limited center dis-*

tances. The position of features of a part, such as holes, slots, bosses, and the like, may be located by giving limited center distances as discussed in this article or by true position dimensioning as discussed in Art. 13.20.

b. Rectangular coordinates. Holes, for example, may be located by giving limit dimensions to their centers from each of two planes at right angles to each other as shown in Fig. 13–15. This method results in a square tolerance zone for the location of centers as shown in Figs. 13–15(*b*). It will be noted in Fig. 13–16 that the tolerance along the diagonal of the square is 1.4 times the tolerance specified. This is not a desirable feature.

c. Polar coordinates. Location tolerances may also be specified in polar coordinate form by giving limits on the radial and angular dimensions as shown in Fig. 13–17(*a*). This results in a sector tolerance zone, as shown in Fig. 13–17(*b*).

d. Accumulation of tolerances. If chain dimensioning

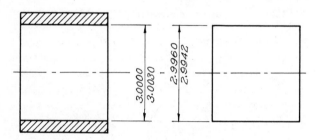

(a) BASIC HOLE METHOD

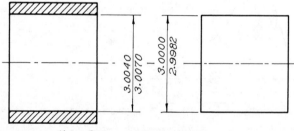

(b) BASIC SHAFT METHOD

Fig. 13–14. Basic hole and basic shaft methods of computing limits.

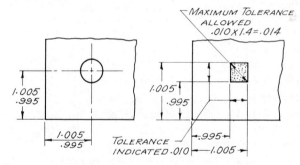

Fig. 13–16. Greater tolerance on the diagonal than specified. (Courtesy ASA.)

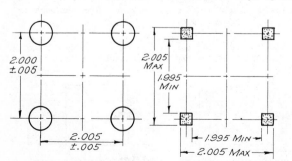

Fig. 13–15. Limited center distances give rectangular tolerance zones. (Courtesy ASA.)

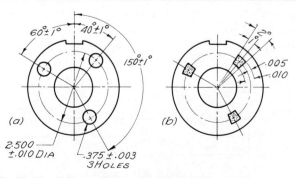

Fig. 13–17. Polar coordinates give sector tolerance zones. (Courtesy ASA.)

is used an undesirable accumulation of tolerances results as shown in Fig. 13–18. The tolerance between any two holes is not that specified on the drawing. Thus between *A* and *B* in Fig. 13–18 the variation in position could be from 1.95 inches to 2.05 inches.

e. Datum dimensioning. The accumulation of tolerances can be controlled by referring each location dimension to a datum surface as shown in Fig. 13–19. Note that now the tolerance between any two holes is the sum of the two tolerance zones, or 1.98 to 2.02.

f. Selection of a datum. Features which are selected to serve as datums must be clearly identified and easily recognizable. To be useful for measuring, a datum on an actual piece must be accessible during manufacture, so that measurements from it can be made readily. Also, corresponding features on mating parts must be used as datums to insure assembly and facilitate tool and fixture design.

g. Accuracy of datum surfaces on actual pieces. A datum surface on an actual piece must be more accu-

rate than any locations established by measuring distances from the datum. Thus, if measurements are made from a datum surface to establish hole locations with a tolerance of .010, the total effect of surface inaccuracies on the measurements must be less than .010, or the locations will not have the specified accuracy. It may be necessary to specify the accuracy of a datum surface by giving tolerances on features such as straightness, flatness, and roundness, to assure that locations can be established with the specified accuracy.

h. Location of surface finished first on a casting. Since most machined parts begin with a casting or a forging, it is necessary for the machinist to locate the first surface to be finished from some relatively rough surface on the original casting. This surface should therefore be located only once from some suitable unfinished surface. The finished surface thus established may be the datum for the location of other finished features. See Fig. 13–20.

13.20   True position dimensioning. In this system the

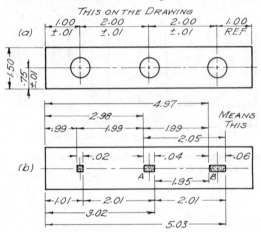

Fig. 13–18.   Cumulative tolerances.

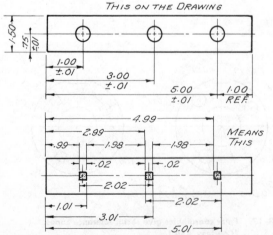

Fig. 13–19.   Datum dimensioning reduces cumulative tolerances.

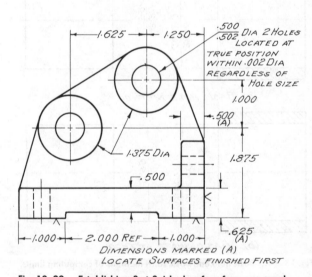

Fig. 13–20.   Establishing first finished surface from one rough surface only.

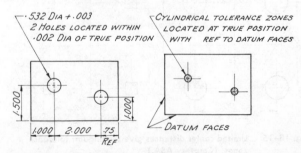

Fig. 13–21.   True position tolerance zones.

location of features is given by basic or untoleranced dimensions. These dimensions give the true position of the features, and the tolerance around these centers is given by a note along with the size of the feature as shown in Fig. 13–21. This method results in a circular tolerance zone as shown in the figure. This method has the following advantages over the method of limited center distances.

1. It corresponds to the distribution of errors which normally arise in production.

2. It corresponds to the control established by fixed position gages.

3. It permits the use of chain dimensioning without the accumulation of tolerances.

4. It makes possible the specification of different tolerances for each of a number of features lying on a common center line.

5. It makes it simpler to determine the clearance between mating components because equal deviation is permitted in all directions.

13.20.1   *Size of fixed position gage pins.* The size of the gage pin for circular holes is equal to the minimum size of the hole minus the diameter of the positional tolerance zone as can be seen from an examination of the extreme position of the holes as shown in Fig. 13–22. The size of the pin would also be the maximum size of a bolt that could be passed through matching holes, without clearance. Normally a small clearance would be allowed.

13.20.2   *Two methods of specifying true position tolerances.* As has been mentioned before, a tolerance is the total variation permitted; hence for location, the diameter of the tolerance zone is the total tolerance, and the note should be unmistakable in this respect.

1. Hence one method of specifying the true position tolerance is to give the diameter of the tolerance zone as shown in Fig. 13–23.

2. Because of long practice in some industries, the specification of the radius of the tolerance zone is also approved as shown in Fig. 13–24. The radius, however,

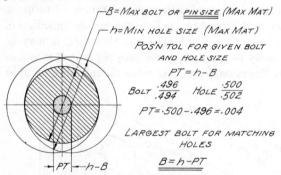

Fig. 13–22.   Maximum size of pin for gaging holes with given positional tolerance.

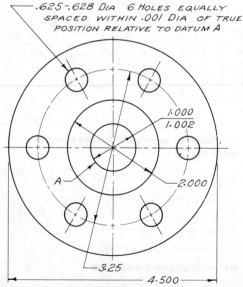

Fig. 13–23.   Specifying tolerance by diameter of zone.

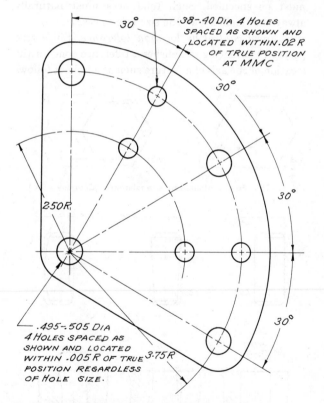

Fig. 13–24.   Specifying tolerance by radius of zone. (Courtesy ASA.)

must be recognized as a deviation from true position and the tolerance is twice the radius.

13.21   Form tolerances controlled by size and location tolerance. *a. Control by size tolerance.* In the past the geometric form of parts was assumed to be as shown by the drawing; that is to say, when two faces of a part are shown at right angles to each other on a drawing these faces were assumed to be made at right angles to each other in the shop. When there is any doubt that ordinary shop practice will produce this form, then it should be controlled in some way by a form tolerance. In many instances, the size tolerance given a part is sufficient to control the form. Thus in Fig. 13–25 the form implied by the drawing is a true hexagon and the size tolerance given will control the shape within the limits shown at (*b*) in the figure. In Fig. 13–26, straightness of a pin and hole is controlled by size tolerance only and illustrations of permissible departure from straightness are shown in parts *b, c, e,* and *f* of this figure. Where greater accuracy of form is required, form tolerances must be specified. Such tolerances must naturally always be smaller than the size tolerances.

b. Form control by location tolerance. Since true position tolerancing establishes a tolerance zone for the location of the axis of a feature such as a hole, it follows that the axis must lie within this tolerance zone throughout its length and thus location tolerance automatically controls squareness of the axis of the hole with the surface with which the drawing shows it to be perpendicular, as shown in Fig. 13–27. It will also control the parallelism of one hole with another.

13.22   Tolerancing of form. When closer control for form is required, the methods shown in this article may be used. In Figs. 13–28 through 13–42, the methods of specifying tolerances of form are shown with an accompanying illustration indicating the meaning or interpretation. The interpretation is never placed on a shop drawing.

13.22.1   *Straightness.* The method of specifying straightness is shown in Fig. 13–28(*a*). The meaning is shown at (*b*). The axis must lie within a cylindrical tolerance zone of the specified size, but usually the part will be gaged on the surface and must fit into a gage. If no other specification is given, the form tolerance must be held regardless of the size of the part.

In practice, applications of tolerances of form, as given on the drawing, apply to the surface regardless of length or area. For long parts, therefore, it may be necessary to specify the tolerance per unit of length or area. For example, on long tubes the tolerance could be

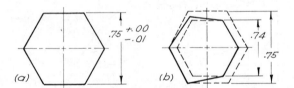

Fig. 13-25.   Form controlled by size tolerance. (Courtesy ASA.)

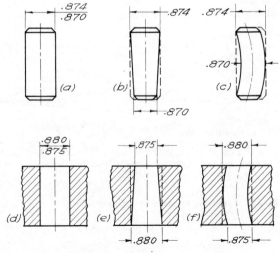

Fig. 13-26.   Straightness controlled by size tolerance. (Courtesy ASA.)

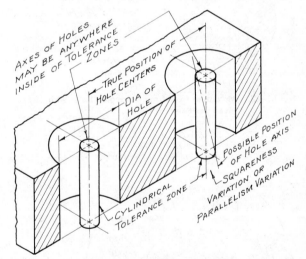

Fig. 13-27.   Form tolerance controlled by location tolerance. (Courtesy ASA.)

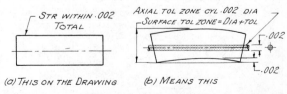

Fig. 13-28.   Method of specifying straightness.

specified as "Straight within .001 per ft." This would permit greater variation over the total length, if it is functionally permissible.

13.22.2 Flatness. The tolerance governing the flatness of a plane surface is the zone between two parallel planes at the specified distance apart. All bearing points of the surface must lie within this zone. The methods of specifying flatness are shown in Fig. 13–29. If applicable a note such as "must not be convex" or "must not be concave" may be added.

13.22.3 Parallelism. The methods for specifying parallelism are shown in Fig. 13–30. If the surface must not be concave, the notes must be expanded to cover this feature. The same is true if the surface is not to be convex. It should be noted that in this case as well as in others such as squareness the datum or reference surface is determined by the high points of contact of the surface.

13.22.4 Squareness. The method and meaning of specifying squareness of one surface with another are shown in Fig. 13–31. When size is also involved, as is usually the case, the squareness variation must lie within the size zone as shown in Fig. 13–32.

13.22.5 Perpendicularity. The methods of specifying perpendicularity are shown in Fig. 13–33. In the illus-

tration for the meaning of the specification, two schemes are shown, one applying to the imaginary axis and the other to the outside surface where gaging must take place.

13.22.6 Angularity. Two systems for specifying the tolerance on angles are in use. One system gives an angular zone of tolerance and the other a zone between two parallel planes. Both systems are shown in Fig. 13–34. The draftsman must be governed by the practice of his shop in his selection of the method to use.

Applications of angularity tolerance are shown in Fig. 13–35. Thus in Fig. 13–35(*a*) and (*b*) the gage

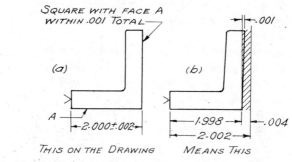

Fig. 13–32. Specifying size and squareness tolerance.

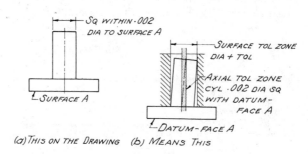

Fig. 13–33. Specifying perpendicularity.

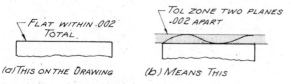

Fig. 13–29. Method of specifying flatness.

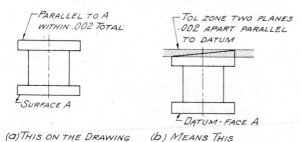

Fig. 13–30. Specifying parallelism.

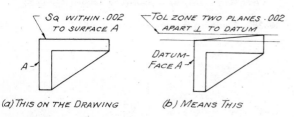

Fig. 13–31. Specifying squareness.

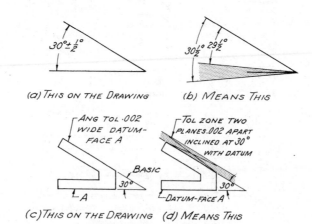

Fig. 13–34. Methods of specifying angularity.

diameter on the taper is not toleranced since to do so would give a cumulative tolerance. There are four possible dimensions which may be used to specify a taper. Any three may be employed, but the fourth can be given for reference only.

13.22.7 Concentricity. The tolerance governing the concentricity of axes is the diameter of the tolerance zone within which the axis must lie, as shown in Fig.

13–36. The zone for the outside surface where gaging must be done is also shown. It should be noted that the actual eccentricity of the axis will be just one-half of the diametral tolerance. The total indicator reading will likewise be just twice the eccentricity.

Figure 13–37 gives an illustration of concentricity specifications when two datum surfaces are involved. The datum axis is then the mean axis of the two parts involved.

13.22.8 Symmetry. Illustrations for the specifications for symmetry are shown in Fig. 13–38. The notes for symmetry as well as all notes for other conditions should state exactly what is meant. Thus, to say that the part is symmetrical within .001 would normally be interpreted to mean that it could vary by this amount on either side of the axis, thus making a tolerance zone .002 wide. Hence the correct specification should read "symmetrical with *A* within .003 total or within .002 wide zone."

13.22.9 Roundness. Roundness may be specified as shown in Fig. 13–39, using either the radius or the diameter in describing the tolerance zone. Gaging, how-

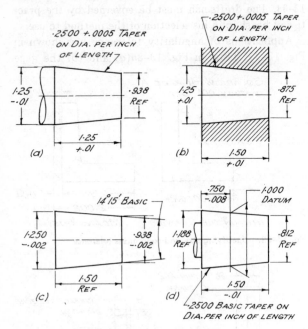

Fig. 13–35. Specification of taper tolerances.

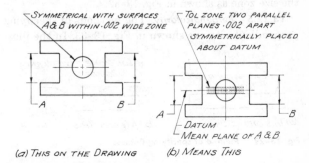

Fig. 13–38. Specifying symmetry.

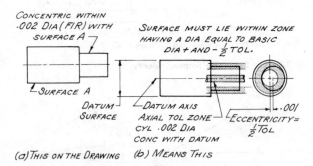

Fig. 13–36. Specifying concentricity.

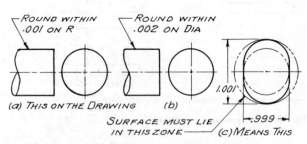

Fig. 13–39. Specifying roundness. (Courtesy ASA.)

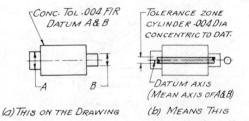

Fig. 13–37. Specifying concentricity with two data surfaces.

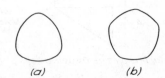

Fig. 13–40. Lobed shapes with constant diameters.

ever, cannot be done with a micrometer caliper since the lobed figures in Fig. 13–40 will measure the same as a true circle. Gaging should be done with three-point devices as shown in Fig. 13–41.

13.23 Application of the MMC principle to true position dimensioning. Since bolt and pin sizes are usually given limit dimensions and hole sizes must likewise be given certain limits in production, it follows that for interchangeable assembly the least favorable condition exists when both parts are at maximum material condition, that is, the bolt at its largest size and the hole at its smallest size.

When the functioning of a part does not prohibit it, a wider tolerance for acceptance of parts is available when the parts are not at maximum material condition. In such cases this should be specified by a general note on the drawing or by adding the phrase "at MMC" to the size and position specification of the part as shown in Fig. 13–42.

Thus, if a pin gage is to be used to gage the holes in the part shown, then the two conditions shown in Fig. 13–42 are possible. In Fig. 13–42(b), the holes are at

maximum material condition (minimum diameter) and the conditions of the drawing are fulfilled. In Fig. 13–42(c), with the holes at minimum material (maximum diameter) the part will still pass the acceptance gage although the tolerance zone for the centers has been increased. The phrase "at MMC" on the drawing indicates that this is acceptable.

When this additional tolerance is *not permissible,* the following phrase should be added to the drawing note "Regardless of feature or hole size" as shown in Fig. 13–20.

13.24 Application of MMC principle to form tolerancing. If the function of the part permits, additional tolerance is also available in form tolerancing as shown for straightness in Fig. 13–43 and for squareness in Fig. 13–44.

13.25 Symbols for form and true position tolerancing. In order to shorten the note for form and positional tolerancing, symbols for these items have been suggested. They are shown in Mil. Std. 8B and are used by the armed services but have not as yet been approved as American Standards. The symbols shown in Fig.

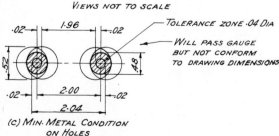

Fig. 13–41. Practical methods of checking roundness. (Courtesy British Standards Institution.)

(a) DRAWING

(b) MAX. METAL CONDITION ON HOLES

VIEWS NOT TO SCALE

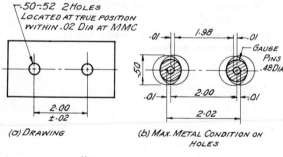

(c) MIN. METAL CONDITION ON HOLES

Fig. 13–42. Tolerance at maximum and minimum material condition.

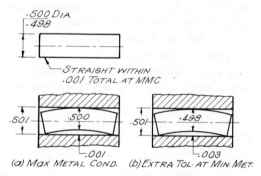

(a) Max METAL COND. (b) EXTRA TOL. AT MIN. MET.

Fig. 13–43. Extra tolerance made available by MMC specification.

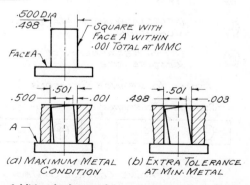

(a) MAXIMUM METAL CONDITION (b) EXTRA TOLERANCE AT MIN. METAL

Fig. 13–44. Additional tolerance for squareness made available by MMC specification.

13–45(a) are from Mil. Std. 8B.

The economy of time made possible is shown by comparison of the symbolic call-out and the note for the same information in Fig. 13–46. An application of the symbols to a drawing is shown in Fig. 13–47.

13.26   Surface finish. The engineer should understand clearly that the specification of surface finish is entirely distinct from specifying tolerances and limits. The finish of a surface determines its quality as to smoothness, surface marks, and the like, whereas tolerance refers to size and position only.

In certain applications the quality and degree of finish must be specified very clearly so that manufacturing processes may be determined and cost estimates prepared. Special operations must be employed to obtain very fine finishes, and consequently the cost increases rapidly as the finish is improved.

13.27   Finish marks and specifications. One of the oldest methods of indicating a finished surface on a drawing is by placing the letter *f* across the edgewise view of the surface to be finished. The *f* is made as shown in Fig. 13–48(*a*), and the correct method of placing it on the drawing, as well as several incorrect methods, is shown in Fig. 13–48(*b*). This symbol calls for an ordinary machine finish and makes no attempt to indicate the quality of the surface.

On some drawings this symbol is improved by adding a circle to the tail of the *f*, in which a number is placed,

as shown in Fig. 13–48(*c*). A note indicating the meaning of the number is placed on the drawing. By this means more specific information may be given concerning the character of the finish desired for that surface.

For some years the American Standards have recommended the *V* symbol for indicating finish. The simplest form of this symbol is constructed as shown in Fig. 13–48(*d*). Although not considered the best form, Fig. 13–48(*e*) shows one method of using the *V* symbol. The *V* is placed with its point touching the line which represents the edgewise view of the surface to be finished. The letters *R* and *G* mean "rough finish" and "grind." Other letters may be used to indicate certain operations or finishes.

The symbol for a finished surface should be placed wherever the surface shows edgewise as a visible or invisible line. This means that the symbol for finishing a single surface may be repeated in several views.

The more complete form of the *V* in which roughness, waviness, and lay are specified is shown in Fig. 13–48(*f*), (*g*), (*h*), and (*i*).

Roughness may be defined as the closely spaced surface irregularities produced by machining or grinding operations.

Waviness refers to the more widely spaced irregularities which may be produced by vibration, deflection of the part in machining, warping, or the release of strains in the material.

⌒   FLATNESS & STRAIGHTNESS

∠   ANGULARITY

⊥   PERPENDICULARITY OR SQUARENESS

‖   PARALLELISM

⊙   CONCENTRICITY

⊕   TRUE POSITION

○   ROUNDNESS

≡   SYMMETRY

Ⓜ   (MMC) MAXIMUM MATERIAL CONDITION

Ⓢ   (RFS) REGARDLESS OF FEATURE SIZE

FORM TOLERANCE SYMBOLS

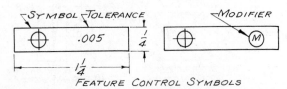

FEATURE CONTROL SYMBOLS

**Fig. 13–45.   Symbols for form and positional tolerance.
(Courtesy Mil Std 8B—1959.)**

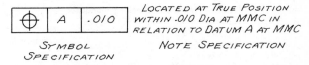

SYMBOL   NOTE SPECIFICATION
SPECIFICATION

Fig. 13–46.   Comparison of note and symbol type of tolerance specification.

Lay refers to the direction of the surface pattern of irregularities produced in the finishing of the surface.

The roughness height may be specified as the peak-to-valley height or as the average arithmetic deviation from the mean surface. Measurements are taken across the lay pattern. Roughness is specified in microinches (millionth of an inch). The values given in the tables below (from ASA B46.1—1955) are commonly used in roughness and waviness specifications.

Waviness specifications are given in inches. Roughness width, as contrasted to depth, is also specified in

inches, and this number appears after the lay symbol as shown in Fig. 13–48(*i*).

WAVINESS HEIGHT VALUES (INCHES) TO BE USED WITH SYMBOL

0.00002	0.00008	0.0003	0.001	0.005
0.00003	0.0001	0.0005	0.002	0.008
0.00005	0.0002	0.0008	0.003	0.010

In addition to roughness and waviness, it is sometimes necessary to specify the lay or the direction of the dominant lines of the surface. This is done by means of a set of symbols which may be placed to the right of the

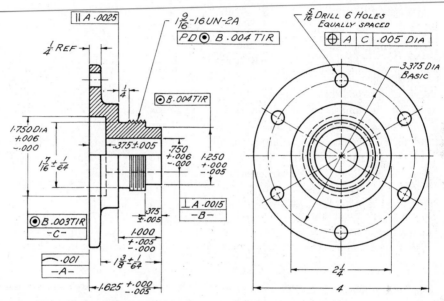

Fig. 13–47. Use of symbols for form and position tolerance specification. (Courtesy Mil Std 8B—1959.)

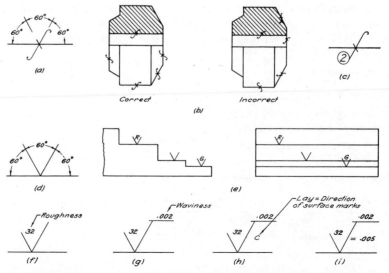

Fig. 13–48. Finish marks.

V as shown in Fig. 13–48(h). The meaning of these symbols is explained as follows:

$\sqrt{=}$ Lines to be parallel to the boundary line representing the surface on the drawing to which the symbol is attached.

$\sqrt{\perp}$ Perpendicular to the boundary line.

$\sqrt{x}$ Angular in both directions to the boundary line.

$\sqrt{M}$ Multidirectional.

$\sqrt{c}$ Approximately circular relative to the center of the surface indicated.

$\sqrt{R}$ Approximately radial relative to the center of the surface indicated.

The final addition to this symbol is the roughness width placed to the right of the lay symbol as shown in Fig. 13–49. The meaning of all these terms and a complete specification thereof are also shown in this figure.

This symbol may be used completely or any part may be used separately as occasion demands. It should be clearly understood that the specification of surface quality is not the same as specifying limits. In other words, a surface may be given both limit dimensions and surface quality specifications, as indicated in Fig. 13–50.

13.28   Checking a drawing. Before a drawing is released for production or construction it must be very carefully checked. Men selected to do this work must be thoroughly familiar with construction methods or shop processes as well as being absolute masters of the theory and practice of drafting.

It is good practice for the checker to have an established routine to follow in order that he may not overlook some phase of his work. The following checking routine slightly modified is used by a large manufacturing concern. Corrections are usually noted on a *print* of the drawing which is returned to the person who made the original drawing. This also makes it simpler for the checker to ascertain that all corrections have been made.

1. Does the general appearance of the drawing conform to the standard drafting practice?

2. Is the part sufficiently strong and suitable for the function it has to perform?

3. Can the weight be reduced without sacrificing strength or function?

4. Does the drawing represent the most economical method of manufacture?

5. Are all the necessary views and sections shown, and are they in proper relation to one another?

6. Are all necessary dimensions shown?

7. Do the dimensions agree with the layout and related parts, and are duplicate and unnecessary dimensions avoided?

8. Is the drawing to scale?

9. Is the drawing dimensioned to avoid unnecessary calculations in the shop?

10. Are stationary and operating clearances adequate?

11. Can the part or parts be assembled, disassembled, and serviced by the most economical methods?

12. Are proper limits or tolerances specified to produce the desired fits?

13. Have undesirable limit accumulations been avoided?

14. Are proper draft angles, fillets, and corner radii specified?

15. Are all necessary symbols for finishing, grinding, etc., shown?

16. Are locating points and proper finish allowances provided?

17. Are sufficient notes, including concentricity, parallelism, squareness, flatness, etc., shown?

18. Is the approximate developed length shown?

19. Is the stock size specified?

20. Are material and heat treatment specifications given?

21. Are plating and painting specifications, either for

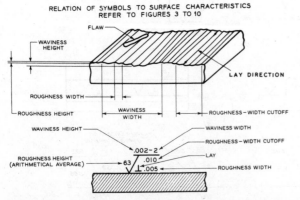

Fig. 13–49.   Meaning of surface finish specifications, roughness, waviness, and lay. (Courtesy ASA.)

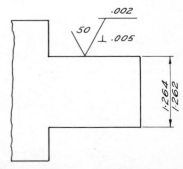

Fig. 13–50.   Application of limit dimensions and finish mark.

protective or decorative purposes, given?

22. Are company trade mark, part number, and manufacturer's identification shown according to divisional requirements?

23. Has the title block been filled in completely and is the information correct?

24. Are primary and secondary part numbers identical?

25. Are necessary part numbers of detail parts and subassemblies shown on assembly drawings?

26. Have original lines and drawing information damaged by erasures been properly restored?

27. Are revisions properly recorded?

28. Have all related drawings been revised to conform?

13.29 Simplified drafting. Because of the high costs of drafting and its effect on total production costs, industrial drafting rooms are making efforts to reduce these costs by simplifying their drafting practice as much as possible without sacrificing clarity of meaning.

The first consideration in making any drawing should

be the question. *Who will use the drawing?* With this question always in mind, the following list will suggest means of reducing drafting costs. Many of these are illustrated in this book.

1. Make freehand sketches of simple objects instead of instrumental drawings.

2. Take advantage of symmetry to reduce drawing time and drawing size.

3. Avoid the use of repetitive detail.

4. Omit unnecessary views and sections. Use partial views and sections where necessary for clarity.

5. Eliminate unnecessary use of letters and notes.

6. Use standard symbols wherever possible, for example, threads and welding symbols.

7. Eliminate inch marks—retain foot marks.

8. Omit drawing of standard bolts, nuts, and other hardware—list them.

9. Reduce hand lettering to a minimum.

10. Avoid ink drawings.

11. Use coordinate dimensioning where applicable.

PHYSICAL SPECIMENS OF SURFACE ROUGHNESS AND LAY

Type of surface	Roughness height (microinches)	Lay	Feed (inches)	Minimum roughness-width cutoff (inches)
Honed, lapped or polished	2	Parallel to long dimension of specimen	. . .	.030
	4		. . .	.030
	8		. . .	.030
Ground with periphery of wheel	4	Parallel to long dimension of specimen	. . .	.030
	8		. . .	.030
	16		. . .	.030
	32		. . .	.030
	63		. . .	.030
Ground with flat side of wheel	4	Angular in both directions	. . .	.030
	8		. . .	.030
	16		. . .	.030
	32		. . .	.030
	63		. . .	.030
Shaped or turned	32	Parallel to long dimension of specimen	0.002	.030
	63		0.005	.030
	125		0.010	.030
	250		0.020	.100
	500		0.030	.100
Side milled, end milled, or profiled	63	Circular	0.010	.030
	125		0.020	.100
	250	Angular in both directions	0.100	.300
	500		0.100	.300
Milled with periphery of cutter	63	Parallel to short dimension of specimen	0.050	.300
	125		0.075	.300
	250		0.125	1.000
	500		0.250	1.000

Extracted from American Standard Surface Roughness, Waviness and Lay, ASA B46.1—1955, with permission of the publisher, The American Society of Mechanical Engineers, 29 West 39th Street, New York 18, New York.

PROBLEMS

The illustrations for the problems of this chapter show the complete details of two subassemblies. In each case, the student is to make the necessary correct and complete shop drawings. *All required dimensions are shown on the pictorial drawings but not necessarily in the place or form in which they should appear on a working drawing.* The student must therefore exercise his judgment in applying the rules for dimensioning instead of copying the illustrations.

Where moving parts assemble together, a class RC7 fit should be used. The basic sizes are given in the illustrations, and the tolerances may be obtained from tables in the Appendix. Finished surfaces must be indicated, and all other information necessary for manufacturing, including part numbers, should be incorporated in the drawings.

The exploded views indicate the order of assembling the parts, and if time permits an assembly drawing with the assignment of part numbers should be made.

Where the material of the part is not indicated in the pictorial drawing, the part should be made of steel or cast iron as the shape and function of the part would indicate. Dimensions of rounded corners and fillets are left to the discretion of the student.

1. Make a complete set of details of all the parts of the governor shown in Figs. 13–51 to 13–60.

2. Make an assembly drawing of the governor detailed in Problem 1.

3. Make a complete set of details of the pump shown in Figs. 13–61 to 13–70.

4. Make an assembly drawing of the pump as detailed in Problem 3.

5. Make a complete set of details of any other simple assembly assigned by your instructor.

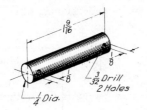

Fig. 13-51.   Weight pin.

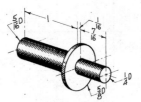

Fig. 13-52.   Pin.

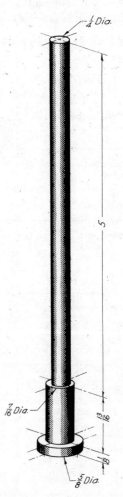

Fig. 13-53.   Plunger.

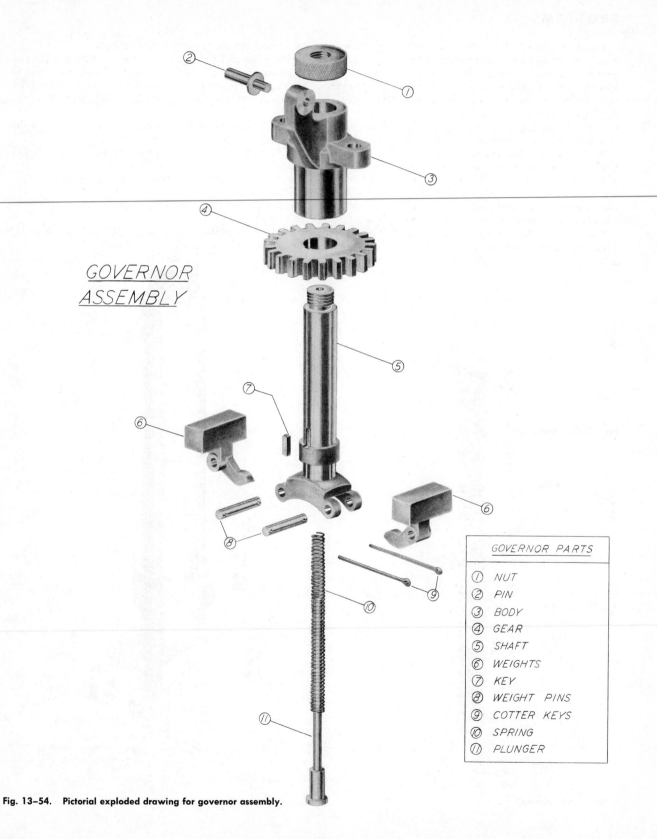

GOVERNOR
ASSEMBLY

GOVERNOR PARTS	
①	NUT
②	PIN
③	BODY
④	GEAR
⑤	SHAFT
⑥	WEIGHTS
⑦	KEY
⑧	WEIGHT PINS
⑨	COTTER KEYS
⑩	SPRING
⑪	PLUNGER

Fig. 13-54.   Pictorial exploded drawing for governor assembly.

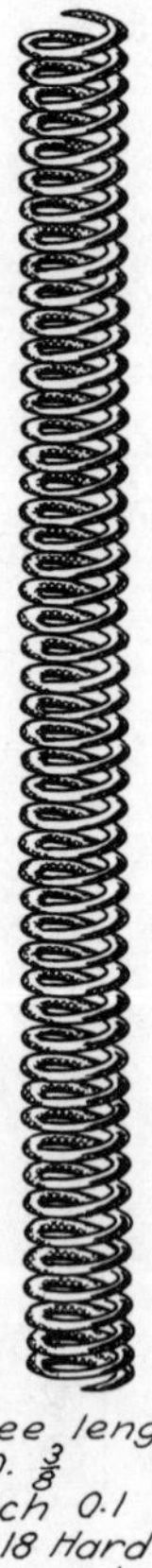
Free length 5 1/4
O.D. 3/8
Pitch 0.1
No. 18 Hard drawn spring steel wire.

Fig. 13–55. Spring.

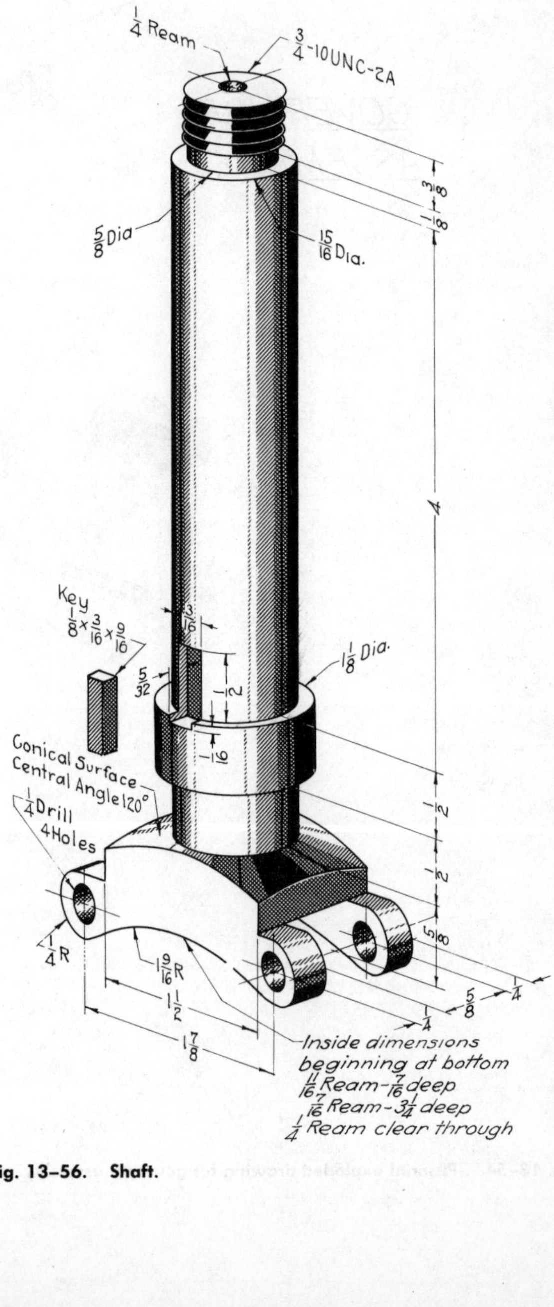
1/4 Ream
3/4-10UNC-2A
5/8 Dia
15/16 Dia.
3/8
1/8
4
Key 1/8 x 3/16 x 9/16
3/16
5/32
1/2
1/16
1 1/8 Dia.
Conical Surface Central Angle 120°
1/4 Drill 4 Holes
1/2
1/2
5/8
1/4 R
1 9/16 R
1 1/2
1 7/8
5/8
1/4
1/4
Inside dimensions beginning at bottom
11/16 Ream-7/16 deep
7/16 Ream-3 1/4 deep
1/4 Ream clear through

Fig. 13–56. Shaft.

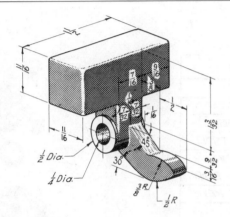

Fig. 13-57. Weight.

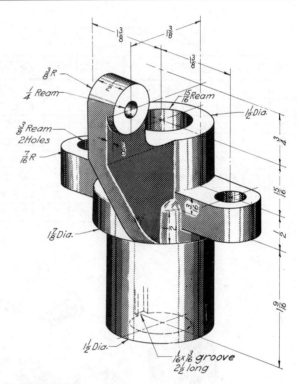

Fig. 13-59. Body.

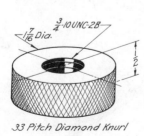

33 Pitch Diamond Knurl

Fig. 13-58. Nut.

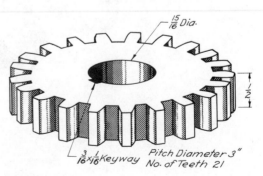

Pitch Diameter 3″
No. of Teeth 21

Fig. 13-60. Gear.

WATER PUMP

NO.	REQ.	DESCRIPTION	NO.	REQ.	DESCRIPTION
1	4	$\frac{15}{8}$"×1" HEX-HEAD BOLTS	9	1	PUNGER BOLT
2	1	OUTLET FLANGE	10	1	ECCENTRIC STRAP
3	2	STEEL BALLS	11	1	ECCENTRIC (INSIDE)
4	1	PUMP BODY	12	1	ECCENTRIC (OUTSIDE)
5	1	PACKING RING	13	1	FLAT HEAD SCREW
6	1	PUMP PACKING GLAND	14	1	CAMSHAFT REAR BEARING
7	1	PUMP PLUNGER	15	2	NO. 9 WOODRUFF KEYS
8	1	COTTER PIN	16	1	INTAKE FLANGE

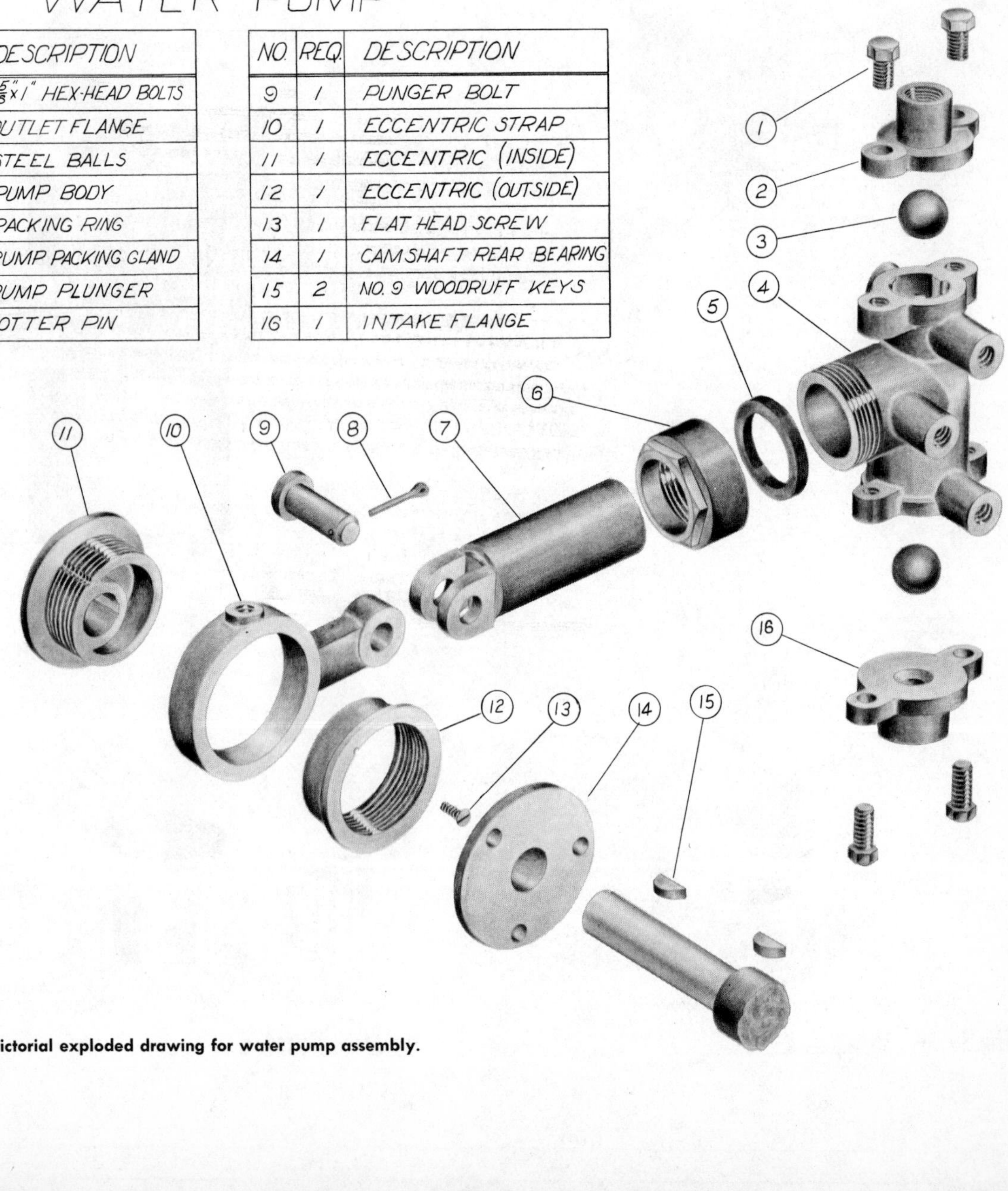

Fig. 13-61. Pictorial exploded drawing for water pump assembly.

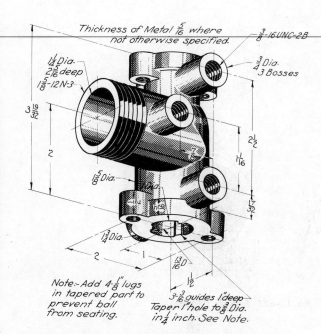

Thickness of Metal $\frac{5}{16}$ where not otherwise specified.

$\frac{3}{8}$-16UNC-2B

$\frac{1}{4}$ Dia. $2\frac{5}{16}$ deep

$1\frac{5}{8}$-12N-3

$\frac{3}{4}$ Dia. 3 Bosses

$3\frac{19}{32}$

2

$2\frac{1}{2}$

$1\frac{1}{16}$

$\frac{5}{16}$ Dia.

$1\frac{7}{32}$

$1\frac{3}{4}$ Dia.

2

1

$\frac{13}{16}$ D

$\frac{1}{2}$

Note:- Add 4-$\frac{1}{8}$" lugs in tapered part to prevent ball from seating.

$3-\frac{3}{16}$ guides 1"deep Taper 1" hole to $\frac{3}{8}$ Dia. in $\frac{1}{4}$ inch. See Note.

Fig. 13-62.   Pump body, two views showing front and rear.

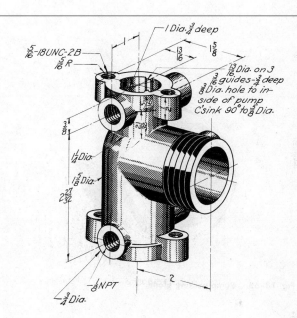

$\frac{5}{16}$-18UNC-2B

$\frac{5}{16}$ R

1 Dia. $\frac{3}{4}$ deep

$1\frac{3}{16}$

$1\frac{5}{8}$

$\frac{13}{16}$ Dia. on 3 guides-$\frac{3}{4}$ deep $\frac{3}{8}$ Dia. hole to inside of pump C'sink 90° to $\frac{5}{8}$ Dia.

$\frac{3}{8}$

$1\frac{1}{4}$ Dia.

$1\frac{5}{8}$ Dia.

$2\frac{27}{32}$

$\frac{1}{8}$ NPT

2

$\frac{3}{4}$ Dia.

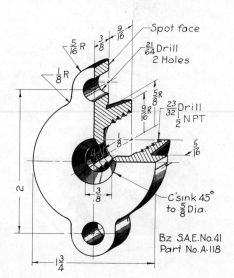

$\frac{5}{16}$ R

$\frac{3}{8}$

$\frac{9}{16}$

Spot face

$\frac{21}{64}$ Drill 2 Holes

$\frac{1}{8}$ R

$\frac{5}{8}$ R

$\frac{9}{16}$ R

$\frac{23}{32}$ Drill $\frac{1}{2}$ NPT

$\frac{3}{8}$

$\frac{5}{16}$

2

$\frac{3}{8}$

C'sink 45° to $\frac{5}{8}$ Dia.

Bz S.A.E. No. 41 Part No. A-118

$1\frac{3}{4}$

Fig. 13-63.   Intake flange.

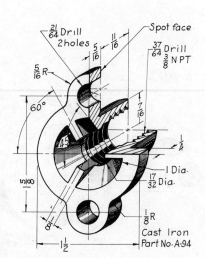

$\frac{21}{64}$ Drill 2 holes

$\frac{5}{16}$

$\frac{11}{16}$

Spot face

$\frac{37}{64}$ Drill $\frac{3}{8}$ NPT

$\frac{5}{16}$ R

60°

45

$7\frac{1}{16}$

$\frac{1}{4}$

1 Dia.

$\frac{17}{32}$ Dia.

$\frac{3}{8}$

$\frac{1}{8}$ R

$1\frac{1}{2}$

$\frac{5}{8}$

Cast Iron Part No. A-94

Fig. 13-64.   Outlet flange.

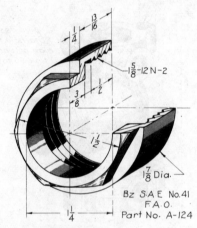

Fig. 13-65.   Pump packing gland.

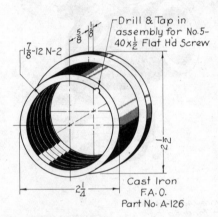

Fig. 13-67.   Eccentric (outside).

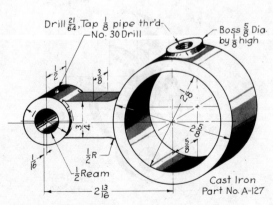

Fig. 13-66.   Eccentric strap.

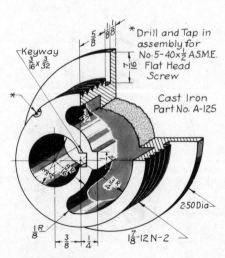

Fig. 13-68.   Eccentric (inside).

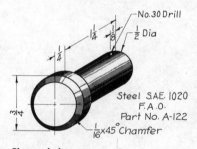

No. 30 Drill

$\frac{1}{4}$ $\frac{1}{8}$ $\frac{1}{2}$ Dia

$\frac{1}{4}$

$\frac{3}{4}$

Steel S.A.E. 1020
F.A.O.
Part No. A-122

$\frac{1}{16}$x45° Chamfer

Fig. 13-69.   Plunger bolt.

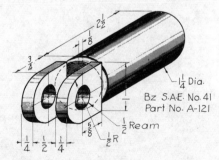

$2\frac{1}{2}$

$\frac{1}{8}$

$\frac{3}{4}$

$1\frac{1}{4}$ Dia.

Bz S.A.E. No. 41
Part No. A-121

$\frac{1}{2}$ Ream

$\frac{5}{8}$ $\frac{1}{2}$ R

$\frac{1}{4}$ $\frac{1}{2}$ $\frac{1}{4}$

Fig. 13-70.   Pump plunger.

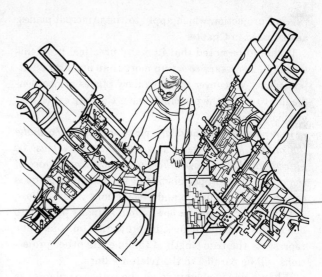

14

Auxiliary Projections

14.1 Need for auxiliary views. On many objects there are lines which do not show in true length and faces which do not show in true size in any of the three principal views. In manufacturing and construction it is also necessary in many cases to know the true value of the angle between lines and between plane faces. When these values do not appear in the three principal views it is necessary to set up additional planes of projection and make views which will give the necessary information. These additional planes are called auxiliary planes.

14.2 Notation of auxiliary planes and views. Since the *H*-, *V*-, and *P*-planes are designated by their initial letters the first auxiliary plane will be numbered *1*, and the second *2*, and so on. The reference lines are marked with the letters or numbers of the planes whose intersection they represent. Thus for an auxiliary plane set up perpendicular to the *H*-plane the reference line is marked *H-1*, for one perpendicular to *V* it is marked *V-1*, and so on, as shown in Fig. 14–1 and those that follow. The projections of points on auxiliary planes are given superscripts corresponding to the number of the plane on which the projection lies. An examination of the figures in this chapter will make clear the system of marking.

14.3 Relation of auxiliary planes to the principal planes. *The first auxiliary plane used in any problem must always be set up perpendicular to one of the principal planes.* The second auxiliary plane must be perpendicular to the first auxiliary plane, as shown in Fig. 14–2. This arrangement makes it possible to follow all the

◄ Machine automatically drills entire oil system in automobile crankshaft in one continuous operation (Ford Motor Company).

rules of projection which apply to the principal planes, as discussed in Chapter 7.

It should be noted that in many practical problems it may be necessary to set up more than one first auxiliary plane. Whenever such auxiliary planes are perpendicular to one of the principal planes they are called first auxiliary planes.

14.4   Relation of auxiliary plane to object. *To make the auxiliary plane serve a useful purpose it must be placed parallel or perpendicular to some line or face of the object.* The proper placing of the auxiliary plane is shown in the discussion and illustrations which follow.

14.5   True length of a line. When a line is parallel to one of the principal planes, its projection on that plane represents the true length of the line. Its other projections will be parallel to the reference lines.

When a line is oblique to all the principal planes, as line *AB* in Fig. 14–3, none of its projections show in true length and none are parallel to the reference lines. *To get*

the true length, an auxiliary plane is placed parallel to the line and its projection on that plane shows the true length of the line. In Fig. 14–3, the position of the auxiliary plane is shown by the reference line *V-1,* which is an edgewise view of the auxiliary plane when viewed from the front. The steps in making this auxiliary view in Fig. 14–3(*b*) are as follows:

1. At any convenient place draw the reference line *V-1* parallel to the projection $a^v b^v$ of the line, and draw perpendiculars to it, of random length, from $a^v b^v$.

2. Measure the distance from a^H to the reference line *V-H,* and set this distance off from *V-1* on the perpendicular from a^v, thus locating a^1. Follow the same procedure to locate b^1.

This construction follows the fact that both the top view and the auxiliary view show the distance of the line *AB* behind the vertical plane.

14.6   Auxiliary plane perpendicular to the H-plane. For a clearer understanding of the method of finding the

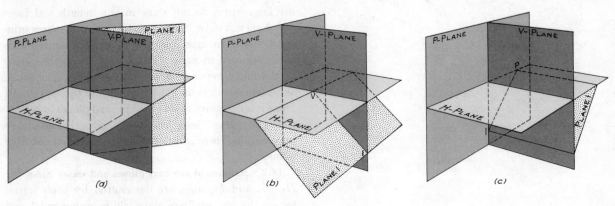

Fig. 14–1.   Position of first auxiliary plane.

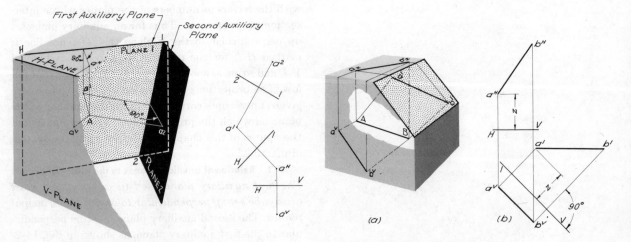

Fig. 14–2.   Position of second auxiliary plane.

Fig. 14–3.   True length of an inclined line.

auxiliary projection, a second problem is illustrated in Fig. 14–4. This pyramid stands in such position that the lines *AB* and *AD* do not show in true length on either the *H*-, *V*-, or *P*-planes. To show the true length of these lines, plane *1* has been placed parallel to the lines and perpendicular to the horizontal plane. In this position the *H-1* reference line is parallel to $a^H b^H$ and $a^H d^H$. The auxiliary projection of the lines, marked $a^1 b^1$ and $a^1 d^1$, has been obtained by drawing projection lines perpendicular to the auxiliary plane. One important fact to be obtained from Fig. 14–4(*a*) is that the distance of the pyramid below the horizontal plane and its vertical height are shown in both the vertical and auxiliary projections. Note that a^V and a^1 are at the same distance below the horizontal plane and that this distance can be measured from the projection to the corresponding horizontal reference line, as a^1 to *H-1* marked *y*. The same thing is true for any point on the pyramid.

In making these projections it is not necessary to think of the rotation of the planes of projection shown in the pictorial views. The engineer thinks of the views simply as the projection or appearance of the object when seen from various points of view. The rotation of planes in Figs. 14–4, 14–5, and 14–6 have been included to demonstrate the correctness of the views and their relationship to each other from a geometrical standpoint. These relationships must always be maintained in engineering drawing.

14.7   True shape of a plane face. Auxiliary plane perpendicular to the V-plane. None of the faces of the pyramid in Fig. 14–5, except the base, is shown in true shape since none is parallel to any of the principal planes of projection. The faces *ABE* and *ACD,* however, appear edgewise in the front view; hence it will be possible to set an auxiliary plane *1* parallel to each of them in turn, project the faces upon these planes, and thus get their true shape. An auxiliary plane parallel to face *ACD* and perpendicular to the vertical plane has been set up in

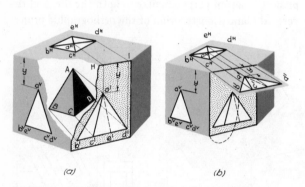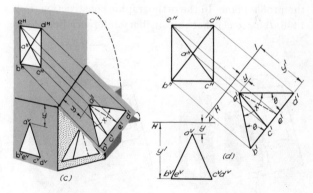

Fig. 14–4.   True length of line and angle between lines.

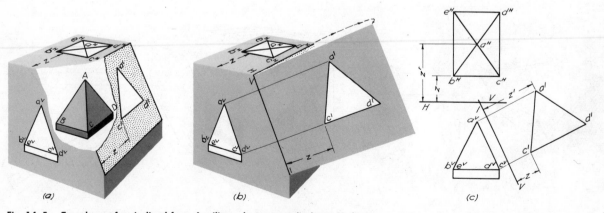

Fig. 14–5.   True shape of an inclined face. Auxiliary plane perpendicular to V-plane.

Fig. 14–5. The pictorial representation in Fig. 14–5(a) shows the projection of face ACD on this auxiliary plane. Since the projecting lines are always perpendicular to this plane, the projections of line CD on both the horizontal plane and on the auxiliary plane will show true length and the distance from any point on the object to the vertical plane will also show in both projections. Such distances may therefore be transferred from the top view to the auxiliary view or vice versa. This figure, parts (b) and (c), also shows that the V-1 reference line is parallel to the edgewise view, $a^v c^v d^v$, of the face and that the projection lines connecting the vertical and auxiliary projections are perpendicular to the V-1 reference line. The orthographic construction necessary for finding the true size of this face is shown completely in Fig. 14–5(c).

14.8 Auxiliary plane perpendicular to the P-plane. To find the true size of face ABCD of the object shown in Fig. 14–6(a), the auxiliary plane must be set up parallel to the edgewise view of the face and perpendicular to the profile plane. In the orthographic construction, Fig. 14–6(d), note (1) that the auxiliary reference line P-1 is

parallel to the edgewise view, $a^p b^p c^p d^p$, of the face; (2) that the projection lines joining the profile and auxiliary projections are perpendicular to the P-1 reference line; and (3) that the distance x from the P-1 reference line to the auxiliary projection of any point is the distance from the point in space to the profile plane. That distance is measured from the horizontal or vertical projection to the vertical reference line.

14.9 Auxiliary plane perpendicular to the axis of a hole. In many problems involving angles between planes, true size of oblique planes, right sections of objects, clearances, and the like, it is necessary to find the endwise view of a line or axis. This is done by setting up an auxiliary plane perpendicular to the line and projecting the necessary parts on that plane.

When the line is parallel to one of the principal planes, the auxiliary plane may be set up at once, perpendicular to both the line and the coordinate plane to which the line is parallel. Thus, in Fig. 14–7(a), the line AB is parallel to the vertical plane, and so the auxiliary plane 1 is set up perpendicular to both the line and the vertical plane. Construction of the orthographic projec-

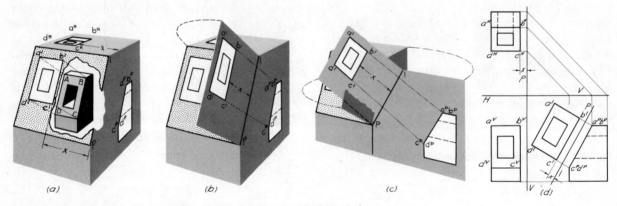

Fig. 14–6. True shape of an inclined face. Auxiliary plane perpendicular to P-plane.

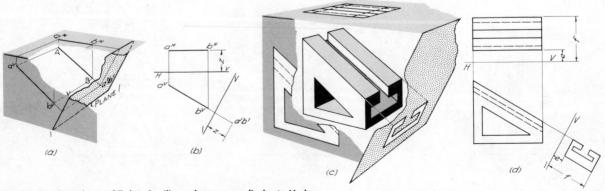

Fig. 14–7. True shape of T-slot. Auxiliary plane perpendicular to V-plane.

tion, Fig. 14–7(*b*), requires the following procedure:

a. Draw the *V-1* reference line perpendicular to $a^v b^v$.

b. Draw projection lines from a^V and b^V, perpendicular to *V-1*.

c. Measure distance *z* from the horizontal projection to the horizontal reference line.

d. Lay out this distance *z* on the projection line drawn perpendicular to *V-1*.

e. Mark this projection $a^1 b^1$. This is the point projection of the line on the plane perpendicular to the line.

An object in which a T-slot has been cut is shown in Fig. 14–7(*c*), and, in order to show the true size of the slot, a plane has been set up perpendicular to the slot. The orthographic projection in Fig. 14–7(*d*) shows the construction necessary for finding the true size of the slot.

When the line is not parallel to one of the principal planes, the solution involves the use of a second auxiliary plane, which is discussed in Art. 14.14.

14.10   Elimination of the reference lines between views. In all the foregoing discussion the planes of projection have been used as reference planes from which measurements were made in constructing the various views. This requires the use of reference lines between views which frequently causes the views to be spaced unnecessarily far apart. In order to avoid this difficulty, planes of symmetry in the object or plane faces of the object may be used as planes of reference. The only condition to be met is that these planes shall be parallel to the coordinate planes that would have been used had reference

lines been drawn. Their representations on the drawing are straight lines parallel to the omitted reference lines of the planes of projection. Figure 14–8(*a*) shows a drawing in which the auxiliary view has been drawn with the use of reference lines, in the usual way. Projecting lines are perpendicular to the reference lines, and measurements are made and laid off from the reference lines. In Fig. 14–8(*b*), the front vertical face of the block has been used as a reference plane. The auxiliary view of this face has been drawn parallel to the edgewise view of the inclined face and at a convenient distance from it. Note that the projection lines for the auxiliary view are perpendicular to the edgewise view and that distances are measured and laid out from the chosen reference face. It is frequently more convenient to use the center line of a symmetrical object as a reference plane. In this event the auxiliary view of the center line is placed parallel to and at a convenient distance from the edgewise view, as shown in Fig. 14–8(*c*). Distances may then be measured and laid out on both sides of the center line, while projection lines are still perpendicular to the edgewise view. The use of center lines is particularly convenient when circles are to be projected, since the projections of four or more points may be located with one setting of the dividers.

14.11   Use of auxiliary views for construction of principal views. The auxiliary view may be used to advantage when the shape of the face in the auxiliary view is known and it is necessary to draw one or more of the principal views, as, for example, the side and front views

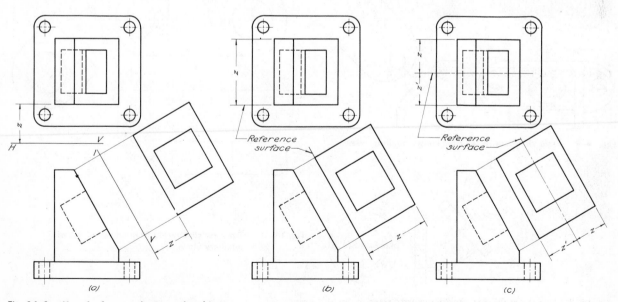

Fig. 14–8.   **Use of reference planes on the object.**

of the object shown in Fig. 14–9. If the dimensions are known it is comparatively easy to draw the side or profile view and the true-size auxiliary view of the inclined face. Note that only one-half of the auxiliary view need be drawn since the object is symmetrical. After the side and auxiliary views have been drawn from known dimensions, the front view can be constructed by projecting back a series of points as illustrated for points *A* and *B*. The following procedures may be used:

1. Choose any points on the upper and lower circles in the auxiliary view, such as a^1 and b^1.

2. From $a^1 b^1$, draw projecting lines perpendicular to the edgewise view of the inclined face in the side view.

3. Mark the positions of a^P and b^P at the place where the perpendiculars cross the edgewise views of the top and bottom faces of the lug.

4. From the positions of a^P and b^P, draw horizontal projecting lines to the front view.

5. Measure the distance x from the center line to a^1 in the auxiliary projection.

6. Lay off the distance x on each of the horizontal projecting lines (drawn in step 4), on both sides of the center line in the front view, to locate the various positions of a^V and b^V.

7. Repeat the process for as many points on the circle as desired.

8. Connect the points in the front view to form the ellipses.

When reference lines are used it is sometimes con-venient to project the points back directly, as illustrated in Fig. 14–10, to avoid the necessity of measuring any distance. This construction may be completed in the following steps.

1. From the point of intersection of the horizontal reference line with the auxiliary reference line, erect a new line to bisect the angle between the two lines.

2. Select points on the auxiliary view, as, for example, a^1 and b^1, and draw a line through the auxiliary view parallel to the *V-1* reference line.

3. From the point where this line intersects the bi-sector, draw a horizontal line.

4. From the projection a^1, draw projecting lines perpendicular to *V-1* to locate projects, $a^V b^V$, etc., on the top and bottom faces of the angle.

5. From projections a^V and b^V, draw vertical projecting lines to locate projections a^H and b^H, on the horizontal line drawn in step 3.

6. Repeat the process to get as many points as desired, and connect them with a smooth curve to complete the horizontal projection.

14.12   Partial views. Objects such as that shown in Fig. 14–11 would be rather difficult to draw if two complete projections were to be made. For this reason it is common practice to show one complete view and two partial views, one of which is an auxiliary. This simplifies the drawing and at the same time makes it easier to read. Since the object is symmetrical, only one-half

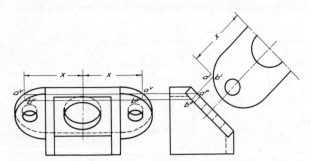

Fig. 14–9.   Front view constructed from known auxiliary view.

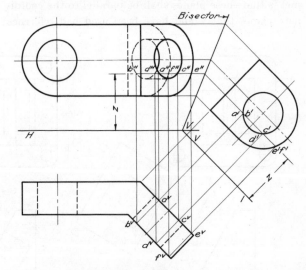

Fig. 14–10.   Top view constructed from known shape of auxiliary view.

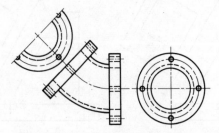

Fig. 14–11.   Partial auxiliary view.

of the auxiliary view is drawn. If the space were limited, the side view could have been drawn as a half view also.

14.13   Procedure in laying out a drawing having one auxiliary view. For speed and efficiency in his work, the draftsman should develop a regular procedure for laying out a drawing. Figure 14–12 gives a step-by-step layout that may be used or may be varied to suit conditions. The object to be drawn is shown pictorially in Fig. 14–12(*a*). The various steps and the order in which they should be taken are listed below with reference to Fig. 14–12.

In Fig. *14–12(b)* the following steps are taken.

1. Draw the front view.

2. Draw the auxiliary projection lines perpendicular to the edgewise view of the inclined face.

3. Locate and outline the top view so that the desired clearance between the top and auxiliary views will be maintained.

Figure 14–12(c) reveals the next two steps.

1. Draw the horizontal center line in the top view.

2. Locate this same center line in the auxiliary view so that the desired spacing between front and auxiliary views will be maintained.

Figure 14–12(d) shows additional construction as follows.

1. Transfer distance *a* with the dividers from the top view to the auxiliary view.

2. Outline the auxiliary view of the inclined face.

Figure 14–12(e) shows the auxiliary view completed in three steps.

1. Locate the center of the circle in the auxiliary view.

2. Draw the circle.

3. Divide the circle into eight (or more) equal parts.

Figure 14–12(f). In this figure the first steps for the completion of front and top views are made.

1. Project the *3–7* center line back to the front view and from there to the top view.

2. Project points *1* and *5*, which are on the original center line, back to the front view and from there to the top view.

Figure 14–12(g). The work of projection is completed in this figure.

1. Project all points from the circle to the edgewise view of the inclined face in the front view.

2. Project those points from the front view to the top view.

3. Transfer distances *b* and *c* from the auxiliary view to the top view on the proper projection line.

Figure 14–12(h) shows the necessary steps for finishing the drawing.

1. Connect the points with a smooth curve showing the proper visibility.

2. Clean up the drawing.

3. Work over the lines to give them the proper weight and character.

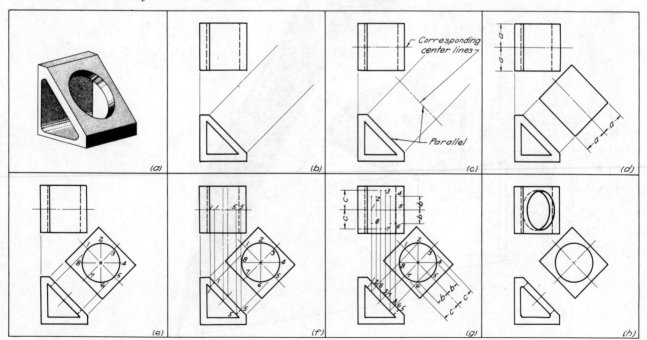

Fig. 14–12.   Constructing the views of an object with the aid of an auxiliary view.

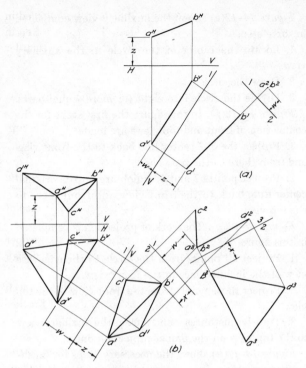

(a)

(b)

Fig. 14-13. Endwise view of a line and angle between planes. Double auxiliary.

14.14 Second auxiliary plane. Perpendicular to an oblique line. When the line is oblique to the principal planes, two auxiliary planes are required. *The first is set up parallel to the line to get the true length as explained in Art. 14.5. The second auxiliary plane is placed perpendicular to the line and to the first auxiliary plane.* The following steps involved in this problem are illustrated in Fig. 14–13(*a*) for a single line.

a. Place *V-1* reference line parallel to $a^V b^V$.

b. Draw projecting lines from a^V and b^V perpendicular to *V-1*.

c. Measure distances from a^H and b^H to the horizontal reference line, and lay them off on the projecting lines, perpendicular to *V-1*, to obtain a^1 and b^1.

d. Place *1–2* reference line perpendicular to $a^1 b^1$.

e. Draw projecting lines from a^1 and b^1 perpendicular to *1–2*.

f. Measure distance *w* from a^V and b^V to *V-1*, and lay it off on the projecting line perpendicular to *1–2* to obtain $a^2 b^2$. This is a point projection which proves that plane *2* is perpendicular to *AB*.

In Fig. 14–13(*b*), the line *AB* is the line of intersection of two plane surfaces *ABC* and *ABD*. By carrying

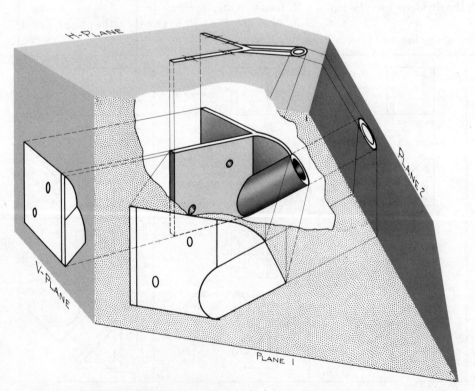

Fig. 14-14. Pictorial drawing of auxiliary planes.

the two additional points C and D to the second auxiliary plane, the edgewise view of each plane is obtained and consequently the true size of the angle between the planes is shown.

As soon as any edgewise view of a plane has been obtained, an additional auxiliary plane may be placed parallel to the plane as shown by plane 3 in Fig. 14–13(b). The projection of ABD on this third auxiliary plane shows the true size of that plane as indicated at $a^3b^3c^3$. The distance that must be laid out to obtain this view is shown for point b, as distance x.

14.15 Procedure in laying out a drawing having two auxiliary views. In theory the procedure is an extension of that used for a single auxiliary plane, but in practice a few difficulties may be encountered that can be cleared up with a step-by-step analysis. The object chosen for this illustration is shown pictorially in Fig. 14–14. Note that the first auxiliary plane 1 is perpendicular to the horizontal plane and parallel to the cylinder, whereas the second auxiliary plane 2 is perpendicular to plane 1 and to the axis of the cylinder, a situation exactly similar to that in Fig. 14–13.

The following step-by-step analysis, illustrated in Fig. 14–15, gives a procedure that may be followed in laying out a drawing of this kind. The steps taken in each part of the figure have been listed in proper order following the figure number.

Figure 14–15(a).

1. Make top and front views of the main body of the casting.

2. Lay out the center line and edge lines of the supporting web in the top view at the proper angle.

Figure 14–15(b).

1. Place auxiliary reference line H-1 parallel to the top view of the web.

2. Draw auxiliary projection of the nearest face of the bracket.

3. Draw center line of the cylinder at the proper angle and at the proper height according to design specifications.

4. Complete the first auxiliary projection of the web by drawing the arc tangent to the surface of the bracket and to the end face of the cylinder.

Figure 14–15(c).

1. Locate the center line, marked x^2, parallel to the edgewise view of the end of the cylinder or perpendicu-

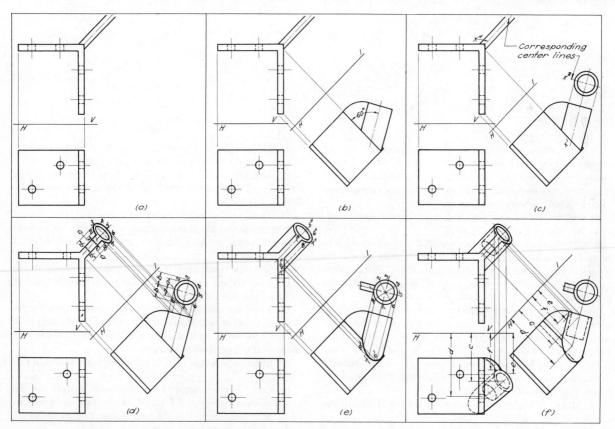

Fig. 14–15. Steps in making complete views of object with the aid of two auxiliary views.

lar to the axis of the cylinder and at a convenient distance from the cylinder. (Note that this is the same center line as the one, marked x^H, in the top view.)

2. Extend the center line of the cylinder to form the other center line for the second auxiliary projection.

3. Draw the circles representing the end view of the cylinder.

Figure 14–15(d).

1. Divide the circles into eight (or more) equal parts.

2. Project these points to the edgewise view of the end of the cylinder in the first auxiliary projection.

3. Project the points from the first auxiliary projection perpendicular to the *H-1* reference line.

4. Measure with dividers the distances marked *a* and *b* in the second auxiliary projection, and lay them out as indicated in the top view.

5. Connect the points with a smooth curve.

Figure 14–15(e).

1. Lay out a portion of the web in the second auxiliary projection.

2. Project the intersection of the web and cylinder from the second auxiliary projection to the first auxiliary projection.

3. Draw elements of the cylinder such as *6*, *7*, and *8* in the top view.

4. Find the points 6^H, 7^H, and 8^H where these elements cut the face of the bracket in the top view.

5. Project these points back to the first auxiliary projection to obtain 6^1, 7^1, and 8^1, etc.

6. Connect these points to form the intersection of the cylinder with the side face of the bracket.

Figure 14–15(f).

1. Project points from the top view of the end of the cylinder vertically to the front view.

2. Measure distances such as *e* and *f* in the auxiliary view, and lay them out as indicated in the front view.

3. Connect these points to form the ellipses representing the end of the cylinder.

4. Locate points on the front view of the web in a similar manner.

5. Locate the intersection of the cylinder with the back face of the bracket and any other necessary lines.

6. Determine the visibility of all lines.

Finally clear up the drawing and erase all construction lines, and then work over all lines, giving them proper weight and character.

PROBLEMS

In the problems of this chapter, it is recommended that the student first make a freehand sketch of the views he plans to make, first, in order that the solution comes within the limits of his drawing paper, and, second, so that the views are planned to make a well-balanced working drawing.

In the interest of drawing for simplification and clarity rounded corners have been omitted.

In each drawing, use the scale specified if the drawing is to be made on an 8½ × 11 inch sheet. Room must be allowed for dimensioning between views and around them. Problems are to be dimensioned, however, only if so specified by the instructor.

1 to 11. Make the orthographic projections including necessary auxiliary views to fully describe the shape of the object assigned from the following figures: 14–16; 14–17; 14–19; 14–20; 14–21; 14–22; 14–23; 14–24; 14–26; 14–27; and 14–30. All views must be planned and drawn so that they may be adequately dimensioned as a shop drawing. Dimension the object if so assigned by the instructor.

12. Make the top and front views of the bin shown in Fig. 14–18, and then find the true shape of the sloping faces assigned by the instructor.

a. Find true size of faces of bin in Fig. 14–18 mathematically. Compare results with those obtained graphically.

13. Make the front and top views of the bin shown in Fig. 14–18, and then find the true value of the angles between the four sloping faces.

14. Make two orthographic views of the roof rafter layout shown in Fig. 14–25. Make a separate layout of the cuts required to frame the hip rafter. Note on a ½ pitch roof the height is ½ the span.

15. Make two orthographic views of the roof framing shown in Fig. 14–31. Make a separate detail showing the cuts required to frame the jack rafter.

16. Draw the necessary orthographic views to describe the shape of the abutment shown in Fig. 14–28. Show in light lines the construction used in making your drawing. Find the true shape of the sloping wing wall face.

17. Same as Problem 16, using the abutment shown in Fig. 14–29.

18.-Find the true shape of the developed pattern for the gusset plate connecting the purlin to the hip rafter in Fig. 14–32. Find also the angle of the bend. Ignore thickness of metal and bend allowance in your layout.

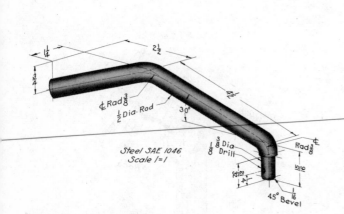

Fig. 14-16. Adjusting rod.

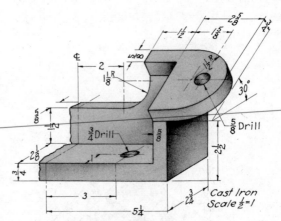

Fig. 14-19. Sand box step base.

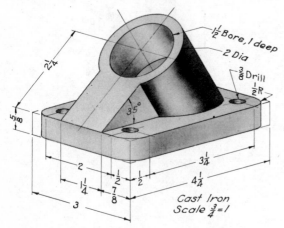

Fig. 14-17. Angle step bearing.

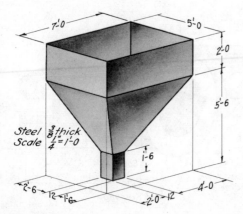

Fig. 14-18. Bin.

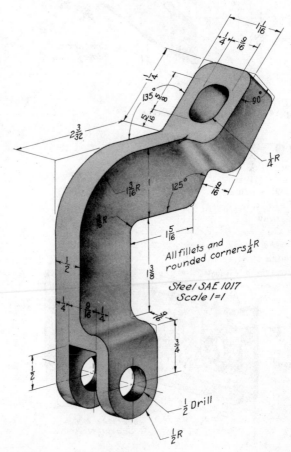

Fig. 14-20. Valve stem clamp.

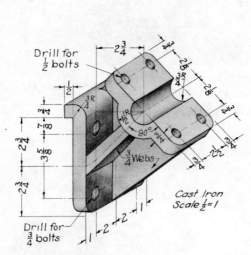

Drill for $\frac{1}{2}$ bolts

$2\frac{3}{4}$

$2\frac{1}{8}$

$2\frac{1}{8}$

$\frac{3}{4}R$

$\frac{3R}{4}$

$\frac{1}{2}$

$\frac{3}{4}$

$\frac{7}{8}$

$2\frac{3}{4}$

$3\frac{5}{8}$

$2\frac{3}{4}$

$\frac{1}{2}R$

90°

$1\frac{1}{4}$

$\frac{3}{4}$ Webs

$\frac{3}{4}$

$2\frac{1}{2}$

$\frac{3}{4}$

Drill for $\frac{3}{4}$ bolts

1 2 2 1

Cast Iron
Scale $\frac{1}{2}=1$

Fig. 14–21. Angle bearing bracket.

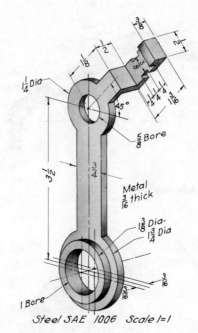

$\frac{3}{8}$

$2\frac{1}{4}$

$\frac{1}{8}$

$\frac{1}{2}$

$1\frac{1}{4}$ Dia

45°

$\frac{5}{8}$ Bore

$1\frac{1}{4}$ $1\frac{1}{4}$ $1\frac{3}{16}$

$3\frac{1}{2}$

$\frac{3}{4}$

Metal
$\frac{3}{16}$ thick

$1\frac{3}{8}$ Dia.

$1\frac{3}{4}$ Dia.

1 Bore

$\frac{3}{16}$

$\frac{3}{16}$

Steel SAE 1006   Scale 1=1

Fig. 14–23. Lever arm.

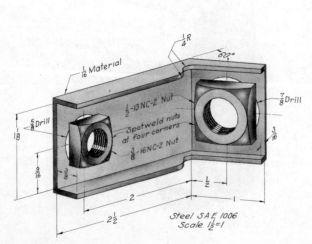

$\frac{1}{16}$ Material

$\frac{1}{4}R$

60°

$\frac{7}{8}$ Drill

$\frac{5}{8}$ Drill

$\frac{1}{2}$–13 NC–2 Nut

Spotweld nuts
at four corners

$\frac{3}{8}$–16 NC–2 Nut

$\frac{3}{16}$

$\frac{1}{8}$

$\frac{9}{16}$

$\frac{1}{2}$

2

1

$2\frac{1}{2}$

Steel SAE 1006
Scale $1\frac{1}{2}=1$

Fig. 14–22. Radiator bracket.

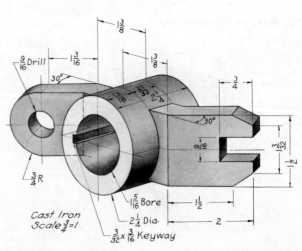

$1\frac{3}{8}$

$1\frac{3}{16}$

$1\frac{3}{8}$

$\frac{3}{4}$

$\frac{9}{16}$ Drill

30°

$\frac{3}{8}$ $1\frac{1}{2}$ $2\frac{1}{4}$

30°

$\frac{9}{16}$

$1\frac{3}{32}$

$1\frac{1}{2}$

$\frac{3}{4}R$

$1\frac{5}{16}$ Bore

$2\frac{1}{4}$ Dia.

$\frac{3}{32} \times \frac{3}{32}$ Keyway

$1\frac{1}{2}$

2

Cast Iron
Scale $\frac{3}{4}=1$

Fig. 14–24. Inclined stop.

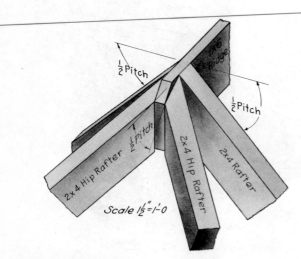

Fig. 14-25.   Roof framing.

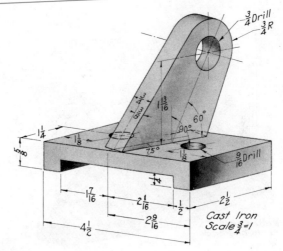

Fig. 14-27.   Anchor bracket.

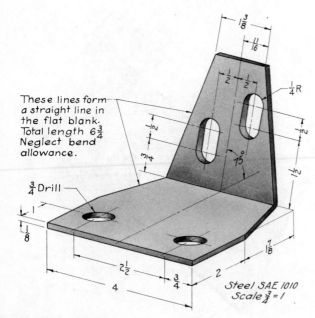

Fig. 14-26.   Bracket.

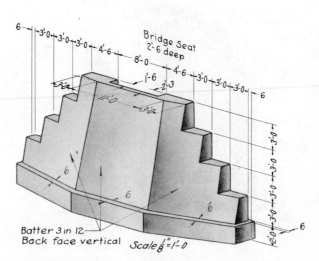

Fig. 14-28.   Stepped abutment wall.

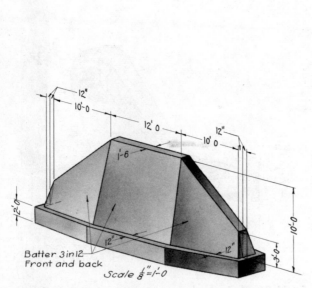

Fig. 14-29. Abutment wall.

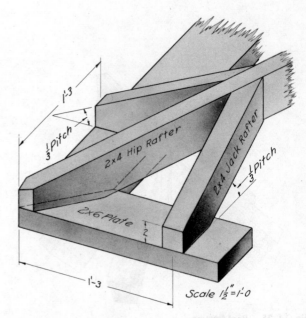

Fig. 14-31. Roof framing.

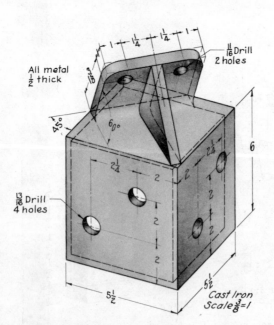

Fig. 14-30. Angle bearing support.

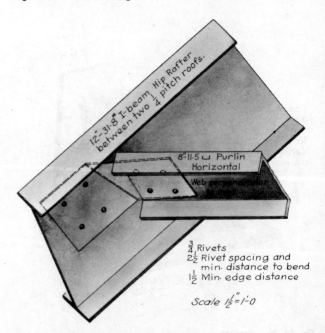

Fig. 14-32. Purlin connection to hip rafter.

Staircase in the Cadet Library, U. S. Air Force Academy, Colorado Springs, Colorado (Skidmore, Owings & Merrill).

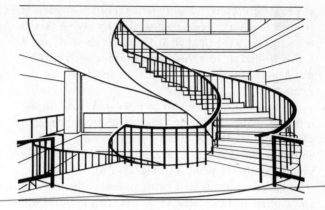

15

Geometry of Engineering Drawing

15.1 Introduction. Many engineering problems dealing with space structures and positions may be solved graphically with sufficient accuracy and in much less time than is required for a mathematical solution. As a basis for these solutions, the engineer must have a thorough understanding of the space relations existing between the various geometrical magnitudes, such as points, lines, planes, surfaces, and solids. In this chapter, these items will be considered in turn and problems relating to them will be solved by the method of auxiliary planes.

Almost all these problems can be solved by one or more of the following basic operations dealing with the use of auxiliary planes.

a. Finding the true length of a line.

b. Finding the point projection of a line.

c. Finding the edgewise view of a plane.

d. Finding the true size of a plane figure.

15.2 Points. A point is simply a space location of infinitesimal size that is located on a drawing by means of two or more projections. It may represent the corner of an object, the intersection of two lines, or a designated spot in space.

15.3 Relationship of points to each other. The only thing to be considered in the relationship of points is the distance and direction from one to another. When actual objects made of solid material are dealt with, the distance must be measured on the surface of the object. This means that it is more convenient to make the measurements along three coordinate axes than along the shortest distance. These distances are measured parallel and perpendicular to the three principal planes of projection. Thus in Fig. 15–1 the position of point *B* relative to point *A* could be described by saying that *B* is 1½ inches to the right of *A*, 1¼ inches above *A*, and 2 inches behind *A*. In a three-view drawing each of these distance is shown in two places as indicated on the figure.

These distances may also be measured from the coordinate planes as in Fig. 15–2(*a*) or from reference planes represented by certain planes on an object as shown by the distances *X, Y, Z,* and *W* which have been used to locate the point *A* in Fig. 15–2(*b*).

In space problems it is often necessary to measure the shortest distance between points. This problem will be considered later as the true length of a line.

15.4   Lines. A line may be defined as the path of a moving point. Lines therefore have location, direction, and length. They may be either straight or curved. In this chapter, straight lines sometimes called right lines will be considered primarily.

15.5   Properties of a line. On the drawing board or in the field, a line may be determined by two points or by one point and a direction. When considered in connection with their relationship to the coordinate or reference planes, lines may be grouped into three distinct classifications, namely, (*a*) perpendicular to one of the coordinate planes and parallel to the other two, (*b*) parallel to one of the coordinate planes and inclined to the other, and (*c*) oblique to all three coordinate planes. The angle that a line makes with the horizontal plane is called θ, with the vertical plane ϕ and with the profile plane π.

15.5.1   *Lines perpendicular to one of the coordinate planes.* When a line is perpendicular to a plane, it projects as a point on that plane, as shown pictorially in Fig. 15–3(*a*) and orthographically in Fig. 15–3(*b*). This line is perpendicular to the horizontal plane. Since it is parallel to the vertical and profile planes, it must show in true length in those projections. The heavy line in

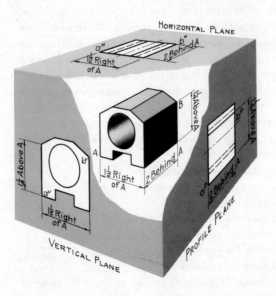

Fig. 15–1.   Space relationship of points.

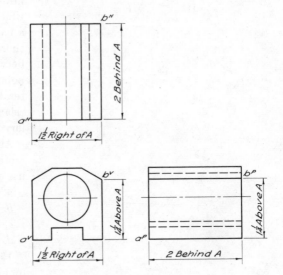

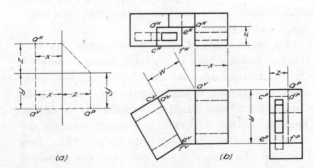

Fig. 15–2.   Distances from points to planes.

Fig. 15–3(c) and 15–3(d) represents such a line on an object.

Similar lines which are perpendicular to the vertical and profile planes are shown in Figs. 15–4, and 15–5, respectively. A careful examination of these figures will enable one to recognize lines of this type wherever they may occur. It should be noted that the true length of the line shows in two views on the planes to which it is parallel, and that two of the projections are parallel to a reference line which indicates that the line is parallel to two of the coordinate planes.

15.5.2   *Lines parallel to a coordinate plane.* If a line is parallel to one coordinate plane, its projection appears

parallel to the edgewise view of that plane as represented by a reference line. If three views are given, it appears parallel in two projections, since in our system of reference lines each coordinate plane appears edgewise in two views. Thus in Fig. 15–6(a) and (b) the line AB is parallel to the horizontal plane, and therefore both the vertical and profile projections appear parallel to the reference line which in those cases represents the edgewise view of the horizontal plane. The horizontal projection must be inclined to the reference lines. In this position the horizontal projection shows the true length of the line and the angle ϕ which the line makes with the vertical plane and the angle π which the line makes

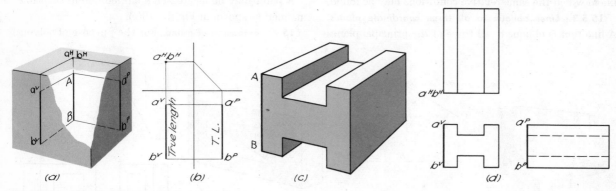

Fig. 15–3.   Line perpendicular to the horizontal plane.

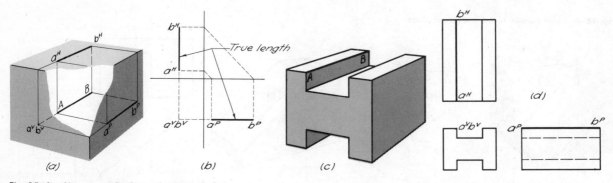

Fig. 15–4.   Line perpendicular to the vertical plane.

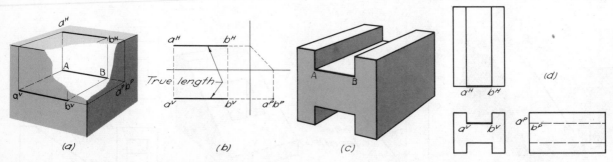

Fig. 15–5.   Line perpendicular to the profile plane.

with the profile plane. When measuring the angle that a line makes with a plane, it is always necessary to have the true length of the line and the edgewise view of the plane in the same view. Figures 15–6(c) and (d) show a line of this type on an object.

In a like manner, a line parallel to the V-plane and inclined to H- and P-planes is shown in Fig. 15–7. Notice that two of the projections are again parallel to a reference line and that the vertical projection shows the true length of the line and the angle θ that the line makes with the horizontal and the angle π that the line makes with the profile.

Likewise, Fig. 15–8 shows a line parallel to the profile in which the same relative conditions may be found.

15.5.3 Lines oblique to all three coordinate planes.

A line that is oblique to all three of the principal planes has all its projections inclined to the reference lines. *Its true length does not show in any of these views nor do the angles that the line makes with the coordinate planes.* Such a line is shown in Fig. 15–9.

15.6 Point on a line. To place a point on a line, it is necessary to locate the projections of the point on the corresponding projections of the line. Thus to locate point C at the center of line AB as in Fig. 15–10(a), it is only necessary to locate the center of any projection such as $a^H b^H$ by scale or geometric construction, and designate the center by a small dot labeled c^H. Then erect a perpendicular to the horizontal reference line from c^H until it crosses $a^V b^V$ which locates c^V.

A point may be located on a curved line in the same manner, as shown in Fig. 15–10(c).

15.7 Extension of a line. For the purpose of solving

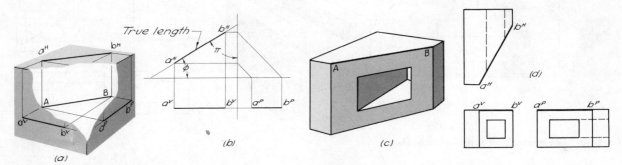

Fig. 15–6. Line parallel to the horizontal plane.

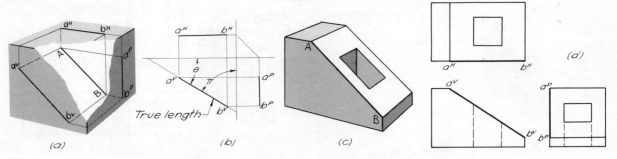

Fig. 15–7. Line parallel to the vertical plane.

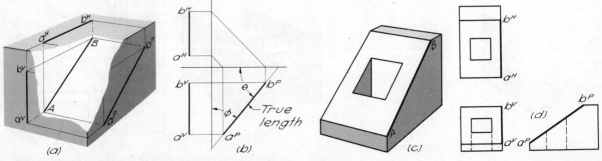

Fig. 15–8. Line parallel to the profile plane.

any problem, straight lines may be extended at either end as far as may be necessary. Points may be located on these extended lines as explained above and as illustrated in Fig. 15–10(*b*).

15.8 True length of an oblique line—auxiliary plane method. Space analysis. *If a line is parallel to a plane, the projection on that plane shows the true length of the line.* Since an oblique line is not parallel to any principal plane, it is necessary to set up an auxiliary plane parallel to the oblique line. Therefore the auxil-

iary reference line must be placed parallel to one of the principal projections of the line.

The relationships between that principal projection and the auxiliary projection must then be exactly the same as those existing between the two principal projections. The *H-* and *V*-projections must always lie on a perpendicular to the *H-V* reference line, and likewise the *H-* and *1*-projections of Fig. 15–11(*a*) must lie on a perpendicular to the *H-1* reference line. See Arts. 14.5, 14.6, and 14.7. Since the distance from the *V*-projection

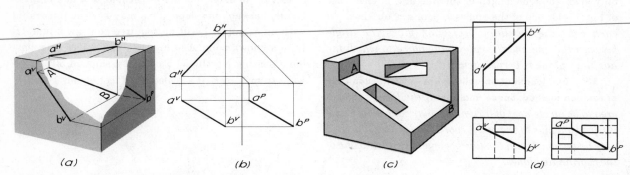

Fig. 15–9. Line oblique to all the principal coordinate planes.

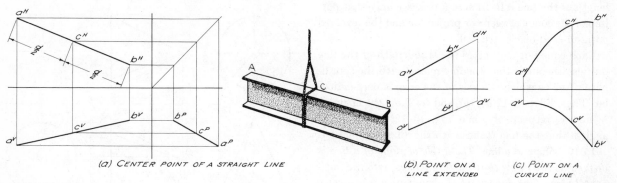

(*a*) CENTER POINT OF A STRAIGHT LINE

(*b*) POINT ON A LINE EXTENDED

(*c*) POINT ON A CURVED LINE

Fig. 15–10. Point on a line.

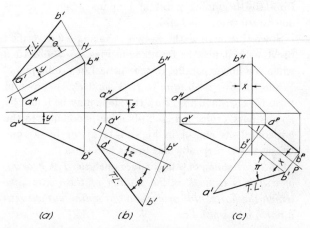

(*a*)   (*b*)   (*c*)

Fig. 15–11. True length of a line by the auxiliary plane method.

to the *H-V* reference gives the distance that the point in space is from the *H*-plane, so the distance from the *1*-projection to the *H-1* reference line must also give the distance from the point in space to the *H*-plane. Therefore, this distance may be transferred from the vertical projection to the auxiliary projection, as shown in Fig. 15–11(*a*). The same reasoning holds when the auxiliary plane is placed perpendicular to the vertical plane or the profile plane, as shown in Fig. 15–11(*b*) and (*c*).

The student should observe that this operation not only gives the true length of the line but, in each case of Fig. 15–11, one of the angles θ, φ, or π is obtained. *In each case the auxiliary projection gives the angle between the line and the coordinate plane to which the auxiliary plane is perpendicular.*

15.9   True length of an oblique line—construction cone or rotation method. Space analysis. *If the line is considered to be an element of a right circular cone whose axis is perpendicular to one of the coordinate planes, the cone may be revolved until the line becomes parallel to one of the coordinate planes.*

In Fig. 15–12, four different cones have been set up, any one of which may be used to determine the true length of the line *AB*. In actual practice only that portion of the cone between the projection and the revolved position need be constructed.

Each cone not only gives the true length of the line but also the angle that the line makes with the coordinate plane to which the axis of the cone is perpendicular. Thus, Figs. 15–12(*a*), (*b*), and (*c*) show the angles θ, φ, and π, respectively, and Fig. 15–12(*d*) shows the angle α that the line makes with the auxiliary plane *1*.

15.10   Slope of a line. *The angle of slope of a line is defined as the angle that the line makes with the horizontal plane. The slope of a line should always be given a plus or minus sign.* It is plus when the line slopes upward from the beginning point and minus when it slopes downward from this point.

Since this angle is the same as the angle θ described previously, it may be found as in Figs. 15–7 and 15–8 when the line is parallel to the vertical or profile plane. When the line is oblique to *H, V,* and *P,* as shown in Figs. 15–11(*a*) and 15–12(*a*), the slope may be found by an auxiliary projection on a plane perpendicular to the horizontal, as shown in Fig. 15–11(*a*), or by a cone whose axis is perpendicular to the horizontal.

15.11   Bearing of a line. Space analysis. *The bearing of a line is defined as the smaller of the two angles which the horizontal projection of the line makes with a north and south line.*

On a drawing the north and south line is usually a vertical line with north at the top. Thus east will be to the right and west to the left. The bearing should be taken from the horizontal projection and marked with the angle and direction as shown in Fig. 15–13(*a*).

The term azimuth is sometimes used to define the direction of a line. This means the angle which the horizontal projection of the line makes with a north and south line, measured clockwise from the north, as illustrated in Fig. 15–13(*b*).

15.12   To determine the projections of a line of given length, bearing, and slope. This may best be illustrated with an example. Let it be required to draw a line *AB* from a known point *A* in Fig. 15–14, 200 feet long, having a bearing North 45° East and a slope of 30° downward from *A* to *B* at a scale of 100 feet equals 1 inch.

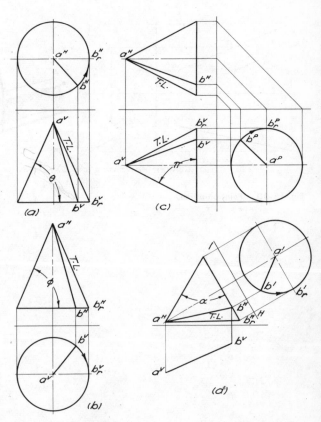

Fig. 15–12.   True length of a line by the rotation method.

The student must analyze the three known facts about this line to determine the order in which he will use the facts to solve the problem. Clearly the *H*-projection of a line having the required bearing can be drawn, but since it is a sloping line its true length cannot be shown immediately. The *H*-projection of a random line $a^H c^H$ will therefore be drawn having the correct bearing as shown in Fig. 15–14(*a*). An auxiliary reference line may be placed parallel to its projection and *A* projected to this plane. The slope can be drawn as shown in Fig. 15–14(*b*). This auxiliary view also gives the true length of the line *AC*, and hence a length of 2 inches (200 ft) can be scaled off from a^1 and the end marked b^1. The projection of *B* can be returned from b^1 to b^H on the horizontal projection of *AC*. From these two views the vertical projection can be constructed, thus completing the problem as in Fig. 15–14(*c*).

15.13   Relationship between lines. If two lines in space intersect, they may be either inclined or perpendicular to each other. If they do not intersect, they may be parallel, non-parallel, or perpendicular to each other. Two non-intersecting lines are said to be perpendicular to each other when one of the lines lies in a plane that is perpendicular to the other line. These relationships are established by means of their projections.

15.13.1   *Intersecting lines. Space analysis.* *If two lines intersect, there must be one point common to both lines.*

The various projections of this point must have the proper alignment with each other and must be on the corresponding projections of both lines, as in Fig. 15–15(*a*). In Fig. 15–15(*b*), the crossing point of the horizontal projections represents two points, *E* and *F*,

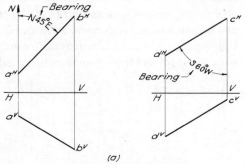
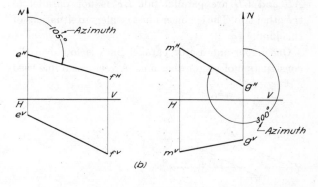

Fig. 15–13.   Bearing and azimuth of a line.

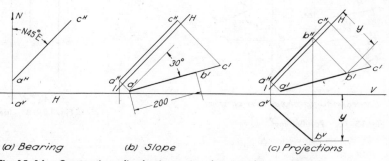

(a) Bearing   (b) Slope   (c) Projections

Fig. 15–14.   Constructing a line having a given bearing, slope, and length.

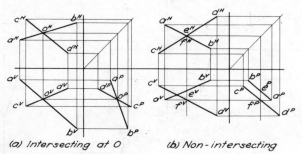

(a) Intersecting at O   (b) Non-intersecting

Fig. 15–15.   Intersecting lines.

since their vertical projections do not coincide, and consequently these lines do not intersect.

15.13.2   *Parallel lines. Space analysis.* *By definition, lines are said to be parallel when they meet at infinity. In projection drawing, two lines are parallel when their respective projections on any and all planes are parallel.*

In Fig. 15–16, this principle has been illustrated for four projections of the lines. In six of the seven possible positions of a line, it is sufficient to consider only two projections. But, when the two projections of each line lie in a single line perpendicular to the reference line between the views, an additional projection is necessary. Thus, in Fig. 15–17(*a*) and Fig. 15–18(*a*), the two views indicate that the lines may all be parallel, but the third view, as shown in Fig. 15–17(*b*) and Fig. 15–18(*b*), indicates clearly which ones are actually parallel. Thus *AB* and *CD* are parallel but *EF* is not parallel to the other two. The engineer must be alert to situations of this kind.

One important use of parallel lines is found in the construction of vector diagrams. A vector is a line used to represent any quantity which has both magnitude and direction, as for example, a force. The direction of the line is the same as the direction of the force, and the length of the line is equal to the magnitude of the force to some convenient scale.

In Fig. 15–19, let it be required to construct the vector diagram to determine the load in the two ropes supporting the 100-pound weight.

Since the ropes are parallel to the vertical plane, the vertical projection will show all lines in true length. Hence, the horizontal projection which is parallel to the reference line need not be considered. In vector diagrams it is customary to letter the spaces between the forces as *D, E,* and *F* shown in Fig. 15–19. The lines of the vector diagram are then designated by the two letters adjacent to them as *DE, EF,* and *FD*. This is known as Bow's notation. To solve the problem, draw first a line *EF* parallel to the vertical rope and make the length equal to 100 pounds to some convenient scale as, for example, 1 inch equals 50 pounds. Then from *E* construct a line parallel to $e^v d^v$ and from *F*, another line parallel to $d^v f^v$.

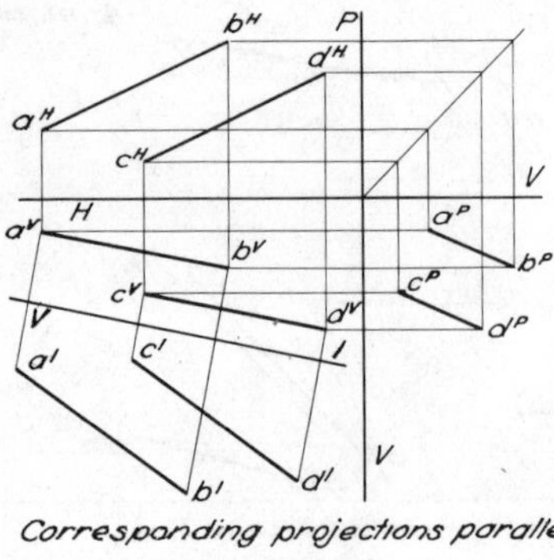

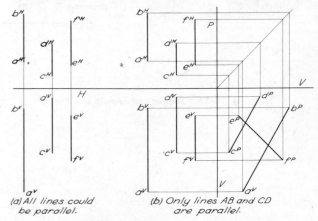

(a) All lines could be parallel.

(b) Only lines AB and CD are parallel.

Fig. 15–18.   Identifying parallel lines.

Corresponding projections parallel.

Fig. 15–16.   Parallel lines.

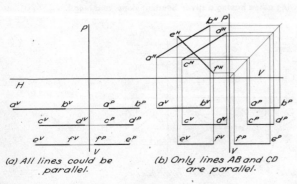

(a) All lines could be parallel.

(b) Only lines AB and CD are parallel.

Fig. 15–17.   Identifying parallel lines.

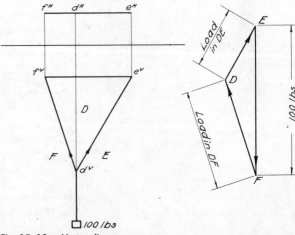

100 lbs

Fig. 15–19.   Vector diagram.

These two lines will intersect at *D,* and the true length of these lines *ED* and *FD* will give the load in the inclined ropes at the same scale used in drawing the first line.

When the ropes are not parallel to one of the principal planes, as in Fig. 15-20, the same construction may be used by setting up an auxiliary plane parallel to the two ropes, as shown in Fig. 15-20.

Frequently it is necessary to find the resultant of several forces which act through one point but all of which do not lie in the same plane. These are called concurrent non-coplanar forces. The resultant is the single force that can be used to replace the entire system of forces. This problem can be solved by constructing a diagram similar to the vector diagram of the previous paragraph with the exception that it will not form a closed polygon and that it must be constructed simultaneously in two views. The line necessary to close the polygon will be the resultant. The equilibrant is a force of the same magnitude but with the direction reversed. Thus, in Fig. 15-21(*a*), a group of three forces whose directions are indicated by the lines *AB, AC,* and *AD* and whose magnitudes are specified in pounds are acting on the point *A.* The solution of this problem is shown in Fig. 15-21(*b*). The spaces between the forces should first be lettered in one view as *O, M,* and *N* in Fig. 15-21(*a*). The forces are laid out in order by proceeding in a clockwise direction around point *A.*

a. Through any point *M,* in Fig. 15-21(*b*), construct a line *MX* parallel to *AD,* and on its true length lay out the magnitude (125 pounds) of force *AD,* thus locating N_r from which the projections of *N* can be found.

b. From *N,* construct a line *NY* parallel to *AC,* and on its true length lay out the magnitude (125 pounds) of the force *AC,* thus locating point *O* in the same manner as before.

c. From *O,* construct a line *OZ* parallel to the third force *AB,* and on its true length lay out the magnitude (150 pounds) of the force *AB,* thus locating a point *P.*

d. The line *MP* joining the first point to the last point gives the direction of the resultant, and the true length of *MP* gives the magnitude of the resultant. This resultant may be used to replace the three original forces.

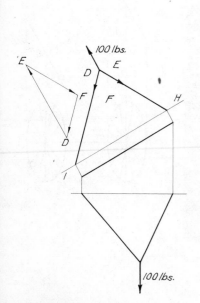

Fig. 15-20.   Vector diagram.

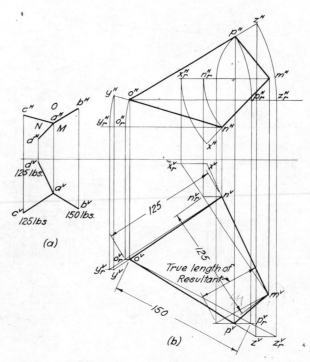

Fig. 15-21.   Resultant of three concurrent forces.

15.13.3   *Perpendicular lines. Space analysis.* *One line is perpendicular to another line when it lies in a plane perpendicular to the other line.* A line constructed perpendicular to another line may have an infinite number of positions. Thus, in Fig. 15–22(a), each spoke of the wheels lies in a plane perpendicular to the axle joining them. When the axle is horizontal, the wheels will project edgewise on the horizontal plane. This edgewise view is perpendicular to the horizontal projection of the axle. *It follows therefore that, if one of two perpendicular lines is parallel to a coordinate plane, the projections of both lines on that plane will be at 90° to each*

other. Thus, in Fig. 15–22(b), the axle AB is parallel to the horizontal plane, and every spoke of the wheel projects in the line $c^H a^H d^H$. Since the wheel may be revolved into any position, the vertical projection of a spoke may have any direction as for example, $a^v e^v$ in Fig. 15–22(b) and 15.22(c). If the length of the perpendicular is to be determined or constructed, this may be done by a single auxiliary projection as shown in Fig. 15–23.

Although the preceding discussion has been limited to the horizontal plane, the same principles apply to any coordinate plane or any auxiliary plane. See Figs. 15–24 and 15–25.

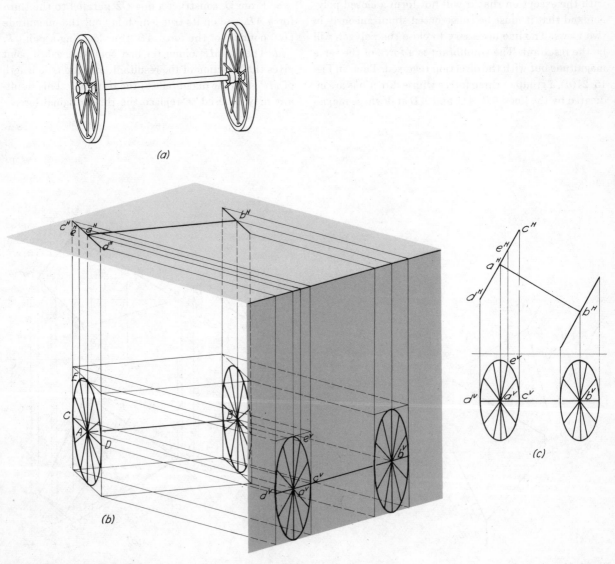

Fig. 15–22.   Perpendicular lines.

If the given line AB in Fig. 15–25, to which another is to be made perpendicular, is not parallel to a principal plane, an auxiliary plane may be set up parallel to the line. The auxiliary view will then show the right angle in true size as shown in Fig. 15–25. After the auxiliary projections have been drawn at right angles to each other the vertical projection of the perpendicular may be drawn in any direction. The horizontal projection is then obtained in the usual manner.

There are three situations in which a line may be drawn at right angles to an oblique line directly. This construction is useful in many problems. Thus, if we

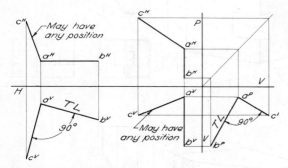

Fig. 15–23. Perpendicular lines.

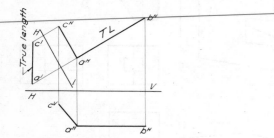

Fig. 15–24. Perpendicular lines.

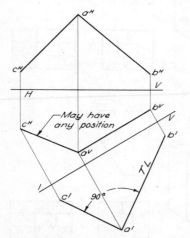

Fig. 15–25. Perpendicular lines.

consider AC in Fig. 15–26(a) to be any spoke of the wheel in Fig. 15–22, then the axle may be drawn by making $a^H b^H$ perpendicular to $a^H c^H$ and $a^V b^V$ parallel to the reference line. The lines BA and AC are then at right angles to each other. Figure 15–26(b) shows another solution in which the axle AB is drawn parallel to the vertical plane, and Fig. 15–26(c) shows a third solution with the axle parallel to the profile plane.

15.14   Properties of planes. A plane surface has length and breadth but no thickness. For practical purposes a plane surface may be extended as far as may be necessary in any direction. A plane is determined by any of the following conditions, that is, two intersecting lines, two parallel lines, a point and a line, three points, or by a line and an angle with some reference plane.

When considered in connection with their relationship with the three principal coordinate planes, all planes may be divided into three groups, namely, (a) parallel to one of the coordinate planes and perpendicular to the other two, (b) perpendicular to one of the coordinate planes and inclined to the other two, and (c) oblique to all three coordinate planes.

15.14.1   Planes parallel to one of the principal coordinate planes and perpendicular to the other two. This group of planes, sometimes called normal planes, may be further subdivided into three subgroups which are very similar in their characteristics and properties. Each of these has two views which show edgewise, and these edgewise views are always parallel to one of the principal reference lines. The third view in each case shows the true size of the plane surface. Thus, in Fig. 15–27(a) and (b), the plane $ABCD$ is parallel to the horizontal plane, and so the horizontal projection will be true size, but the vertical and profile projections are edgewise and parallel to the horizontal reference line. In Fig. 15–27(c) and (d), the shaded area shows such a plane on an object

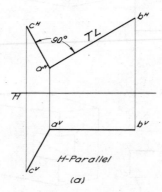

Fig. 15–26. Perpendicular lines.

and on the projection of an object.

The same information for the planes parallel to the vertical and profile is shown in Figs. 15–28 and 15–29, respectively.

15.14.2 *Planes perpendicular to one of the principal coordinate planes and inclined to the other two.* This group of planes, sometimes called inclined planes, may also be subdivided into three subgroups whose proper-

ties and characteristics are very similar. The principal characteristic of these planes is that one view is always edgewise and the other two are areas which are not true size.

Thus Fig. 15–30(*a*) and (*b*) shows a plane that is perpendicular to the horizontal plane and inclined to the other two coordinate planes. The horizontal view is therefore shown edgewise. Since the horizontal refer-

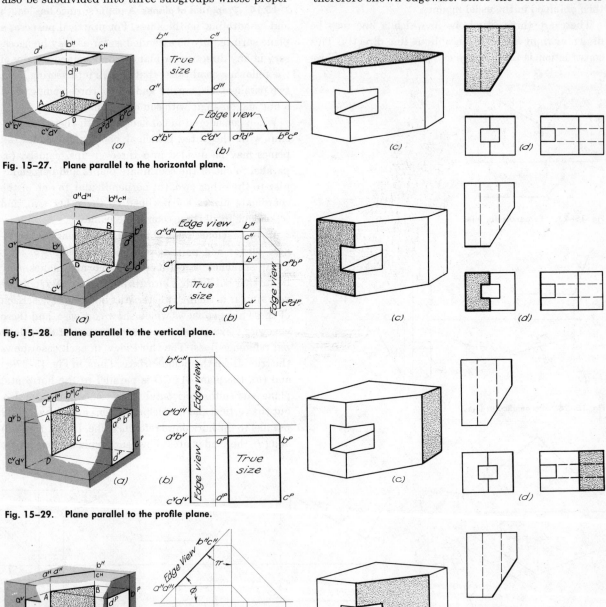

Fig. 15–27.   Plane parallel to the horizontal plane.

Fig. 15–28.   Plane parallel to the vertical plane.

Fig. 15–29.   Plane parallel to the profile plane.

Fig. 15–30.   Plane perpendicular to the horizontal plane.

ence line is the edgewise view of the vertical plane in this view, the angle φ between plane *ABCD* and the vertical plane will show in true size as indicated. Likewise the angle π which plane *ABCD* makes with the profile will show as indicated in the horizontal projection. The shaded areas of Fig. 15-30(c) and (d) show this plane on an object and on the projections of an object.

In the same manner the planes perpendicular to the vertical and the profile are shown in Figs. 15-31 and 15-32, respectively. It should be noticed in each case that the angles between the given plane and the coordinate planes show in the view in which the given plane shows edgewise. Whenever two planes show edgewise in the same view, the angle between these edgewise

views is the angle between the two planes.

15.14.3 *Planes oblique to all three principal coordinate planes.* This group of planes, sometimes called oblique planes, shows as an area in each of the principal projections but none of these is in true size. There is no edgewise view, and the angles between the plane and the coordinate planes do not show in any of the principal views. Figure 15-33 shows a plane of this kind and also shows how this plane will appear on an object and on the projections of an object. Methods for finding the angles, θ, φ, and π and the true sizes of these planes will be discussed later.

15.15   Line in a plane. Space analysis. *A straight line lies in a plane when it joins two points in the plane.*

When a plane is determined by two lines or when two

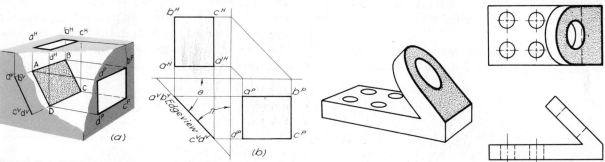

Fig. 15-31.   Plane perpendicular to the vertical plane.

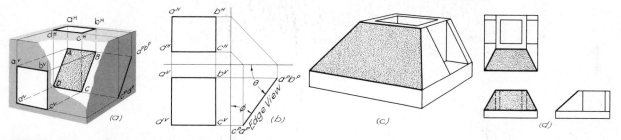

Fig. 15-32.   Plane perpendicular to the profile plane.

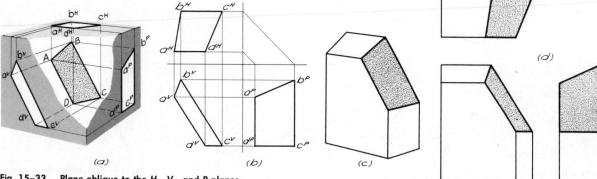

Fig. 15-33.   Plane oblique to the H-, V-, and P-planes.

lines can be located in the plane, any point on one line can be joined to any point on the other line to locate a new line in the plane. Thus in Fig. 15–34(a) the line MN is made to lie in the plane of the triangle ABC by assuming M as a point on AB and N as a point on BC. Since the two points lie in the plane, the line joining them must also lie in the plane.

A horizontal line may be constructed in a plane by making the vertical projection of it parallel to the reference line as in Fig. 15–34(b). The projections e^V and f^V where this vertical projection crosses $a^V b^V$ and $b^V c^V$ are then projected to $a^H b^H$ and $b^H c^H$ to locate the horizontal projection $e^H f^H$.

In a similar manner in Fig. 15–34(c), a V-parallel may be drawn in the plane by making the horizontal projection parallel to the reference line. Likewise the P-parallel can be found by making the H- and V-projections parallel to the vertical reference line, as in Fig. 15–34(d).

15.16   Point in a plane. Space analysis. A *point will lie in a plane if it lies on a line in the plane.*

If one projection of a point in a plane is known, as in Fig. 15–35(a), the other may be found by assuming the projection of a line through the point, as in Fig. 15–35(b). Then by making this line lie in the plane as in Fig. 15–35(c) the remaining projection of the point may be found on the other projection of the line.

15.17   Strike of a plane. *The strike of a plane is defined as the direction or bearing of a horizontal line in the plane.* Hence to obtain the strike of any plane it is only necessary to draw an H-parallel in the plane and measure the angle its H-projection makes with a north and south line. This is illustrated in Fig. 15–36.

15.18   True size of a plane figure when the edgewise view is given. Space analysis. *The true size of any plane figure shows on a plane parallel to the figure.*

When one view of a plane figure shows edgewise parallel to a reference line, the adjacent view across the reference line shows the true shape of the figure and the true angle between any lines in the figures. See Figs. 15–27, 15–28, and 15–29. When the edge view is inclined to the reference lines, an auxiliary plane may be

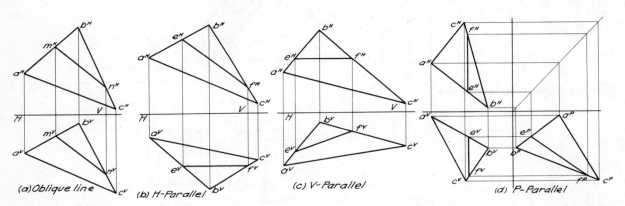

Fig. 15–34.   Line in a plane.

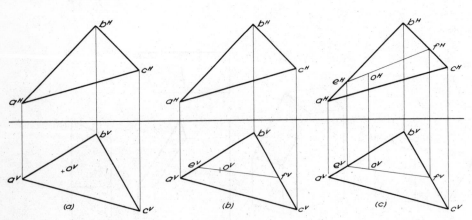

Fig. 15–35.   Point in a plane.

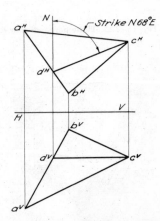

Fig. 15–36.   Strike of a plane.

placed parallel to this view and the true shape of the figure obtained upon it in the usual manner. See Fig. 15-37.

15.19 Point projection of a line. Space analysis. *A line projects as a point on any plane perpendicular to the line.* Many space problems can be solved by obtaining an endwise view of a line or its point projection. If a line is parallel to two of the principal coordinate planes, it projects as a point on the third, as shown in Fig. 15-38(*a*). If the line is parallel to one of the principal coordinate planes and inclined to the other two, as shown in Fig. 15-38(*b*), the point projection may be obtained by placing an auxiliary plane perpendicular to the line. This is done by placing the auxiliary reference line perpendicular to the true length projection.

When the line is oblique to all three of the principal coordinate planes, its point projection may be obtained by using two auxiliary planes. The first step in this problem is to set up an auxiliary plane parallel to the line to obtain its true length, as shown in Fig. 15-39(*a*). The second auxiliary plane is set up perpendicular to

the first and perpendicular to the line. This is accomplished by placing the *1-2* reference line perpendicular to the true length projection a^1b^1, as shown in Fig. 15-39(*b*). Since the adjacent projections, in this case the first auxiliary projection and the second auxiliary projection, must lie on a perpendicular to the *1-2* reference line, the first step is to project a^1 and b^1 perpendicular to the *1-2* reference line. Then the second auxiliary projection can be obtained by laying out on this projection line the distance *W* from the point to the first auxiliary plane. This distance *W* is found as the distance from the horizontal projection to the *H-1* reference line and laid out on the perpendicular from the *1-2* reference line. This will give the point projection of the line.

In these problems it is usually necessary to project other points on the same plane, but the procedure for any other point is the same as for *A* and *B*. However, no other line than *AB* or a line parallel to it will project as a point on this plane.

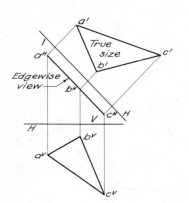

Fig. 15-37. True size of a plane figure.

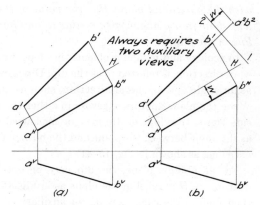

Fig. 15-39. Point projection of an oblique line.

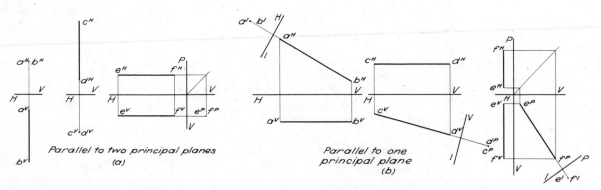

Fig. 15-38. Point projection of a line.

15.20   Edgewise view of a plane. Space analysis. *A plane figure shows edgewise when projected upon a plane perpendicular to any line in the original figure.*

If the line chosen in the figure is inclined to all the principal planes, this will require two auxiliary planes. Therefore for purposes of simplicity a line in the plane which is parallel to one of the coordinate planes is always used.

The construction is as follows:

1. Draw an *H*- or *V*-parallel in the plane. In Fig. 15-40, the *V*-parallel *AD* has been chosen.

2. Set up an auxiliary plane perpendicular to this line to get the edgewise view of the plane. This edgewise view will also give the angle between the given plane and the adjacent coordinate plane, marked ϕ in Fig. 15-40.

To obtain the angles θ and π, the auxiliary plane would have to be set up perpendicular to an *H*-parallel or a *P*-parallel, respectively.

15.21   Dip of a plane. Space analysis. *Since the slope of a plane is defined as the angle which the plane makes with the horizontal plane, the true value of this angle will show in a plane perpendicular to any horizontal line in the plane.*

In geology and mining problems the slope, in a downward direction, is referred to as the dip. Dip is expressed as an angle and a general direction, such as 46° N.W. When the plane appears edgewise in either the front or side views, the slope or dip may be measured directly as the angle between the plane and the horizontal reference line, as shown in Fig. 15-41.

For an oblique plane, the dip may be obtained by drawing an *H*-parallel in the plane as in Fig. 15-36 and then finding the edge view on an auxiliary plane perpendicular to the *H*-parallel as in Fig. 15-41(*c*). The angle between the edge view and the auxiliary reference line is the dip. The method of showing the dip on a map

is illustrated in Fig. 15-41(*c*), and consists of an arrow drawn in the horizontal projection perpendicular to the strike line, pointing down the slope. The angle of the dip is placed near the arrow.

15.22   True size of a plane by the auxiliary plane method. Having obtained the edgewise view of an oblique plane as in Art. 15.20, the true shape of the plane figure may be obtained by setting up a second auxiliary plane parallel to the plane figure and obtaining the projection on that plane. Figure 15-42(*a*) shows the edgewise view of the triangle *ABC* that was obtained by placing the first auxiliary plane perpendicular to the *V*-parallel *CD*. In Fig. 15-42(*b*), the auxiliary reference line *1-2* has been placed parallel to the edgewise view $a^1b^1c^1$. The projection on plane 2, which is the true size of the plane, was obtained by constructing perpendiculars from a^1, b^1, and c^1 to the *1-2* reference line and laying out on those perpendiculars the distance from each point in space to the first auxiliary plane. These dis-

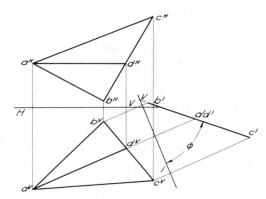

Fig. 15-40.   Edgewise view of a plane.

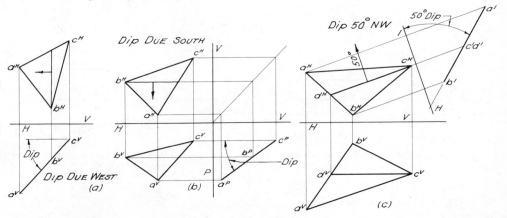

Fig. 15-41.   Dip of a plane.

tances were obtained by measuring the distances from a^V, b^V, and c^V to the 1-V reference line. This procedure will always be followed in obtaining any projection on a second auxiliary plane and will not be discussed in detail in future examples. By similar reasoning, projections on additional auxiliary planes may be obtained.

15.23 True size of a plane by the rotation method. Space analysis. *When a point is revolved about a line, it revolves in a circle which lies in a plane perpendicular to the line and the center of the circle is a point on the line.*

It is sometimes more convenient to find the true shape of a plane figure by revolving it around a line in the plane until it is parallel to one of the principal planes. This requires that the line used as an axis of rotation be parallel to one of the coordinate planes. This has been done in Fig. 15–43 in lieu of making a second auxiliary projection. For an oblique plane it is first necessary to draw an H- or V-parallel in the plane like AF. An aux-

iliary view on a plane perpendicular to this line will show the plane edgewise and the line as a point at a^1f^1. With a^1f^1 as a center or axis of revolution, the edgewise view may be revolved until it is parallel to the H-plane, that is, until e^1, d^1, c^1, and b^1 are in a line parallel to the reference line H-1 at e_r^1, d_r^1, c_r^1, and b_r^1. *It is important to know that the plane must be shown edgewise before this method of rotation can be used.*

The revolved position of these points may now be projected back to the horizontal projection, as illustrated in Fig. 15–43. Since the line AF is the axis of rotation the points in the plane will revolve in planes perpendicular to the axis of rotation. Hence b_r^H is on a line through b^H perpendicular to a^Hf^H. The remaining points c_r^H, d_r^H, and e_r^H are obtained in the same manner and then connected to give the true shape of the figure. It should be observed that since a^H and f^H are in the axis of rotation their position does not change in the revolved view.

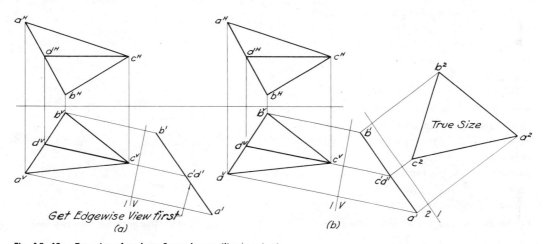

Fig. 15–42.   True size of a plane figure by auxiliary projection.

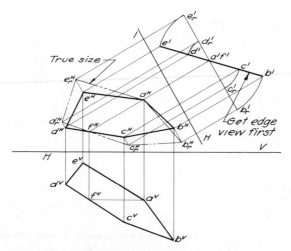

Fig. 15–43.   True size of a plane figure by rotation.

15.24   Angle between two lines. Space analysis. *The angle between two lines shows in its true value on any plane parallel to both lines.*

Whenever two intersecting lines lie in a plane parallel to one of the principal planes, the true size of the angle between them will show in the projection on that plane.

When the two lines lie in a plane which is perpendicular to one of the principal planes as in Fig. 15–44, the projection of the lines on that plane will coincide or lie in a single straight line which is the edgewise view of their plane. An auxiliary plane may be placed parallel to the two lines, and the view on this plane will show the true angle between the lines. If the plane of the two lines is oblique, not edgewise in any view, as in Fig. 15–45, the problem may be solved by the use of two auxiliary planes, the first being perpendicular to the plane of the lines and the second parallel to it.

15.25   Line through a point making a given angle with a given line. Space analysis—see Art. 15.24. The construction is as follows:

1. Draw a *V*-parallel from the point to the line, and obtain an edgewise view as in Fig. 15–46(*a*).

2. On a second auxiliary view, find the true shape of the plane of the point and line and draw the line making the required angle with the given line. See Fig. 15–46(*b*).

3. Return the projection of this new line to the original views. See Fig. 15–46(*b*).

15.26   Distance between two parallel lines by the point projection method. Space analysis. *The distance between the point projections of the two lines will be the shortest distance between the lines.*

Project both lines on an auxiliary plane perpendicular to the lines, and measure the distance between the point projections, as illustrated in Fig. 15–47.

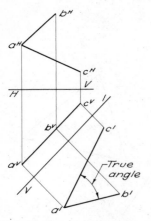

Fig. 15–44.   True angle between two lines.

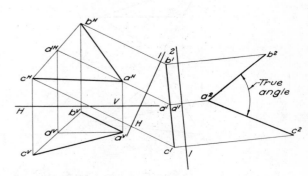

Fig. 15–45.   True angle between two lines.

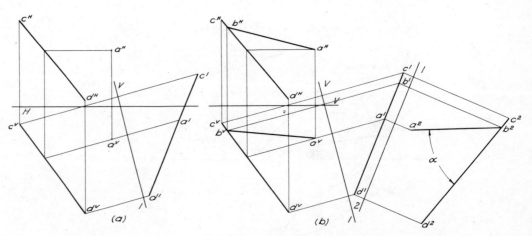

(a)   (b)

Fig. 15–46.   Line making specified angle with another line.

15.27   Distance between two parallel lines by the plane method. Space analysis. *The true distance between the lines will show in that projection which gives the true size of the plane of the two lines.*

Find the edgewise view of the plane and then the true size view by auxiliary planes or rotation as explained in Arts. 15.22 and 15.23. See Fig. 15–48.

15.28   Distance from a point to a line by the point projection method. Space analysis. *The shortest distance from a point to a line will show on a view that gives the point projection of the line.*

Project both the point and the line on an auxiliary plane perpendicular to the line. The distance between the projections is the required distance. Since the shortest distance will be parallel to this auxiliary plane, its projection in the adjacent view must be parallel to the reference line between these views. See Fig. 15–49.

15.29   Distance from a point to a line by the plane method. Space analysis. *The true distance between the point and line will show on a view that gives the true size of the plane of the point and line.*

Project the point and line on an auxiliary plane parallel to the plane of the two. The true length of the perpendicular may be measured on this view and projected back directly. See Fig. 15–50.

15.30   Point in which a line pierces a plane. Edgewise view method. Space analysis. *Whenever a plane appears as an edgewise view the piercing point of a line with that plane can be seen by inspection to be at the crossing point of the proper projection of the line with the edgewise view.*

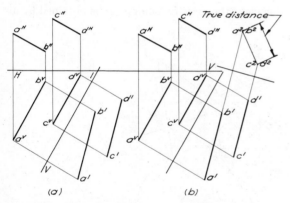

Fig. 15–47.   Distance between two parallel lines. Point projection method.

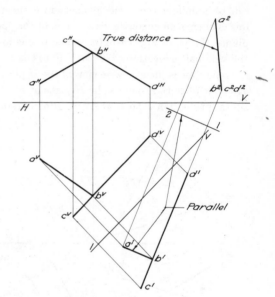

Fig. 15–49.   Distance from a point to a line. Point projection method.

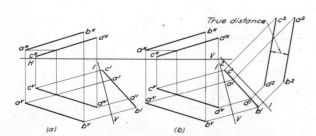

Fig. 15–48.   Distance between two parallel lines. Plane method.

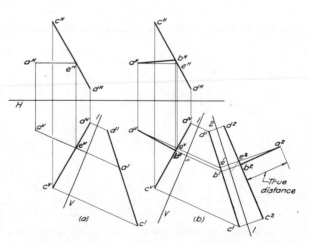

Fig. 15–50.   Distance from a point to a line. Plane method.

Figure 15–51 shows the edgewise view of plane ABC in the vertical projection and therefore the piercing point of the line MN with the plane can be located in that view at p^V.

The remaining projections of the piercing point are carried to the other projections of the line in the usual manner. When the plane does not appear edgewise in any principal view, an auxiliary view can be made which will give an edgewise view of the plane. The point where the auxiliary projection of the line crosses the edgewise view of the plane will be the auxiliary projection of the point where the line pierces the plane. See Fig. 15–51(b).

The piercing point of a line with the coordinate planes can be found in the same manner since the reference line is always an edgewise view of one of the coordinate planes. Thus, in Fig. 15–52(a), when one is looking at the vertical projection, a^Vb^V, of a line, the horizontal reference line is the edgewise view of the H-plane. Hence extend a^Vb^V until it pierces the H-plane at h^V. The horizontal projection is then at h^H on a^Hb^H extended, and

h^P on a^Pb^P extended.

In the same manner, when one is looking at a^Hb^H, the top view of the line in Fig. 15–52(b), the horizontal reference line represents the edgewise view of the V-plane. Hence, extend a^Hb^H until it pierces the V-plane at v^H. The vertical projection v^V is directly below v^H on a^Vb^V extended.

The profile plane appears edgewise in both the front and top views, and the piercing point may be determined simply by extending both projections of AB until they cross the profile reference line at p^H and p^V. See Fig. 15–52(c).

If a line is parallel to one of the coordinate planes it is said to pierce it at infinity. Obviously, this cannot be shown on a drawing. It may, however, be indicated by an arrow with the symbol for infinity at the end of the line, as illustrated in Fig. 15–53.

When a line is parallel to the profile plane its H- and V-piercing points are obtained by making the profile view. Since both the H- and V-planes appear edgewise in this view, the piercing points can be obtained by in-

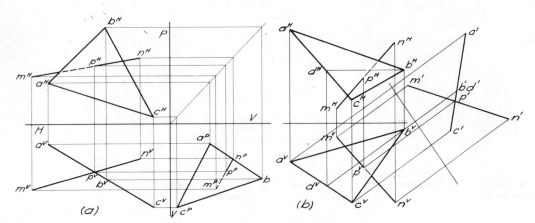

Fig. 15–51.   Point in which a line pierces a plane. Edgewise view method.

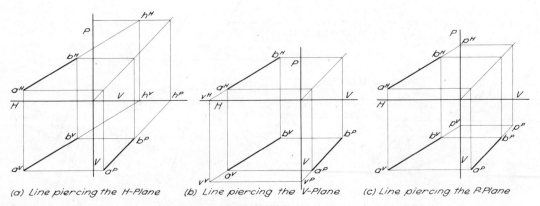

(a) Line piercing the H-Plane   (b) Line piercing the V-Plane   (c) Line piercing the P-Plane

Fig. 15–52.   Points in which a line pierces the coordinate planes.

spection, as shown in Fig. 15–54. The other views can then be obtained by projection.

The piercing point of a line with the coordinate planes has many applications, as, for example, in oblique projection, Fig. 18–4, and perspective, Fig. 19–7.

In other problems such as outcrop problems in mining, see Fig. 25–30, highway or railroad cuts and fills, see Figs. 25–31, 25–32, and intersection problems in Chapter 16, the principle of piercing points of lines with other surfaces must be used.

15.31   Point in which a line pierces a plane. Cutting plane method. Space analysis. *If any plane be passed through the line and the line of intersection of this plane with the given plane be found, the piercing point will be the crossing of the given line with the line of intersection.* This method, as illustrated in Fig. 15–55, is often more convenient than the auxiliary plane method. It is used extensively for finding the intersection of any two surfaces.

The procedure may be stated briefly as follows:

1. Pass a projecting plane through the line as in Fig.

15–55(*a*). A projecting plane always shows edgewise in the view in which it is used.

2. Find the intersection of the given plane with the projecting plane, Fig. 15–55(*b*).

3. Find the point of intersection of the given line with this line of intersection, Fig. 15–55(*c*). Thus, in Fig. 15–55(*a*), the line *XX* is the edgewise view of an *H*-pro-

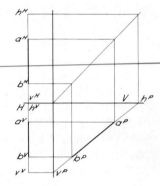

Fig. 15–54.   Piercing points of a P-parallel.

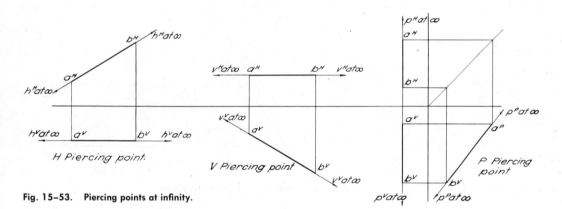

Fig. 15–53.   Piercing points at infinity.

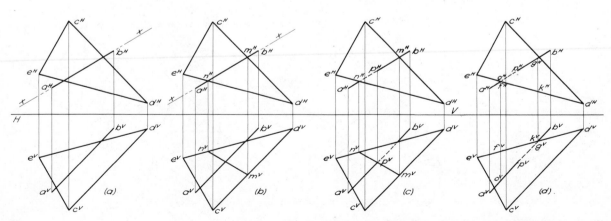

Fig. 15–55.   Point in which a line pierces a plane. Cutting plane method.

jecting plane through the line AB. The piercing points of the lines CD and DE with this plane are located by inspection at M and N, in Fig. 15–55(b). The line MN is therefore the intersection of the cutting plane with plane CDE. Since the lines AB and MN both lie in the plane XX they must intersect or be parallel. In this case they intersect at point P, in Fig. 15–55(c), which is the piercing point of AB with plane CDE. If AB were parallel to MN the line AB would be parallel to the plane.

15.32   Visibility. In order to complete the drawing in Fig. 15–55 it is necessary to show which portion of the line AB is visible. In the top view of Fig. 15–55(d), it is necessary to determine which of the lines AB and DE is above the other by examining the crossing point $o^H f^H$ of their projections. By drawing a vertical projecting line from $o^H f^H$ it can be seen from the front view of f^V on line DE is above o^V on line AB. At this point therefore line AB goes below DE and the plane, and is therefore invisible in the top view from this

point until it emerges above the plane at the piercing point.

The visibility in the front view can be determined in the same manner by observing the crossing point of the vertical projection of the lines AB and DE at $g^V k^V$. By erecting a vertical projecting line from $g^V k^V$ to the top view, it can be seen that k^H on DE is in front of g^H on AB. Hence AB goes behind DE and the plane, and, at this point, becomes invisible until it emerges at the piercing point.

15.33   Outcrop of a plane. *The line in which any plane such as a vein of coal or a bed of stone intersects the surface of the earth is called an outcrop.* The outcrop on a horizontal surface may be found by obtaining the points in which any two lines in the plane of the vein pierce the horizontal surface and joining these two points with a straight line, as shown in Fig. 15–56. This outcrop can also be found by setting up an auxiliary plane perpendicular to the strike line to obtain the

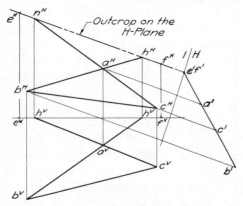

Fig. 15–56.   Outcrop of a plane.

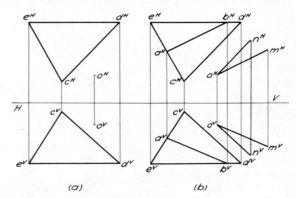

Fig. 15–58.   Lines parallel to a plane.

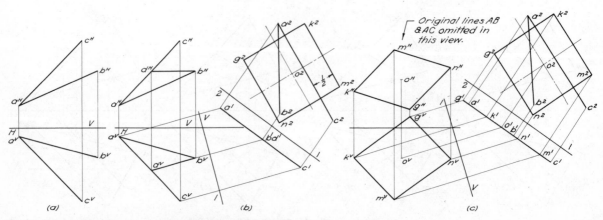

Fig. 15–57.   Construction of a plane figure in a specified position.

edgewise view of the plane.

The point where the auxiliary reference line and the edgewise view of the plane intersect is the point projection, e^1f^1, of a line that lies in the horizontal plane and in the plane of the vein. This line EF is the outcrop which can be located in the horizontal view at e^Hf^H by projecting from e^1f^1 perpendicular to the 1-H reference line. This line is indefinite in length, so the projections e^H and f^H may be placed anywhere along the outcrop as shown in Fig. 15-56. The outcrop on a vertical plane such as the side of an excavation can be found by obtaining the piercing points of any two lines in the vein with the given vertical plane and joining them together. Usually the surface of the earth is defined by contours, in which case the method of finding the outcrop is explained in Art. 25.26.

15.34   Construction of a plane figure in a specified plane. A plane is determined in a number of ways, as was discussed in Art. 15.14, the more common methods being by two intersecting lines or two parallel lines to which all the other methods such as "by three points" can be reduced. In the plane determined by lines AB and AC in Fig. 15-57, let it be required to construct a square of a given size with one side parallel to AC and ½ inch from it. The first step is to find the true value of the angle between the lines AB and AC by means of two auxiliary views, as shown in Fig. 15-57(b). In the second auxiliary view the square may be drawn in its proper size and position. The projections are then carried back to the horizontal and vertical projections in the usual manner, as shown in Fig. 15-57(c).

15.35   Line parallel to a plane. Space analysis. *A line is parallel to a plane when it is parallel to any line in that plane.*

Thus, in Fig. 15-58, if it is required to construct a line through O parallel to the plane CDE, one may draw any line AB in the plane CDE and then through O draw the projections of OM parallel to the corresponding projections of AB. Any edge line of the triangle CDE could also have been used, as for example, ON is parallel to CD.

A line may also be drawn parallel to a plane by making one projection of the line parallel to the corresponding edgewise view of the plane, as shown in Fig. 15-59. The other projections may have any convenient position so long as they are in correct alignment with each other. For example, let it be required to draw a line through O in Fig. 15-59(a) parallel to plane ABC. The edgewise view of the plane with the corresponding projection of O may be obtained by auxiliary projection as shown in Fig. 15-59(b). Through o^1 draw o^1m^1 parallel to $a^1b^1c^1$. The adjacent projection of o^Vm^V may be made in any direction. The projection o^Hm^H is found in the usual way.

15.36   Plane parallel to one or two lines. Space analysis. *If any plane contains a line parallel to a second line, then that plane is parallel to this second line.*

When only one line is involved there are an infinite number of solutions but if two non-parallel lines are involved only one solution is possible.

To construct a plane through a point parallel to a given line it is only necessary to draw a line ON through the point parallel to the given line AB as shown in Fig. 15-60. Any plane such as OMN containing this line satisfies the condition.

If a plane is to be constructed through a point parallel to two given lines, then two lines must be drawn through the point respectively parallel to the two given

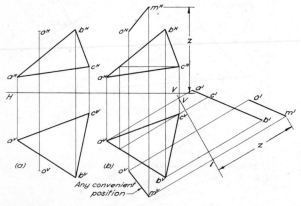

Fig. 15-59.   Line parallel to a plane.

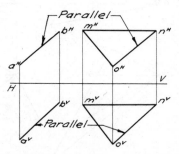

Fig. 15-60.   Plane parallel to one line.

lines, as shown in Fig. 15–61. The plane of the two lines is the required plane. The line *ON* is parallel to *CD,* and *OM* is parallel to *AB,* thus satisfying the conditions.

15.37   Line perpendicular to a plane. Space analysis. *A line is perpendicular to a plane when it is perpendicular to any two non-parallel lines in the plane.*

Theoretically any two intersecting lines may be used but to make the construction as easy as possible, it is best to use an *H*-parallel and a *V*-parallel. Figure 15–62(*a*) shows a plane *ABC* with the *H*-parallel *AD* and the *V*-parallel *AE* already constructed. To make *AG* perpendicular to *ABC,* $a^H g^H$ is drawn perpendicular to $a^H d^H$ and $a^V g^V$ is drawn perpendicular to $a^V e^V,$ as in Fig. 15–62(*b*), thus making *AG* at right angles to both lines *AD* and *AE,* as explained in Art. 15.13.3. Any line parallel to *AG* will also be perpendicular to the plane.

The edgewise view of a plane may also be used to construct a perpendicular. In Fig. 15–63, the plane *ABC* shows edgewise in the front view. Any line perpendicular to this plane must also be parallel to the *V*-plane. The line *DE* is therefore drawn at right angles to plane *ABC* by making $d^V e^V$ perpendicular to $a^V b^V c^V$ and $d^H e^H$ parallel to the reference line.

This method may be used for any plane by obtaining first an edge view by auxiliary projection, as shown in Fig. 15–64. In the auxiliary view, draw $d^1 e^1$ perpendicular to $b^1 a^1 c^1$ and the adjacent view parallel to the auxiliary reference line. The remaining projection is obtained in the usual way.

15.38   Plane perpendicular to a line. This is simply the reverse of the problem in the preceding paragraph and may be solved by either procedure discussed in that paragraph.

The first solution, shown in Fig. 15–65(*a*), consists of drawing two lines *BC* and *BD* each perpendicular to the line *AB,* as explained in Art. 15.13.3 and illustrated in Fig. 15–26. The plane of these two lines is the required plane.

In the second method shown in Fig. 15–65(*b*) and (*c*), the edgewise view of the plane is drawn perpendicular

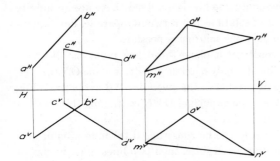

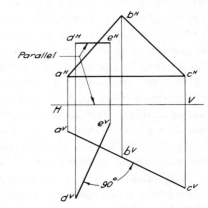

Fig. 15–61.   Plane parallel to two lines.

Fig. 15–63.   Line perpendicular to a plane. Edgewise view method.

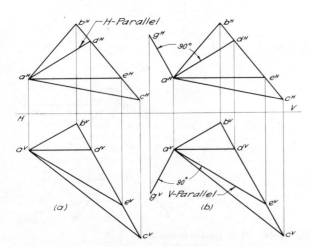

Fig. 15–62.   Line perpendicular to a plane.

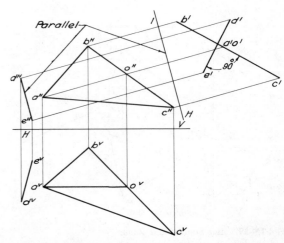

Fig. 15–64.   Line perpendicular to a plane. Edgewise view method.

to the true length view of the line. The adjacent view may be drawn in any position so long as the points are in proper alignment. In Fig. 15–65(*b*), the true length view of the line is the top view or horizontal projection, but the same principles would apply in any view.

For an oblique line as shown in Fig. 15–65(*c*), it is first necessary to obtain a true length view of the line by auxiliary projection. Beginning in the auxiliary view the procedure is the same as outlined above.

15.39   Distance from a point to a plane. Space analysis. *The distance from a point to a plane is the true length of the perpendicular line from the point to the plane.*

This true length will appear in any view which shows the plane edgewise. Hence the problem may be solved by obtaining the edgewise view of the plane together with the corresponding projection of the point. In Fig. 15–66, the perpendicular distance from o^1 to the edge

view of the plane in the auxiliary projection is the required distance. Since o^1p^1 is the true length, o^Hp^H must be drawn parallel to the auxiliary reference line *H-1*.

It should be noted that the shortest level line from a point to the plane can likewise be found in the auxiliary projection by drawing from m^1 parallel to the *1-H* reference line till it pierces the plane at n^1. A line of any slope can be constructed by making the auxiliary projection of the line at the specified slope with the *H-1* reference line. In each case the horizontal projection must be parallel to the *1-H* reference line.

15.40   Distance between two parallel planes. The distance between two parallel planes can be determined by direct measurement between the edge views, as shown in Fig. 15–67.

15.41   Plane parallel to another plane. Space analysis. *One plane is parallel to a second plane when two inter-*

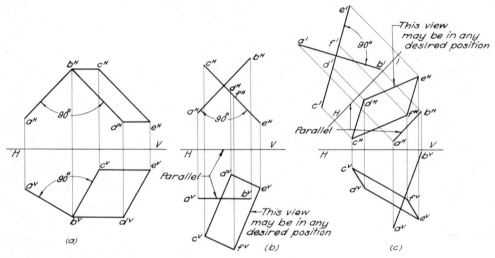

Fig. 15–65.   Plane perpendicular to a line.

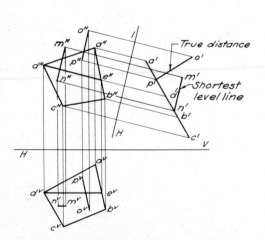

Fig. 15–66.   Distance from a point to a plane.

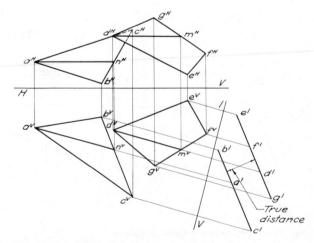

Fig. 15–67.   Distance between two parallel planes.

secting lines in the first are respectively parallel to two lines in the second.

Thus, in Fig. 15-68(a), the hexagon *ABCDEF* is parallel to the triangle *MNO* because *AB* is parallel to *MN* and *CD* is parallel to *NO*. Thus by the simple principle of parallel lines it is possible to lay out one plane parallel to another.

When two planes are parallel they will appear parallel in any principal or auxiliary view in which they appear edgewise. This method may therefore be used to determine the parallel relationship or to construct one plane parallel to another, as shown in Fig. 15-68(b). If the edgewise views are parallel, the other projections may have any shape as long as they remain in projection.

15.42   Plane perpendicular to a plane. Space analysis. *If a line is perpendicular to a given plane any plane containing the line is perpendicular to the given plane.*

Thus in Fig. 15-69(a) the line *AB* has been constructed perpendicular to the plane *DEFG* by the method discussed in Art. 15.37. Since the plane *ABC* contains the line *AB* the plane is perpendicular to *DEFG*. Another method for constructing two planes perpendicular to each other is discussed in the next paragraph.

If an edge view of one plane is found as $a^1b^1c^1$ in Fig. 15-69(b), another plane such as *DEFG* may be set up perpendicular to *ABC*, or at any other angle, by making the edge view $d^1e^1f^1g^1$ at the prescribed angle with

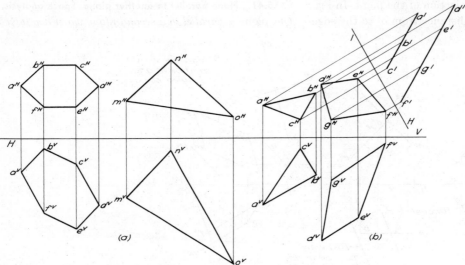

Fig. 15-68.   Plane parallel to a plane.

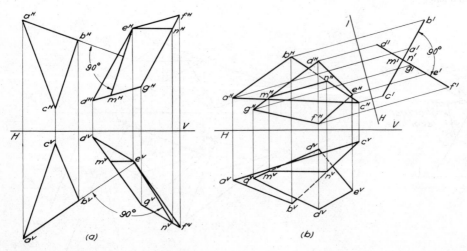

Fig. 15-69.   Plane perpendicular to a plane.

$a^1b^1c^1$. The adjacent projection of *DEFG* may be placed in any convenient position so long as it is in proper alignment with $d^1e^1f^1g^1$.

15.43 Intersection of two planes. Space analysis. *The intersection of two planes is a straight line which is determined by two points each common to both planes.*

The problem, therefore, resolves itself into finding two points common to both planes. Using the method described in Art. 15.31, the point *O* in Fig. 15–70(*a*), where line *BC* pierces the plane *DEFG,* is found. The point *P* in Fig. 15–70(*b*) in which *DG* pierces plane *ABC* locates the second point of the line *OP*. The line *OP* shown in Fig. 15–70(*c*) is the required line of intersection. Visibility may be determined as described in Art. 15.32 and shown in Fig. 15–70(*c*) and (*d*).

Another method for determining the line of intersection of two planes is useful for geologists when the planes are determined by strike and dip. In Fig. 15–71, two planes through point *A* are determined by their strikes and dips as they would appear on a map. By placing an auxiliary plane perpendicular to *AB,* the edgewise view of one of the planes can be obtained by laying off the dip as indicated in Fig. 15–71.

Another auxiliary plane perpendicular to *AC* will make it possible to construct the edgewise view of the second plane by laying off the dip as shown in Fig. 15–71. If a cutting plane *TT* be passed parallel to the horizontal, the edgewise views of this plane may be shown in both auxiliary views. The line of intersection of this cutting plane with the plane through *AB* is *DE* and with the plane through *AC* is *KG*. The point *F* where these two lines intersect is a point on both planes and therefore one point on their line of intersection. The line *AF* is therefore the line of intersection of the two given planes.

15.44 Angle between two planes. Space analysis. *When two planes show edgewise on the same plane of projection, the true angle between the planes will show*

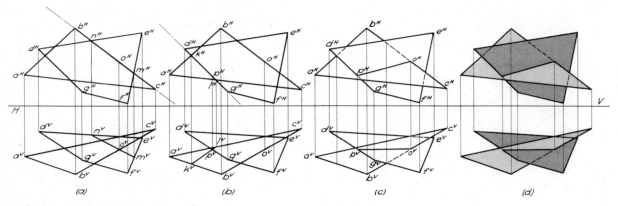

Fig. 15–70. Intersection of two planes.

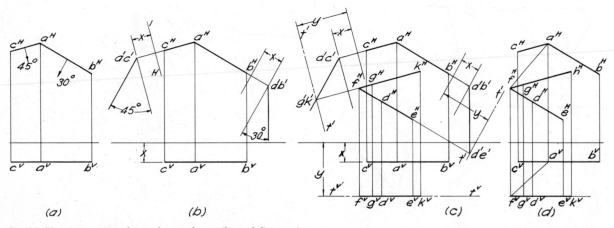

Fig. 15–71. Intersection of two planes when strike and dip are given.

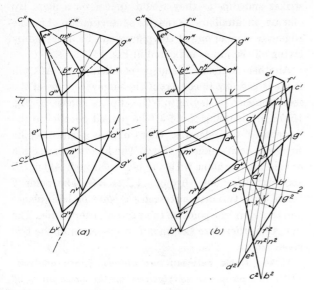

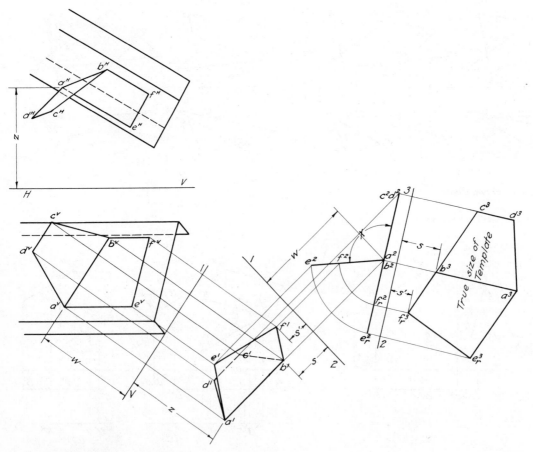

Fig. 15-72. **Angle between two planes.**

between the edge views.

When the angle between two given planes is required the edge views of both planes can be found on an auxiliary plane perpendicular to their line of intersection. In Fig. 15-72(a), it is therefore necessary to find the line of intersection MN of the two planes by the usual methods. In Fig. 15-72(b), the first auxiliary plane is set up parallel to MN and a second auxiliary plane perpendicular to MN, thus giving the edge view of both planes and the angle between them.

A common problem of this type is the layout of a gusset plate connecting two structural members. Since the gusset plate must be cut from a flat piece of steel, the true size of each part must be obtained in addition to the angle between them.

Having the true angle X between the faces in the second auxiliary view as shown in Fig. 15-73, find the true shape of one face on an auxiliary plane parallel to it. Then revolve the other face about the line of inter-

Fig. 15-73. **True size of gusset plate.**

section, until it is also parallel to the same auxiliary plane as explained in Art. 15.23. This layout will give the true size of the plate before bending.

15.45 Angle between a line and a plane. Space analysis. *The true angle between a line and a plane will show on an auxiliary plane which is simultaneously parallel to the line and perpendicular to the plane.* The solution of this problem may require three auxiliary views as illustrated in Fig. 15-74. First, secure an edge view of the plane. Second, make a true shape view of the plane as in Fig. 15-74(*a*). Third, construct another edge view of the plane on an auxiliary plane parallel to the line. See Fig. 15-74(*b*). This view gives the required angle. This angle can also be found by revolving the line *AB* about an axis, *BG,* perpendicular to the plane *CDEF* until it is parallel to the first auxiliary plane as shown at $a_r^2 b^2$ in Fig. 15-74(*b*). In this case the angle will show between the edgewise view of the plane $c^1d^1e^1f^1$ in the first auxiliary projection and the revolved position of the line

$b^1 a_r^1$ as shown in the dashed lines in Fig. 15-74(*b*).

15.46 Construction of a solid in a specified position. As an illustration, let it be required to construct a right pentagonal pyramid with line *AB* of Fig. 15-75(*a*) as an axis and point *C* as one corner of the base. To solve this problem, the following steps are necessary.

a. Project the point and line on an auxiliary plane perpendicular to the line. See Fig. 15-75(*a*).

b. Construct the true size of the base in the second auxiliary projection. See Fig. 15-75(*b*).

c. Construct the elevation of the pyramid in the first auxiliary projection. See Fig. 15-75(*b*).

d. Project the pyramid back to the vertical projection as shown in Fig. 15-75(*c*).

e. Project the pyramid back to the horizontal projection as shown in Fig. 15-75(*d*).

f. Determine the visibility in each view.

15.47 Shortest distance between two non-parallel, non-intersecting lines. Space analysis. *The shortest distance*

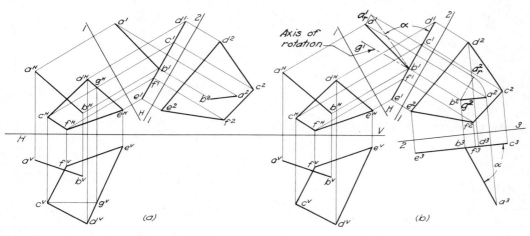

Fig. 15-74.   Angle between a line and a plane.

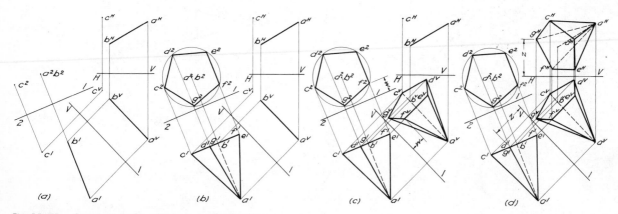

Fig. 15-75.   Construction of a solid in a specified position.

between two *non-parallel, non-intersecting lines is the true length of their common perpendicular.* Lines of this type are sometimes called skew lines. This problem can be solved by projecting both lines on a plane perpendicular to one of them as in Fig. 15–76(a). Having this projection, draw a line from a^2b^2 perpendicular to c^2d^2 as in Fig. 15–76(b) and letter it m^2n^2. Point n^1 may be found on c^1d^1 by direct projection. Construct m^1n^1 parallel to reference line *1–2* since *MN* is perpendicular to *AB* and hence parallel to plane *2*. Return the projections of *M* and *N* to the original views by the usual methods.

15.48   Line parallel to a given line and intersecting two non-parallel, non-intersecting lines. Let it be required to draw a line parallel to *EF* and intersecting *AB* and *CD* as shown in Fig. 15–77(a).

Analysis. If the point of projection of one of the lines is found, the required line can be drawn in that projection through the point and parallel to the given line until it intersects the other of the two skew lines.

The solution for this particular problem is found by projecting all three lines on a plane perpendicular to *AB*, as shown in Fig. 15–77(b). Since parallel lines always have their projections parallel, draw a line from a^2b^2

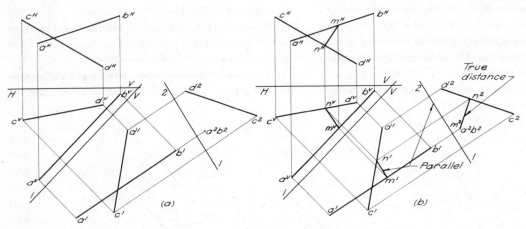

Fig. 15–76.   Shortest distance between two non-parallel, non-intersecting lines.

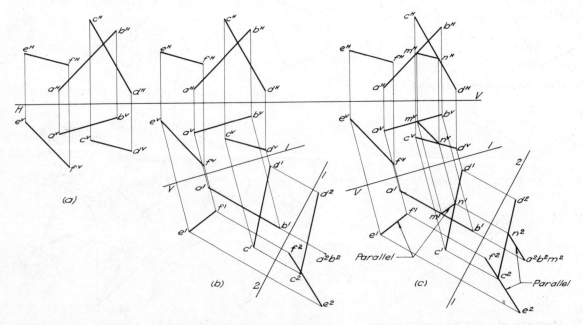

Fig. 15–77.   Line parallel to a given line and intersecting two skew lines.

parallel to e^2f^2 until it intersects c^2d^2 at n^2, as in Fig. 15–77(*c*). In the first auxiliary view, draw a line from n^1 parallel to e^1f^1 until it intersects a^1b^1 at m^1, thus determining a line between *AB* and *CD* parallel to *EF*. Return the line *MN* to the original views in the usual manner.

The solution could also have been obtained by placing an auxiliary plane perpendicular to the line *EF,* in which case the required line *MN* would have shown as a point in the second auxiliary view.

15.49 Construction cone. When a line is to be established making a specified angle with a given plane or line, the right circular cone provides a convenient working tool for the solution. The following problems illustrate its use.

15.49.1 *Line through a point making a given angle with H-, V-, or P-plane. Space analysis.* A right circular cone having the specified base angle may be set up with its vertex at the given point and its axis perpendicular to the required plane. Any element of this cone will satisfy the conditions of the problem.

As an illustration, let it be required to draw a line through point *A* in Fig. 15–78 making an angle of 45° with the *H*-plane. Through *A* draw a line *AB* of any convenient length perpendicular to the *H*-plane. With *AB* as an axis, draw a right circular cone whose elements make 45° with the base. Any element such as *AC* will satisfy the conditions of the problem.

A similar construction for the vertical and profile planes can be made by drawing the axis of the cone perpendicular to either of these planes.

15.49.2 *Line through a point making given angles with both H- and V-planes. Space analysis.* If two cones are drawn from the same point as a vertex with one having its axis perpendicular to H and the other perpendicular to V and each having the proper base angle, the intersection of these cones will satisfy the conditions of the problem.

For simplicity of solution the bases of both cones should be on the surface of a sphere whose center is at the given point through which the line is to be constructed. The outer circles in Fig. 15–79 represent the projections of the sphere. Every element of both cones is therefore a radius of the sphere and consequently they are of equal length. If the solution is possible, the cones will intersect and since the elements are all the same length and the bases lie on the surface of the sphere, the bases will intersect each other at one or two points. These points, when connected with the apex of the cones, will be the required lines since they are elements of both cones.

Let it be required to construct a line through the point *A* in Fig. 15–79 making an angle of 30° with the *H*-plane and 45° with the *V*-plane. With point *A* as a center draw the *H* and *V* projections of a sphere whose radius will be equal to the desired length of elements for the cones. With *A* as a center, construct a right circular cone with its axis perpendicular to the *H*-plane and its elements equal to the radius of the sphere, and making an angle of 30° with the *H*-plane. With the same apex, construct another cone with its axis perpendicular to the *V*-plane, and with its elements making 45° with the

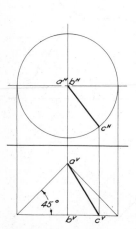

Fig. 15–78. Line making a specified angle with the H-plane. Cone method.

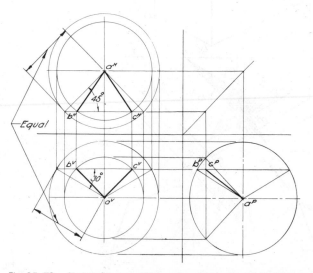

Fig. 15–79. Line making specified angles with the H- and V-planes.

V-plane and equal in length to the radius of the sphere. The bases will now intersect each other at points *B* and *C* in Fig. 15–79. Joining these points to the apex gives the lines *AB* and *AC* which satisfy the conditions of the problem.

In this problem the profile view is useful since both axes are parallel to profile and consequently both cones show as triangles.

15.49.3   *Line through a point making a given angle with any two planes.* The solution of this problem, illustrated in Fig. 15–80, is the same as the preceding one but represents a more general case. Here the line of intersection of the two planes has been made perpendicular to the *V*-plane. The solution involves the construction of two cones with axes perpendicular respectively to the two planes as shown in Fig. 15–80.

If the line of intersection of the two planes is not perpendicular to one of the coordinate planes, then the first step in the solution will be to find the edge view of both planes on a plane perpendicular to their line of intersection. This auxiliary plane will be parallel to the axes of both cones and therefore will show both cones as triangles. The remainder of the solution is similar to that shown in Fig. 15–80.

15.50   Line intersecting two skew lines and making specified angles with two given skew lines. Space analysis. *Since the elements of a right circular cone make a constant angle with the axis, construction cones may be used to draw a line making a given angle with another line or two separate lines. Lines parallel to these constructed lines may then be drawn intersecting the two given skew lines.*

Let it be required to construct a line intersecting *AB* and *CD* in Fig. 15–81 making 60° with *AB* and 45° with *CD*. The solution is as follows:

a. Through any point *O* construct twolines, *OE* and *OF*, respectively parallel to *AB* and *CD*. Figure 15–81(*a*).

b. Project both lines on plane *1* to get the edgewise view at $o^1e^1f^1$ and on plane *2* to get the true size at $e^2o^2f^2$ in Fig. 15–81(*a*).

c. In the second auxiliary view construct one view of the desired sphere, and using o^2e^2 and o^2f^2 as axes draw the cones using the specified angles. Figure 15–81(*b*).

d. Set up a third auxiliary plane parallel to either one of the bases of the cones and draw the circle representing that base. Figure 15–81(*b*).

e. In the second auxiliary projection the bases of the cones intersect at m^2n^2. The lines *OM* and *ON* are lines

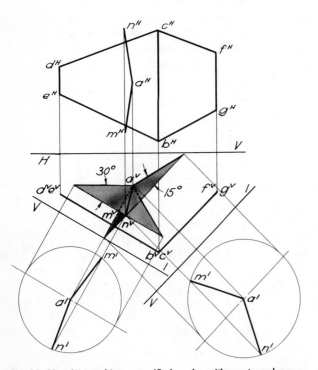

Fig. 15–80.   Line making a specified angles with any two planes.

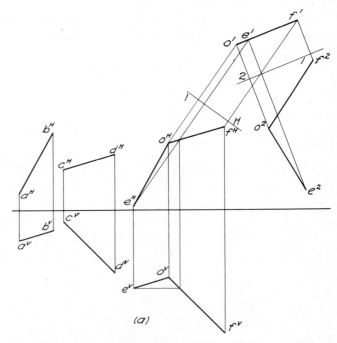

(a)

Fig. 15–81.   Line intersecting two skew lines and making specified angles with them.

through point O parallel to the required line, and they may be projected back to the H and V projections. Figure 15–81(b).

f. In Fig. 15–81(c) project $AB, CD, OM,$ and ON on a plane perpendicular to AB. In the second auxiliary projection the required lines ST and XY may be constructed as explained in Art. 15.48.

15.51   Plane making a specified angle with a given line or plane. Space analysis. *The plane may be made tangent to a construction cone that has been set up so that its elements make the desired angle with the given line or plane.*

As an example, let it be required to construct a plane containing the line AB in Fig. 15–82 and making 60° with the horizontal plane. Choose any point on AB, and make that point the apex of the cone. In this case, the apex is at A and a cone whose elements make 60° with the H-plane has been constructed. The size of the cone is not important but it should be large enough to get accurate results. Next find the point $P,$ where AB pierces the plane of the base. From this point, construct a line PC tangent to the base of the cone. The lines AP and PC determine the required plane. The line PC can be drawn tangent to the circle on either side.

15.52   Planes making specified angles with two given planes. Space analysis. *If a line be constructed making angles with two planes that are complements of the required angles, the required plane may be constructed perpendicular to this line.*

It is first necessary to find the edgewise view of both planes by setting up an auxiliary plane perpendicular to the line of intersection of the two planes. In Fig.

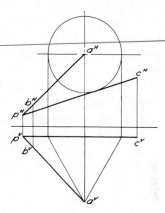

Fig. 15–82. Plane containing a given line and making specified angle with the *H*-plane.

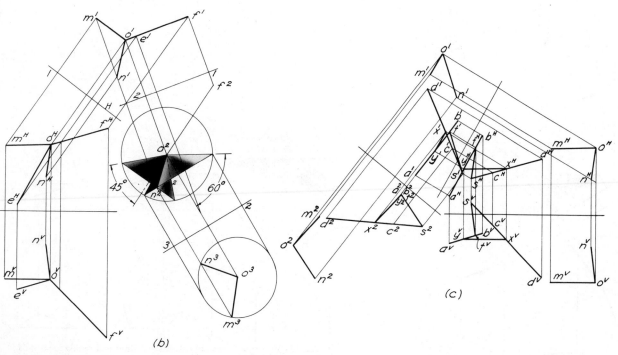

(b)

Fig. 15–81. **(Continued)**

(c)

15–83 this has been completed, and the resulting views are shown as horizontal and vertical projections although in a general problem they would probably be auxiliary projections one and two. The steps in the solution are as follows when it is desired to obtain a plane making 60° with *ABCD* and 40° with *CDEF*.

a. By means of construction cones, determine the lines *OM* and *ON* that make an angle of 30° with *ABCD* and 50° with *CDEF*. This is illustrated in Fig. 15–83(*b*) and explained in Art. 15.49.3.

b. Construct the plane *ORS* perpendicular to *OM* and the plane *OXY* perpendicular to *ON*. This is explained in Art. 15.38 and illustrated in Fig. 15–83(*c*). These planes *ORS* and *OXY* contain the point *O* and make the required angles with the given planes.

15.53   Shortest line having any given slope and intersecting two non-parallel, non-intersecting lines. Space analysis. *The shortest line having a given slope will be parallel to a plane that is perpendicular to the horizontal plane and upon which the two skew lines appear parallel.*

Let it be required to construct the shortest line from *AB* to *CD* that has an angle of slope of −15°.

Construction. Through point *A* in Fig. 15–84, draw a line *AE* parallel to *CD*. In the plane of these two lines, construct the *H*-parallel *EF* and set up an auxiliary plane perpendicular to this line. The projections a^1b^1

and c^1d^1 on this plane will appear parallel as specified in the space analysis. Since any line that is parallel to plane *1* must have its horizontal projection parallel to the *1-H* reference line, the true slope of the line will show between the projection of the line on plane *1* and the *1-H* reference line. See Art. 15.10.

The next step must be to set up any line that is parallel to plane *1* and has a slope of −15°. *TW* is such a line. An auxiliary plane perpendicular to *TW* will show the required line as a point. Plane *4* is therefore set up by making the *1–4* reference line perpendicular to t^1w^1. When the lines *AB* and *CD* are projected on plane *4*, they will intersect in a line which shows as a point x^4y^4. The line *XY* is the required shortest line drawn from *AB* to *CD* with a −15° slope. Since all points on it are the same distance from plane *1*, the horizontal projection x^Hy^H must be parallel to *1-H*, and therefore the projection x^1y^1 shows the true slope.

Other planes may be set up perpendicular to plane *1* to determine lines having other slopes. Plane *3* has been set up so that the projection lines are parallel to reference line *1-H*, and consequently the line *RS* obtained from this projection is the shortest horizontal line that can be drawn intersecting the lines *AB* and *CD*.

Plane *2* has been set up parallel to *AB* and *CD* to obtain the shortest perpendicular between the two lines. Another construction for this was given in Art. 15.47.

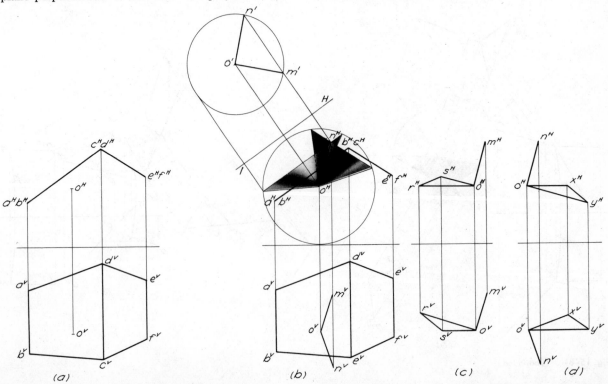

Fig. 15–83.   Plane making specified angles with two planes.

The intersection of $a^H b^H$ and $c^H d^H$ gives a line GK that is the line intersecting the two lines and perpendicular to the horizontal plane.

It should be noted that the projections of all these lines on plane 1 intersect in a point marked $o^1 p^1$. This point may be found by means of any two of the planes H, 2, 3, or 4, and thereafter lines of any desired slope may be drawn through this point in that projection. OP actually represents a line that is the axis of an hyperbolic paraboloid of which all these lines are elements. The hyperbolic paraboloid is further discussed in Art. 15.55.1 and also shown in Fig. 4–37.

15.54 Locus problems. The concepts of loci appears in some descriptive geometry problems. The solution of such problems usually requires that the general locus be determined first and then that further limiting conditions be applied. For example, let it be required to find the locus of points equidistant from two given points and in a given plane. The general locus of points equidistant from two given points is the plane perpendicular bisector of the line joining the points. This plane must be determined first. The second condition limits the locus to points lying in a particular given plane. Hence the answer is the line of intersection of the two planes.

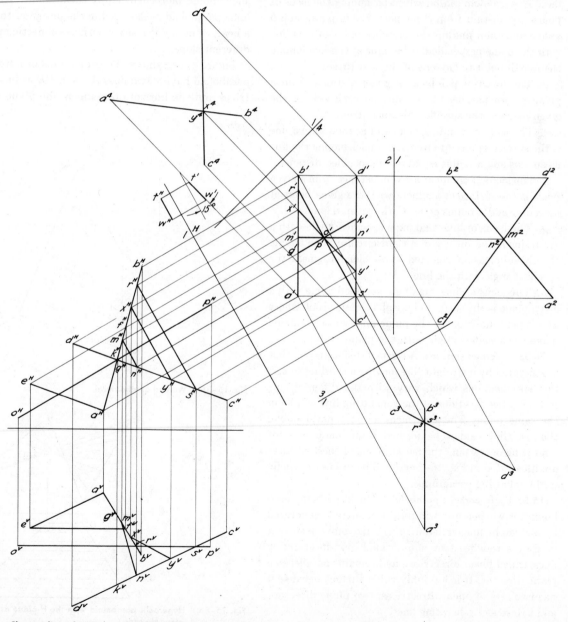

Fig. 15–84. Shortest line of a given slope intersecting two skew lines.

The loci most commonly used are listed below.

a. The locus of points equidistant from two given points is the plane perpendicular bisector of the line joining the points.

b. The locus of points equidistant from three given points is the line of intersection of the two plane perpendicular bisectors of the two lines joining the three points. This line will be perpendicular to the plane of the three points.

c. The locus of points equidistant from four given points (not lying in a plane) is a single point, which is the center of a sphere having the four points on its surface. This problem can be solved by finding the locus of points equidistant from three points as in paragraph *b* above and then finding the piercing point of this line with the plane perpendicular bisector of the line joining the fourth point to any one of the first three.

d. The locus of points at a given distance from a plane is two parallel planes, one on each side of the given plane at the specified distances from it.

e. The locus of points at a given distance from a line is the surface of a right circular cylinder having the line as an axis and a radius equal to the specified distance.

f. The locus of points at a given distance from a given point is the surface of a sphere with the given point as its center and a radius equal to the given distance.

g. The locus of lines making a specified angle with a given line is the surface of a right circular cone having the given line as an axis, and whose elements make the specified angle with the line.

h. The locus of lines making a specified angle with a given plane is the surface of a right circular cone whose axis is perpendicular to the plane and whose elements make the specified angle with the plane.

15.55   Warped surfaces. A warped surface is one that is generated by a straight line moving according to certain specifications which vary with the different surfaces. No two positions of the generating line will lie in the same plane. These surfaces are non-developable; that is, they cannot be formed from metal without stretching or warping the metal. Some of these surfaces are illustrated in Fig. 16–1 and will be discussed briefly in the following paragraphs.

15.55.1   *Hyperbolic paraboloid.* The hyperbolic paraboloid or warped quadrilateral is a surface generated by a straight line, called a generatrix, moving so that it always touches two non-parallel, non-intersecting lines, called linear directrices, and remains parallel to a plane director. It is a doubly ruled surface because it has two sets of linear directrices, two plane directors, and two sets of generating lines.

If the surface is defined by giving four bounding lines as *ABCD* in Fig. 15–85, it is called a warped quadrilateral. Elements may be drawn in the surface by dividing either set of linear directrices (opposite sides) into the same number of equal spaces and drawing lines connecting the division points. If a plane be passed through *AB* parallel to *CD*, this plane will be one of the plane directrices and one set of elements will all be parallel to that plane. The other plane may be found by passing a plane through *AD* parallel to *BC*.

The hyperbolic paraboloid is sometimes used as the basis or framework of some practical structure and as such should be recognized by the student. The hyperbolic paraboloid is also used in the design of the bow of a boat, or in any transition surface connecting planes of different slope.

Figure 15–86 shows the projections of a hyperbolic paraboloid having two lines *AB* and *CD* as linear directrices and the horizontal plane as the plane director.

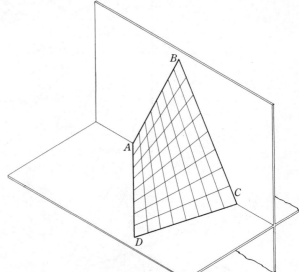

Fig. 15–85.   Warped quadrilateral.

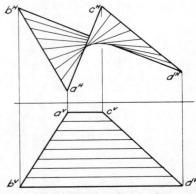

Fig. 15–86.   Hyperbolic paraboloid with the *H*-plane as the plane director.

Since the horizontal reference line represents the edgewise view of the horizontal plane in the vertical projection, that projection of the elements may be drawn parallel to the reference line. Therefore, to construct one view of any hyperbolic paraboloid, it is only necessary to find the edgewise view of the plane director by means of one or more auxiliary planes and draw the elements in that view. They may then be projected to the other views by means of their intersections with the linear directrices as was done in Fig. 15–86.

Note that the true length lines of various slopes in Fig. 15–84 are elements of a hyperbolic paraboloid which are perpendicular to and intersect the line *OP*.

15.55.2 *Hyperboloid of revolution of one sheet.* This surface is generated by a right line which revolves about another non-parallel, non-intersecting right line as an axis. It may also be generated by a line touching three circles whose planes are perpendicular to a common axis through their centers. When the radius of the mid-

dle, or gorge, circle becomes zero, the surface is a cone, and, when this radius becomes the same as the radius of the other two circles, the surface is a cylinder. Thus the cone and cylinder become the limits of the hyperboloid of revolution. Since this is a surface of revolution, a plane passed perpendicular to the axis of revolution cuts a circle from the surface.

The surface is doubly ruled, since two different lines may be revolved about the axis to give the same surface. These lines make equal angles with the base but slope in opposite directions. Figure 15–87 gives the projections of a hyperboloid of revolution, showing both sets of generatrices, *AB* and *CD*. The other elements shown are of the *AB* generation, no other positions of *CD* being shown.

The hyperboloid of revolution may be generated also by revolving a hyperbola about its conjugate axis. The surface is sometimes represented by showing its contour lines as illustrated in Fig. 15–88, these contour lines be-

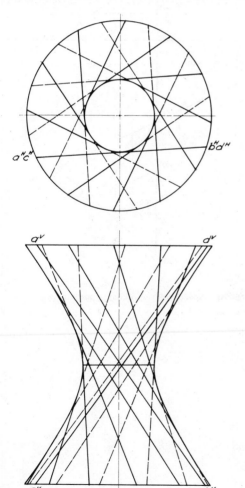

Fig. 15–87. Hyperboloid of revolution.

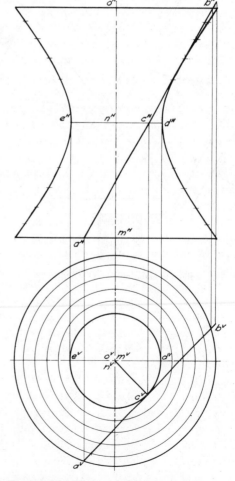

Fig. 15–88. Hyperboloid of revolution.

ing the opposite branches of the hyperbola.

a. *Construction 1*. Having given three curvilinear directrices, as in Fig. 15–87, divide the base circle into a number of equal parts in the plan view and draw the horizontal projection of the elements through these points tangent to the gorge circle. Project the ends of the elements to the elevation, and draw in the elements.

b. *Construction 2*. Having given the axis OM and the generatrix AB, as in Fig. 15–88, draw the gorge circle with a radius CN equal to the perpendicular distance from OM to AB. Project c^V up to c^H on $a^H b^H$, and through c^H draw the vertical projection of the gorge circle perpendicular to the axis. Then locate the limiting points D and E on the gorge circle, the vertices of the

contour hyperbola. By drawing other circles in the horizontal projection this process is repeated and other points on the hyperbola obtained.

The hyperboloid of revolution has practical applications in mechanism, the most important being found in the pitch surfaces of skew gears. If any two right lines not in the same plane be taken as axes, a third line may be taken in a plane parallel to the other two lines so that the hyperboloids formed about the two axes by using the third line as a generatrix will be tangent to each other. They will operate together as the pitch surface of gears, since all elements will in turn assume positions common to both surfaces. Figure 15–89 illustrates this use of the hyperboloid of revolution or roll-

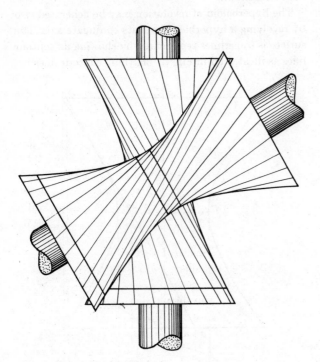

Fig. 15–89.   Rolling hyperboloids.

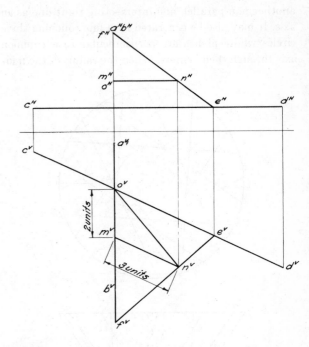

Fig. 15–90.   Speed ratios of rolling hyperboloids.

ing hyperboloid.

c. Construction of rolling hyperboloids for a given speed ratio. Let it be required to find the line of generation of two mating rolling hyperboloids so that axis AB (Fig. 15–90) will make two complete revolutions while axis CD makes three complete revolutions.

To solve this problem each line should be projected on a plane that is parallel to both lines. Thus, in Fig. 15–90, both lines AB and CD are parallel to the vertical plane. In this figure, AB is perpendicular to the H-plane. This makes the construction of the hyperboloids as simple as possible.

Construction. In the vertical projection, construct $o^V m^V$, 2 units long at any convenient scale. This repre-

sents the angular velocity of axis AB. From m^V, construct $m^V n^V$ parallel to $c^V d^V$, 3 units long at the same scale. This represents the angular velocity of axis CD. The line $o^V n^V$ is the vertical projection of the generating line. Point N is therefore on the surface of both hyperboloids. A perpendicular to these surfaces must intersect both axes. Therefore through n^V construct $e^V f^V$ perpendicular to $o^V n^V$ to intersect AB at F and CD at E. The line $e^V f^V$ is the vertical projection of a perpendicular to both surfaces at point N. The horizontal projection of EF may be found by projection to be at $e^H f^H$ on the axis. Projection n^H must lie on $e^H f^H$. Since the line of generation must be in a plane parallel to both lines AB and CD, the horizontal projection of ON may be constructed parallel to the reference line. ON is then the required generating line. The hyperboloids may be constructed as was discussed in Construction 2, Art. 15.55.2*b*. For more detailed discussion, see page 334 in *Practical Geometry and Graphics* by D. A. Low.

Only a small portion of the rolling hyperboloids is used as the pitch surface when skew bevel gears are constructed. If that portion near the gorge circle is used, the pitch surfaces of the gears will be approximately cylindrical, but if a section well removed from the gorge circle is used the pitch surfaces will be approximately conical. This can be observed in Fig. 15–89.

15.55.3   *The helicoid.* A surface generated by a right line moving so that it always touches a helix and its axis, and making a constant angle with its axis, is called a helicoid and is the warped surface most frequently encountered in drafting. It occurs in the surface of screw threads, screw propellers, conveyors, circular staircases, and chutes. If the generatrix is perpendicular to the axis of the helix, the surface is a right helicoid as illustrated by the surface of a Square thread. If the generatrix is inclined to the axis, it is an oblique helicoid such as the surface of a *V* thread. The helicoid is actually a limitless surface, but is usually considered only as the portion contained within a cylinder concentric with the helix.

Construction of a right helicoid. The first step is to construct the helix with a given pitch on the surface of a given cylinder. To do this the pitch is divided into equal parts, and the circle representing the cylinder is divided into the same number of equal parts (24 parts is very convenient), as shown in Fig. 15–91. The points on the circle are then projected up to the horizontal line drawn through the corresponding point on the axis. From the points on the helix, lines are drawn intersecting the axis and perpendicular to it. These lines form

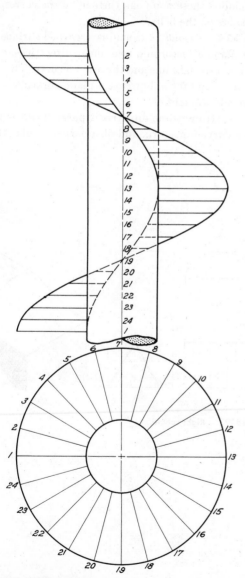

Fig. 15–91.   Right helicoid.

elements of the right helicoid.

Construction of an oblique helicoid. Given the limiting cylinder, the pitch of the helix, and the angle that the elements make with the axis, first construct the helix in the same manner as explained for Fig. 15–91. Then draw in the element AB, Fig. 15–92, making it parallel to the horizontal plane. In this position the true angle that the element makes with the axis shows in the horizontal projection, and the horizontal projection $a^H b^H$ can be drawn. As each element must move the same proportionate distance along the axis as it does along the curve, the other elements are drawn by laying out horizontal distances starting at b^H equal to the horizontal distances between the points on the helix, and joining these points on the axis to the corresponding points on the helix.

15.55.4 *Conoids.* A conoid is a warped surface having a plane director and two linear directrices, one of which is a straight line and the other a curve. The curve may have any form, but closed plane curves are most commonly thought of.

If the straight-line directrix is parallel to the plane of the curved directrix and also perpendicular to the

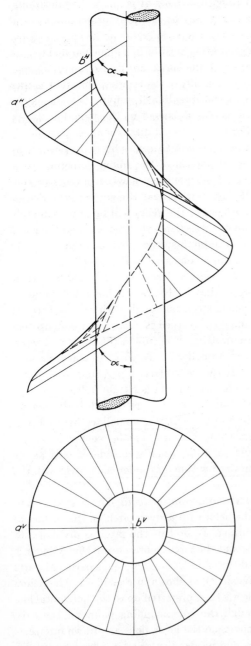

Fig. 15–92. Oblique helicoid.

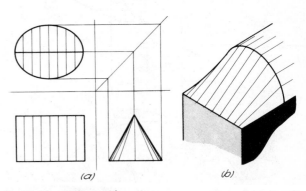

Fig. 15–93. Right conoid.

plane director, the surface is called a right conoid, as shown in Fig. 15-93(*a*). A common application of this form is shown in Fig. 15-93(*b*), where a roof must change from a curved to a flat section.

When the linear directrix, the curved directrix, and the plane director are oblique to each other, the surface is called an oblique conoid. Figure 15-94 shows the projections of an oblique conoid.

15.55.5   *Cylindroid.* A surface generated by a straight line moving so that it always remains parallel to a plane director and at the same time touches two plane curves, not lying in the same plane, is called a cylindroid. These curves are usually parts of circles or ellipses.

Construction. Since this problem is more frequently encountered in arch construction where the plane director is likely to be the horizontal plane, it is so illustrated here. However, it should be clear that any plane director and any plane curves, not lying in the same plane, can be used. Elements of the surface can be found by obtaining the edgewise view of the plane director and drawing elements in that view to intersect the two curvilinear directrices. See Fig. 15-95.

In Fig. 15-95, the two curvilinear directors *ABC* and *DEF* are to be joined by a cylindroid whose plane director is the *H*-plane. This means that elements can be drawn in the vertical projection by making them parallel to the reference line. They may then be carried to the *H*-projection to complete the required views.

15.55.6   *General procedure.* There are many more varieties of warped surfaces and other methods of generation, but the drawing of the surfaces usually consists of drawing elements touching certain curved or right-line directrices or parallel to certain directors. With a general knowledge of engineering geometry the student should be able to follow any of the necessary constructions. Accurate development of warped surfaces is not possible, but it is frequently necessary to get an approximate development. This is done by dividing the surface into small triangles and laying out these triangles side by side in true size. This is called the method of triangulation.

Intersections of warped surfaces with other surfaces may be found by following the general procedure given in Chapter 16 for all intersections. Usually the best method is to find the points where elements of the warped surface pierce the other surface.

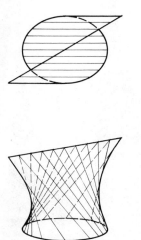

Fig. 15-94.   Oblique conoid.

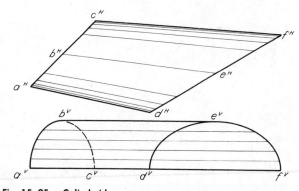

Fig. 15-95.   Cylindroid.

Tank used for the storage of liquid petroleum gas (Shell Oil Company).

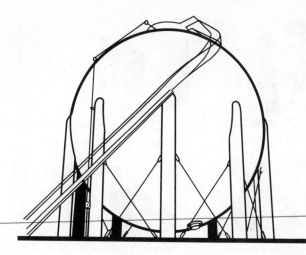

16

Intersections and Developments

16.1 The problems involved in finding the intersections of surfaces and in developing surfaces of various kinds into flat patterns and templates have many applications in a wide range of industries. In some instances intersections are shown in a conventional way as illustrated in Art. 16.21, but in other cases it is necessary to find these intersections with accuracy. Boilers, smokestack breeching, ducts, and ventilators also involve problems of this kind. In ship, automotive, and aircraft drafting the problems are numerous and the intersections must be laid out full size. In aircraft work the layouts on the loft floor are held to a tolerance of .005 inch.

In this chapter we shall discuss not only a variety of practical problems but also the general method of procedure which may be used to solve any problems of this type.

16.2 Geometrical surfaces. Most structures involved in engineering practice are bounded by simple geometric surfaces or more complex combinations of them. The engineer should be familiar with these surfaces and the terminology connected with them. A classification of the more common surfaces shown in Fig. 16–1 is given in the adjacent column.

Many of the surfaces in the accompanying table are often found in practice to exist as the surface of solid objects. In dealing with them, however, the engineer is concerned only with their properties as surfaces. In this book the prisms and pyramids are treated as solids, and cylinders and cones are considered surfaces.

16.3 Finding intersections. The intersection of two surfaces is the line common to both surfaces. The process of finding this line consists of drawing elements of one

CLASSIFICATION OF SURFACES

Ruled surfaces (which can be generated by moving a straight line)
- Plane surfaces
  - Five regular polyhedrons
  - Prisms
  - Pyramids
- Single curved
  - Cylinders
  - Cones
  - Convolutes
- Warped surfaces
  - Cylindroids
  - Conoids
  - Hyperbolic paraboloid
  - Hyperboloid of revolution of one sheet
  - Helicoid

Double-curved surfaces (generated by revolving a curved line)
- Sphere
- Spheroids
  - oblate
  - prolate
- Hyperboloid of two sheets
- Paraboloid
- Torus

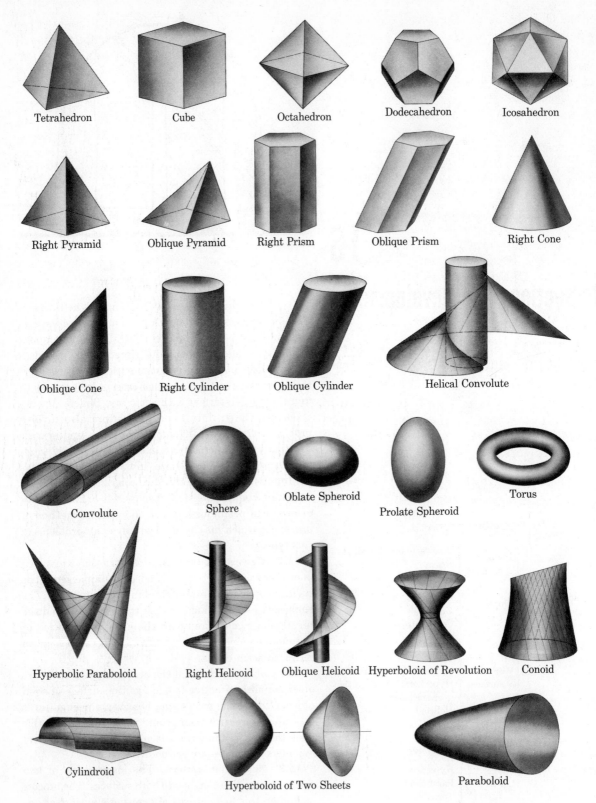

Fig. 16–1. Geometric surfaces.

Tetrahedron Cube Octahedron Dodecahedron Icosahedron

Right Pyramid Oblique Pyramid Right Prism Oblique Prism Right Cone

Oblique Cone Right Cylinder Oblique Cylinder Helical Convolute

Convolute Sphere Oblate Spheroid Prolate Spheroid Torus

Hyperbolic Paraboloid Right Helicoid Oblique Helicoid Hyperboloid of Revolution Conoid

Cylindroid Hyperboloid of Two Sheets Paraboloid

surface and locating the point at which this element pierces the other surface. An element of a surface is any line lying wholly in the surface. It may be either curved or straight. In all ruled surfaces, the straight-line element is preferable since it is the easiest to draw. On double-curved surfaces, the circle is the most practical element which may be used. On some double-curved surfaces, other elements must be used. The general method of finding intersections is explained in detail in the following paragraphs and illustrations.

16.4   Intersection of two planes. For a discussion of this topic, see Art. 15.43.

16.5   Intersection of a plane and prism. The simplest method of finding the piercing points of the edges (elements) of a prism with a plane is to obtain an edgewise view of the plane. The piercing points can then be located by inspection. In Fig. 16.2(a), the plane $ABCD$ shows edgewise in the front view and the piercing points can be seen at e^V, f^V, and g^V. These points can be projected to the side view on the corresponding edges of the prism, giving the view of the intersection $e^P f^P g^P$. The true shape of the truncated face can be found by auxiliary projection from the front view as shown at $e^1 f^1 g^1$.

By assuming only a front and top view given in Fig. 16-2(b), an auxiliary projection is necessary to obtain an edgewise view of the plane. The auxiliary plane is placed perpendicular to the line AB. This can be done since AB is parallel to the H-plane as shown by the projection $a^V b^V$ which is horizontal. Having an edgewise view of the plane, the piercing points can be seen by inspection at $e^1 f^1 g^1$ and then projected back to the corresponding edges in the original views.

The cutting plane method of finding these piercing points, as discussed in Art. 15.31 is frequently very convenient. In Fig. 16–2(c), the cutting planes have been passed through the elements of the prism and perpendicular to the H-plane. (Perpendicular to the V-plane would have been equally satisfactory.) The intersection of these cutting planes with the plane $ABCD$ is then found and the points where these lines of intersection cross the given elements are located. These are the points on the desired intersection. When all of these points have been determined, they can be connected in order, to give the intersection of $ABCD$ with the prism.

16.6   Intersection of a plane and pyramid. The same method of procedure may be used for pyramids as discussed above for prisms.

In Fig. 16–3(a), the plane shows edgewise in the front view but is not outlined in the top view. The piercing points are seen by inspection in the front view and projected to the corresponding lines in the other two views.

When the plane does not appear edgewise in the given views, the chief problem is to obtain such a view. In Fig. 16–3(b), for example, a horizontal line can always be drawn across the plane by making the vertical projection $b^V d^V$ horizontal. From this the horizontal projection $b^H d^H$ is then located and the auxiliary plane set up perpendicular to BD by drawing the reference line H-1 perpendicular to $b^H d^H$. The plane then shows edgewise at $a^1 b^1 c^1 d^1$, and the piercing points may be found by inspection and carried back to the other views as shown in the figure.

16.7   Intersection of a plane and cylinder. This problem again is similar to the preceding ones, the only new feature being that the cylinder has no edges and there-

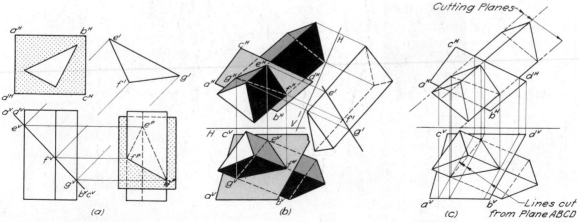

Fig. 16–2.   Intersection of plane and prism.

fore a series of elements must be chosen whose piercing points with the plane will determine the curve of intersection. For most problems of this type twelve equally spaced elements will suffice, as shown in Fig. 16-4. Note that, if the upper part of the cylinder is detached and turned 180° and then again fastened to the lower part, a right-angled elbow would be formed.

A second illustration for an oblique cylinder requiring an auxiliary view is shown in Fig. 16-4(b).

In this illustration, the plane $ABCD$ has the line AB parallel to the H-plane. The auxiliary plane reference line may therefore be placed perpendicular to $a^H b^H$. The piercing points can be seen by inspection in the auxiliary view and then projected to the top view and from there to the front view.

16.8 Intersection of a plane and cone. In making an auxiliary projection to obtain an edgewise view of the plane, it will facilitate the solution a great deal if the base of the cone (cylinder, prism, or pyramid) also appears edgewise in the auxiliary view. In Fig. 16-5, two solutions have been presented, the first of which, Fig. 16-5(a), shows the auxiliary plane perpendicular to V, thus making the base of the cone an elliptical figure.

The position of the auxiliary plane was determined by drawing line AD in the plane parallel to V and making the auxiliary plane perpendicular to this line. Although this solution is correct, a less tedious solution is shown in Fig. 16-5(b).

In the second solution, the line AD was drawn in the plane parallel to H and the auxiliary plane placed per-

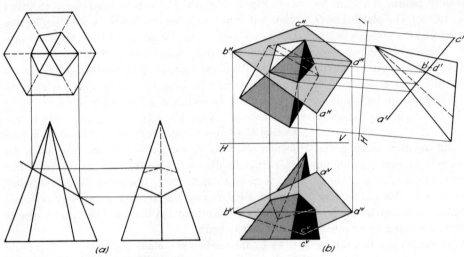

Fig. 16-3. Intersection of plane and pyramid.

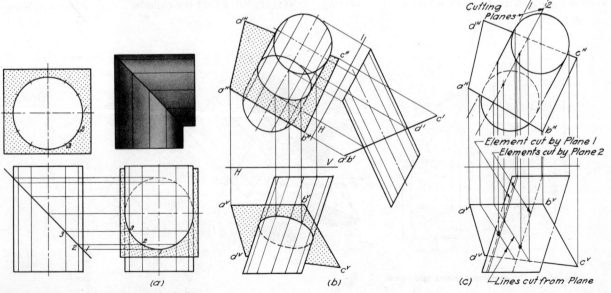

Fig. 16-4. Intersection of plane and cylinder.

pendicular to this line. It can be observed that since the base of the cone is parallel to *H* it will also appear as a straight line or edgewise in the auxiliary projection, thus making the solution much simpler.

16.9 General principles of finding the intersection of any two surfaces. The method discussed in the preceding problems is satisfactory for the types of intersections thus far presented, but when neither of the two surfaces is a plane, that is, where both consist of a series of broken planes (prisms or pyramids) or curved surfaces, some additional aid is necessary in finding the piercing points of the elements of one surface with the other.

The additional aid consists of passing a cutting plane which will cut straight lines or curves from both surfaces which will show in projection as straight lines or

circles. These lines, since they both lie in the same cutting plane, will cross each other at points on the curve of intersection. This process, of passing cutting planes, is repeated a sufficient number of times to locate accurately the curve of intersection.

Sometimes the surfaces are of such nature that circles or straight lines cannot be cut from them, in which case other curves must be used as, for example, those in Fig. 16–34. At times it is possible to use cutting cylinders in lieu of planes.

16.10 Intersection of plane and surface of revolution. To find the intersection of the plane *ABCD* and the sphere in Fig. 16–6(*a*), a cutting plane *MN* has been passed through both surfaces. This cuts a circle from the sphere which appears as a straight line in the front

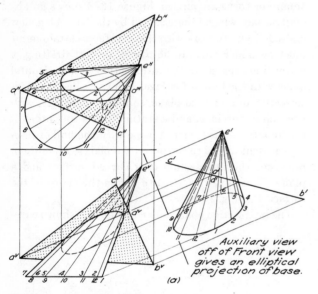
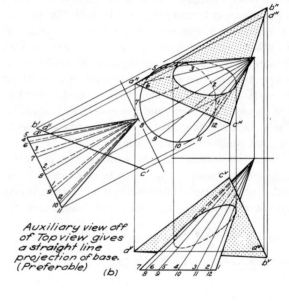

Fig. 16–5.   Intersection of plane and cone.

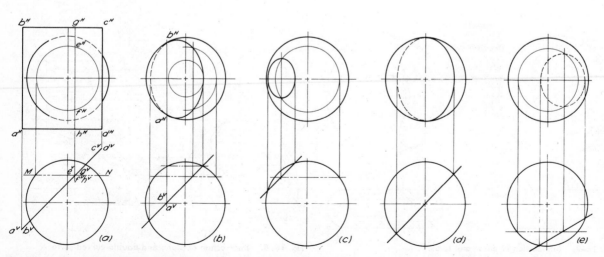

Fig. 16–6.   Intersection of plane and sphere.

view and a circle in the top view. The two planes intersect in the line *GH*. The intersection of the line and circle can be seen by inspection at $e^V f^V$ in the front view and e^H and f^H in the top view. A sufficient number of points to determine the curve of intersection may be obtained by repeating this process as shown in Fig. 16–6(*b*). The curve is tangent to the great circle in the top view at the points a^H and b^H where the cutting plane crosses the great circle at a^V and b^V in the front view.

The curve of intersection of a plane and sphere is always a circle but in our illustration it appears as an ellipse. In Figs. 16–(*c*), (*d*), and (*e*), the plane forming the intersection has been shown edgewise in three different positions. Note the effect on the visibility of the ellipse and its tangency to the great circle in the different positions of the intersecting plane. In Fig. 16–6(*c*), since the intersection lies entirely above the great circle, it is entirely visible in the top view. In Fig. 16–6(*d*), the intersection plane passes through the center of the sphere and the curve is tangent to the great circle at the ends of the corresponding diameter in the top view. The upper half is visible but the lower half is invisible. The student should study these illustrations and clearly visualize each situation for himself.

A similar construction for the intersection of a plane and torus is shown in Fig. 16–7. In this case the true outline of the curve of intersection is not a circle. It may have a wide variety of shapes, depending upon the

position of the intersection plane. The method of construction, however, is the same as for the sphere and is clearly shown in the figure. It should be noted that each construction plane, except the top and bottom ones, cuts two circles from the torus. Open circles indicate invisible points, and black circles indicate visible points.

16.11   Intersection of plane and double-curved surface. Many practical problems involve finding the intersection of planes with curved surfaces which are considerably more complex, as, for example, the determination of station lines and water lines in ship and aircraft construction. The principles involved, however, are exactly the same, the only difference being that in many surfaces straight-line elements cannot be drawn. For example, the simplest elements which may be drawn on a sphere or torus are circles. Figure 16–8 shows an aircraft surface which is determined by the body plan view and side view. To work with these surfaces certain terms must be understood. In ship and aircraft drafting, a water line represents the intersection of a horizontal plane with the hull or fuselage. A buttock line is the intersection of a vertical plane, running lengthwise, with the hull or fuselage, and a station line is the intersection of a transverse vertical plane with the hull or fuselage at right angles to the other two planes. All of them represent the intersection of a curved surface and a plane. These lines are used to define the shape of the surface. See Fig. 16–8.

The intersection of an inclined plane *MN* shown edge-

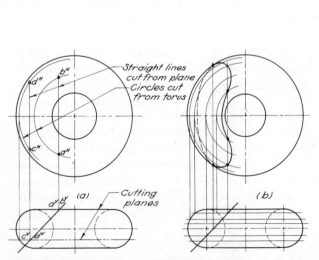

Fig. 16–7.   Intersection of plane and torus.

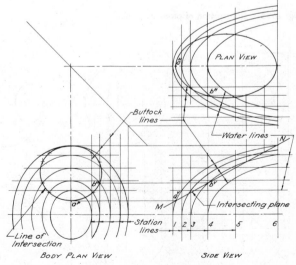

Fig. 16–8.   Intersection of plane and double-curved surface.

wise in the side view with the surface, represented in Fig. 16–8, appears in the plan view and the body plan view. The central buttock line which pierces the plane at a^V is projected to a^P and a^H. The intersection of station line 4 with the plane MN appears at b^V which is projected at b^P and b^H. Any number of points required to determine the curve can be found in the same manner, using water lines, buttock lines, and station lines.

16.12   Intersection of two prisms. The first example, Fig. 16–9, shows the intersection of two prisms. The top view shows the four faces of the square prism edgewise; hence, the projections of the points in which the three edges of the triangular prism pierce these faces are shown directly in the top view at points 1, 2, 4, and 6, 8, and 9, with the points 1, 2, 4, 6, 8, and 9 in the front view located on the corresponding projections of the same edge lines of the triangular prism. (Note that numbered points in this illustration and in succeeding ones are not given superscripts since the connection between the views is obvious.) It remains then to find where the two edges AE and CG of the square prism pierce the faces of the triangular prism. The construction is as follows:

a. Extend the plane of the face $AEDH$ and use it as a cutting plane.

b. Find the intersection, $4UT$, where this cutting plane intersects the triangular prism.

c. The points where the element AE intersects the triangle $4UT$ give the points 3 and 5 on the intersection of the two prisms.

d. Using a cutting plane through $BCGF$, the same procedure can be used to locate points 7 and 9 on the right half of the intersection.

When one of the prisms is shown endwise as in Fig. 16–9, it is possible to determine the general shape of the intersection and also to number the points consecutively so that they may be connected in order. In this case, it can be seen that the triangular prism goes completely through the square prism, which shows that there will be two completely separate parts to the intersection. Since the square prism shows endwise in the top view, all lines of the intersection must show on the outline of the square in the top view and cannot cut across the square. Thus the planes AB and AD will form one part of the intersection and those planes must intersect the top part of the triangular prism, planes $MNOP$ and $OPRS$ first and then the bottom part, plane $MNRS$.

To number the points properly, it is best to start with point 1 in the top view and proceed around the square prism and on the top faces of the triangular prism first. Therefore, the numbering would go from 1 to 2, to 3 which is on plane $MNOP$, to 4 and then back on the bottom to 5, which is on plane $MNRS$ and finally to point 1. When the two points 3 and 5 have been obtained, as previously explained, it is essential that the higher point in the front view be marked 3 because that was taken as the point on the upper surface of the triangular prism.

In the same manner, the points 6, 7, 8, 9, and 10 may be numbered on the right side of the intersection. When they have been numbered in this manner, they may be connected in order to give the correct intersection. If the end view of one of the prisms is not given, it is usually best to take enough auxiliary views to get an endwise view.

For visibility each line must be checked to see if it is on the front or back of both surfaces. If on the front of both surfaces, the line will be visible. All other combinations give an invisible line in the front view.

16.13   Rules for visibility. The visibility of points on each of two lines is determined simply by ascertaining which of the points is closest to the observer. Thus, in Fig. 16–10(*a*), it can be observed from the top view, that at the crossing point of the two rods in the front view, the point 1 on rod AB is in front of point 2 on rod CD. Therefore, the rod AB is visible and must be shown passing in front of CD. In Fig. 16–10(*b*), an examination of the front view shows that rod AB is higher than CD at the crossing point shown in the top view. In the

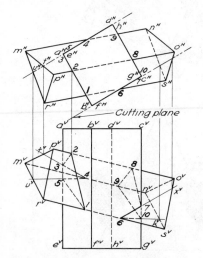

Fig. 16-9.   Intersection of two prisms.

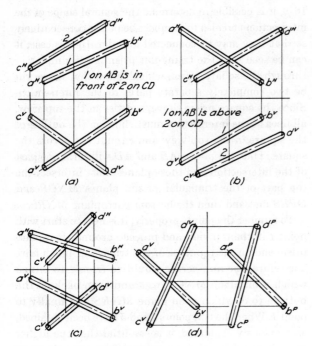

Fig. 16–10. Determining visibility.

top view, *AB* is entirely visible and must be shown passing over *CD*. The student should verify the visibility of the rods as shown in Fig. 16–10(*c*) and (*d*).

It will be noted from the foregoing discussion that the visibility of a line in any view is always determined by reference to the adjacent view. In Fig. 16–9, since the line *BF* is in front of the line *RS*, the latter enters the prism at point *1* and emerges again at point *6*. Between these two points it is invisible. For the same reason line *PO* enters the prism at point *2* and emerges at point *8*. Point *8*, however, is invisible since it lies on the rear surface of the prism, and the line *PO* does not become visible again until it passes the edge *CG* of the prism.

From Fig. 16–9 and subsequent figures, the following principles can be observed:

1. To be visible a point must lie on a visible edge or element of both intersecting surfaces.

2. For a line of intersection to be visible it must connect two visible points. If it connects one visible and one invisible point, it is entirely invisible.

3. A line of intersection can change from visible to invisible or vice versa only upon the outlines of one or the other of the two intersecting surfaces.

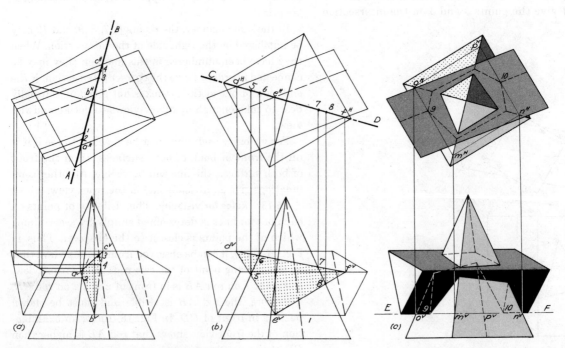

Fig. 16–11. Intersection of prism and pyramid.

16.14   Intersection of prism and pyramid. The cutting plane method is illustrated again in this problem. Thus, in Fig. 16–11(a), the cutting plane AB through two edges of the pyramid cuts the triangle ABC from the prism. This triangle intersects the two edges of the pyramid in points 1, 2, 3, and 4, thus locating four points on the line of intersection. In a similar manner cutting plane CD in Fig. 16–11(b) cuts another triangle DEF from the prism, thus locating four more points 5, 6, 7, and 8 with corresponding projections in the top view. Finally a cutting plane EF in Fig. 16–11(c) through the lower edge of the prism cuts a square MNOP from the pyramid, which locates the points 9 and 10. Connecting the points in proper order and showing the visibility complete the process.

The first points 1 to 8 in the problem above could have been found quite conveniently by making an endwise view of the prism in an auxiliary projection. The simplest method for the remaining two points, 9 and 10, is by the cutting plane method used in Fig. 16–11(c).

Had the prism in Fig. 16–11 been inclined to both H and V, the auxiliary plane method would have required two auxiliary views whereas the cutting plane method could be applied without additional work.

16.15   Intersection of two pyramids. The method of cutting planes, to obtain elements of both surfaces which intersect each other, is further illustrated in determining the intersection of two pyramids as shown in Fig. 16–12. The cutting plane AB passing through the front edge of the horizontal pyramid in Fig. 16–12(a) cuts the shaded quadrilateral $a^V b^V c^V d^V$ from the other pyramid, thus locating points 1 and 2 of the intersection on the edge of the horizontal pyramid.

In Fig. 16–12(b), the plane CD cuts a line from the upright pyramid and the shaded triangle RST from the other, thus locating points 3 and 4 of the intersection. Other points obtained in a similar manner give the final intersection shown in Fig. 16–12(c).

16.16   Possible types of intersections. It is of considerable value to the draftsman if he knows, before beginning construction, what general form the intersection will have. Only four forms are possible, and the type which any problem will give may be easily determined for cylinders, if an endwise view of one of the cylinders is obtained. The four types are shown in Fig. 16–13, with the cylinders placed in the most advantageous positions possible relative to the principal coordinate planes. With a complete penetration of one cylinder by the other, as

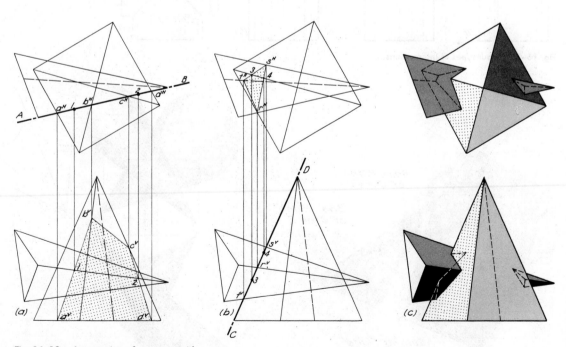

Fig. 16–12.   Intersection of two pyramids.

in Fig. 16–13(*a*), two closed curves are formed, with a partial penetration, as shown in Fig. 16–13(*b*), one continuous closed curve is formed. With a partial penetration in which one cutting plane is tangent to both cylinders, as in Fig. 16–13(*c*), a crossed curve with one point common to both parts like a figure 8 is formed; and finally, with a complete penetration of two cylinders of the same size with two cutting planes tangent to both cylinders, as in Fig. 16–13(*d*), two closed curves are formed which cross each other at two points. In right circular cylinders and cones these curves are ellipses. The above statements concerning intersecting cylinders apply equally to two cones, or to a cone and a cylinder, or to prisms and pyramids, when under the same conditions as regards penetration and tangency of cutting

planes. The determination of the form of the intersection can be readily made either from an auxiliary view or from the position of the limiting cutting planes, as shown in Fig. 16–28, where the first cutting plane, No. *1*, is tangent to both cylinders and the last is tangent to one and cuts the other, thus giving a crossed loop as in Fig. 16–13(*c*).

16.17   The intersection of two cones. The intersection of two cones is a common practical problem. In this case, if straight-line elements are to be cut from both surfaces, the cutting planes must pass through the vertices of both cones.

Thus, in the pictorial drawing of Fig. 16–14, the line *AD* passes through the vertices of *B* and *C*. Line *ED* in the plane of the base of cone *B* cuts elements *1* and *2*

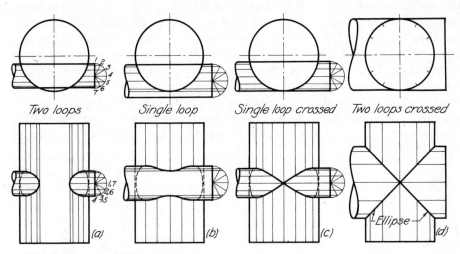

Fig. 16–13.   Four types of intersections.

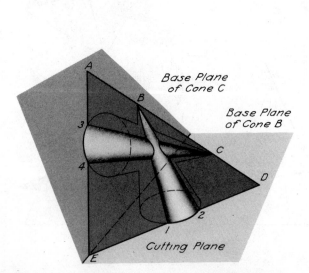

Fig. 16–14.   Intersection of two cones.   Pictorial drawing.

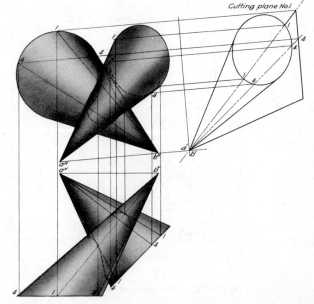

Fig. 16–15.   Intersection of two cones, using auxiliary view.

from this cone, and the line *EA* in the plane of the base of cone *C* cuts elements *3* and *4* from cone *C*. The two pairs of elements, all lying in this one cutting plane, cross each other to give four points on the curve of intersection.

From Fig. 16–14, it can be observed that the crux of this problem lies in finding the foot of the elements cut by one plane. The method of procedure will depend upon the situation in which the cones occur. In general the steps of the solution are as follows.

1. Draw a line through the vertices of both cones.

2. Pass a cutting plane through this line, and find the elements cut from each cone. These elements cross in points on the curve of intersection. A variety of procedures may be required to accomplish this second step. These are illustrated in the five following examples.

If the line joining the vertices of the cones is an *H*- or *V*-parallel, an endwise view of this line can be obtained in a first auxiliary view as shown in Fig. 16–15. The cutting planes then appear edgewise in the auxiliary view, and the foot of the elements cut from the cones can be obtained by inspection. See elements *1* and *4* in this figure.

When the bases of both cones lie in the same plane, the cutting planes may be located by constructing a line joining the two apexes and finding the point where this line pierces the plane of the bases. In Fig. 16–16, the line *AB* pierces the plane of the bases at point *C*. From this

point, any number of lines may be drawn on the base plane so that they cut across both bases. Each of these lines when taken with the line *AC* determines an inclined plane containing both apexes. One such line is shown in Fig. 16–16 which locates the points *D, E, F,* and *G* on the bases of the cones. From each of these points elements of the cones may be drawn to locate four points on the line of intersection of the two cones. The elements should be drawn showing their proper visibility in their own surface only, without regard to the other cone. Then when two visible elements cross, the point on the intersection will be visible. All other combinations will give an invisible point.

The problems occurring in engineering practice often involve frustums of cones. In cases of this kind the vertices must be found by extending two or more elements. An illustration of this type of problem is shown in Fig. 16–17. Here the two cones have a common base which is, of course, one of the lines of intersection. When cones have a common base or common base plane, the solution is much simplified because elements cut out by any cutting plane are very easily found. The procedure is as follows: Extend the line joining the two vertices until it pierces the plane of the bases as at *P*. From this point draw a line across the bases. The intersections of this line with the curve of the bases locate the foot of all elements lying in the cutting plane determined by the two

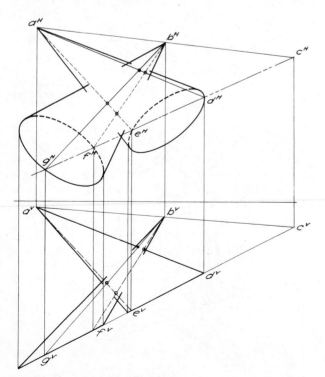

Fig. 16–16.   Intersection of two cones.

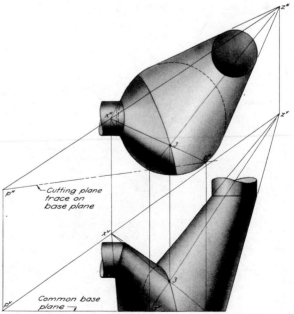

Fig. 16–17.   Intersection of two cones with common base.

intersecting lines, i.e., the one through the vertices and the one drawn across the bases. The elements cut by one such plane intersect in points on the curve of intersection. The construction for one cutting plane is shown in the figure. The line XZ pierces the plane of the bases at point P. PB is the line across the bases. The elements XB and ZA are cut from the cones. They intersect at point 3 on the surfaces of the cones. The other two elements which intersect at A and B on the common base have not been shown. Other points on the curve of intersection were obtained in a similar way.

In Fig. 16–18, two cones are illustrated with bases which appear edgewise in the top view. To determine the elements which lie in a cutting plane, proceed as follows:

a. Draw a line AB connecting the vertices of the cones, and extend it until it pierces the planes of both bases at C and D.

b. Find the line of intersection EF of the planes of the bases. It appears endwise at $e^H f^H$ in the top view and as a vertical line $e^V f^V$ in the front view.

c. Draw a line from d^V across the base of the cone up to the line of intersection at g^V and from this point across the other base to the point c^V. These lines determine the elements 3 on both cones and the points on the curve of intersection, as shown in the figure. The entire curve has not been shown.

In Fig. 16–19, one cone has its base edgewise in the top view and the other cone has its base edgewise in the front view. The procedure is exactly the same as in the preceding problem. It should be noted that the projections of the line of intersection of the base planes lie in the edgewise views of the bases since one is an H-projecting plane and the other a V-projecting plane.

When the base of only one cone shows edgewise, the elements determined by a single cutting plane may be found as illustrated in Fig. 16–20. The procedure is as follows:

a. Extend the line AB joining the vertices of the two cones until it pierces the plane of the base of the cone which shows edgewise as at D.

b. Choose an element in the other cone as AC in Fig. 16–20, and extend it until it likewise pierces the plane of the edgewise base at E.

c. Draw the line DE which crosses the base of the cone at F and G. The cutting plane through the vertices is thus determined by the lines DE and AE.

d. Draw the elements BF and BG which cross the element AC at points on the curve of intersection. The curve is not shown in the figure.

e. Repeat the process with a succession of elements in the cone A.

If neither base appears edgewise in any view, an auxiliary plane can be set up perpendicular to one of the bases and both cones projected to this auxiliary plane.

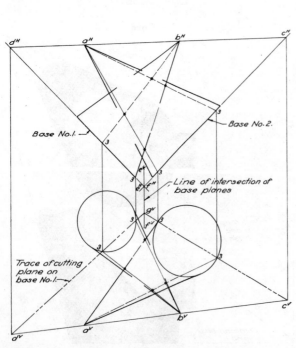

Fig. 16–18.   Intersection of two cones.

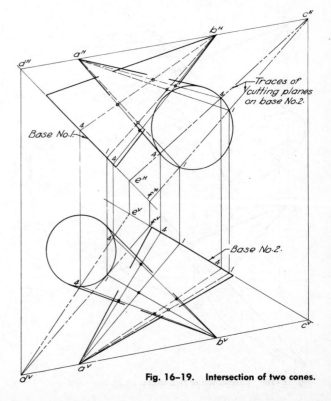

Fig. 16–19.   Intersection of two cones.

When this is done the procedure above can be followed. Another method of solution would be to extend both cones to some common base plane and then proceed as in Fig. 16–16.

16.18 Intersections of cylinders and cones. To cut straight lines from both a cone and a cylinder at the same time requires (1) that the cutting plane pass through the vertex of the cone and (2) that it be parallel to the elements of the cylinder. This can be accomplished by inspection if an endwise view of the cylinder can be obtained as in Fig. 16–21. Here the points obtained with one typical cutting plane have been shown.

When the cone is right circular and the cylinder is par-

allel to the base of the cone, as in Fig. 16–22, the cutting planes can be chosen so that they cut straight lines from the cylinder and circles from the cone which intersect in pairs to locate points on the curve of intersection.

When the cone and cylinder are so situated that neither of the schemes used above can be readily applied, then the cutting planes must be passed through a line drawn from the vertex of the cone and parallel to the elements of the cylinder. Any plane through this line will cut straight lines from both cone and cylinder if it cuts them at all. This is illustrated pictorially in Fig. 16–23.

A solution based on this method is shown in Fig.

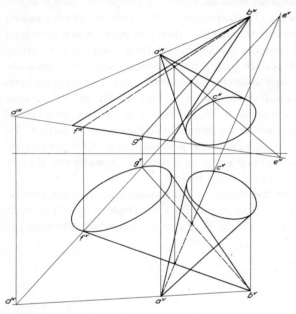

Fig. 16–20.   Intersection of two cones.

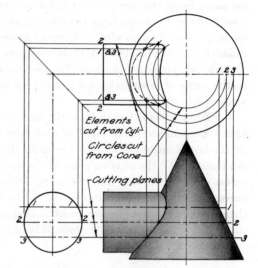

Fig. 16–22.   Intersection of cone and cylinder.

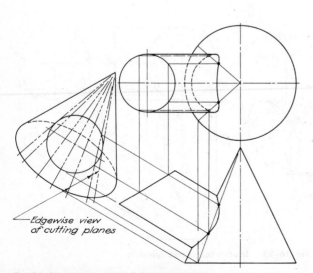

Fig. 16–21.   Intersection of cone and cylinder.

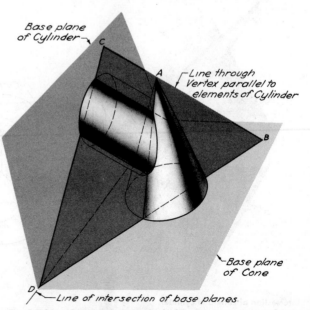

Fig. 16–23.   Cutting plane method of finding intersection of cone and cylinder.

16–24. To find the foot of the elements cut from each surface by such a plane, it is necessary:

   a. To draw the line *AB* through the apex of the cone parallel to the elements of the cylinder.

   b. To find the points *B* and *C* where this line pierces the bases of the cone and cylinder.

   c. To find the line of intersection of the two bases. In Fig. 16–24, both projections of the line of intersection are in the horizontal reference line since one base is in the *V*-plane and the other in the *H*-plane.

   d. To draw a line from *b^V* (the piercing point of the line from the apex with the base of the cone) across the base of the cone to locate *d^V*. This locates elements on the cone. From the point *D* which lies on the line of intersection of the bases, draw the line *CD,* the horizontal projection of which *c^Hd^H* will cross the base of the cylinder, thus locating the foot of the elements cut from the cylinder. One cutting plane (No. *4*) and the points on the curve of intersection determined by this plane are shown in the figure.

It may be observed that after the first three steps have been completed the plane of each base contains (1) the line of intersection of the bases, (2) the curve of one base, and (3) the piercing point of the line from the vertex of the cone with the base plane. Hence, a line drawn from the line of intersection of the bases across the base curve to the piercing point in that plane will cut the curve in the foot of the elements lying in the cut-

ting plane. A line drawn from the same point on the line of intersection of the bases across the other base to the corresponding piercing point will cut the foot of the elements from the other surface lying in the same cutting plane. Hence, all these elements lie in one cutting plane and must cross each other on the curve of intersection of the surfaces.

16.19   Intersection of two cylinders. Another illustration of the general method involving the intersection of two cylinders is shown pictorially and orthographically in Fig. 16–25. The cutting plane *AB* shown edgewise in the top view cuts elements numbered *3* and *7* from one cylinder and the element *3* only from the other. These elements cross each other at two points *c* and *d* on the curve of intersection. If the inclined cylinder passed entirely through the other, four points would have been determined by this one cutting plane. Other cutting planes are passed until enough points have been obtained to determine a smooth curve. Two other common situations are shown in Figs. 16–26, and 16–27 with the method of solution indicated. When the two cylinders are of the same size and their axes intersect, the curve of intersection is one-half of each of two ellipses, unless the penetration is complete, in which case the two ellipses are also complete.

In the preceding illustrations the cylinders were so placed that planes which cut straight lines from both cylinders could be drawn by inspection. Although the

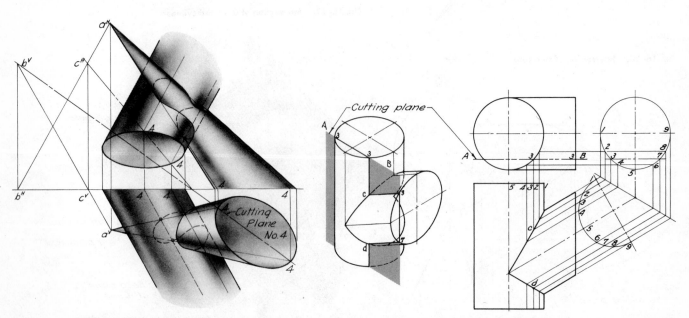

Fig. 16–24.   Intersection of cone and cylinder.   **Fig. 16–25.   Intersection of two cylinders.**

draftsman can, many times, draw intersecting cylinders in positions like these, sometimes this may not be convenient. To cover other situations, four illustrations are shown and discussed in the following paragraphs.

In Fig. 16–28, two oblique cylinders are shown having a common vertical base plane. Up to this point it has been possible to draw the cutting plane by inspection since all of them have been *H-* or *V-*projection planes. In this problem and those which follow, the cutting planes are oblique and hence cannot be determined by inspection. It is necessary therefore to determine the position of the cutting planes which will cut straight lines from the cylinders or cones.

To cut straight lines from two cylinders, the plane must be parallel to the elements of both cylinders. In Fig. 16–28, the plane *ABC* shown at the right has been constructed parallel to the elements of both cylinders and the line of intersection *BC,* with the plane of their bases determined. All cutting planes must be parallel to this guide plane.

It now becomes necessary to find the elements which these planes cut from each cylinder. This is done by drawing lines across the bases parallel to the line of intersection (trace) of the guide plane with the plane of the bases. Two typical cutting planes with the points determined by them have been shown in Fig. 16–28.

In Fig. 16–29, the bases of the cylinders are in different planes but both appear edgewise in the top view. To find

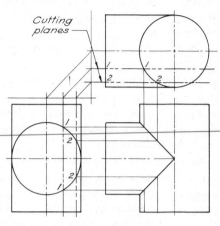

Fig. 16–27. Intersection of two cylinders of same size.

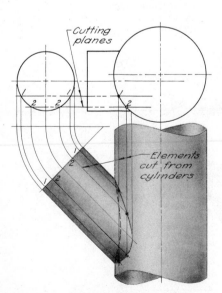

Fig. 16–26. Intersection of two cylinders.

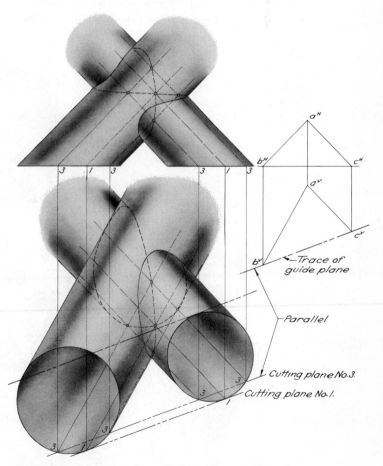

Fig. 16–28. Intersection of two cylinders with common base plane.

the position of the cutting planes which will cut straight-line elements from both cylinders, it is necessary to establish a guide plane which is parallel to the elements of both cylinders. This is done by assuming a point as O at the left in Fig. 16–29 and drawing two lines through it as OA and OB respectively parallel to the elements of the cylinders.

The second step is to find the lines of intersection of this plane with each of the base planes. These are found by locating the piercing points of the two lines with the planes of the two bases at a^V and b^V for base No. 1 and c^V and d^V for base No. 2. Note that these lines meet at F in the line of intersection of the base planes which must also be found.

Having these lines established, other lines can be drawn parallel to them across the bases like planes No. 1 and No. 5, thus locating the foot of the elements cut from both cylinders by these planes. Note once again that these lines meet in the line of intersection of the base planes.

If the position of the bases is such that the construction for the guide plane would run off the board, other planes parallel to the original ones may be set up and the construction carried out as at the right in Fig. 16–29.

This entire procedure has been illustrated pictorially in Fig. 16–30.

A third situation is shown in Fig. 16–31, where the base of one cylinder shows edgewise in the top view and the base of the other appears edgewise in the front view. The direction of the traces of the cutting plane on the base planes is shown in the construction at the right. In this construction, it should be noted that one actual base plane has been used (base No. 1) and for convenience a second plane parallel to base plane No. 2 has been set up. The line of intersection of the base planes has its horizontal projection in the edgewise view of base No. 1 and its vertical projection in the edge view of base No. 2.

To determine where a single cutting plane crosses both bases, observe cutting plane No. 6. The vertical projection 6–6 is drawn across base No. 1 parallel to the guide trace $b^V c^V$ until it crosses the vertical projection of the line of intersection of the bases at f^V. Then, from f^H on the horizontal projection of the line of inter-

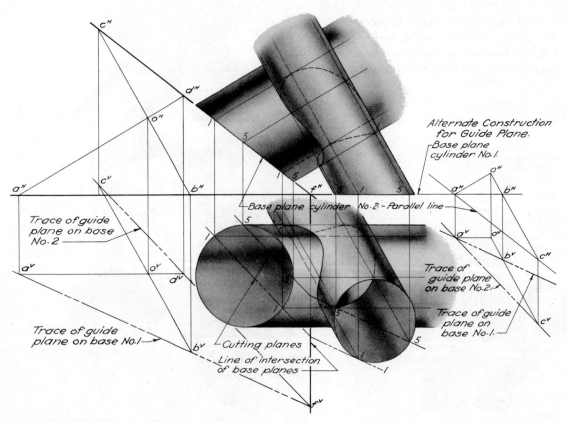

Fig. 16–29.   Intersection of two cylinders.

section of the bases, the cutting plane is drawn across the other base parallel to guide trace $d^H e^H$, thus locating the foot of the elements in both cylinders which lie in a single cutting plane. Having the elements located, the rest of the solution is the same as in the preceding examples.

In Fig. 16–32, two cylinders are shown in which neither base appears edgewise. As before, the problem is to determine cutting planes which will cut straight lines from both cylinders.

Several methods of solution are possible.

a. A plane could be chosen arbitrarily to cut across both cylinders, and the intersection of this plane with both cylinders could be found, thus making the new bases of both cylinders lie in the same plane similar to the situation in Fig. 16–28. This having been done the

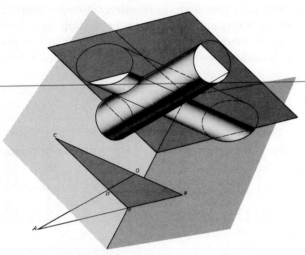

Fig. 16–30. Cutting plane method of finding intersection of two cylinders.

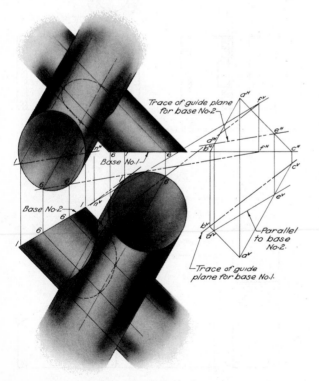

Fig. 16–31. Intersection of two cylinders.

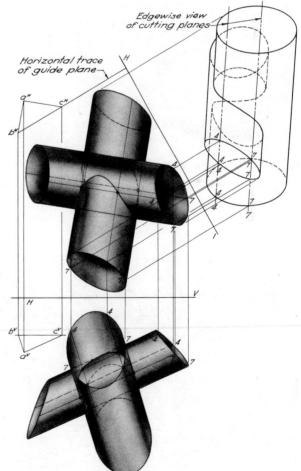

Fig. 16–32. Intersection of two cylinders.

problem would be reduced to that of Fig. 16–28. This method has not been shown for Fig. 16–32.

b. A second method consists of constructing the guide plane *ABC* in Fig. 16–32. An auxiliary plane perpendicular to this guide plane will show the edgewise view of all cutting planes. By making the views of both cylinders on this auxiliary plane the elements may be determined.

In Fig. 16–32, the direction of the horizontal trace of the guide plane has been determined at b^Hc^H. The reference line *H–1* is drawn perpendicular to this line. Both cylinders are then projected in the auxiliary view. Here

cutting planes like *4* and *7* are drawn edgewise to determine the foot of the elements in both cylinders. From an inspection of the auxiliary view it can be seen that the intersection will be a single continuous curve.

16.20   Cylinder with a double-curved surface. A simple illustration of the intersection of a cylinder and sphere is shown in Fig. 16–33. Here the cylinder and sphere have been chosen in such position that the planes, which cut straight lines from the cylinder, cut circles from the sphere which project as circles in the top view. Two typical cutting planes are shown. In this position the problem becomes very simple. It scarcely need be said

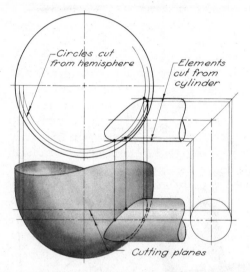

Fig. 16–33.   Intersection of sphere and cylinder.

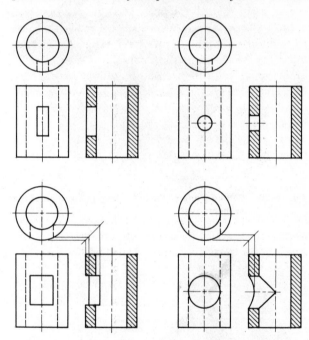

Fig. 16–35.   Conventional intersections in sectioned views.

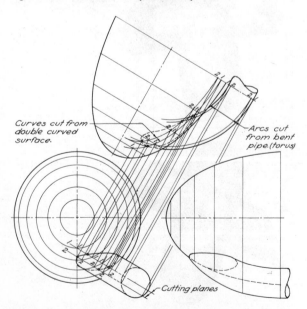

Fig. 16–34.   Intersection of curved pipe and double-curved surface.

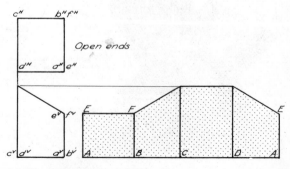

Fig. 16–36.   Development of a right prism.

that by one or two auxiliary views the draftsman can always reduce the problem to the situation shown in Fig. 16–33.

Another more complex situation is shown in Fig. 16–34, where a curved pipe (geometrically a partial torus) passes through a double-curved surface. In this case by a careful selection of the cutting plane and the auxiliary view, parts of circles are cut from the pipe and more complex curves from the other surface. The method for finding the curve on the larger surface is illustrated for two cutting planes in Fig. 16–34. The process must be repeated a sufficient number of times to determine the curve. In any event it is a long and tedious process.

16.21 Conventional intersection. On many machine parts intersections occur which are automatically produced by machining operations. Thus a small hole drilled into a tube, for example, produces the intersection, and hence such intersections can be shown conventionally, as in Fig. 16–35. If the intersection is relatively large, an approximation may be made by locating three points and using an irregular curve, as shown in the lower right-hand illustration of Fig. 16–35.

16.22 Development of surfaces. Another practical problem which arises frequently in construction work and which is commonly associated with the work in intersections is the development of surfaces. The term development means the laying out of flat patterns from which curved surfaces can be formed without stretching the material.

The method of making developments is best explained by concrete examples. One fundamental principle, however, may be noted, namely, that every line used in making a development must represent the true length of that line on the actual surface.

The two methods of finding the true length of a line will be found in Arts. 15.8, and 15.9 which should be thoroughly reviewed at this time.

16.23 Development of a prism. If the prism in Fig. 16–36 is cut along the edge AE and unfolded into a flat surface, the resulting pattern is called a development. In this case all the edges show in their true lengths in one or the other of the two original views. The plane of the base is perpendicular to the edges; hence this base line develops into a straight line perpendicular to the edges as shown in Fig. 16–36.

If the prism had been an oblique prism, then neither base would have developed as a straight line and it would be necessary to lay out the development so that a right section (a section at right angles to the edges) would roll out as a straight line. Thus, in Fig. 16–37(a), the elements show in their true length in the front view but, since neither base is at right angles to the elements, these lines of its bases cannot be used even though some of them show in their true length in the top view, because their position relative to the elements is not convenient to use. The true shape of the right section is shown at $a^1b^1c^1d^1$, and this section develops as a straight line as shown at $ABCDA$. Here $AB = a^1b^1$, $BC = b^1c^1$, etc.

In Fig. 16–37(b), none of the edges of the prism show

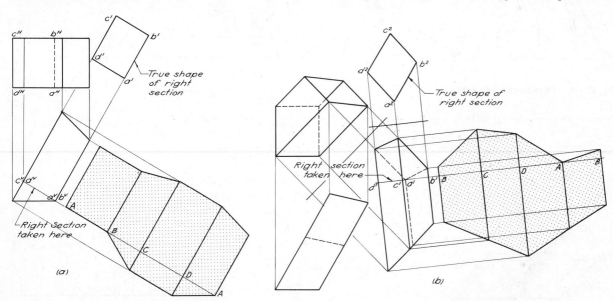

Fig. 16–37. Development of an oblique prism.

in true length in the front and top views. The true lengths of the four corner edges, however, are obtained in the first auxiliary view, and the true shape of the right section in the second auxiliary view. These true lengths have then been used to obtain the development as shown. For convenience the development has been projected from the first auxiliary but obviously it could have been laid out in any position by the use of dividers.

16.24   Development of a pyramid. Each face of a pyramid is a triangle except the base which may have any shape. It is therefore necessary to get the true length of the edges and lay out the series of triangles in the proper sequence, as shown in Fig. 16–38. In Fig. 16–38(*a*), because of symmetry the true lengths of all edges are known. Note that the projection of o^V to o^V_r and then up to the plan view to o^H_r and the revolution back to o^H to obtain the position of this projection in the top view is the equivalent of revolving the element *BE* until it is parallel to the plane. The true length of the truncated portion *BO* is obtained at the same time at $a^V o^V_r$.

In the oblique pyramid in Fig. 16–38(*b*), it was necessary to obtain the true length of the four edges by rotation as shown. The edges of the base appear in true length in the top view. Study carefully the method of obtaining the true lengths of the truncated portions. The true lengths having been obtained, the development is made as in the foregoing example. As in previous

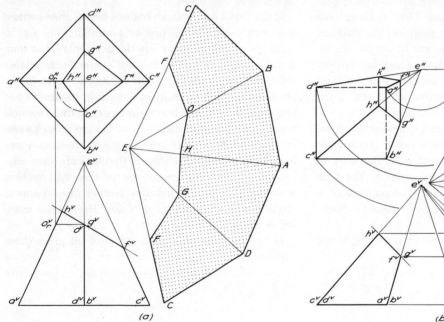

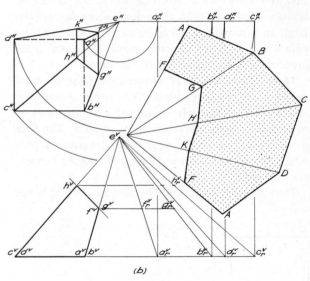

Fig. 16–38.   Development of a pyramid.

Fig. 16–39.   Pictorial of development of a right cylinder.

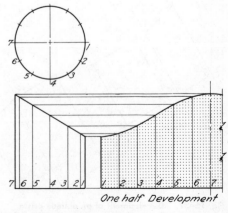

One half Development

Fig. 16–40.   Development of a right cylinder.

cases the pyramid is cut on the shortest element *FA* of the truncated portion.

16.25 Development of a cylinder. The cylinder is a very common surface encountered in design. If its bases are parallel and perpendicular to the axis, it is easily seen that when split along any element and rolled out flat, as in Fig. 16–39, a rectangle is formed. The width of this rectangle is equal to the length of the cylinder, and its length is equal to the circumference of the cylinder. Both measurements are easily found from a working drawing.

A truncated right circular cylinder has been developed in Fig. 16–40. Here the elements, 12 in number, show in their true length in the front view and may be projected directly to the development. The lower base shows the true size of the right section as a circle in the top view, and the true shape of the inclined face may be obtained by auxiliary projection if desired.

In stepping off the 12 spaces between elements with a divider it is well to check the accuracy of the setting by stepping it off six times halfway around the true size of the base. If this does not check with the semicircle, the setting should be adjusted until a perfect check is obtained.

16.26 Oblique cylinder. An oblique cylinder, that is, one that has its bases inclined to the elements, requires first, the true length of all elements and second, the true size of a right section similar to that explained in the discussion of the oblique prism. The right section may be taken at any convenient point and its true length obtained by auxiliary projection as in Fig. 16–41. In this case, the elements show in their true length in the front view and may be projected to the development in a direction at right angles to their length as illustrated for three of them or they may be transferred into another position with dividers as shown for the half-development. The right section rolls out as a straight line, and the spaces between elements, obtained from the auxiliary view, may be laid out on this line.

A still more general case of the oblique cylinder is shown in Fig. 16–42. In this instance it was necessary to obtain the true length of the elements in the first auxiliary view and the size of the right section by a second auxiliary view. These having been determined, the construction follows in the usual manner. A practical application is shown in Fig. 16–43 in the layout of patterns for an elbow.

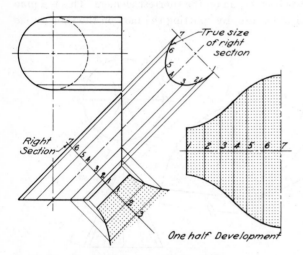

Fig. 16–41. Development of an oblique cylinder.

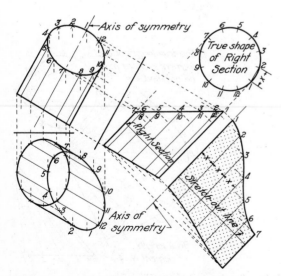

Fig. 16–42. Development of an oblique cylinder.

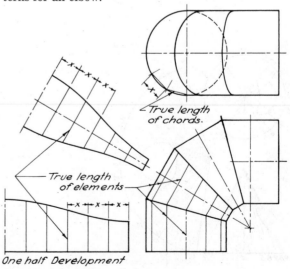

Fig. 16–43. Patterns for making an elbow.

16.27   Development of a cone. The right circular cone develops into a sector of a circle as shown in Fig. 16–44. The front view shows the true length of the elements as *y*. The lengths of the chords of the base may be obtained from the top view. With *y* as a radius, an arc of indefinite length is drawn and on it a length equal to the chord *x* is stepped off twelve times. If these points are connected to the center we have in reality 12 small triangles which approximate very closely the actual cone. This is the usual graphical method of development. A closer approximation can be obtained by dividing the base into a greater number of parts or the length of the base of the cone may be computed and laid out on an arc. The development of a cone intersected by a cylinder is shown in Fig. 16–45.

16.28   Oblique cone. The oblique cone requires that the true length of all elements be found, and if the base is not parallel to one of the planes of projection the true length around the base may also be found, preferably by auxiliary projection. Figure 16–46 illustrates the first type with the base parallel to *H*. Note again that the development consists of a series of triangles, the length of whose sides have been determined and which have been joined in consecutive order, beginning with the shortest element.

A second cone is shown in Fig. 16–47, in which the true shape of the base has been determined by auxiliary projection and the true length of the elements by rotation as usual. As soon as these things have been accomplished, the solution follows the customary procedure.

In several of the proceding figures the development has been begun on the shortest element. This is a practical feature. By splitting the part on the shortest ele-

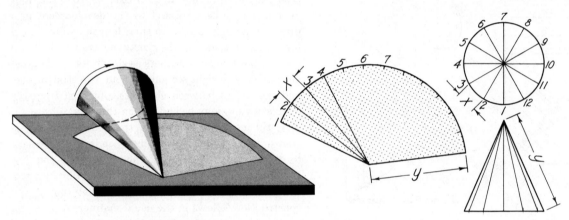

Fig. 16–44.   Development of a right circular cone.

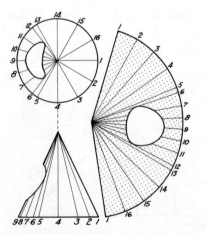

Fig. 16–45.   Development of an intersected cone.

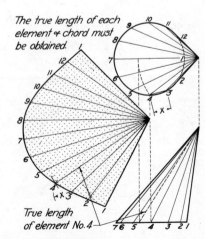

Fig. 16–46.   Development of an oblique cone.

ment the least labor is required in welding or riveting the seam. Whenever possible, therefore, the shortest element should be chosen as the beginning of a development or template.

16.29 Development of transition pieces. A large amount of sheet metal layout work consists of transition pieces or reducers as they are sometimes called. When it becomes necessary to join ducts of different shapes the portion by which this change is accomplished is called a transition piece. If there is a change in size the sections are commonly called reducers. Thus one may connect rectangular parts in different planes or change a section from square to round and so on through a wide range of combinations.

The problem in making these pieces lies first in recognizing and identifying the various component shapes, that is, cylinders, cones, convolutes, and planes,

of which the transition pieces are composed. The second step lies in the development of the several parts and connecting them to the proper order. It is also desirable to identify axes of symmetry since a pattern of one-half will suffice if there is one axis of symmetry and one-fourth may be enough if there are two axes of symmetry.

A series of reducers connecting rectangular sections is shown in Fig. 16–48. In the first three of these the reducer is composed entirely of plane sections. In the last, Fig. 16–48(*d*), two of the faces are warped quadrilaterals. Theoretically, warped surfaces cannot be formed without stretching the material, but, practically, a development can be made if the warping is not too severe. In Fig. 16–48(*d*), the warped surface can be made into two plane triangular surfaces by bending slightly along the line between the triangles.

The axes of symmetry have also been shown in Fig. 16–48 by center lines. A little study of these illustrations and those that follow will be an aid in analyzing similar problems in practice.

The development of a reducer similar to Fig. 16–48(*b*) is shown in Fig. 16–49. Each part consists of a quadrilateral. To lay these out it is necessary to have the true length of the edges and a diagonal unless some of the edges are at right angles to each other. This piece having only one plane of symmetry will be split on that plane and only one-half need be developed. Parts *1* and *4* each have two edges perpendicular to the central plane of symmetry, and hence a diagonal is not essential. Face *2–3*, however, cannot be developed without one of the diagonals as shown.

The three parts must be laid out in their proper relationship to each other. Although it would seem impossible for anyone to put them together in the wrong order, nevertheless this sometimes happens. If the

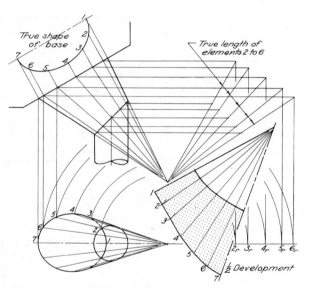

Fig. 16–47. Development of a frustum of an oblique cone.

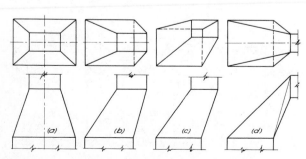

Fig. 16–48. Rectangular reducing sections.

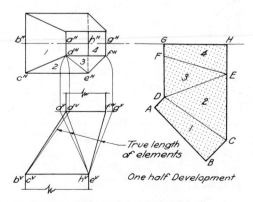

Fig. 16–49. Development of one-half of a reducing section.

draftsman is not sure of himself, it is suggested that the corners be lettered on the two views and that these letters be carried through to the development as shown in Fig. 16-49.

In Fig. 16-50, transition pieces connecting circular cylinders have been shown. In the first two cases the connector is a part of a cone because the circles at the top and bottom lie in parallel planes. In the last two cases, Fig. 16-50(c) and (d), the surfaces are convolutes and may be developed by dividing the circular ends into an equal number of parts, beginning at any known element of the surface and then connecting the points on each end, making a series of quadrilaterals which can be developed as explained in Art. 16.30.

Reducers which change in shape from rectangular to circular are shown in Fig. 16-51. These are commonly found on the roofs of buildings as ventilators. In each

case the reducing section consists of four partial cones and four triangular plane surfaces. The vertices of the cones lie at the corners of the rectangle. A typical development is shown in Fig. 16-52.

Another group of transition pieces involving parts of cylinders and planes and cones is shown in Fig. 16-53. The end part of the one in Fig. 16-53(d) is a portion of an oblique cone. With the vertex downward the chords of both bases show in true length in the top view; hence it is only necessary to obtain the true length of the segments of the elements.

In all cases developments should be made exactly to the planes of symmetry. If additional material is needed to make a joint, this should be added as a narrow strip in the developed pattern and not on the original two- or three-view drawing.

The reducer shown in Fig. 16-54 consists of parts of

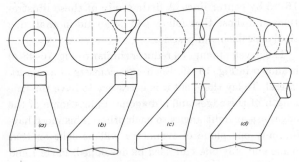

Fig. 16-50.   Reducer between cylindrical surfaces.

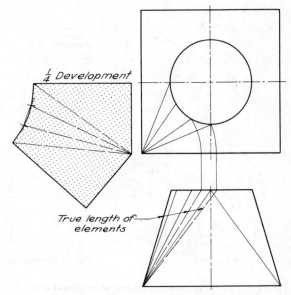

Fig. 16-52.   Development of one-fourth of a transition piece.

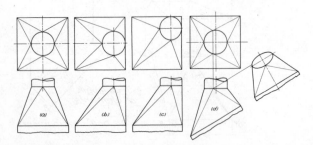

Fig. 16-51.   Transition sections.

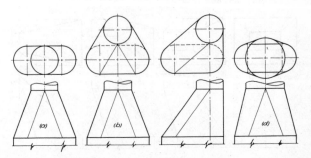

Fig. 16-53.   Transition between cylindrical surfaces.

two oblique cylinders and two triangular plane sections. Note that the auxiliary view used to determine the length of the elements of the cylinder could be projected from either the front or top view. The top view was chosen because this makes the bases come out as straight lines in the auxiliary view, rather than curves. The right section is obtained in the second auxiliary view. Again, care must be exercised to connect the two triangular parts to the cylinder in proper order.

When it becomes desirable to design a transition surface to connect two cross sections composed of straight lines and curves, the surface must be divided into planes, cones, cylinders, or convolutes as necessary. In each case there will be only one solution that will give a perfectly smooth surface although other subdivisions might be used to form a closed surface. The best procedure is to determine the plane surfaces first, after which the remaining surfaces are usually quite evident. A few simple rules will help in making the divisions.

a. Every straight line in either base must lie in a plane surface. Determine the plane surfaces first.

b. When there are curves in one base but none in the other, there will be cones in the surface.

c. When there are circles in both bases of equal radius, there will probably be cylinders in the surface.

d. When there are circles of different radii or other curves in both bases or when the bases are not parallel, there may be frustums of cones or convolutes.

16.30 Development by triangulation. In many cases a transition piece cannot be divided into cylinders, cones, and planes. For example, Fig. 16–50 is composed entirely or in part of frustums of cones or convolutes. Such surfaces can be developed by a method commonly called triangulation. This method is frequently applied to cones if the vertex is too far removed for practical use. The method consists in dividing the surface into small triangles which will approximate the surface and then in laying out these triangles in their true size and proper relative order.

This method is illustrated for a reducer connecting a circular and an elliptical section in Fig. 16–55. Beginning at any common element, usually on a plane of symmetry, the upper and lower bases are divided into the same number of equal parts and these points connected in a manner similar to the elements of a cone. This divides the surface into a series of quadrilaterals. Next these quadrilaterals are divided into triangles by drawing diagonals. It is customary to keep all the diagonals running in the same general direction. This method is simple but it cannot be regarded as a short cut since it is still necessary to find the true length of every line used in the development. The method of finding the true length has again been illustrated for a few of the lines in Fig. 16–55.

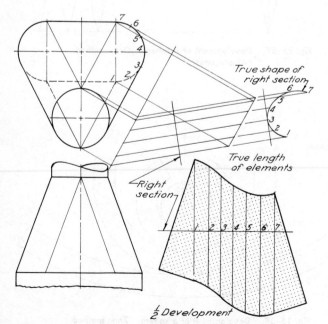

Fig. 16–54. Development of one-half of reducing section.

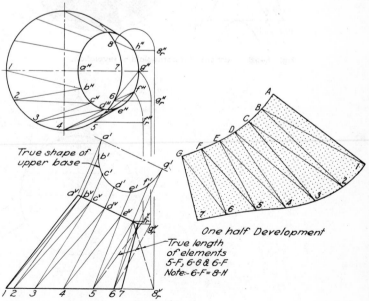

Fig. 16–55. Development by triangulation.

16.31   Development of double-curved surfaces. Spheres and other double-curved surfaces can only be roughly approximated by development. If these surfaces are to be accurately reproduced, as many of them are, in aircraft work, the material must be stretched by forming in dies with a drop hammer, or hydropress, or by spinning.

The construction of these dies involves a knowledge of intersections as illustrated in Fig. 16–56, where the templates used in forming a plaster mold for a paraboloid of revolution are shown. The sections are taken at right angles to each other. The templates are cut from sheet metal and firmly joined together. Circular sections may be added to give accuracy to the shaping of the plaster cast. The spaces between the templates are filled with wire netting and excelsior over which

the plaster can be placed. As the plaster dries it can be scraped to the exact contour. It is then used to make a metal die, and from the die a metal punch similar to the plaster mold can be made. Allowance must be made for the thickness of metal to be formed.

Surfaces of revolution may be approximated in one or two ways as illustrated in Figs. 16–57 and 16–58. When the sections are cut along meridian curves as in Fig. 16–57, the method is called the gore method and each section is referred to as a gore. When the sections are cut perpendicular to the axis of revolution as in Fig. 16–58, the scheme is referred to as the zone method. In either case the accuracy will obviously depend upon the number of sections made. The greater the number, the closer will be the approach to the true surface. True lengths must again be used throughout.

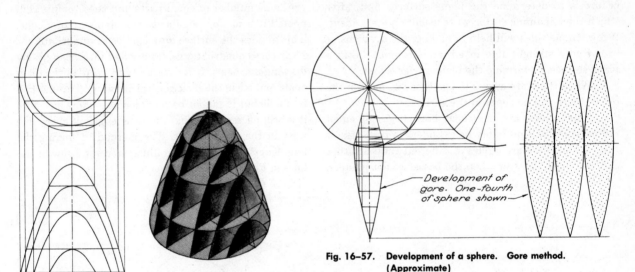

Fig. 16–56.   Sections of a paraboloid of revolution.

Fig. 16–57.   Development of a sphere.   Gore method. (Approximate)

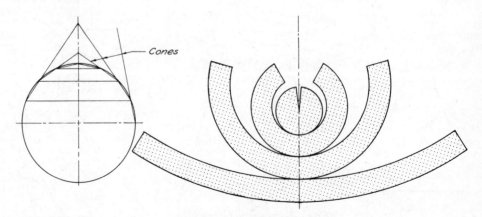

Fig. 16–58.   Development of a sphere.   Zone method. (Approximate)

The zone method of development is in general similar to the polyconic system of map projection used for topographic maps of the United States and gives a good basis for further study of that system of map making.

16.32   Sheet metal joints. Sheet metal developments and templates would be of little value unless the ends could be fastened together. A wide variety of methods are used in sheet metal work. Seams may be made by bending, welding, or soldering and riveting, as shown in Fig. 16–59. Allowance must be made beyond the theoretical line of development to provide the necessary overlap to make these joints.

16.33   Bend radii and bend allowance. In bending or forming sheet metal parts the minimum radius to which the sheet can be bent is deterned by the type of material, the thickness, and the equipment available. In any bend, the material on the outer portion of the bend is stretched and that on the inside is compressed. Somewhere between the two sides there is a line that has not been changed in length. This is referred to as the neutral line or surface. Experience has shown that this line is approximately 44% of the thickness from the inner or compressed side. In making a flat pattern therefore this line will develop in its true length.

Since the circumference of a circle is $2\pi r$, the length

of a curve of 1 degree will be $(2\pi r)/360$ or $(\pi r)/180$. This reduces to $.01745r$ where r is the radius to the neutral surface and is equal to $(R + 0.44t)$. If this quantity is multiplied by the angle of bend in degrees, the total length of material required to make the bend may be readily computed as $.01745rA$, where A is the angle of bend. A simple illustration is shown in Fig. 16–60. To save the labor of computation, tables of bend allowances for 1 degree are usually used.

16.34   Development based on mold lines. It will be noted in the preceding illustration that the distance to the bend line must be known to make use of the formula and table mentioned in the preceding article. Frequently, however, the distance to the mold line is known rather than to the bend line. Under these conditions it is simpler to use the distance between mold lines, called the setback, in determining the length of a flat pattern.

The mold line is the line of intersection of the two faces on each side of the bend as shown in Fig. 16–61. Although there is a mold line for the inside surfaces as well as the outside surface, the outside mold line is generally used. It will be noted that, although there is only one outside mold line for the part in its bent condition, there are two mold lines in the flat shape. In other

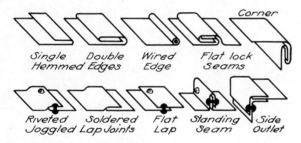

Fig. 16–59.   Sheet metal joints.

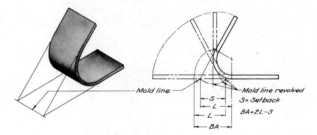

Fig. 16–61.   Mold lines and setback.

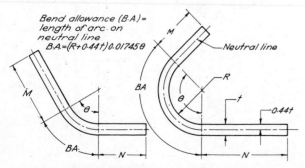

Fig. 16–60.   Bend allowance.

words, there is a mold line for each face. The method of computing the setback and of using it in determining the developed length is shown in Fig. 16–61. The meaning of open and closed bevels is illustrated in Fig. 16–62.

16.35 Bend relief. When two edges of a flat pattern are bent up, the corner is subjected to stresses which may tear the material. In order to avoid tearing, the corner is cut out on a circular arc to relieve this strain. This curve is frequently drawn tangent to the bend lines although it need not be. The chief purpose is to remove material that is subject to bending in two directions. A few simple layouts for the development of patterns have been shown in Fig. 16–63.

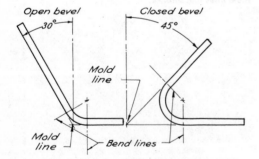

Fig. 16-62. Open and closed bevels.

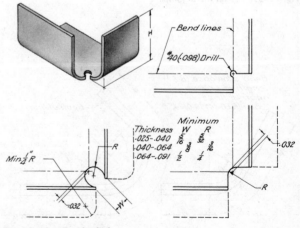

Fig. 16-63. Bend relief.

PROBLEMS

All the problems in this group have been laid out to be drawn on an 8½ × 11-inch sheet with the front and top views arranged along the long dimension of the sheet. Dimensions have been given to borderlines so that the student may make his layout to come within the borders of the sheet. Space between borderlines is assumed to be 7½ × 10½ inches by allowing a ¾-inch margin on the left long edge and a ¼-inch margin on the other three edges.

If it is desired to include developments with the intersection problems, an 11 × 17-inch sheet should be used, the intersec-tion portion of the problem being kept at the left.

In each problem the student must reproduce the figure as shown and then find the intersection specified. These instruc-tions are not repeated in the problem statements.

The location of reference lines for making auxiliary views to show the true shape of some intersections have also been defi-nitely located. In some instances these reference lines are cen-ter lines. In the intersections of surfaces the elements are not terminated where they actually disappear. The student is to determine this as a part of his problem.

1. Find the intersection of the Plane *A* and the square pyra-mid of Fig. 16–64. Show the true shape of the intersection.

1a. Develop the lower portion of the pyramid.

2. Same as Problem 1, using Plane *B*.

3. Same as Problem 1, using Fig. 16–65. Plane *A*.

3a. Develop the lower portion of the pyramid.

4. Same as Problem 1, using Fig. 16–65. Plane *B*.

5. Same as Problem 1, using Fig. 16–66. Plane *A*.

5a. Develop the lower portion of the cone.

6. Same as Problem 1, using Fig. 16–66. Plane *B*.

7. Same as Problem 1, using Fig. 16–66. Plane *C*.

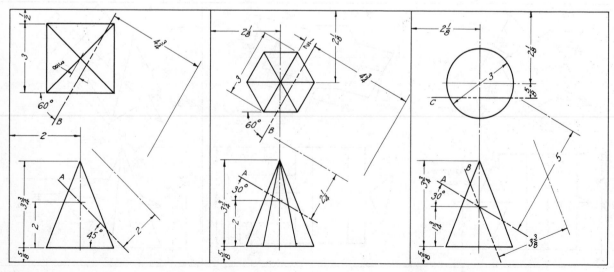

Fig. 16–64   Fig. 16–65   Fig. 16–66

8. Find the intersection of the Plane *A* with the hexagonal prism of Fig. 16–67.

8a. Make a development of the prism.

9. Find the intersection of the Plane *A* with the cylinder of Fig. 16–68.

9a. Make a development of the cylinder.

10. Find the intersection of the Plane *A* and the pentagonal prism of Fig. 16–69.

10a. Make a development of the prism.

11 to 13. Find the intersection of the surfaces as assigned from Figs. 16–70 to 16–72. Show visibility correctly on your finished drawing. Note that the edges of the prisms and pyramids are not necessarily terminated where they actually disappear.

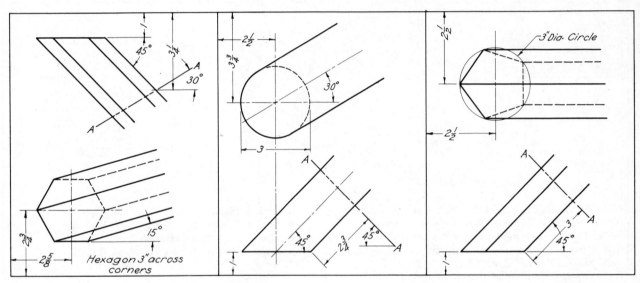

Fig. 16–67   **Fig. 16–68**   **Fig. 16–69**

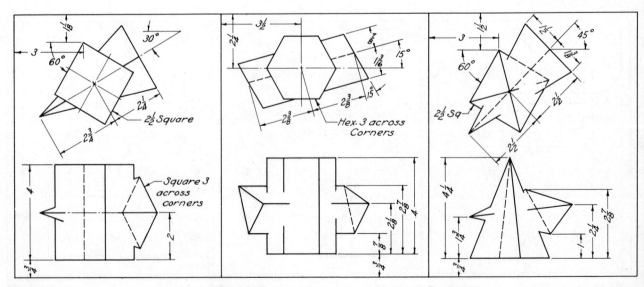

Fig. 16–70   **Fig. 16–71**   **Fig. 16–72**

14 to 16. Find the intersection of the cylinders as assigned from Figs. 16–73 to 16–75. Show visibility.

17 to 19. Find the intersection of the surfaces as assigned from Figs. 16–76 to 16–78.

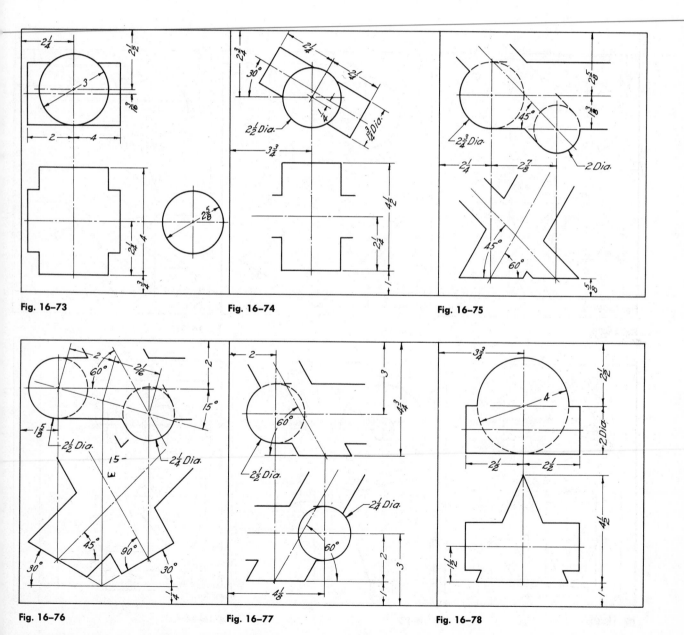

Fig. 16–73   Fig. 16–74   Fig. 16–75

Fig. 16–76   Fig. 16–77   Fig. 16–78

20 to 22. Find the intersection of the cones as assigned from Figs. 16–79 to 16–81.

23 to 24. Find the intersection of the surfaces as assigned from Figs. 16–82 to 16–83.

25. Develop the pattern for the cone of Fig. 16–82, showing the opening required for the intersecting cylinder.

26. Make a development of the small cylinder in Fig. 16–82, showing the proper shape for connecting to the cone.

27. Find the intersection of the cone and circular pipe in Fig. 16–83.

28. Make a development of the cone in Fig. 16–83, showing the opening required for the intersecting pipe.

29. Make a development of a symmetrical portion of the upper reducing section in Fig. 16–84.

30. Make a development of the convolute section of the reducer in Fig. 16–84 by the triangulation method.

31. Make a development of the small cylinder in Fig. 16–84.

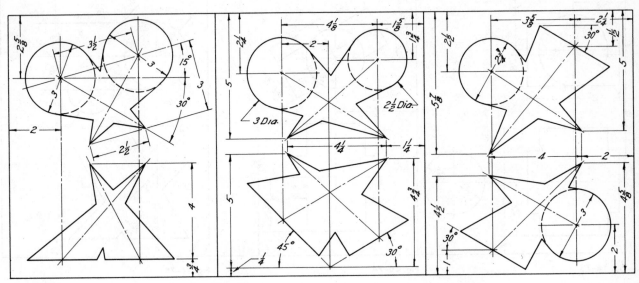

Fig. 16–79   Fig. 16–80   Fig. 16–81

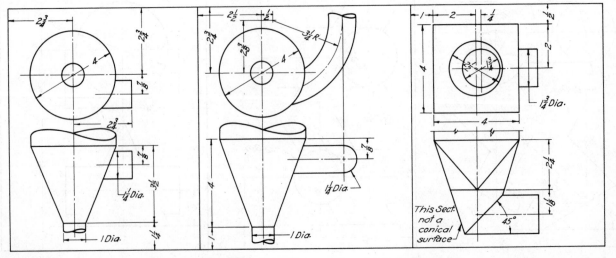

Fig. 16–82   Fig. 16–83   Fig. 16–84

32. Make a three-view working drawing of the connecting rod end shown in Fig. 16–85. Find accurately all curves of intersection in your drawing.

33. Same as Problem 32, using the connecting rod end of Fig. 16–86.

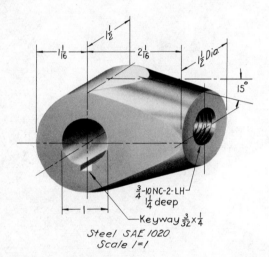

Fig. 16–85.   Connecting rod end.

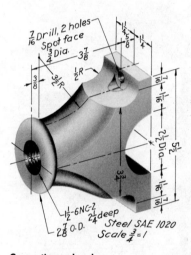

Fig. 16–86.   Connecting rod end.

Trimetric Projection Board (Wayne L. Shick).

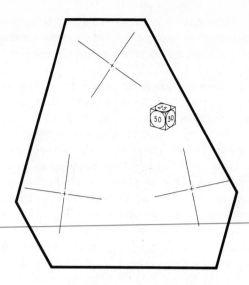

17

Axonometric Projection

17.1 **Definition.** An axonometric projection may be defined as an orthographic projection upon a plane oblique to the three principal planes, as shown in Fig. 17–1. The object represented is usually assumed to have its principal faces parallel to the three principal planes of projection. Three types of views or projections may be obtained by varying the position of the axonometric plane. When this plane makes equal angles with the principal planes, an isometric projection results. The axes, or edges of the cube, are therefore equally foreshortened and make angles of 120° with each other.

When the axonometric plane is equally inclined to two of the principal planes, two of the axes project equally and the third is foreshortened by a different amount. In this case two of the angles between the axes are equal, whereas the third is different.

When the plane is unequally inclined to all three principal planes a trimetric projection results. When this happens, the axes are all foreshortened by different amounts and the angles between the axes are all unequal. In no case can any of these angles be 90° or less.

Projections of this kind can be made in a variety of ways. For example, it will be noted that the body diagonal of the cube in Fig. 17–1 is perpendicular to the axonometric plane and the three edges will therefore make an angle of 120° with each other. Consequently an isometric projection may be made upon a plane which is set up perpendicular to this diagonal either by auxiliary projection, as shown in Fig. 17–2, or by revolving the cube until its body diagonal is perpendicular to the vertical plane, as in Fig. 17–3. These methods, however, are not practical for more complicated objects, but from them certain rules may be derived which make possible simple methods of construction. This scheme based upon simple rules of construction is called the conventional method.

17.2   Isometric projection compared with isometric drawing. In Fig. 17–3, it may be noted that the edges of the projection of the cube at the right are shorter than those of the cube itself as shown on the three-view drawing at the left. The correct ratio of this foreshortening could be obtained by constructing an isometric scale as shown in Fig. 17–4(*a*). A second method of construction is shown in Fig. 17–4(*b*). Scales of this type, however, are not on the market, and it would be tedious to make them and not worthwhile since an isometric drawing on which the regular normal scales are used has exactly the same appearance as a projection except for size. By making measurements along the three isometric axes with a normal scale the drawing becomes about 1¼

times as large as a true projection, as shown in Fig. 17–5.

A line parallel to any one of the isometric axes (edges of the cube in Fig. 17–5) is called an isometric line. All other lines are non-isometric.

17.3   Isometric of plane figures. *a. Straight-line figures.* The isometric drawing of a solid object consists mainly in representing three more or less irregular plane faces, which are parallel to the faces of the isometric cube. In these faces there may be any number of non-isometric lines. The outlines of the plane faces including the non-isometric lines in them constitute a series of plane geometrical figures which must be drawn in isometric. As a prelude to the drawing of more complicated solids the construction of plane figures in isometric will be considered.

In Fig. 17–6(*a*) an irregular seven-sided figure is shown. In Fig. 17–6(*b*), this figure has been enclosed in a rectangle and the coordinates of the corners of the

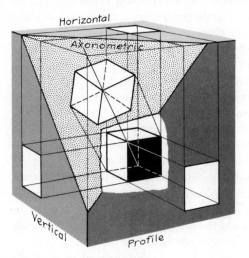

Fig. 17–1.   Theory of isometric.

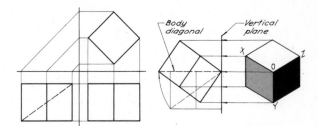

Fig. 17–3.   Isometric view by turning cube.

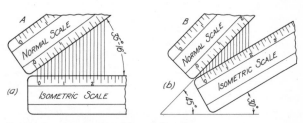

Fig. 17–4.   Construction of isometric scales.

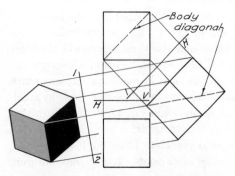

Fig. 17–2.   Isometric view by auxiliary projection.

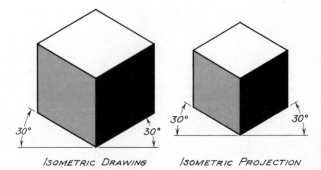

ISOMETRIC DRAWING   ISOMETRIC PROJECTION

Fig. 17–5.   Isometric projection and isometric drawing compared.

figure relative to the box have been indicated. In Fig. 17–6(c) and (d), an isometric of the rectangle has been made in two different positions and the seven-sided figure constructed therein by making measurements as indicated.

b. Circles and curves by coordinate method. A circle may be constructed in isometric by the coordinate method, as shown in Fig. 17–7. The procedure is as follows: (1) Divide the circle into 12 equal parts; (2) enclose it in a square, and draw coordinates through these points in two directions; (3) construct the isometric of the square and the coordinates, thus locating the 12 points in the isometric; (4) draw a smooth curve through the points.

Another very convenient method of drawing an ellipse which represents a circle in isometric or any kind of projection is illustrated in Fig. 17–7(f). First draw a parallelogram which is the projection of a square circumscribing the circle and then draw a semicircle, using one of the sides of the parallelogram as a diameter. Divide the semicircle into an even number of parts and project them perpendicularly to the side of the parallelogram. From these points draw lines in the parallelogram parallel to the adjacent side. Draw a diagonal of the parallelogram. Draw lines from the points of intersection of the diagonal, parallel to the side of the parallelogram on which the circle is drawn. The intersections of those two sets of parallel lines give points on the isometric of the circle. This method may be used in any type of pictorial.

c. Circles by the four-center approximate method. An approximate isometric of a circle may be drawn by the method shown in Fig. 17–8. This construction depends upon the fact that the center of a circle which is tangent to a straight line lies on the perpendicular to the line at the point of tangency. Hence if we erect perpen-

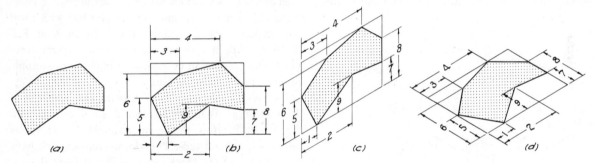

Fig. 17–6.   Construction of plane figures in isometric.

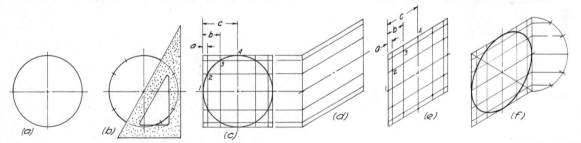

Fig. 17–7.   Construction of circle in isometric.

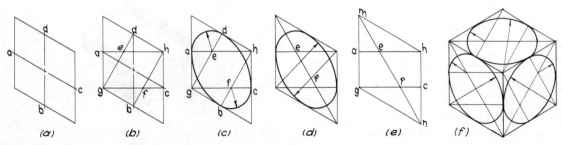

Fig. 17–8.   Four-center method of representing a circle in isometric.

diculars at the midpoints *a, b, c,* and *d* of the sides of the isometric square, these perpendiculars will intersect in pairs, thus locating the centers of the four arcs, *e, f, g,* and *h,* which will approximate the correct ellipse. It will be noted that in isometric two of these centers lie on the corners of the square and the other two lie on the long diagonal. Use of these facts enables the draftsman to shorten the construction considerably by drawing only the lines *ah, gc,* and *mn,* as in Fig. 17–8(*e*). This construction can be used in any isometric face of a cube, as illustrated in Fig. 17–8(*f*). The method involves less labor than the coordinate method and is sufficiently accurate for most isometric work. This approximate ellipse has a shorter major axis and longer minor axis than the true ellipse as shown in Fig. 17–9.

17.4 Isometric drawing of solids. Box method. From the drawing of plane figures to the drawing of solid objects in isometric is but a simple step, involving only the use of a third coordinate distance. The steps in the procedure are as follows:

a. Draw the orthographic views of the object to the same scale as that to be used on the isometric.

b. Enclose the views in the smallest enclosing rectangular box.

c. Draw the enclosing box in isometric in the position which will best reveal the shape of the object, making the three edges at 120° with each other.

d. Draw the simple parts of the object which lie in or adjacent to the faces of the box.

e. Plot the curves and interior points by the coordinate method.

f. It is the usual practice to omit all invisible lines in pictorial drawing.

17.5 Isometric of a block. Box method of construction. An isometric drawing of the block shown by three orthographic views in Fig. 17–10(*a*) may be readily constructed in the following manner. The first step as outlined above consists of enclosing the orthographic views of the object in the smallest rectangular box which will just enclose it as shown by the light lines of Fig. 17–10(*a*). This box serves as a reference frame from which dimensions can be measured in the orthographic views and plotted in the isometric.

The second step consists of drawing the isometric of the enclosing box in the position desired, as shown in Fig. 17–10(*b*). Here the front orthographic view has been made the left face. The various parts which have been cut out of the block can now be cut from the isometric box in any order desired. Thus, in Fig. 17–10(*c*), the distance (a^H–*1*) on the top view has been measured

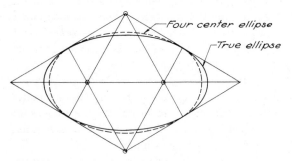

Fig. 17–9. True ellipse and four-center ellipse compared.

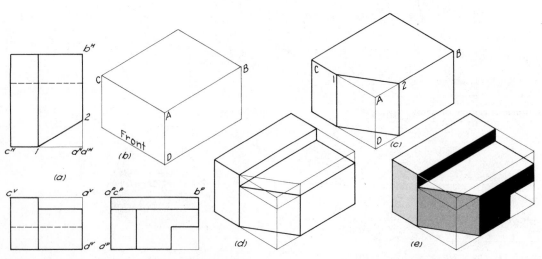

Fig. 17–10. Box method of drawing a solid in isometric.

on the same line, AC, in the isometric and the distance $(a^H$–$2)$ along the line AB. The diagonal line 1–2 can now be drawn in the isometric view. From the points 1 and 2 in the isometric, vertical lines can be dropped to the bottom of the box and then the diagonal in the bottom face can be drawn.

In a similar manner the other cutouts can be transferred by direct measurement from the orthographic to the isometric, as illustrated in the successive Figs. 17–10(d) and 17–10(e). It should be carefully noted that in all cases measurements are made on or parallel to the three isometric axes. They can be made in no other manner for no other lines are foreshortened in the same ratio as these lines.

As a second illustration, the construction of a truncated hexagonal pyramid is shown. In Fig. 17–11(a), the object is shown enclosed in a rectangular box, and, in Fig. 17–11(b), the box has been drawn in isometric and the hexagonal base shown in the bottom of the box. The measurements a and b for constructing this plane figure are obtained from the top view as shown in the figure.

Whenever an object has a plane of symmetry, advantage should be taken of this fact to speed construction. Hence, in Fig. 17–11(c), the central plane of symmetry has been established and the two points 2 and 9 located in it to give the center line of the truncated face (2–9). For example, the point 2 is located by measuring the coordinate 1–2 in the central plane as indicated. The point 9 is located by going up along the center line from 0 to 9, using the distance 0–9 in the front view. Points

3, 4, and 5 are located by taking the measurements (1–3), (1–4), and (1–5) from the top and front views. By dropping perpendiculars from 3, 4, and 5 to the center line (2–9), the points 6, 7, and 8 are located as shown in Fig. 17–11(c). Isometric horizontal lines can then be drawn through points 6 and 7. Points 10 and 11 can be located by stepping off from point 6 on these lines the distances (6–10) and (6–11) which are equal. A similar procedure locates points 12 and 13 as shown in Fig. 17–11(d). All these measurements are taken from the top view. The six points in the truncated face are then connected to form the sloping truncated face. The corners of this face are then connected to the corresponding corners of the base, thus completing the isometric as shown in Fig. 17–11(e). It is customary in isometric drawing, as in all other pictorials, to omit hidden lines unless they are necessary to make clear the shape of the object. Note again that all measurements were taken on or parallel to isometric lines.

17.6   Solid objects involving circles. The objects illustrated thus far have been composed entirely of straight lines. Many objects, however, involve circles either singly or in groups. The following suggestions will assist in speeding up construction and in avoiding common errors.

17.6.1   *Parallel circles or other curves.* In actual drawing, circles nearly always occur in pairs. Since rapidity in construction is always important, the suggestions for speeding up the layout of circles parallel to each other, as shown in Fig. 17–12, are valuable.

In the four-center method the centers for the first cir-

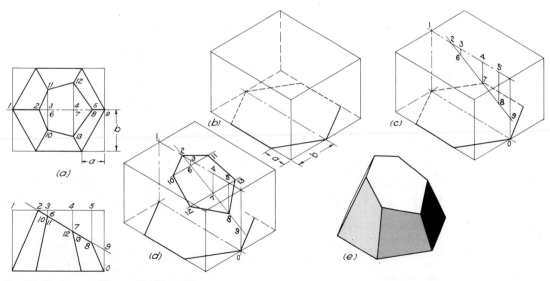

Fig. 17–11.   Truncated pyramid in isometric.

cles are found in the usual way. Circles parallel to the first may be quickly found by drawing isometric lines from the original four centers and stepping off on them the distance between the circles, to locate the new centers, as shown in Fig. 17–12.

The same scheme may be used for a curve plotted by the coordinate method, as shown in Fig. 17–13, for a non-circular curve. One curve is drawn in the usual way, and isometric lines are drawn from the plotted points. Each successive curve may be stepped off with one setting of the divider.

17.6.2   *Tangent circles and arcs.* The four-center method may be used for tangent circles or arcs only when they are tangent to each other at the midpoint of the sides of their enclosing rectangles, as shown in Fig. 17–14(*a*). If the tangency points occur at other places, the circles will overlap or miss, as shown in Fig. 17–14(*b*), because of their departure from the true ellipse. In such cases the coordinate method should be used or other approximations made.

17.6.3   *Common errors in drawing circles.* Two common errors are frequently made by the student in drawing

circles on various objects. One of these consists of drawing the circle out of the proper isometric plane, as shown in Fig. 17–15(*a*). This can be avoided by making sure that the sides of the enclosing parallelogram are parallel to the isometric lines of the plane in which the circle lies, as shown for the circle in the lower face of the object in Fig. 17–15(*a*).

A second error occurs in the drawing of short cylinders or cylindrical parts where the student fails to put in the isometric tangent line between the circles, as shown in Fig. 17–15(*b*). The far side of small holes is omitted many times.

17.7   Steps in construction illustrated. The simple bearing shown in Fig. 17–16 will serve to illustrate further the method of construction which has again been broken down into a series of successive steps, following the method previously suggested. Figure 17–16(*a*) shows the orthographic views enclosed in a box. Figure 17–16(*b*) shows the box in isometric with the base and cylindrical bearing partly completed. The circles are drawn in their proper planes by the four-center method based on the enclosing rectangles which are shown.

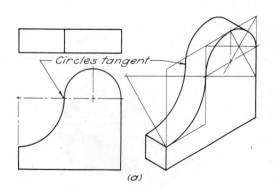

Fig. 17–12.   Short cut in drawing parallel circles in isometric.

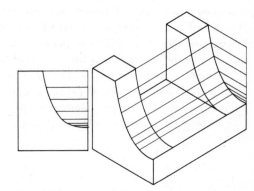

Fig. 17–13.   Short cut in drawing parallel curves in isometric.

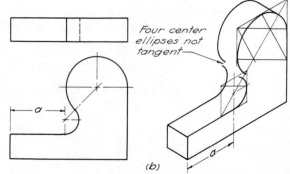

(*a*)   (*b*)

Fig. 17–14.   Limitation of four-center method.

In an object of this kind, considerable time can be saved by using the plane of symmetry and noting that much of the construction falls naturally into isometric planes. To plot the vertical and sloping webs, a series of horizontal planes *d, e, f,* etc., are drawn in the orthographic views locating points *1* to *12* on the curves. In Fig. 17–16(*c*), the end view of the vertical web is drawn in the end of the isometric box, and on it the points *d, e, f,* etc., are located by measurements (*0–d*), (*0–c*), etc. From these points *d, e, f,* etc., isometric horizontal lines are drawn and measurements (*d–1*), (*e–2*), etc., made on them, thus locating points *1, 2, 3,* etc., on the curve which can then be drawn as in Fig. 17–16(*c*).

The front view of the sloping web is next constructed in the right face of the isometric box, as shown in Fig. 17–16(*d*). It is a simple matter to carry the *m, n, o, p* horizontal planes around the box from *d, e,* etc., to locate the points (*5, 6, 9,* and *10*), etc. From these points horizontal lines can be drawn in isometric, and the distances (*m–5*), (*n–6*), etc., obtained from the three-view drawing in Fig. 17–16(*a*), can be measured on them, thus establishing points *5, 6, 7,* etc. The other curves may be

found in a similar manner. The completed drawing with all construction removed is shown in Fig. 17–16(*e*).

17.8   Isometric of a double-curved surface. On some objects such as the pipe return bend shown in Fig. 17–17, an enveloping curve representing the outstand-

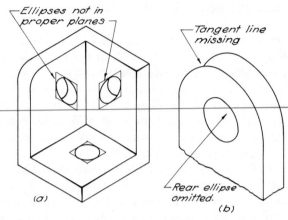

Fig. 17–15.   Common errors made in drawing isometrics of circles.

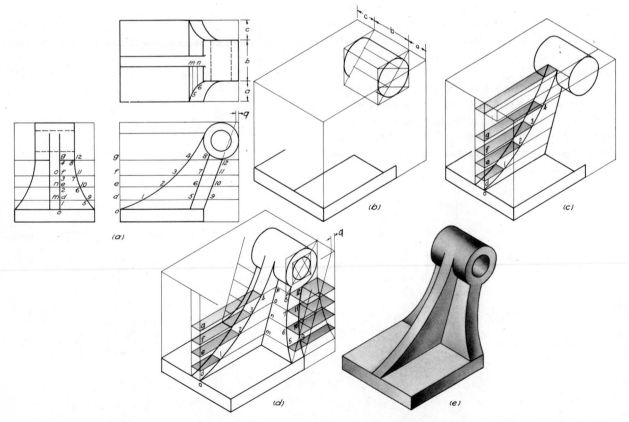

Fig. 17–16.   Construction in isometric planes speeds drawing.

ing contour of the object must be drawn. This curve does not lie in a single plane and hence cannot be constructed by plotting points in the usual way.

Since a sphere projects as a sphere in isometric a simple method of making this, or any similar construction, is shown in Fig. 17–17. A series of spheres may be imagined lying in the bend just tangent to it. The centers of five or six of these spheres may be located on the isometric of the center-line circle, as shown in the illustration by points *a, b,* etc. Next the size of the isometric sphere is obtained, as shown in Fig. 17–17(*a*), by making the circle tangent to the isometric ellipse. Only the major axis of the ellipse needs to be drawn to determine the diameter of the spheres. With the radius thus determined the arcs may be drawn and a smooth curve drawn tangent to them.

17.9   Construction by the center-line layout. The box method of construction discussed in preceding paragraphs may be used for any type of object. When, however, the object consists of a number of circular parts lying in the same or parallel planes, the center-line layout shown in Fig. 17–18 is a convenient and rapid method of construction. In Fig. 17–18(*a*) the orthographic views are shown, and in Fig. 17–18(*b*) the isometric layout of the principal center lines are drawn. In Fig. 17–18(*b*) the parallelograms for some of the circles are drawn, and in Fig. 17–18(*c*) the drawing is completed.

17.10   Dimensioning. For shop purposes, other than assembly work, an isometric drawing must be dimensioned. The regular rules and suggestions for dimensioning two- or three-view working drawings hold for isometric drawing in a general way, but, in addition, the following rules must be observed.

17.10.1   *Pictorial plane dimensioning.* Dimensions on isometric drawings should be placed in such a way that they can be read from one point of view, which should be from the bottom of the sheet. This may be said to encompass all other rules in regard to the direction on which dimensions should read, and it is the only safe one to follow at all times. It is best to dimension the visible faces.

a. All dimension lines must be isometric lines and lie in isometric planes. This point must be carefully observed. Difficulty usually occurs in objects having nonisometric lines. Figure 17–19(*a*) illustrates a very com-

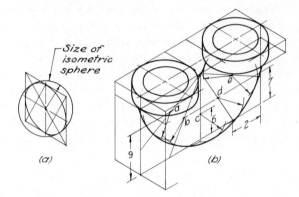

Fig. 17–17.   Tangent sphere method of drawing a double-curved surface.

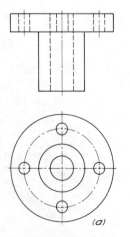

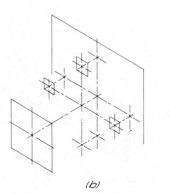

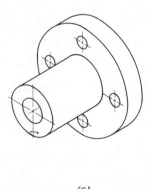

Fig. 17–18.   Center-line method of constructing cylindrical objects.

mon error. The dimension line and the two witness lines do not lie in an isometric plane even though the dimension line is vertical. Figure 17–19(*b*) illustrates the correct method.

b. Figures and lettering of notes should be made to lie in isometric planes. Only vertical-style lettering should be used in isometric. Figure 17–20 shows how the parallelogram enclosing a letter or figure may be used as an aid in isometric lettering. The front views of the small cubes show the letters and their enclosing parallelograms orthographically; the two isometrics of the cubes show the six possible positions in which these

parallelograms and figures may appear. Figure 17–21(*a*) illustrates the dimensioning of a rectangular object, placing the numerals in one or another of the positions shown in Fig. 17–20.

17.10.2 *Unidirectional dimensioning.* The American Standards Association has recently approved the placing of all dimensions and notes in one plane as illustrated in Fig. 17–21(*b*). When using this system only vertical letters or numerals should be used. This method is simple and more rapid for production purposes.

17.11 Screw threads in isometric. Screw threads could be accurately drawn in isometric but the process is so

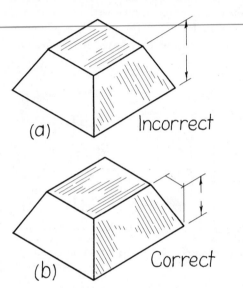

Fig. 17–19. Dimension lines in isometric planes.

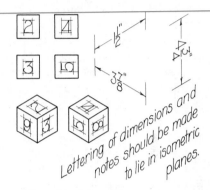

Fig. 17–20. Lettering and dimensions in isometric.

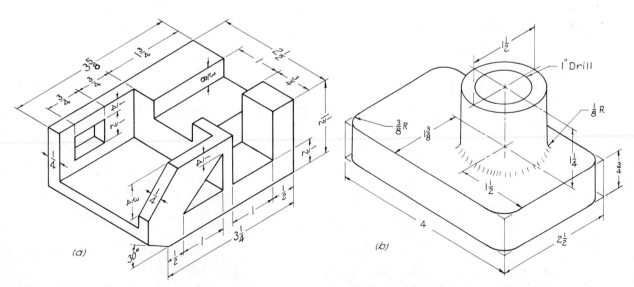

Fig. 17–21. Two approved systems of dimensioning.

laborious that a conventional scheme which is quite satisfactory has been adopted. Arcs of a series of parallel circles are used to represent the crest and root lines although the root lines need not be shown. Any method of drawing the circles may be used but the construction for the four-center method is illustrated in Fig. 17–22.

Because of symmetry of construction Square threads and Acme threads cannot be clearly shown in isometric. Dimetric or trimetric layouts are much more suitable for this purpose.

17.12   Section views. As in orthographic drawings,

the interior construction of complicated objects is best shown by sectional views. Half and full sections may be made by removing one-fourth or one-half of the object, respectively. The cutting planes should always be isometric planes as shown in Fig. 17–23(*a*). In a half section the crosshatching lines should be drawn in a position to give the effect of coincidence if the two sectioned faces were revolved together. Correct and incorrect examples are given in Figs. 17–23 and 17–24 to illustrate this point. No new principles of construction are involved in making section views.

The step-by-step construction of a sectional view is shown in Fig. 17–25. By beginning with the sectioned parts, as shown in Fig. 17–25(*b*) and (*c*), a minimum number of construction lines need be used. Careful study

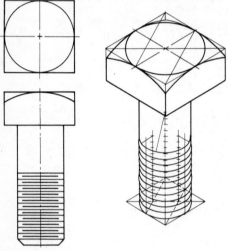

Fig. 17–22.   Screw threads and Square bolt head in isometric.

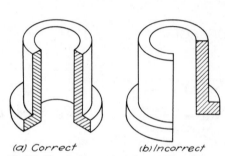

(a) Correct   **(b) Incorrect**

Fig. 17–23.   Section cutting planes in isometric.

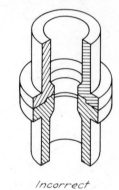

Incorrect

Fig. 17–24.   Incorrect crosshatching.

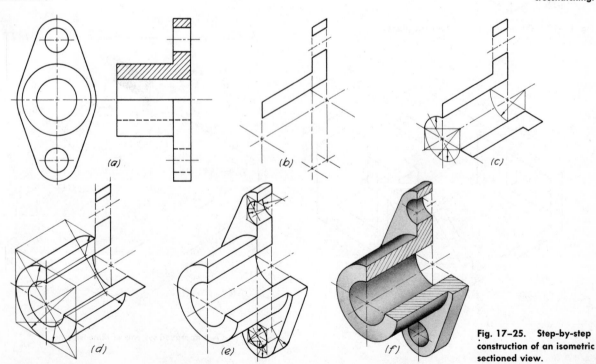

(a)   (b)   (c)

(d)   (e)   (f)

Fig. 17–25.   Step-by-step construction of an isometric sectioned view.

of the figure will show the procedure. The finished sectional drawing is shown in Fig. 17–25(*f*).

17.13 Position of isometric axes. Thus far we have considered isometric drawing with the object always in one position. The three axes, however, may be drawn in an infinite number of positions so long as they always make equal angles with each other. Four easily drawn positions, as shown for the object and enclosing box, in Fig. 17–26, are most commonly used.

The choice of the position of these axes will depend upon the nature of the object. When the top and sides of the object contain most of the details, the position used thus far is best. If, on the other hand, the bottom contains the more important details, the position of Fig. 17–26(*b*) is by far the best. The object should, of course,

be shown in the natural or normal position if it has one.

17.14 Spheres and other curved parts. Spherical parts occur on pieces of machinery and can readily be drawn in isometric. The sphere appears as a true circle. A simple lever involving spheres and curved handle is shown in Fig. 17–27.

In some objects such as gears and conveyors, it is desirable to divide a circle into a large number of equal parts. This must be accomplished first in the orthographic layout and then transferred to the isometric, using the outlines of the isometric square as shown in Fig. 17–28. Isometric protractors are on the market, and where such an instrument is available it may be used to make the divisions directly in the isometric.

17.15 Advantages of isometric. As compared with

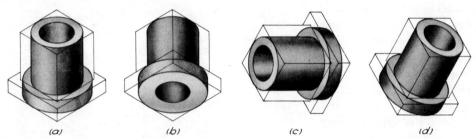

(a)   (b)   (c)   (d)

Fig. 17-26.   Choice of position for isometric view.

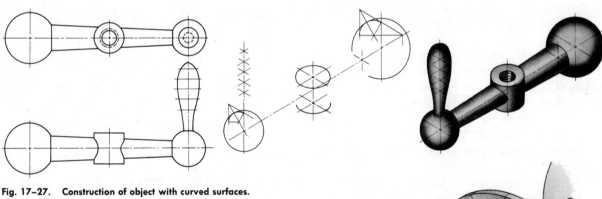
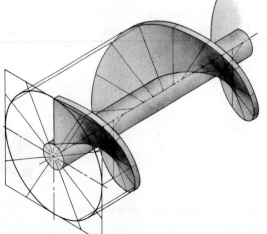

Fig. 17-27.   Construction of object with curved surfaces.

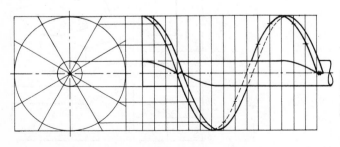

Fig. 17-28.   Construction of a right helicoid in isometric.

two- and three-view orthographic projections, isometric has the advantage of showing three sides of the object in one view, thus giving a more realistic picture of it.

As compared with other forms of pictorial drawing, isometric has the advantage of being easily constructed since the same scale is used on all sides. Circles can be readily approximated by the four-center method. It can be scaled and dimensioned. It is flexible in the position in which an object may be shown but not as flexible as other types, particularly oblique projection described in a later chapter. Circles are not distorted as in oblique and sometimes in perspective.

Against these advantages may be placed definite disadvantages which limit its usefulness in certain situations. Long objects with parallel sides show a disagreeable distortion since the eye is accustomed to the perspective effect of long parallel lines which appear to approach each other. There is also an exactness of symmetry causing an overlaying of lines in some symmetrical objects which makes the isometric difficult to read.

17.16   Dimetric drawing. Somewhat the same distinction exists between dimetric projection and dimetric drawing as obtained between isometric projection and isometric drawing, namely, that scales approximating the projected scales are used in making the drawing. In Fig. 17–29(a), the conventional cube has been shown rotated from the position for isometric projection to a convenient dimetric position. The dimetric projection is shown at (b).

In Fig. 17–30, four convenient positions for the dimetric axes are illustrated, with the approximate proportion of angles and scales for each axis indicated. The construction in conventional dimetric is carried on in the same manner as in isometric, except that on one axis the scale is changed. The simplest way of making a dimetric drawing is to proceed in the following manner:

a. Make the orthographic views to the scale desired for the two equal dimetric axes, and then enclose the views in the smallest possible rectangular box as shown in Fig. 17–31.

b. Draw the box in the desired dimetric position by transferring overall dimensions with dividers directly from the orthographic views for the equal axes and to the proper scale for the third axis. The scale to be used for this third axis is shown in Fig. 17–31 at the left side of the top view. In this case the scale on the short axis was made ⅝ that of the other axes.

c. Plot points locating the corners and curves of the object just as in isometric, taking care to use the proper scale.

d. It should be noted that the four-center method of drawing circles can be used only in the face having equal scales on both sides.

17.17   True axonometric projection. A simple method of making true axonometric projections was published by Theodor Schmid in 1922 and Professor L. Eckhart

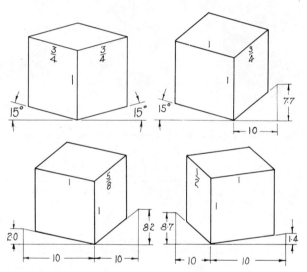

Fig. 17–30.   Four convenient positions for dimetric drawing.

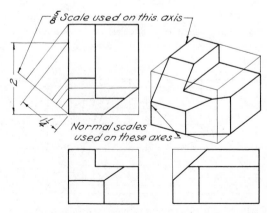

Fig. 17–31.   Construction of a dimetric drawing.

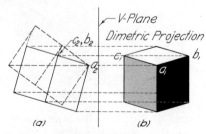

Fig. 17–29.   Dimetric projection and drawing.

in 1937. This method was presented in the United States by the authors in 1942 and has since been widely used. The method is applicable to isometric, dimetric and trimetric projections, and is particularly useful when orthographic views of an object are available. The question of scale on the various axes is automatically determined.

17.18 Theory of axonometric projections. In Fig. 17–32, the position of the axonometric plane relative to the three principal planes is shown pictorially for each of the three types of projection. In each case the picture plane coincides with the axonometric plane. Therefore the axonometric triangle in each drawing is true size. The relative positions of the three principal views and the axonometric view are also shown. It should be noted at the beginning *that axonometric projection as*

here discussed is orthographic projection, that is, the projection lines are perpendicular to the plane of projection. The following principles of orthographic projection are involved in an understanding of axonometric projection.

a. If a point is projected orthographically upon any two intersecting planes, as in Fig. 17–33, the two projections, when one of the planes is revolved into coincidence with the other, fall on a line which is perpendicular to the line of intersection of the two planes. Thus in Fig. 17–33, the two projections o^H and $o_r{}^A$ lie on the same perpendicular to AB. This principle has been illustrated again for all principal planes in Fig. 17–34.

In Fig. 17–35, the three principal planes, together with the projections of an object on them, have been

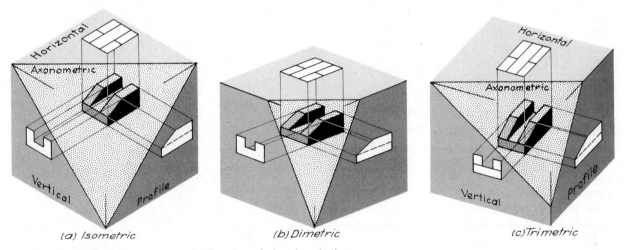

Fig. 17–32. Position of plane for isometric, dimetric, and trimetric projection.

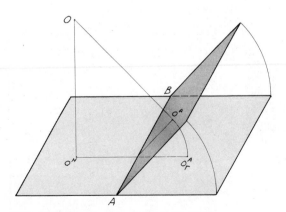

Fig. 17–33. Theory of axonometric projection.

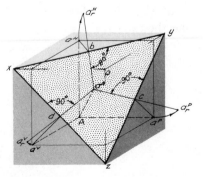

Fig. 17–34. H-, V-, and P-projections of a point revolved into axonometric plane.

successively revolved into the plane of the axonometric triangle. From Fig. 17–35(c) it can be seen that the axonometric projection can be obtained by direct projection from any two of the three revolved views. The following things should be noted:

1. The projecting lines are always perpendicular to the axis of rotation.

2. In each case, the revolved positions of the orthographic views have their principal edges parallel to the edges of the corresponding revolved plane.

b. One other geometric principle is involved. If three mutually perpendicular lines, as, for example, three intersecting edges of a cube, *ox*, *oy*, and *oz*, in Fig. 17–36(*a*), are made to pass through the three corners of a triangle, *xyz*, the projections of these lines on the tri-

angle will be perpendicular to the side opposite the corner through which the line passes, that is, *ox* will be perpendicular to *yz*, *oy* will be perpendicular to *xz*, and *oz* will be perpendicular to *xy*. This is shown in Fig. 17–36(*a*).

c. Finally, in order to determine the position of right triangle *OYZ*, of Fig. 17–36(*a*), when revolved into the plane *XYZ*, it is necessary to use the geometric principal that any two lines drawn from the ends of a diameter of a circle to a point on the circumference make a right angle with each other. Then since it is known that the angle *YOZ* is a right angle, its true size must show where the plane has been revolved into the axonometric plane which has been set up to show in its true size. Hence if a semicircle be constructed with *YZ* as a diame-

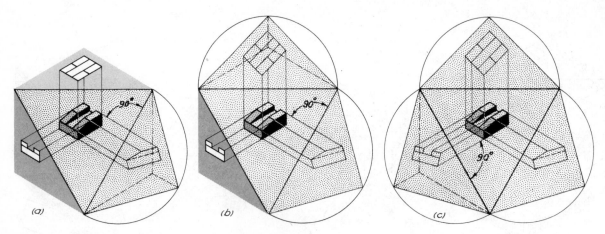

Fig. 17–35.   Rotation of coordinate planes into axonometric plane.

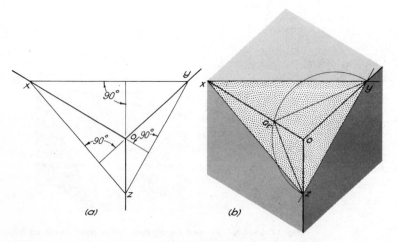

Fig. 17–36.   Finding revolved position of the edges of coordinate planes.

ter, as in Fig. 17–36(b), point O must move out along the line OX to the point O_r on the semicircle. This construction enables the draftsman to determine the position of the orthographic views by revolving the front corner instead of the rear corner as was done in Fig. 17–35. This construction is much easier since the work usually begins with the position of the axes rather than the entire box.

17.19 Constructing a trimetric projection. Having these principles in mind, a step by step construction for making a trimetric projection may be made as follows. See Fig. 17–37.

a. Select the position of the three axes as in Fig. 17–37(a). Note that the edges of the object in the finished drawing will be parallel to these lines. The angles between the lines may have any value greater than 90° except 180°.

b. Draw lines at right angles to the axes across the opposite angles as shown in Fig. 17–37(b). All three may be used but any two will be sufficient.

c. Determine the revolved position of the axes as shown in Fig. 17–37(c) and (d). Note that this construction has been translated to a parallel position in order to leave the central area free.

d. Place the front and side views with the edges parallel to the revolved positions of the respective axes, as shown in Fig. 17–37(e). Project from these views to form the axonometric projection.

As a further illustration of this method, the bearing bracket of Fig. 17–38 has been drawn in dimetric in Fig.

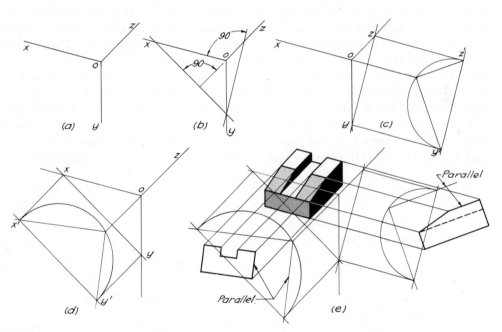

Fig. 17–37. Step-by-step construction of a trimetric projection.

17-39. The details of projection have been omitted. In order to orient the orthographic views properly, it is best to make a freehand thumbnail sketch of the axes and orthographic views in the position in which they are to be shown, as in Fig. 17-39(a).

In Fig. 17-39 the top and front views have been used to make the construction. In drawing the circles with ellipse guides or by the trammel method, it is only necessary to find the location of the center and the major and minor axes in the pictorial. The length of the major axis is always equal to the diameter of the circle and its direction will be perpendicular to the axis of the right cylinder of which the circle is a base.

17.20   Selection of axes. The axes may be chosen in any position provided the angles between them are over 90° but not 180°. However, certain positions have been found by experience to be very satisfactory. When the axes are 120° apart, the result is an isometric projection, which is useful because everyone is accustomed to seeing isometric drawings. A good dimetric is formed by making one axis vertical and the other two at an angle of 15° with the horizontal. A trimetric with one axis vertical, one at 15° with the horizontal and the other 30° with the horizontal, makes a very flexible layout and has the advantage that the lines may be drawn with readily available triangles. By rotating the axes

and reversing them, total of twelve different positions can be obtained which will allow an object to be viewed from almost any position. When the orthographic two- or three-view drawings are available, the projected axonometric becomes much easier and faster than making an isometric drawing. For a simple object, there is little advantage, but as the complexity increases, the savings in time become very real.

17.21   Drawing circles in axonometric. The drawing of circles in any pictorial is usually the slowest part of the work. In axonometric projection the points on a circle may be projected quite rapidly, but it is then necessary to connect them with an irregular curve which is very time consuming. To avoid this, ellipse guides have been developed, by means of which the entire ellipse can be drawn by projecting only the center of the circle and the axis of the cylinder. The Lietz Ellipse guides are made with ten different proportions and a wide range of sizes. They are numbered in degrees ranging from 15° to 60° by 5° intervals. The degree gives the angle that the line of sight makes with the plane of the circle, which is the complement of the angle between the plane of the circle and the picture plane. With 5° intervals on the ellipse guides, the greatest error possible is 2°-30′, which does not impair the accuracy of the drawing for most purposes.

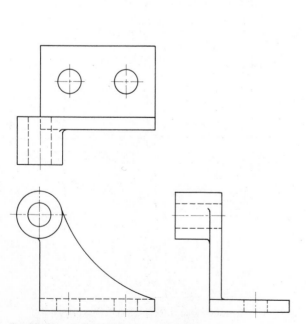

Fig. 17-38.   Orthographic views of bracket.

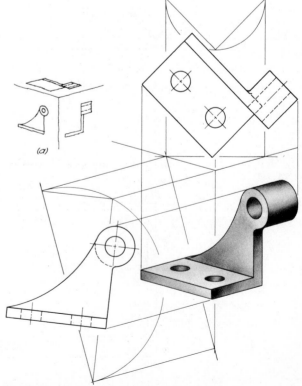

Fig. 17-39.   Axonometric projection of bracket.

To use the ellipse guides, it is necessary to determine the angle between the picture plane and the various faces of the object. Figure 17–40 shows two methods for doing this. The profile projection determined by using the semicircle to lay out a right angle as in Fig. 17–37, gives the angle between the top face and the picture plane. Auxiliary planes perpendicular to the other sides of the triangle may be used to determine the corresponding angles by the same method.

By the second method, a plane is passed through OX perpendicular to the picture plane, XYZ. This plane is then revolved about the line OS in the picture plane until it coincides with the picture plane. The triangle $O^v O^v_r S$ is the revolved position and shows the angle between the two planes and also the Lietz Ellipse angle as indicated in Fig. 17–40.

17.21.1   Selection of axes for predetermined ellipse angles. It is possible to determine the direction of axes so that two of the three sides will have ellipse angles that fit perfectly with the guides but the third face must be accepted as found by the construction. Thus suppose it is desired to use 20° ellipse guides on the top face and 40° guides on the left face, the construction is then as follows.

a. Assume a horizontal line, MN, of indefinite length, and a vertical line with a definite point, B, at the lower

end. See Fig. 17–41(*a*).

b. The plane containing MN and point B is the picture plane which shows edgewise in the profile view. Through $m^p n^p$ construct a line making 70° (the complement of the specified 20°) with the picture plane. This line represents the edgewise view of the top face of the cube. See Fig. 17–41(*b*).

c. In the profile view construct a semicircle with $m^p n^p - b^p$ as a diameter. This semicircle locates O^p so that BO is perpendicular to the top plane. The line BO

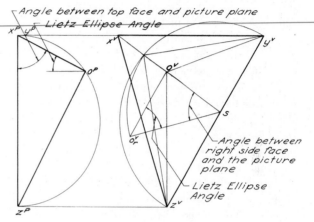

Fig. 17–40.   Determining Lietz ellipse angle.

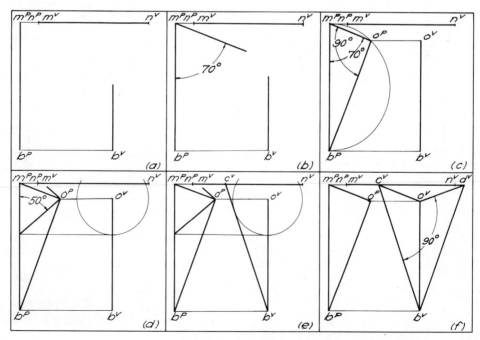

Fig. 17–41.   Determining axes for specified ellipse angles.

is the front edge of the cube, and O is the origin of the axes. See Fig. 17–41(c).

d. With O as the apex construct a right circular cone whose base lies in the picture plane and whose elements make an angle of 50° (the complement of the specified 40°) with the picture plane. The two views of the cone are shown in Fig. 17–41(d).

e. Through b^V, construct a line tangent to the circular base and extend it to c^V on the horizontal line MN. See Fig. 17–41(e).

f. Through O^V, construct a line perpendicular to to $b^V c^V$ and continue it to the horizontal line at d^V. The triangle $b^V c^V d^V$ is the picture plane triangle and $o^V b^V$, $o^V c^V$, and $o^V d^V$ are the axes. See Fig. 17–41(f). The angle that the right face makes with the picture plane may be found as previously explained.

17.22   Special drawing boards. Several special drawing boards have been developed at the University of Illinois, chiefly by Professor Wayne Schick, to make the use of axonometric projection simpler and more comprehensive. Boards similar to the one shown in Fig. 17–42 may be designed for any set of axes. The positions of the various views and the ellipse guides to be used on the various faces are marked clearly on the face of the board. The corners of the board are cut off perpen-

dicular to the three axis so that all projection lines can be drawn with a T-square. If a blueprint of the object is available, the use of this board to make a trimetric projection may save up to 50% of the time required to make an isometric drawing of a complicated object.

17.23   The united drawing system. By means of the specially designed board, shown in Fig. 17–43, it is possible to construct three orthographic views of an object and an isometric projection at the same time. This board was invented and patented by Professor W. L. Schick of the University of Illinois. It consists of a basic equilateral triangle on which the quadrangle slides. The quadrangle is a transparent plastic tool so designed that two sides may be used for projecting between two of the orthographic views, whereas the third side projects from one view to the isometric view. Since the angles are all equal in isometric, the quadrangle may be used on each of the three sides of the triangle for projection purposes. The advantages of the system are that direct projection is obtained between any two views and also that the isometric acts as a very positive check on the accuracy of all projections. The disadvantage is that the three-view drawings are not arranged in horizontal and vertical alignment as is customary in regular multiview projection.

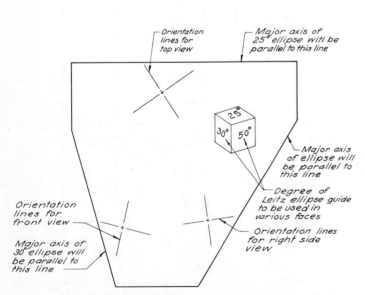

Fig. 17–42.   Trimetric board.

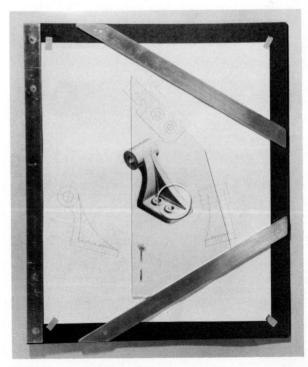

Fig. 17–43.   Unified drawing system.

PROBLEMS

The problems in the following group may be made as axonometric drawings by the conventional method or as true projections by the exact method.

The scales given under each figure are for the solution of isometrics on 8½ × 11-inch paper by the conventional method. When dimetrics or trimetrics are made, the other scales should normally be smaller than the one given.

For exact projections the original orthographic views may be made at a slightly larger scale since the projected axonometric is foreshortened in all its dimensions. Thus, for example, a problem with scale specified as ⅜″ = 1″ may have the ortho-

graphic views made at ½″ = 1″ for the construction of true projections.

1. Make an isometric drawing by the conventional method of an object assigned from Figs. 17–44 to 17–55.

2. Make a true isometric projection of an object assigned from Figs. 17–44 to 17–55. Note that two correct orthographic views must first be made for this method.

3. Make a true dimetric projection of an object assigned from Figs. 17–44 to 17–55. Use axes as desired.

4. Make a true trimetric projection of an object assigned from Figs. 17–44 to 17–55. Use axes as desired.

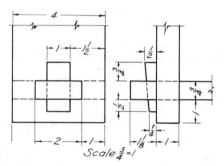

Fig. 17–44.   Tenon joint.

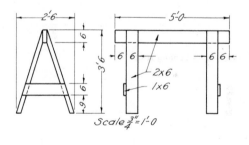

Fig. 17–46.   Horse.

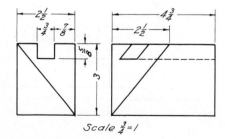

Fig. 17–45.   Cut-block.

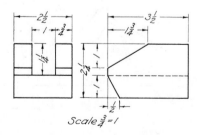

Fig. 17–47.   Cut-block.

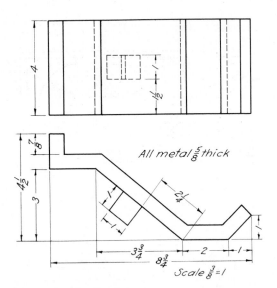

Fig. 17–48. Truss-bearing strap.

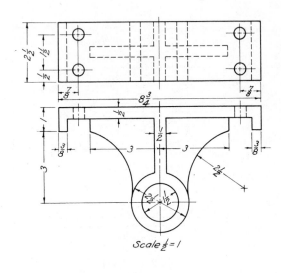

Fig. 17–50. Conveyor bearing support.

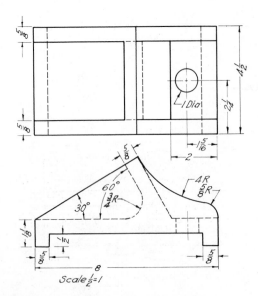

Fig. 17–49. Truss block.

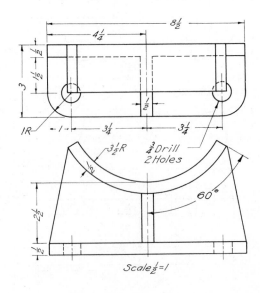

Fig. 17–51. Saddle.

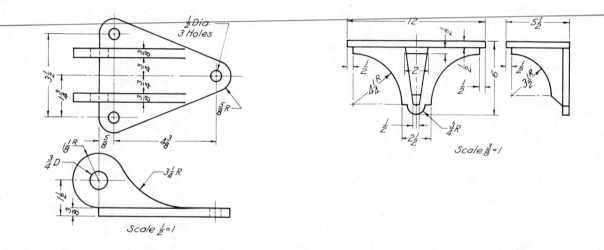

Fig. 17–52. Hinge.

Fig. 17–54. Shelf.

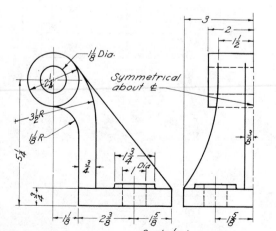

Fig. 17–53. Bearing bracket.

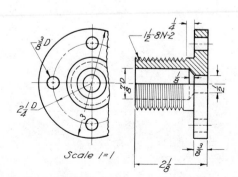

Fig. 17–55. Stuffing box body.

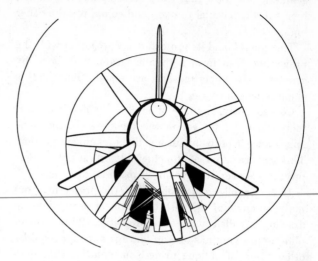

18

Oblique Projection

18.1 In both orthographic and axonometric drawing, already discussed in previous chapters, the projecting lines have been at right angles to the plane or planes of projection. We shall now consider a kind of drawing in which, as in axonometric, only one plane of projection is used, but in which the projecting lines, although parallel to each other, are oblique to the plane of projection. The object may be placed in any position, but, for convenience and to obtain the full advantage of this method of drawing, it is customary to have the front face of the object parallel to the vertical plane or picture plane as it is sometimes called.

18.2 Projecting lines. As noted above, the projecting lines may make any angle with the plane of projection except 90°. There are several types of oblique projection. They are distinguished from each other solely by the angle which the projecting line makes with the plane of projection as discussed in the following paragraphs. Because the projecting lines in any one drawing are always parallel to each other, the point of sight is said to be at infinity, since by definition parallel lines meet at infinity.

Because the projecting lines are parallel to each other, any line which is parallel to the picture plane will project in its true length. The projection will also be parallel to the original position of the line, as shown in Fig. 18–1.

This can readily be seen to be true if we remember that two parallel lines determine a plane. If we think of a plane through the lines *AB, BC,* etc., parallel to the plane of projection, then the plane of the projecting lines is a third plane intersecting these two, and from geometry we know that the intersections are parallel; hence AB is parallel to a_ob_o, and so on, for the other lines.

The line AB and its projection a_ob_o together with the projecting lines form a parallelogram, and again by geometry the opposite sides are equal. Hence AB is equal in length to a_ob_o.

Consequently, any face of an object which is parallel to the plane of projection will have exactly the same appearance in both oblique and orthographic projection. This feature is one of the chief advantages of oblique projections over other forms of pictorial drawing.

18.3 Cavalier projection. When the projecting lines make an angle of 45° with the plane of projection the drawing is called a Cavalier projection. This form of oblique drawing has one advantage not possessed by other types of oblique projection, namely, that lines which are perpendicular to the picture plane also project in their true length as well as those which are parallel to the plane.

In Fig. 18–2, the line AB, which is perpendicular to the plane, has its end B in the plane and the end A in front of the plane. The end B therefore coincides with its projection. When the end A is projected to the plane by a line making 45° with the plane in any direction, the projection of the line is exactly as long as the line itself. It should be definitely noted in this figure that, whereas the projecting lines Aa_1, Aa_2, Aa_3, etc., all make 45° with the plane of projection like the elements of a cone, the projections Ba_1, Ba_2, Ba_3, etc., may make any angle with the horizontal.

Receding axis. As in isometric the rectangular box furnishes an excellent reference frame for construction. The three edges of such a box, which meet at a corner, when represented in oblique drawing, are referred to as the axes of the drawing. Two of them are always in the front face at right angles to each other, and the third, which represents an edge perpendicular to the plane of projection, may be at any convenient angle. This inclined line is called the receding axis. In Cavalier projection all these three axes will project in their true length, and therefore the same scale may be used on all of them in making constructions. This is the distinguishing feature of Cavalier projection.

As noted above and as illustrated in Fig. 18–3, the receding axis may make any angle with the horizontal. This angle is not to be confused with the 45° angle which the projecting line makes with the plane of projection.

18.4 Theoretical construction. An oblique projection of an object may be constructed from its orthographic views by drawing the oblique projecting lines from these

views and finding where they pierce the plane of projection, as shown in Fig. 18-4. Any two views could be used, but all three have been shown in the figure in order to illustrate the theory.

Since the vertical plane appears edgewise in both the side and top views, the piercing points of the projecting lines can be seen in these views by inspection. Thus, in the pictorial top view of Fig. 18-4(a), the projecting line from a^H pierces the plane at $a_o{}^H$, and the front view of this piercing point must lie in the perpendicular from $a_o{}^H$. Likewise in the side view the projecting line from a^p pierces the picture plane at $a_o{}^p$, and the front view of this piercing point must lie horizontally across from $a_o{}^p$. The intersection of these two perpendiculars determines $a_o{}^V$, which is the oblique projection of point A on

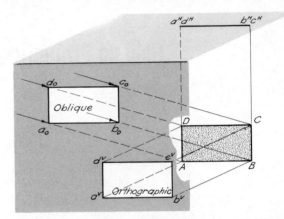

Fig. 18–1. Oblique projection of lines parallel to plane of projection.

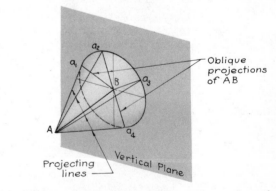

Fig. 18–2. Oblique projection of line perpendicular to plane of projection.

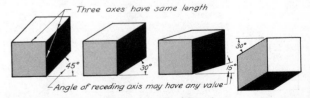

Fig. 18–3. A few positions of the receding axis.

the object. The same procedure is used for all other points.

The orthographic construction of an oblique projection and the completed oblique projection are shown in heavy outline in Fig. 18–4(*b*). Although this theoretical method can be used for so simple an object as a cube, it would be too cumbersome for more complicated objects. A conventional method of construction similar to that used in isometric is explained in the following paragraphs.

It may be noted, in passing, that the true value of the angle which the projecting lines make with the *V*-plane does not show in any one of the three views of Fig. 18–4(*b*). It may be found, however, by dropping a perpendicular to the *V*-plane from *B* in Fig. 18–4(*b*) and

revolving the shaded triangle to BCB_o around the line BC until it is parallel to the *H*-plane. The true value of the angle then shows in the *H*-projection at $b_{or}{}^H$.

18.5   Conventional construction of Cavalier projections. Since the same scale may be used on the three axes of a Cavalier projection, a method of construction similar to that used in isometric may be employed.

a. Plane figures. One of the advantages of oblique projection is that plane figures in the front face of an object, or parallel thereto, project in their true shape just as shown in the orthographic views and hence require little further explanation.

The only difficulty experienced lies in getting the contours which lie behind the front face into their proper planes. Thus, in the block shown in Fig. 18–5(*a*),

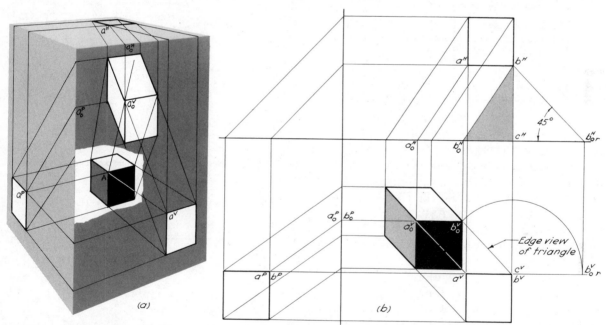

Fig. 18–4.   Theory of oblique projection.

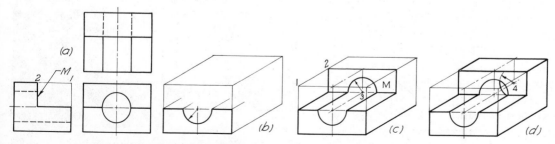

Fig. 18–5.   Box method of constructing oblique projections.

the circle, lying in the face *M,* while showing as a circle, must be located at the proper place. This is accomplished by measuring back a distance *1–2* and drawing a plane across the box, as indicated in Fig. 18–5(*c*). The center line of the front circle can now be carried back to this plane, thus locating the center of the required circle at *3.*

The center of the circle in the back face is formed by carrying the center line from *3* up over the top of the box and down the back until it intersects the receding center line through *3,* thus establishing the center *4.*

In the top and side receding planes, the coordinate method of construction may be used, as shown in Fig. 18–6. Circles may be plotted by the coordinate method in the same manner as for isometric, or they may be approximated by the four-center method of construction.

b. Four-center approximate method of representing circles. A circle may be enclosed in a square, and since it is always tangent to the square at the midpoint of the sides, the Cavalier projection will show an ellipse which is tangent to the midpoint of the sides of the enclosing rhombus. Hence, to find the centers of the four arcs,

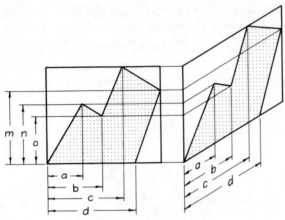

Fig. 18–6. Coordinate methods of construction.

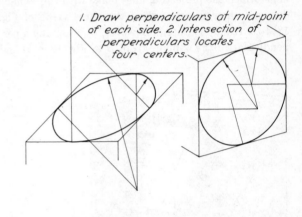

1. Draw perpendiculars at mid-point of each side. 2. Intersection of perpendiculars locates four centers.

Fig. 18–7. Four-center approximate method of representing circles.

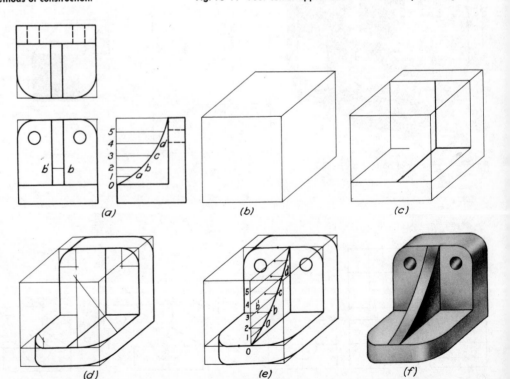

(a)   (b)   (c)

(d)   (e)   (f)

Fig. 18–8. Construction of curves in a receding plane.

erect perpendiculars to the midpoints of the four sides of the rhombus, and find their intersections, as shown in Fig. 18–7. It should be noted that as the ratio of the major to the minor axis increases the approximation becomes less accurate.

c. Solid objects. The steps in making a Cavalier projection of a solid or three-dimensioned object are illustrated in Fig. 18–8. They may be listed as follows:

1. Enclose the orthographic views of the object in the smallest possible rectangular box whose faces are parallel to the principal faces of the object. See Fig. 18–8(*a*).

2. Draw this enclosing box in Cavalier projection, making the front of the box like the orthographic front view and the receding axis to the same scale as the front and at an angle that will show the side and top to the best advantage. See Fig. 18–8(*b*).

3. Draw lightly all lines in the front face, and establish position of planes parallel to the front face. See Fig. 18–8(*c*).

4. Draw all lines in faces parallel to the front at the proper distances from the front face, as shown in Fig. 18–8(*d*).

5. Construct coordinates for curves not in the front face in the orthographic view as shown at *1–a, 2–b, 3–c*, etc., in Fig. 18–8(*a*), and then transfer these coordinates to the oblique as shown for one curve in Fig. 18–8(*e*). Since the second curve is parallel to the first, points on it may be located by stepping off the thickness of the web (see front view) as *bb′*, in Fig. 18–8(*e*).

6. Complete all lines, and erase construction. After erasure make heavy the visible outlines of the drawing, producing the finished drawing of Fig. 18–8(*f*).

18.6   Position of object. *a. For simplicity of construction.* Since any face of an object which is parallel to the picture plane appears in its true shape in an oblique projection, the construction of many drawings can be kept quite simple by showing the face of the object which has the most circles, arcs, or other curves as the front face. This rule should be adhered to whenever possible for it can be readily seen that the object in the position of Fig. 18–9(*a*) is not only easier to draw but also looks much better than the same object as represented in Fig. 18–9(*b*).

b. To reduce distortion. Unpleasant distortion in Cavalier projection frequently can be reduced by placing an object which has one dimension much greater than the others with this long dimension parallel to the picture plane, as shown in Fig. 18–10. Some discrimination must be exercised, however, for this may not work so well with some objects as with others. A better method to reduce distortion is to reduce the scale on the receding axis.

18.7   Cabinet drawing. A second type of oblique projection which has been specifically named is produced when the angle which the projecting line makes with the plane of projection is 63°-26′. The tangent of this angle is 2, which means that a line perpendicular to the vertical plane is just twice as long as its projection, or stated in another way the projection is one-half as long as the line. This result will be produced automatically if the scale used on the receding axis is just one-half that used on the front face. A drawing made in this way is called a Cabinet drawing. Again it should be mentioned that the angle which the receding axis makes with the horizontal may have any value just as

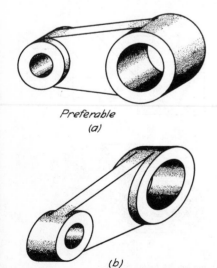

Preferable
(a)

(b)

Fig. 18–9.   Circles preferably parallel to front face.

Fig. 18–10.   Long dimensions parallel to plane of projection.

in Cavalier projection.

a. Construction of a cabinet drawing. A Cabinet drawing may be made in the same manner as a Cavalier projection with the exception that the scale on the receding axis must be reduced one-half. The steps in this procedure are shown in Fig. 18–11, which, though not a Cabinet drawing, illustrates the method of construction. Where curves are involved in the receding faces a convenient scheme for obtaining the foreshortened or one-half-scale dimensions from the orthographic views is shown in Fig. 18–11.

Thus, for a Cabinet drawing, if the total length *ab* on the receding axis is 3 inches, the line *ac* will be 1½ inches long. This line may be laid out in any convenient direction from either end of line *ab*, as illustrated. The point *c* is then connected with *b*, and all other points to be plotted are transferred to line *ac* by lines parallel to *bc*. This device for making proportional divisions of any line should be thoroughly understood by the student.

The four-center approximate method of drawing circles cannot be used in Cabinet drawing since the sides of the enclosing parallelogram are not equal. A circle can be plotted, however, without referring to the original orthographic projections except to get the dimensions and position of the enclosing parallelogram. The

method of plotting coordinates by means of a semicircle and a diagonal of the parallelogram is shown in Fig. 17–7.

18.8   General oblique. Obviously, other scales than those mentioned could be used on the receding axis. For example, if the scale on the front face is 1″ = 1″, a scale of ¾″ = 1″ could be used on the receding axis. A drawing made in this manner is neither a Cavalier projection nor a Cabinet drawing and is simply referred to as an oblique projection. The angle which the projecting lines make with the plane of projection can be determined by comparing the length of a perpendicular with the length of its projection. Thus, in Fig. 18–11, a perpendicular 1 inch long would project ¾ inch long. Hence the tangent of the angle which the projecting line makes with the plane of projection would be 1 ÷ ¾ or 1.333. This angle is 53°-8′. Its value, of course, is of theoretical interest only since it does not enter into the actual construction of the drawing.

The construction of any oblique drawing follows the same pattern as the construction of a Cavalier projection, with the exception that the scale on the receding axis is changed to suit the conditions.

18.9   Center-line layout. When an object is composed of more or less cylindrical parts like the rocker arm in

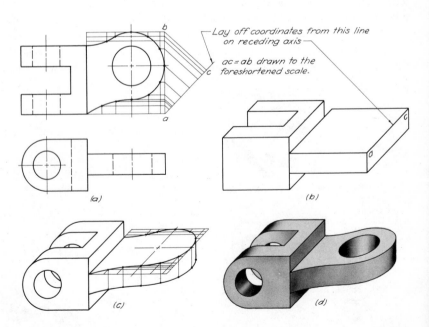

Fig. 18–11.   Method of foreshortening the scale on the receding axis.

Fig. 18-12(a), the construction can be based upon a center-line framework instead of the box construction previously explained. With the direction of the three axes chosen, the centers of all circular parts can be laid out as illustrated in Fig. 18-12(b), using the proper scale on all axes. At each center, circles of the proper size can be drawn, as shown in Fig. 18-12(c). The straight lines tangent to them can be drawn quickly, giving the final result shown in Fig. 18-12(d).

18.10   Sectioning oblique drawings. As in all pictorial drawing, hidden lines are not shown since it is very difficult to interpret them. Interior construction is best shown by making sectional views with either one-fourth or one-half the object removed. The cutting planes, in general, should be parallel to the oblique planes or faces of the enclosing box, as shown in Fig. 18-13. Other illustrations may be found in the problem sections of various chapters.

The crosshatching lines lying in two planes which are at right angles to each other should be sloped in such a way that they would seem to coincide if the planes were rotated together. Correct section lining is shown in Fig. 18-13.

18.11   Dimensioning oblique drawings. The principles of dimensioning studied in connection with working

drawings apply in general to oblique projections, with the following additions:

a. Dimensions should be made to read from the bottom and right-hand side of the sheet so far as possible. See Figs. 18-12 and 18-14(b).

b. Dimension lines and witness or extension lines

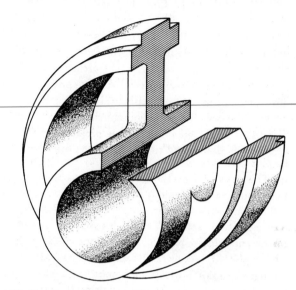

Fig. 18-13.   Sectional view in oblique projection.

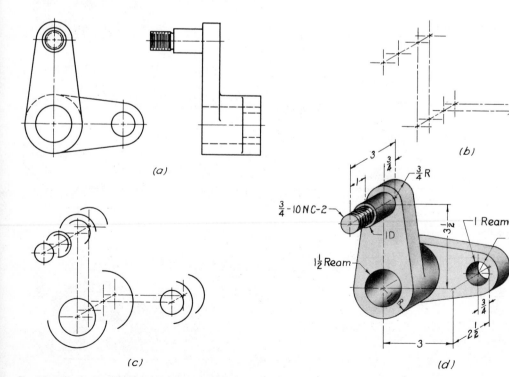

Fig. 18-12.   Center-line method of construction.

must lie in the same oblique plane. See Figs. 18–14 and 18–15.

c. Dimensions must lie in the oblique plane determined by the dimension lines and extension lines.

d. Only vertical lettering and numerals should be used. Numerals and letters may be made to lie in oblique planes in the same manner as shown for isometric. The unidirectional system is also approved.

e. As far as possible, dimensions should be placed in the front face or parallel thereto since this makes the dimensioning similar to that in the orthographic views.

f. When notes are extensive and are not on the figure, they may be lettered neatly in slant style. In general, however, vertical lettering is preferred.

18.12   Screw threads in oblique projection. Since circles which are parallel to the plane of projection show as true circles in oblique projection, screw threads may be easily represented by a conventionalized scheme, if the axis of the thread is made parallel to the receding axis of the drawing. The axis of the bolt or nut, as in Fig. 18–16, becomes the line of centers for a series of circles representing the crests of the threads. The root line does not show. The spacing of the circles is made the same as the pitch of the thread until the pitch becomes too fine, in which case the smallest convenient spacing is used.

Whenever possible, bolts, screws, or nuts should be drawn in the position shown in Fig. 18–16. When placed with the axis parallel to the picture plane, the circles representing the thread crests must be plotted as ellipses and drawn with an irregular curve or ellipse guide, which is a slow process.

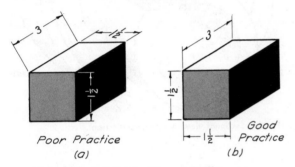

Poor Practice
(a)

Good Practice
(b)

Fig. 18–14.   Dimensioning in oblique projection.

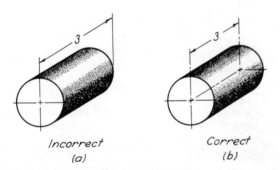

Incorrect
(a)

Correct
(b)

Fig. 18–15.   Dimensions in oblique plane.

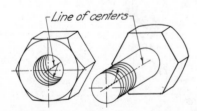

Line of centers

Fig. 18–16.   Screw threads in oblique projection.

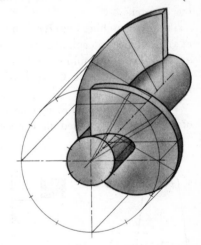

Fig. 18–17.   Helicoid in oblique projection.

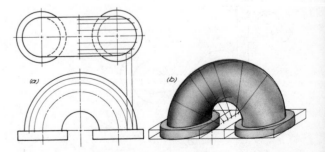

(a)   (b)

Fig. 18–18.   A double-curved surface in oblique projection.

18.13 **Three-dimensional curves.** Three-dimensional curves, such as the conveyor shown in Fig. 18–17, can be drawn with comparative ease if the axis of the conveyor is placed on the receding axis of the drawing. The method is illustrated in the figure. The circles are first divided into 12 equal parts, and the pitch is likewise divided into the same number of parts. On the center line, step off intervals equal to one-twelfth the pitch. From these points radial lines can be drawn parallel to those used in dividing the circles. The construction is shown for the first four points on the curve. After the first turn has been completed, successive turns can be made by stepping off distances equal to the pitch from the previous curve. The thickness of the blade can also be stepped off at equal intervals from the first curve. In cases of this kind the orthographic views are not required to make the construction.

If, on the other hand, the three-dimensional curve is irregular in shape, it may be necessary to resort to the box construction and plot three rectangular coordinates.

18.14 **Double-curved surfaces.** The outline of a double-curved surface is represented by an enveloping curve tangent to imaginary curves in the surface. Thus a return pipe bend can have a series of semicircles drawn on its surface, as shown in Fig. 18–18(*a*). These curves are then drawn in oblique and the enveloping curve drawn tangent to them.

18.15 **Advantages of oblique drawing.** From the foregoing paragraphs it is quite clear that oblique drawings have several distinct advantages over other pictorial forms.

a. The front face of an object or any face parallel to it may be drawn like its true orthographic projection, and hence circles may be drawn as true circles.

b. Distortion may be largely overcome by a careful foreshortening of the scale on the receding axis.

c. Dimensioning is simpler since only one set of dimensions need be made in an oblique plane.

d. There is a greater range of choice of positions of the axes than in the other forms except trimetric. See Fig. 18–3.

To offset these advantages it should be noted that oblique projections even though foreshortened on the receding axis have an unpleasing distortion. This is particularly true when circles must be shown in the receding faces.

PROBLEMS

Problems in the following group may be assigned as Cavalier projections (*note:* this does not mean that the receding axis must slope at an angle of 45°), Cabinet drawing, or general oblique projection. The student should note that the only practical difference in drawing the different types of projection lies in the scale used on the receding axis.

For general obliques, it is recommended that the scale on the receding axis be in the ratio ¾ to 1 of that used for the front face. The most convenient slope for the receding axis is 30° up to the right, but any other direction may be used.

The selection of all scales and the slope of the receding axis has been left to the student unless specifically directed by the instructor.

1. Make a Cavalier projection of an object assigned from Figs. 18–19 to 18–29.

2. Make a Cabinet drawing of an object assigned from Figs. 18–19 to 18–29.

3. Make a general oblique projection of an object assigned from Figs. 18–19 to 18–29.

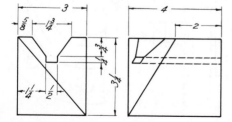

Fig. 18–19. Cut block.

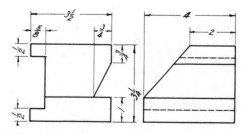

Fig. 18–20. Cut block.

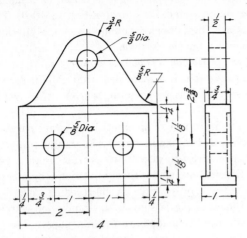

Fig. 18-21.   Conveyor attachment.

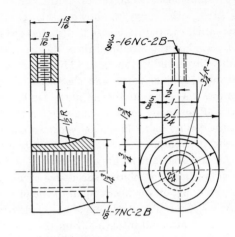

Fig. 18-24.   Flue hole cutter holder.

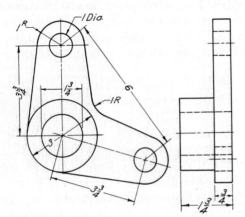

Fig. 18-22.   Rocker arm.

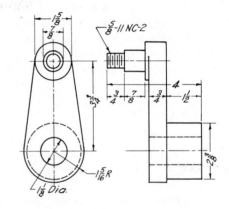

Fig. 18-25.   Bell crank.

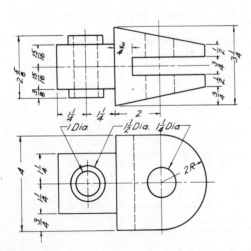

Fig. 18-23.   Link.

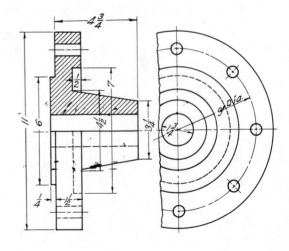

Fig. 18-26.   Cylinder end.

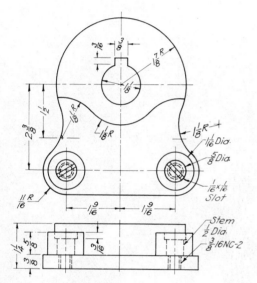

Fig. 18–27. Cam follower.

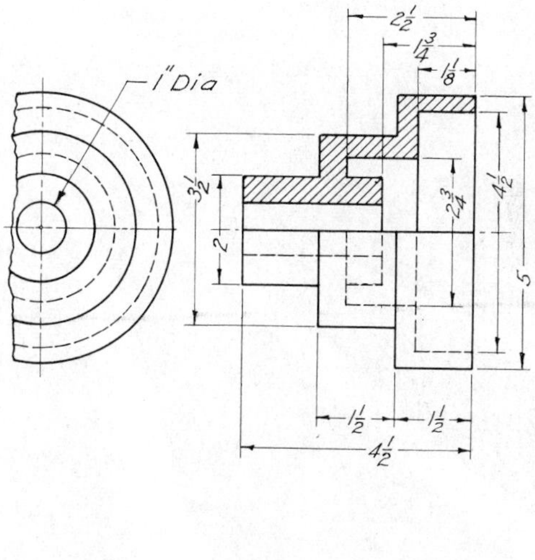

Fig. 18–28. Step pulley.

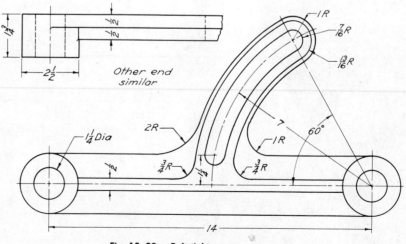

Fig. 18–29. Belt tightener.

Perspective view of irrigated fields (Charles P. Cushing).

19
Perspective

19.1   When a person looks at an object, the light rays (visual rays) from the object are focused by the eye so that the picture is formed on the spherical rear surface of the eye known as the retina. Perspective is the form of pictorial drawing which most nearly approaches the picture as seen by the eye. Thus, if we imagine a vertical plane between the eye and the cube, in Fig. 19–1, the visual rays from the cube to the eye, if intercepted by the vertical or picture plane, will form an image which exactly coincides with the edges of the cube. This produces the same image as the cube itself if viewed from this one particular position.

It will be observed that the major difference between perspective projection and the forms studied heretofore lies in the fact that the point of sight is at a finite distance from the object. *The visual rays or projecting lines from the object therefore converge to the point of sight instead of being parallel to each other as in other forms of projection.* This type of drawing is sometimes called scenographic projection or central projection since the lines of sight converge to a single point or center.

The picture or perspective obtained will depend upon the relative position of the object, picture plane, and point of sight.

19.2   **Location of the picture plane.** Normally the picture plane is placed between the object and the point of sight, as in Figs. 19–2(b) and (c). In these positions all the lines of the drawing are shorter than their true length on the object.

By comparing Figs. 19–2(b) and (c) it can be seen that the picture becomes smaller as the picture plane is moved away from the object and closer to the point of sight.

If the object is between the observer and the picture plane, as in Fig. 19–2(a), the image will be larger than the object. Finally, if the point of sight is between the object and the plane, as in Fig. 19–2(d), the image is inverted and reversed. This is what takes place in a camera where the lens is the point of sight.

19.3   Location of the point of sight. With the picture plane and object in a definite relationship to each other the perspective can be greatly altered by a change in position of the point of sight. For example, the point of

sight could be chosen above the object to show the top, or below the object to show the bottom, as in Fig. 19–3. Likewise it could be chosen to the right or left of the object to reveal either side, as in Fig. 19–4. A proper choice of the point of sight is therefore very important in making an attractive perspective.

It has been observed from experience that when the eye is focused on a certain point the eye will see clearly all the picture contained within a right circular cone having its apex at the eye and an interior angle at the apex of approximately 30°. This condition is satisfied when the point of sight is placed at a distance from the

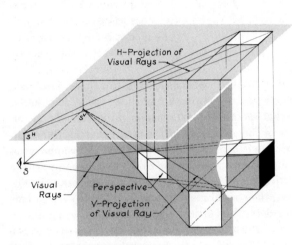

Fig. 19–1.   Theory of perspective.

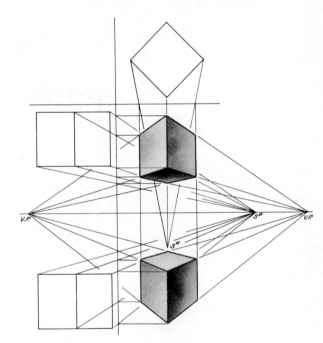

Fig. 19–3.   Object above and below point of sight.

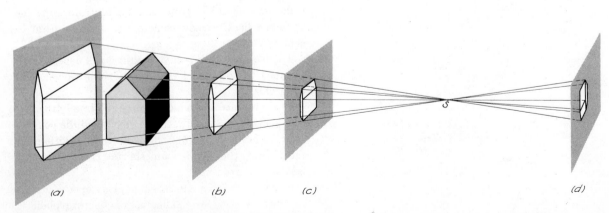

Fig. 19–2.   Relationship of object, picture plane, and point of sight.

object at least twice the longest dimension of the object, as shown in Fig. 19–5. For a good perspective, the point of sight should be located in front of the center of the object.

19.4 Position of object. The angular position of the object relative to the plane of projection will also make a great difference in the appearance of the finished perspective, as can be noted from an examination of Figs. 19–3 and 19–4. The position of the object gives rise to three types of perspective, as follows:

a. Parallel perspective. When the principal face of the object is parallel to the picture plane, as in Fig. 19–4 a

parallel or one-point perspective is formed. The term one-point refers to the fact that such perspectives have only one principal vanishing point.

b. Angular perspective. When two faces of the object are inclined to the picture plane, as in Fig. 19–3, an angular or two-point perspective is formed. There are two principal vanishing points.

c. Oblique perspective. When all faces of the object are oblique to the picture plane, an oblique or three-point perspective results. There are three principal vanishing points, as shown in Fig. 19–6.

19.5 Visual-ray method. Perspective may be constructed in a number of ways. The simplest method, though not the most practical for complicated objects, is the visual-ray method which is based on all the definition of Art. 19.1. By this method it is only necessary to draw the visual rays from the object to the point of sight and find where they pierce the picture plane. This method has been used in Fig. 19–7(a) where visual rays from A to the point of sight, $S,$ have been drawn in the top and front views. The vertical projection $A_p,$ of the point where this line pierces the vertical plane is the perspective of A. In Fig. 19–7(b), the piercing point is found by using the top and side views of the point $A,$ and the point of sight. A vertical line through v^H intersects a horizontal line through v^P to locate v^V, which is the perspective, $A_p,$ of point A.

The perspectives of the other corners of the cube have been located in the same manner. Since the perspective

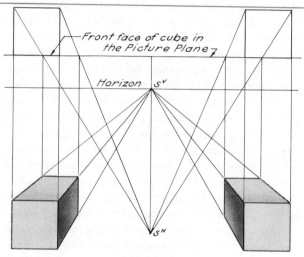

Fig. 19–4. Object right and left of point of sight.

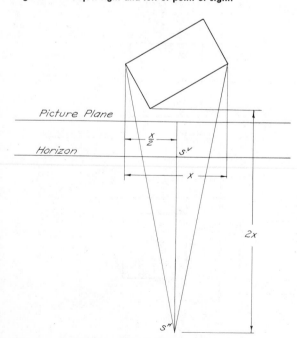

Fig. 19–5. Location of point of sight.

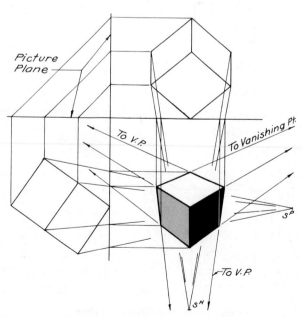

Fig. 19–6. Three-point perspective.

tends to overlap the front view in Fig. 19-7(a), the method used in Fig. 19-7(b) is preferable.

19.6   Vanishing points. It will be observed in a number of the preceding figures that lines which are not parallel to the picture plane converge to a point. *By definition parallel lines meet at infinity. The perspective of this meeting place is called the vanishing point of the lines.*

To find the vanishing point of any group of parallel lines it is necessary to draw a line through the point of sight parallel to the group of lines and then find where this line pierces the picture plane. In a step-by-step procedure the method is as follows:

a. Through the point of sight, draw a line parallel to the group of lines. It should be recalled that to draw one line parallel to another the corresponding projections are made parallel and that at least two projections are required.

b. Find the *V*-piercing point of this line.

This method of finding the vanishing points is shown pictorially in Fig. 19-8, where an object, the picture plane, the point of sight, the vanishing points, and the final perspective are represented. Lines have been drawn from *S*, parallel to several sets of parallel lines on the object to locate the vanishing points of these lines. The perspectives of these lines are then shown to vanish at the points thus found. From this figure it can be seen that horizontal lines vanish at a point on the horizon,

lines sloping up to the rear vanish above the horizon, and lines sloping down to the rear vanish below the horizon.

In Fig. 19-9, the construction is shown for finding vanishing points as the draftsman does it. In Fig. 19-9(a), the line is parallel to the horizontal, and consequently the vanishing point falls on the horizon because the vertical projection is parallel to the reference line. In Fig. 19-9(b), the line slopes up to the rear, and so the V.P. is above the horizon.

19.7   Perspective of a line. *To find the perspective of a line, it is necessary to find the perspective of two points on the line.* Those two points may be corners of an object or any other points, real or imaginary, on the line. When two projections of the object, in its desired position, are given, as in Fig. 19-7, the perspective of two points can be found by the visual-ray method. However, when the front face is not parallel to the picture plane, it requires considerable time to rotate the object and obtain the desired views. To avoid this difficulty, two other points on the lines are commonly used. *They are the vanishing point of the line and the point where the line pierces the picture plane.* Since the vanishing point is the perspective of a point at the infinite end of the line, it may always be used as one point on the perspective of the line. The point where the line pierces the picture plane must lie in the picture plane, and consequently the vertical projection of this point must be its own perspective. For purposes of explanation, the hori-

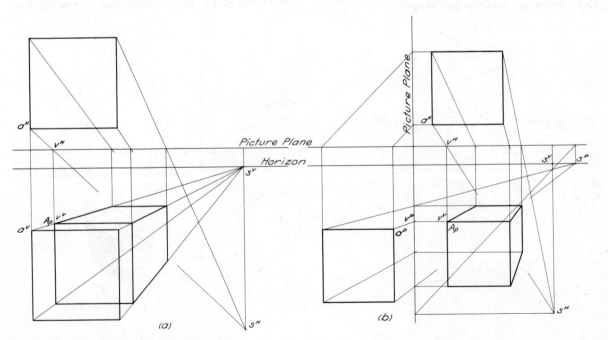

Fig. 19-7.   Perspective of cube. Visual-ray method.

zontal and vertical projections of an inclined line AB are given in Fig. 19–10. The vanishing point, VP, is found as explained in Art. 19.6. The vertical piercing point, v^V, of the line AB is found as shown in Fig. 19–10(a). The perspective of the complete line extending from the picture plane to infinity will be the line joining v^V and VP.

To find the desired points A and B on this line, the horizontal projections of visual rays from S to A and from S to B may be constructed as shown in Fig. 19–10(b). From the points where these visual rays pierce

the picture plane, projecting lines may be drawn vertically to locate A_p and B_p on the perspective v^V–VP.

The greatest advantage of this method in practical applications is obtained when the lines are horizontal. In that case the vertical projection of the line is not necessary since it is known to be parallel to the reference line, and the vanishing point must therefore lie on the horizon. Any elevation of the object will give the height of the vertical projection of any horizontal line and consequently the height of the V-piercing point. This is illustrated in Fig. 19–11, where the perspective of the

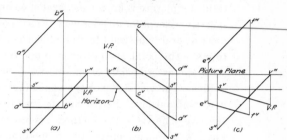

Fig. 19–9.   Method of finding vanishing points.

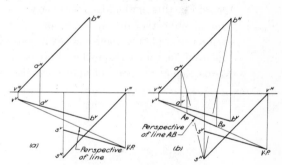

**Fig. 19–10.   Perspective of an inclined line.
Vanishing-point and visual-ray method.**

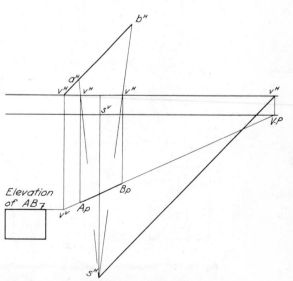

**Fig. 19–11.   Perspective of a horizontal line.
Vanishing-point and visual-ray method.**

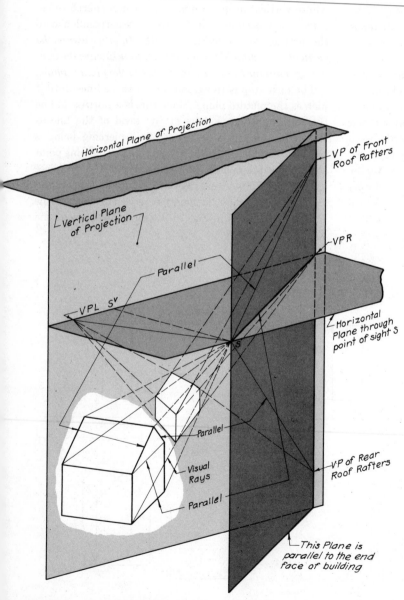

Fig. 19–8.   Theory of vanishing points.

line *AB*, the upper line of the rectangle, is found without actually drawing its vertical projection. This method is particularly convenient since many of the lines of an object are horizontal.

Even when such horizontal lines do not exist on the object it is possible and convenient to assume such imaginary lines for purposes of construction as shown for points on the circle in Fig. 19–16.

19.8   Parallel or one-point perspective. When the object is placed so that one face is parallel to the picture plane and the others perpendicular to it, the resulting picture is known as parallel or one-point perspective. Except for interior views this is not usually the most desirable position for the object because it tends to move the point of sight over to one side in order to show two exterior sides of an object.

Either the visual-ray or the vanishing-point method or a combination of the two may be used to find the perspective. The visual-ray method has been illustrated in Fig. 19–7. Consequently, the more practical method involving the use of vanishing points will be discussed here. For this method it is necessary to have the horizontal projection drawn in the proper relation to the reference or picture plane and any elevation in its proper relation to the horizon. The horizontal and vertical projection of the point of sight must also be given. This

information for a small house is shown in Fig. 19–12(*a*).

The first step in the solution is always to find the vanishing points of the principal lines of the figure. In this case the lines parallel to the picture plane will have vanishing points at infinity, which means that *any face parallel to the picture plane will show in the perspective in true shape but reduced in size,* depending on the distance of the object behind the picture plane. The lines perpendicular to the picture plane will have a vanishing point which may be found by the method explained in Art. 19.6. In this case the lines drawn through *S* parallel to the given line must pierce the picture plane at a point whose vertical projection is at s^V, which therefore becomes the vanishing point for all lines perpendicular to the picture plane, as in Fig. 19–12(*b*). *In other words, the vertical projection of the point of sight is always the vanishing point for lines perpendicular to the picture plane.*

The next step is to extend one of these lines until it pierces the picture plane. Since this is a horizontal line the piercing point will be at the level of the line as shown in the given elevation. This piercing point is marked v^V in Fig. 19–12(*b*). By joining the piercing point to the vanishing point the perspective of the complete line is formed. By visual rays the required points A_p and B_p on the line may be found to give one line on the building, as shown in Fig. 19–12(*b*). Other lines on the

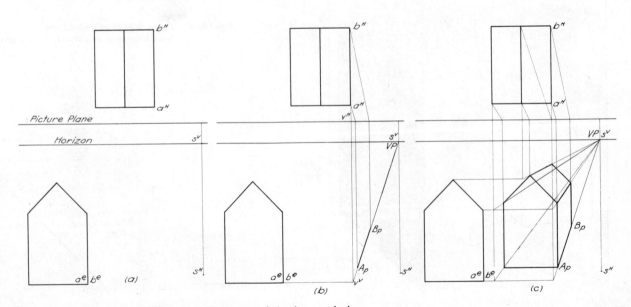

Fig. 19–12.   Perspective of building. Vanishing-point and visual-ray method.

building may be found in the same manner, as illustrated in Fig. 19–12(c). It should be noticed that the front face of the building is true shape but not true size.

An architectural parallel perspective is shown in Fig. 19–13.

19.9 Angular or two-point perspective by the combination method. When one of the principal axes of the object is parallel, and the other two inclined to the picture plane, the resulting picture is called two-point perspective. In this case the required information, which is the same as for parallel perspective, is shown in Fig. 19–14(a). Note that a true profile projection is not required.

To find the perspective of any point it is necessary to

Fig. 19–13. One point perspective of McGregor Lounge, Wayne State University. Courtesy of Minoru Yamasaki & Associates, Archs. and Baltazar Korab, photographer.

find the perspective of a line through the point and then locate the point on the line by a visual ray. Any two points on the line will determine the line, but the best ones are the vanishing point and the *V*-piercing point.

The first step is to find the vanishing points of both sets of inclined lines that are parallel respectively to *AB* and *AC*. These vanishing points have been located at *VPR* and *VPL* in Fig. 19–14(*b*). Then any line of the drawing such as *AB* in Fig. 19–14(*b*) may be extended to find its *V*-piercing point at v^V. By connecting v^V with *VPL*, the vanishing point of *AB*, the perspective of the entire line is found. Visual rays drawn to points *A* and *B* will serve to locate points A_p and B_p on the perspective of the line. These will be the perspectives of two corners of the building. Another corner of the building, such as *C* in Fig. 19–14(*c*), may be located by connecting A_p with *VPR*, which is the vanishing point of line *AC*, and drawing the visual ray through *C*, thereby locating C_p on the line *AC*. Corner *D* of the building must be located exactly as was done for point *A*.

19.10   Two-point perspective by the vanishing-point method. It is possible to find the perspective of an object without the use of visual rays. To do this two lines are constructed through each point so that the intersection of these lines determines the point. Thus, in Fig. 19–15, the perspective of the line *AB* may be found as explained in the previous paragraph by joining v^V with *VPL*. The perspective of *AC* may be found in a similar manner. The intersection of these two lines will locate the perspective of *A* at A_p in Fig. 19–15. All other points on the object may be located similarly. The entire construction is shown in Fig. 19–15. This construction is used exclusively in the measuring-point method which

is explained in Art. 19.13.

19.11   Perspective of a circle or curve. To find the perspective of any circle or curve it is necessary to have a series of points on the plan view and the same points located on any elevation. Figure 19–16 shows a circle in two positions, one of which has been solved by the combination visual-ray and vanishing-point method and the second by the vanishing-point method only. A series of points is first numbered in either view, and the position of each point is marked in the other view by the same number. Horizontal lines are assumed through these points. These lines may be in the plane of the circle, or they may be perpendicular or inclined to it, so long as

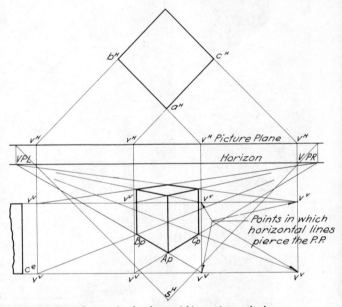

Fig. 19–15.   Perspective by the vanishing-point method.

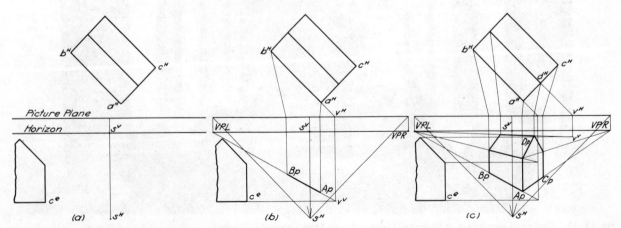

Fig. 19–14.   Angular perspective. Vanishing-point and visual-ray method.

they pass through the points on the circle. The perspective of these lines is determined in the usual manner. The points on these lines can then be found either by visual rays, as in Fig. 19–16(*a*), or by intersecting lines, as in Fig. 19–16(*b*), to determine the perspective of the curve.

19.12 Vanishing point traces. In perspective a vanishing point may be found for any line. Ordinarily they are useful only when it is necessary to find the perspective of a group of parallel lines. When two or more lines lie in a plane, the intersection of that plane with the plane of projection or picture plane forms a line. That line is the locus of vanishing points of all lines lying in that

plane, and is called a vanishing point trace. Thus the plane *ABCD* in Fig. 19–17 is a vertical plane that intersects the picture plane in the vertical line marked *VPL–VPCD*. This line then becomes a locus on which the piercing point or vanishing point of every line in plane *ABCD* will be found.

Any two points will determine a straight line; therefore, if it is possible to find any two vanishing points in a plane, the line joining them will be the vanishng point trace for that plane. Thus since the vanishing point of *CD* is at *VPCD* and the vanishing point of *DN* is at *VPR*, then the line joining *VPCD* with *VPR* will be the vanishing point trace for plane *CDNM*. In a similar

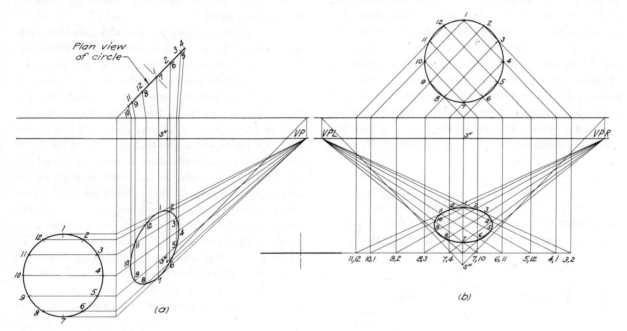

Fig. 19–16.   Perspective of a circle.

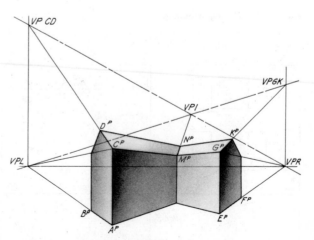

Fig. 19–17.   Vanishing point traces.

manner it can be shown that *VPL–VPGK* is the vanishing point trace for plane *GKNM*. It follows then that the intersection of these two traces will be the vanishing point for the line *MN* which is the line of intersection of the two planes.

This principle is frequently useful in finding intersections of planes and in locating the shadows in perspective.

19.13   Measuring points and lines. When a vertical face that is inclined to the picture plane, such as face *ABCD* in Fig. 19–18, is rotated until it lies in the picture plane, the vertical projection of this face in the revolved position $a^V_r b^V_r c^V_r d^V_r$ is coincident with the perspective of the revolved position. If the vanishing point of the line joining b^H to b^H_r in Fig. 19–18 is found, the perspective of this line can be used to carry points from the revolved position to their correct position in the perspective. The vanishing point *MPR*, of the line $b^H b^H_r$ is therefore called a measuring point. Since the vertical projection of the revolved position $a^V_r b^V_r c^V_r d^V_r$ is in true size, the horizontal lines $a^V_r b^V_r$ and $c^V_r d^V_r$ are true length and any desired distances from *A* or *D* can be laid off along these projections. The projection $a^V_r b^V_r$ is therefore called a measuring line. The projection $c^V_r d^V_r$ could

have been used equally well as a measuring line. In fact, a horizontal line can be drawn through any point that lies in the picture plane and used as a measuring line.

A simpler method for finding the measuring point *MPR* is illustrated in Fig. 19–18. If, through v^H, the *H*-projection of *VPR*, an arc having a radius $v^H s^H$ is drawn from s^H to the picture plane, this point on the picture plane may be projected straight down to *MPR* on the horizon.

Proof. Since $a^H b^H b^H_r$ was constructed as an isosceles triangle and since $v^H s^H v_1^H$ has its sides respectively parallel to $a^H b^H b^H_r$, the triangle $v^H s^H v_1^H$ is similar and also an isosceles triangle. Therefore $v^H s^H$ is equal to $v^H v_1^H$, and v_1^H may be located by constructing the arc shown on the figure.

19.14   Construction of a perspective by the measuring-point method. The great advantage of this method over all other methods of perspective is that it is not necessary to set up the projections in any particular position and work from them by projection or visual rays. The vanishing points right and left are usually taken as far apart as convenient, the picture plane and horizon are made to coincide, the angles that the sides of the object make with the picture plane are chosen, and a front corner of the object is selected at a certain place on the picture plane. If the vanishing points are chosen first, then s^H is located by drawing lines from the vanishing points parallel to the sides of the object, which are usually at right angles to each other.

In Fig. 19–19(a), the projections of an object are given. The problem is to draw the perspective so that the corner marked *A* will be in the picture plane 6 inches below the horizon and 1 inch right of the point

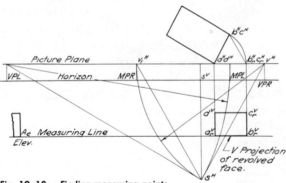

Fig. 19–18.   Finding measuring points.

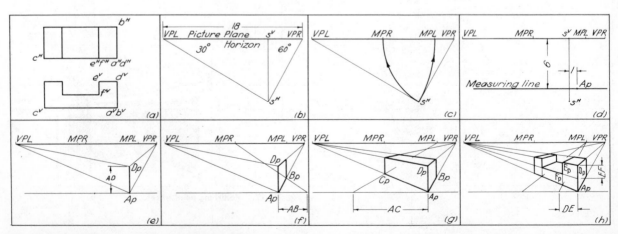

Fig. 19–19.   Perspective by the measuring-point method.

of sight. The side AB is to make an angle of 60° with the picture plane, and the vanishing points are to be 18″ apart. The construction will then proceed in the following steps:

a. Figure 19–19(b). Draw a horizontal line near the top of the sheet, and mark off the vanishing points 18″ apart.

b. Figure 19–19(b). Through VPR construct a line at 60° with the picture plane and through VPL a line making 30° with the picture plane. The intersection of these two lines will locate s^H. The vertical projection s^V will be on the horizon. This assures that the faces of the block will form the specified angles with the picture plane.

c. Figure 19–19(c). Using VPR as a center, swing an arc through s^H to the picture plane to locate MPR. Using VPL as a center, swing an arc through s^H to the picture plane to locate MPL.

d. Figure 19–19(d). Measure 6″ below the horizon and 1″ right of the point of sight to locate the perspective of point A. Through this point draw a horizontal line which is the measuring line for horizontal distances.

e. Figure 19–19(e). On a vertical line through A_p, lay out the height of the object AD to locate D_p. Draw lines from these points to VPR and VPL.

f. Figure 19–19(f). Lay out the distance AB on the horizontal measuring line to the right of A_p. From this point, draw a line to MPR to intersect the line from A_p to VPR, thus locating B_p. Erect a vertical line through B_p to give the right edge of the object.

g. Figure 19–19(g). Lay out the distance AC on the horizontal measuring line to the left of A_p. From this point, draw a line to MPL to intersect the line from A_p

to VPL. This locates C_p. Erect a vertical line through C_p to give the left edge of the object. Complete the outline of the figure by drawing to the proper vanishing points.

h. Figure 19–19(h). From D_p, lay out on the vertical line the distance FE, which is the depth of the slot. From this point, draw a line to VPL. From A_p, lay out the distance DE on the horizontal measuring line to the left of A_p. Connect this point to MPL to intersect the line from A_p to VPL. Erect a perpendicular to locate points E_p and F_p, which establishes the right side of the slot. In a similar manner locate the left side of the slot.

i. Connect these points to the proper vanishing points to complete the picture.

19.15 Perspective of a circle by the measuring-point method. By taking measurements from the orthographic projections, points on a circle may be located in perspective by the use of coordinates, but this is a tedious process and should be avoided if possible.

The better method is to find the perspective of a square circumscribing the circle and then obtain the ellipse by the diagonal method. For a circle lying in a vertical face the procedure is illustrated in Fig. 19–20, and the steps are listed below.

a. Figure 19–20(b). Find the perspective of the front face of the object shown in Fig. 19–20(a) by the method given in the preceding paragraph.

b. Figure 19–20(c). On the measuring line through A_p, lay out the horizontal distance A–2, from A to the center line of the circle, to the left of A_p. On either side of this point, lay out the radius of the circle to locate points 1 and 3. Carry those three points back into the picture by drawing lines to MPL.

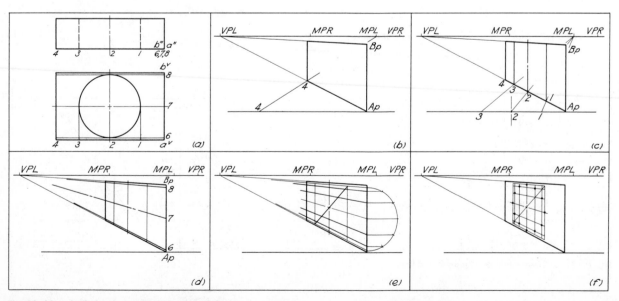

Fig. 19–20. Circle by the measuring-point method.

c. Figure 19–20(*d*). From A_p, lay out the vertical distance A–7, from A to the center line of the circle, on the front corner of the object. On either side of this point, lay out the radius of the circle to locate points *6* and *8*. From those three points, draw to *VPL* to form the perspective of the square circumscribing the circle.

d. Figure 19–20(*e*). On either of the vertical lines, construct a semicircle as shown. Divide the semicircle into 6 equal parts, and project these points horizontally to the vertical line that was used as the diameter of the construction circle. From these points on the vertical line, draw lines to *VPL*.

e. Figure 19–20(*f*). Construct the diagonal of the square and complete the grid by constructing vertical lines through the points where the horizontal lines cross the diagonal of the square, and mark the points as shown in the figure.

When the circle lies in a horizontal plane, the pro-cedure is similar except that the semicircle must be drawn on the measuring line, as illustrated in Fig. 19–21. When the points have been carried back into the perspective by means of the measuring points and vanishing points, the grid is constructed by using the diagonal as previously explained.

19.16   One-point measuring point and line. It is sometimes convenient to use the same measuring point for distances on both sides of an object in perspective. However, to be able to do this, it is necessary to locate a new measuring line.

The construction for this method is illustrated in Fig. 19–22. The steps are as follows:

a. Figure 19–22(*a*). This figure shows the two vanishing point method for finding a perspective. The vanishing point, *VP* 45°, for a line making 45° with the two principal lines has been added. In all of this construction the picture plane and the horizon are coincident.

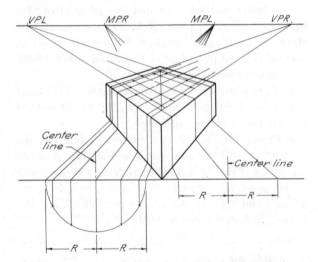

Fig. 19–21.   Horizontal circle by the measuring-point method.

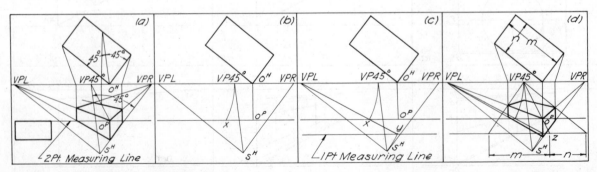

Fig. 19–22.   One-point measuring point and line.

b. Figure 19–22(*b*). With *VPL* as a center, an arc is drawn through *VP* 45°. The intersection of this arc with the two-point measuring line locates the point *X*.

c. Figure 19–22(*c*). A line is constructed from *VPL* through "*X*" and continued until it intersects an arc drawn through S^H with its center at *VPL*. Through the point of intersection marked "*y*," the one-point measuring line may be constructed parallel to the picture plane.

d. Figure 19–22(*d*). If a line is drawn from *VP* 45° through O^P and continued until it intersects the one-point measuring line the point *Z* is located. *Z* is the point from which distances *m* and *n* may be laid out in opposite directions on the one-point measuring line. From the points thus obtained lines may be drawn to *VP* 45° to cut off the perspective lines through O^P to determine the size of the perspective. Visual rays have been added to show that both methods give the same results.

19.17   Three-point perspective. When all three of the principal axes of an object are oblique to the picture plane, the resulting picture is called a three-point perspective. The theory of perspective as it has been developed for one- and two-point perspective can be extended to three-point. However, the actual construction is more complicated because the picture plane does not appear edgewise in the top view. It is possible to solve the problem by visual rays, as shown in Fig. 19–6, but the solution is tedious and will not be discussed here. If it is desired to specify the angle of tilt of the picture plane and the angle of rotation of the object, the reader should refer to the texts: *Industrial Production Illustration* by Hoelscher, Springer, and Pohle or *Perspective* by Moorehead.

The customary procedure is to select the three vanishing points as far apart as convenient and work from these points in the manner illustrated in Fig. 19–23 and as explained below.

a. Figure 19–23(*a*). Select the three vanishing points, and draw the triangle connecting them. Through each corner construct a line perpendicular to the opposite side of the triangle. These three lines intersect at point *S*, which is the projection of the point of sight as determined by the selected vanishing points.

b. Figure 19–23(*b*). Revolve the top plane into the picture plane as explained in Art. 17.18 for axonometric. With *VPR* as a center and VPR-S_r as a radius, swing an arc to locate *MPR*. With *VPL* as a center and VPL-S_r as a radius, swing an arc to locate *MPL*.

c. Figure 19–23(*c*). Revolve the right side plane *S*, *VPR*, *VPV* into the picture plane as explained in Art. 17.18. With *VPV* as a center and VPV-S_r as a radius, swing an arc to locate *MPV*. If desired, another *MPR* may be located but this is not necessary since one has already been found.

d. Figure 19–23(*d*). Select A_p as a point in the picture plane in such a position that the center of the picture will come approximately at *S*.

Through A_p, draw a line parallel to *VPL–VPR*. This is a measuring line, and distances may be laid out for right or left distances and front or back distances just as explained for two-point perspective in Art. 19.14. The top of the box is obtained as shown in Fig. 19–23(*d*).

e. Figure 19–23(*e*). Construct a line through A_p parallel to *VPR–VPV*, and on this line lay out the height of the box from A_p. From the point, draw to *MPV* to intersect the line from A_p to *VPH*. This determines the height of the box in the perspective.

f. Figure 19–23(*f*). From the points already located,

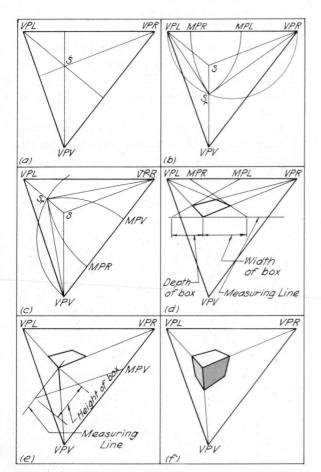

Fig. 19–23.   Three-point perspective.

draw to the proper vanishing point to complete the perspective of the box.

19.18   Isometric three-point perspective.* For the special case of three-point perspective in which the three principal vanishing points lie on the corners of an equilateral triangle, an easy construction has been developed that has the same relation to the theoretical three-point perspective that isometric drawing has to isometric projection.

The construction is as follows:

a. Figure 19–24(*a*). Lay out an equilateral triangle of the size desired, usually the maximum a drawing board will accommodate, and let the corners be the three vanishing points.

b. Figure 19–24(*b*). Select a point A_p in the picture plane and through this point construct two measuring lines, one parallel to *VPL–VPR* and the other parallel to *VPR–VPV* (or *VPL–VPV*).

c. Figure 19–24(*c*). On the horizontal line, lay out the right and left or length dimension of the box to the left of A_p. Lay out the front and back dimensions or depth of the box to the right of A_p. Draw to the vanishing point as shown. This determines the top of the enclosing box for any object.

d. Figure 19–24(*d*). On the measuring line parallel to *VPR–VPV*, lay out the height of the box, and draw to the vanishing point *VPR* as shown. The lower corner of the box is located at the point where this line crosses

* This method was developed by Professor Wayne Shick of the University of Illinois and is reproduced by his permission.

the line from A_p to *VPV*. Complete the box by drawing to the proper vanishing points. Other dimensions of an object may be laid out in the same manner.

19.19   Alternate method for three-point perspective. When the orthographic projections of the object are available at a scale which is convenient for use, the method illustrated in Fig. 19–25 is very convenient. In using this construction it is best to work on tracing paper placed directly over the appropriate views of the object. The procedure is as follows:

a. On the tracing paper, layout the three vanishing points as far apart as convenient, and join them to form the triangle, *VPL–VPR–VPV*.

b. Revolve the top plane as shown in Fig. 19–25 to obtain *Sr*.

c. Assume point A^P, which is one corner of the object, in the picture plane.

d. Arrange the horizontal projection or plan view under the tracing paper with sides parallel respectively to $S_r - VPR$ and $S_r - VPL$.

e. Join A^P to *VPR* and *VPL*.

f. Join a^H, b^H, c^H, and d^H to S_r.

g. The perspective of *B* is located at B^P where $b^H S_r$ intersects A^P–*VPR*, and the perspective of *D* at D^P where $d^H S_r$ intersects A^P–*VPL*.

h. This locates the top plane of the object at $A^P B^P C^P D^P$.

i. By revolving one of the side faces and proceeding in a similar manner the vertical faces of the object can be located.

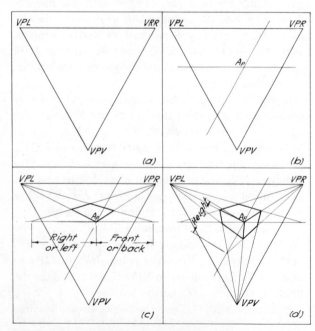

Fig. 19–24.   Three-point perspective drawing.

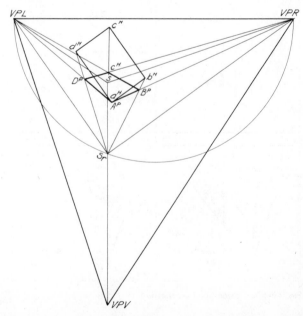

Fig. 19–25.   Alternate method of three-point perspective.

19.20 Shades and shadows in perspective. When light shines on an object, a part of the surface will be lighted and the remaining part will be dark. That part of the surface on which no light shines is said to be in shade. The lines on the object that separate the light areas from the shaded areas are called shade lines. When the object rests on or is adjacent to some other object, it casts a shadow which may be outlined by finding the shadow of the shade lines. To find the shadow of an object, therefore, two things are necessary: first, to pick out the shade lines, and second, to find the shadow of these lines on the surfaces on which the shadow falls.

To recognize the shade line requires a knowledge of the direction of the light ray and the ability to visualize the object as it stands in space. In case of doubt it is possible to find the shadow of every line on the object, after which the largest area outlined by these shadows will be the shadow of the object.

When the light rays are tangent to any surface, that surface is said to be in shade.

19.21 Shadow of a vertical line. A vertical line resting on a horizontal plane is used as the basic line in determining shadows. One reason for this is that, since the horizontal projection of a vertical line is a point, the horizontal projection of the shadow of the line must coincide with the horizontal projection of a light ray. When the direction of the light ray is specified by two projections of one ray, as MN in Fig. 19–26, the shadow of the line AB in the horizontal projection must be a line through $a^H b^H$ parallel to $m^H n^H$. Since that shadow

is a horizontal line, it must have its vanishing point on the horizon. That vanishing point may be found at VPS in the usual manner, as shown in Fig. 19–26. Then the shadow of AB on the horizontal plane must vanish at VPS, and, since B is on the horizontal plane, the shadow must start at B_p. By joining B_p to VPS, the shadow of a vertical line of infinite height is obtained. To find the shadow of A, it is then necessary to draw the perspective of the light ray through A and find the point where it intersects the shadow line. The vanishing point of the light ray MN, found as explained in Art. 19.6, is located at the point marked $VPLR$. Then, by joining A_p to $VPLR$, the point A_{sp} is located, and the actual shadow of the line lies between B_p and A_{sp}.

In finding shades and shadows in perspective, it is always necessary to locate first the vanishing points VPS and $VPLR$. *Always remember that VPS is the vanishing point of the shadow of the vertical line on a horizontal plane and nothing more.*

When the vertical line casts a shadow on a vertical plane, the shadow must be parallel to the line and in two-point perspective will show as a vertical line. The best way to find this shadow is to find the shadow of the line on the horizontal base plane until it crosses the base line of the vertical plane. From there the shadow will be vertical, as illustrated by the shadow or the flag pole in Fig. 19–27. The location of this vertical shadow can also be found by means of a visual ray from the plan or top view, as indicated in the figure.

When the shadow falls on an inclined surface such as the roof of the building in Fig. 19–27, it is necessary to locate two points on the shadow of the line or the line extended. One point on the eave line has already been located, and another can easily be located on the ridge line. One method is by visual ray, as shown in Fig.

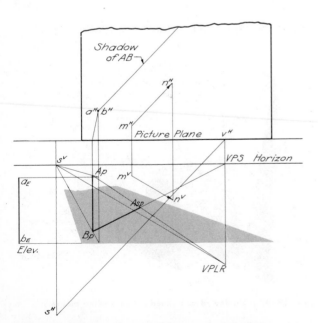

Fig. 19–26. Shadow of a vertical line on a horizontal plane.

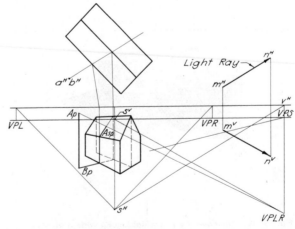

Fig. 19–27. Shadow of a vertical line on a vertical and inclined surface.

19-27. The other method, which is better since it can also be used when working by measuring-point method, involves cutting a vertical plane through the center of the building, as indicated by the dotted line. Then by imagining the front of the building removed the shadow on the section plane can be found, which will locate the desired point on the ridge line. This construction is shown in dashed lines in Fig. 19–27. The shadow of the flag pole on the roof will be the line joining the point on the eave line to the point on the ridge line, and a light ray through the top of the flag pole to *VPLR* will locate the end of the shadow.

19.22   Shadow of a horizontal line. *When a horizontal line casts a shadow on a horizontal plane, the shadow will be parallel to the line itself. In perspective this means that the two lines will have the same vanishing point.* Thus, in Fig. 19–28, the line *AB* vanishes at *VPR,* and consequently its shadow must also vanish at *VPR. BC* vanishes at *VPL,* and its shadow also vanishes at *VPL.*

When a horizontal line casts a shadow on a vertical or inclined plane, the shadow of two points on the line, or one point and the direction, must be found on the given plane. Thus, in Fig. 19–29, the line *AB* casts a shadow on the horizontal, inclined, and vertical planes. The shadow on the horizontal plane vanishes at *VPR,* and if the inclined plane were removed it would continue to the base of the vertical plane and from there would go to B_p because B is actually on the vertical face. The intersection of this shadow on the vertical face with the top line of the inclined face gives a second point on the inclined plane to determine the shadow of the horizontal line on the inclined plane.

19.23   Shadow of an inclined line on a horizontal surface. To find the shadow of an inclined line it is usually best to assume as many vertical lines as necessary through points on the line and find the shadows of these vertical lines. For example, in Fig. 19–30, a vertical line was assumed through B_p. By means of this vertical line, the shadow of B_p on the ground was found at B_{sp}. Note that the vertical line through B_p is an imaginary line.

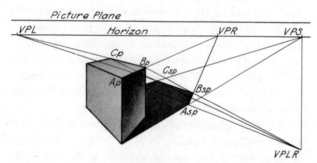

Fig. 19–28.   Shadow of a horizontal line on a horizontal plane.

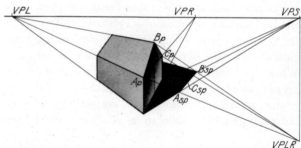

Fig. 19–30.   Shadow of an inclined line on a horizontal plane.

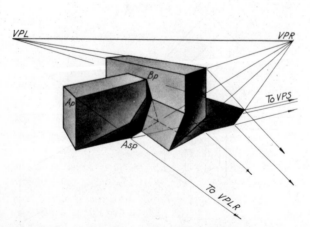

Fig. 19–29.   Shadow of a horizontal line on various planes.

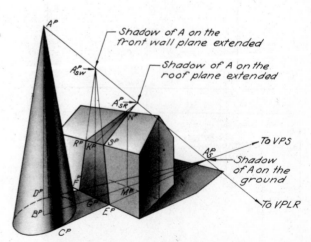

Fig. 19–31.   Shadow of an inclined line on various planes.

19.24   Shadow of an inclined line on horizontal, vertical, and inclined planes. The conical structure in Fig. 19–31 will cast a shadow on the house, but the actual lines that cast the shadow, called the shade lines, are elements of the cone and they must be found as a part of the first step. As in the preceding illustration, it is necessary to establish a vertical line, which in this case is the altitude of the cone called AB. The shadow of AB on the ground is found in the usual manner, by drawing from B^P to VPS and from A^P to $VPLR$. The intersection of these two lines $A_s{}^P$ gives the shadow of A on the ground. Since the base of the cone rests on the ground, the entire shadow of the cone on the ground can be found by drawing from $A_s{}^P$ tangent to both sides of the base. The points of tangency, C^P and D^P of those lines with the base, locate the shade lines A^PC^P and A^PD^P on the cone. The problem then is to find the shadow of these inclined shade lines on the various planes.

The shadow of the shade lines on the ground has already been determined, and from these shadows the points E^P and F^P at the base of the wall may be located.

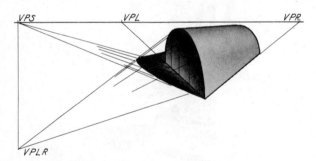

Fig. 19–32.   Shadow of a curved line.

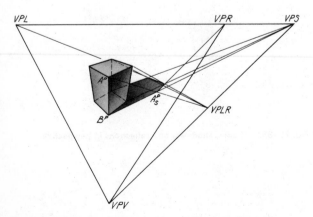

Fig. 19–33.   Shades and shadows in three-point perspective.

Next the imaginary shadow of A on the wall extended is found at $A_{sw}{}^P$ by use of the vertical line AB. By joining this point with E^P and F^P the shadow of the cone on the vertical wall is found.

The shadow of AB on the inclined roof is found to be K^PN^P as explained in Art. 19.21. By extending K^PN^P until it intersects the light ray through A^P the shadow of point A on the inclined roof is located at $A_{SR}{}^P$. By connecting $A_{SR}{}^P$ to R^P and S^P the shadow of the cone on the inclined roof is completed. The various parts of the shadow may be shaded to give the complete picture as shown in Fig. 19–31.

19.25   Shadow of a curved line. The shadow of a curved line may be found by assuming a series of vertical lines through points on the curve. The shadow of these vertical lines may be found in the usual manner and the shadow of the point located on the shadow of the line. This is illustrated in Fig. 19–32.

19.26   Shadows in three-point perspective.* The shadow of a vertical line on a horizontal plane is the basis for determining shadows in three-point perspective just as it is in two-point perspective. In Fig. 19–33, a simple object has been drawn in three-point perspective for the purpose of illustrating the method of locating the shadows.

Since the line VPL–VPR is the vanishing point trace for horizontal planes, the vanishing point of the shadow of a vertical line on a horizontal plane must lie on this trace. Therefore if it is desired to have the shadow fall to the right of the object, VPS is selected on this trace far enough to the right of VPR to give the desired effect.

By joining the vanishing points of any two lines in a plane the vanishing point trace for that plane is obtained. Therefore, by joining VPS with VPV the vanishing point trace of a plane containing a vertical line and its shadow is obtained and consequently the vanishing point of the light ray will lie on this trace. $VPLR$ may be chosen any place on the trace VPS–VPV to give the desired effect.

After having VPS and $VPLR$ located, the procedure is the same as for two-point perspective. From B^P the base of a line A^PB^P draw a line to VPS and from the top A^P draw a line to $VPLR$. The intersection of these lines gives $A_s{}^P$ the perspective of the shadow of A.

19.27   Reflections. Whenever water appears in the foreground of a perspective, the building or structure shown in the picture will also show in the water as a reflection. To obtain the perspective of the reflection,

* This method was devised by Professor Wayne Shick.

the elevation of the structure being shown may be reversed about the water line, and the complete perspective of this inverted object constructed in the same manner as the original perspective. Figure 19–34 shows the elevation of the corner of a building standing on the bank of a body of water, with the picture plane and water surface shown edgewise. Point C is the corner of a building, C_w is the projection of C on the surface of the water, and C_R is the position of C in the reversed elevation.

Point S is the point of sight for the perspective, and, therefore, the piercing points of the visual rays in the picture plane will locate the perspectives of C, C_w, and C_R at C_p, C_{wp}, and C_{Rp}, respectively. By plane geometry it can be shown that, since the two distances, y, were constructed equal, the three angles marked α must be equal. Then the perspective of C_R must coincide with

the perspective of the reflection of C on the water surface, thus proving that the reflection of an object may be obtained in this manner.

By geometry it can also be shown that, since the two distances marked y were constructed equal, then the two distances marked y' must also be equal. Since these distances are measured directly in the perspective, it then becomes possible to locate the reflection of any point in a two-point perspective by measuring the distance, y', from the perspective of the point, C_p, to the perspective of its projection on the water surface, C_{wp}, and laying that distance below C_{wp} on the water surface to locate C_{Rp}, which is the reflection of point C. This gives a rapid method of finding the reflection of any point, without drawing the reversed elevation. In a three-point perspective, the reversed elevation must be drawn and the reflection found in the same manner as

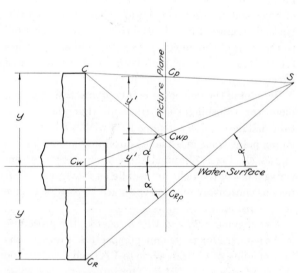

Fig. 19–34.   Theory of reflections.

Fig. 19–35.   Shades, shadows, and reflections in perspective.

the real perspective.

The lines in the reflection should be made irregular and broken to represent wave action. The surface of the water can be indicated by a series of irregular horizontal lines whose spacing increases toward the front of the drawing. Figure 19–35 shows a perspective with shades, shadows, and reflections. Figure 19–36 shows the method for finding reflections by reversing distances in the perspective.

19.28   Three-point perspective board. The big disadvantage of three-point perspective is that it is very difficult to get the vanishing points far enough apart to avoid excessive perspective effect. Even on a very large drawing board the triangle is so small that the lines vanish too rapidly for a good appearance. To avoid this, it is fairly easy to construct a special board by means of which the vanishing points can be widely separated. The

appearance of the board is shown in Fig. 19–37. The three arcs are constructed with their centers at the three vanishing points. Then by means of a special T-square so arranged that one edge is exactly centered between the two bearing points of the head, lines may be drawn that always point to the center of the circle. The use of this T-square is illustrated in the figure.

By means of the construction explained in Art. 19.16, the 45° vanishing points are located for each face together with the corresponding one-point measuring lines. These lines are marked off in unit divisions as illustrated, and from these divisions the accurate perspective can be found directly. In this figure a rectangular solid 3 × 4 × 5 has been drawn. With three measuring points and lines, it is possible to make each measurement in two different ways. Lines showing both sets are shown in the figure.

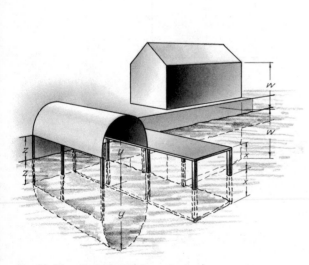

Fig. 19–36.   Method of finding reflections.

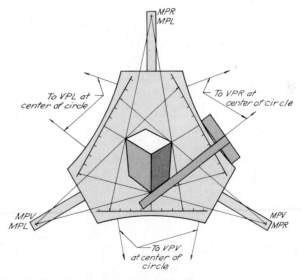

Fig. 19–37.   Three-point perspective board.

PROBLEMS

The problems in the following group may be solved by any method discussed in this chapter. The layouts have been made for angular perspective. These can be drawn most rapidly by the combination vanishing-point and visual-ray method.

Dimensions for the location of the plan view have been given to the borderlines of standard sheets, and the scale for each size of sheet has been specified. This arrangement will normally bring the point of sight (s^H) and the vanishing points on the sheet.

For parallel perspectives, notes have been added on each of the simpler drawings specifying the location and position of the plan view. In all cases the elevation should be placed out

of the range of the perspective at the left or right.

For shades and shadows in perspective, the direction of the light ray has been specified verbally for some of the simpler objects.

1. Make an angular perspective of the outdoor fireplace shown in Fig. 19–38 by the combination visual-ray and vanishing-point method.

2. Same as Problem 1, using vanishing-point method only.

3. Make a parallel perspective of the outdoor fireplace shown in Fig. 19–38. See note in the figure for position of object relative to the picture plane and the point of sight.

4. Make the perspective specified in Problem 1, and then

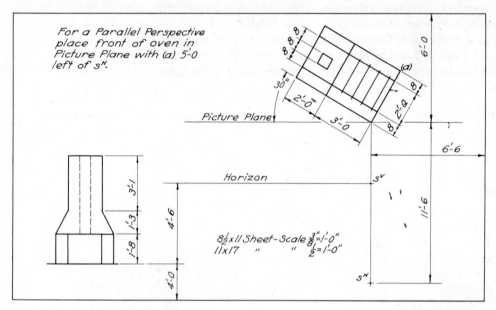

For a Parallel Perspective place front of oven in Picture Plane with (a) 5-0 left of s^H.

$8\frac{1}{2}$x11 Sheet-Scale $\frac{3}{8}$"=1'-0"
11x17 "   " $\frac{1}{2}$"=1'-0"

Fig. 19–38. Outdoor fireplace.

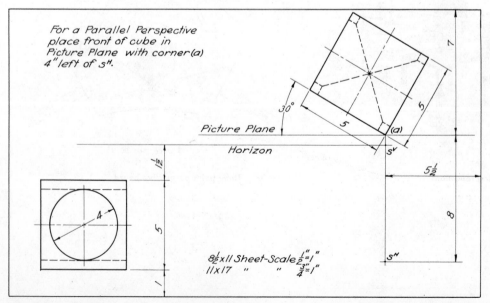

For a Parallel Perspective place front of cube in Picture Plane with corner (a) 4" left of s^H.

$8\frac{1}{2}$x11 Sheet-Scale $\frac{1}{2}$"=1"
11x17 "   " $\frac{3}{4}$"=1"

Fig. 19–39. Drilled cube.

find the shades and shadows, assuming the light ray to be parallel to the vertical plane and to make an angle of 45° with the horizontal plane, down to the right.

5. Make an angular perspective of the cube shown in Fig. 19–39 by any assigned method.

6. Make a parallel perspective of the cube shown in Fig. 19–39. See note in the figure for the relative position of the object and point of sight.

7. Make a perspective of the monument shown in Fig. 19–40 by the visual-ray method only.

8. Make a perspective of the monument that is illustrated in Fig. 19–40 by using the combination visual-ray and vanishing-point method.

9. Make the perspective assigned in Problem 8, and then find the shades and shadows, assuming the light ray to have the following position. Horizontal projection 30° with ground line, up to the right. Vertical projection 45° with ground line, down to the right.

10. Make an angular perspective of the memorial fountain shown in Fig. 19–41 by the combination vanishing-point and visual-ray method.

11. Make a parallel perspective of the memorial fountain shown in Fig. 19–41. See note in the figure for the relative position of object and point of sight.

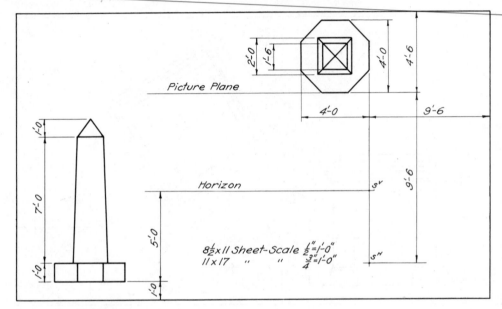

Fig. 19–40. Monument.

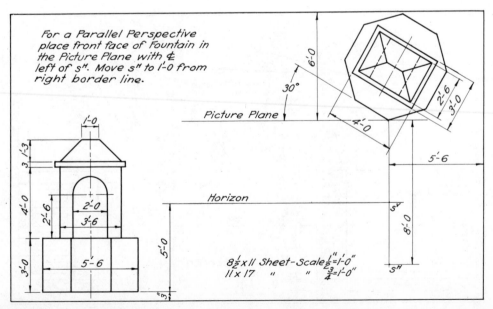

Fig. 19–41. Memorial fountain.

12. Make an angular perspective of the arch shown in Fig. 19–42 by the combination vanishing-point and visual-ray method.

13. Make an angular perspective of the garage shown in Fig. 19–43 by the combination vanishing-point and visual-ray method. Find and use the vanishing points for the rafters.

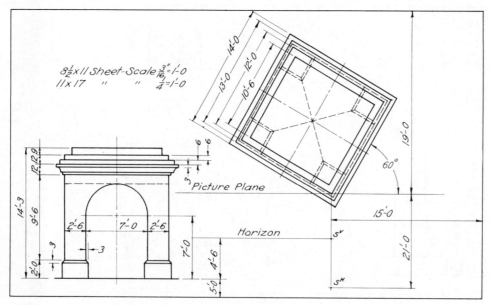

Fig. 19–42.   Memorial arch.

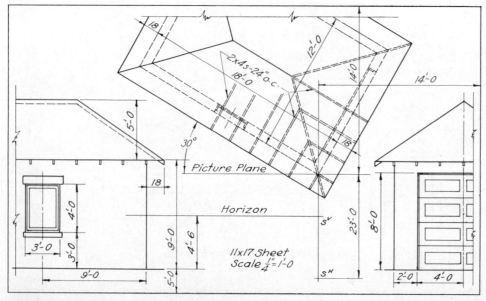

Fig. 19–43.   Garage.

Part Three
Technical Charts and Graphic Computation

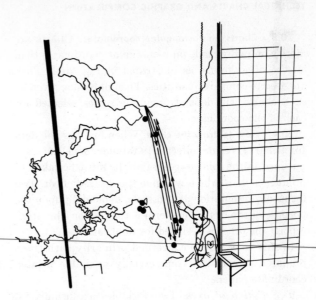

20

Charts and Diagrams

20.1 Uses of charts. The purpose of charts and diagrams is to present facts and their significance in a more easily interpreted form than could be done with words or tabular data. A technical or business publication scarcely appears today without charts of some kind. Some of the more common uses of charts are as follows:

a. To present results of test data obtained in experiments.

b. To correlate the observations of natural phenomena.

c. To present business statistics.

d. To determine trends in business.

e. To present equations graphically for computation uses.

f. To derive empirical equations.

20.2 Classification of charts. According to the method of presentation or drawing, with which this chapter is primarily concerned, charts may be readily classified in the following form:

a. Plane curves on rectangular coordinates, logarithmic, semilogarithmic, trilinear, polar coordinates, and others.

b. Bar charts of all kinds.

c. Pie or sector charts.

d. Computation charts, vector diagrams, and nomographs.

e. Flow charts and distribution diagrams.

f. Three-dimensional charts.

g. Map or distribution diagrams.

All of these are illustrated in the various figures of this chapter.

◀ Strategic Air Force Command plotting room (U. S. Air Force).

20.3   Charts on rectangular coordinates. Charts are more commonly made on rectangular coordinates than on the other forms, as illustrated in Fig. 20–1. They are used to compare quantities. The impression given by such charts will depend upon the scales selected for each of the coordinates.

20.4   How to draw the chart. When one has the data for a chart given or collected in tabular form, the steps outlined in the following paragraphs must be taken to produce a chart which will give the desired effect. Two forms of presentation are possible, depending upon the purpose of the chart. One form is the test or laboratory report; the other is designed for publication.

In this book we are concerned primarily with those prepared directly on commercially available printed coordinate papers.

a. Selection of axes. Two variables are usually involved in a chart. It is therefore necessary to decide which variable will be placed on the vertical or *Y*-axis and which on the horizontal or *X*-axis. It is general practice to place the independent or controlled variable on the horizontal axis. One exception to this rule, established by custom, is the so-called stress-strain curve. When time is one of the variables this is usually placed on the *X*-axis.

The location of the zero point or intersection of the axes must be so chosen that all values of the variables can be plotted. When only positive values are involved, this point is placed in the lower left corner of the chart about 1 inch in from the printed border, as shown in Fig. 20–2. This allows room for numerals and legends.

b. Choice of scales. The choice of scales materially affects the impression given by the chart. See Fig. 20–3. The scales on the two axes should be chosen to take maximum advantage of the space available. If the chart is to be made upon printed coordinate paper, the scale units should be chosen to come upon the heavy printed lines. These units should be multiples of 1, 2, 4, or 5. Interpolation of the smaller divisions on the paper should be easy to make. If the chart is to be made for formal publication, coordinates are usually ruled upon blank paper. For this type of work the reader should consult the ASA publications, Y15–1—1959 *Illustrations for Publication and Projection* and Y15–2—1960 *Time Series Charts.*

c. Marking coordinates. Unit values of the coordinates should be marked on each axis, as shown in Fig. 20–2. A legend should indicate what the units are and the unit of measurement, as, for example, inches, feet, etc., or time in days, hours, or minutes. Note in Fig. 20–2 that the smaller ruled divisions have been used as guide lines for the lettering.

d. Showing plotted points. The plotted points are indicated by open circles about $\frac{1}{10}$ inch or a little less in

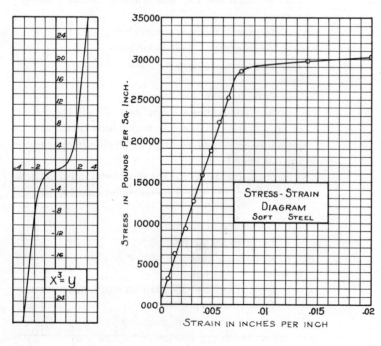

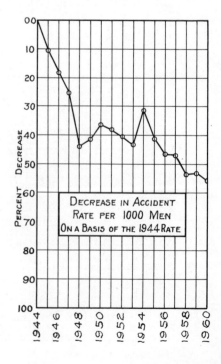

Fig. 20–1.   Types of plane curves.

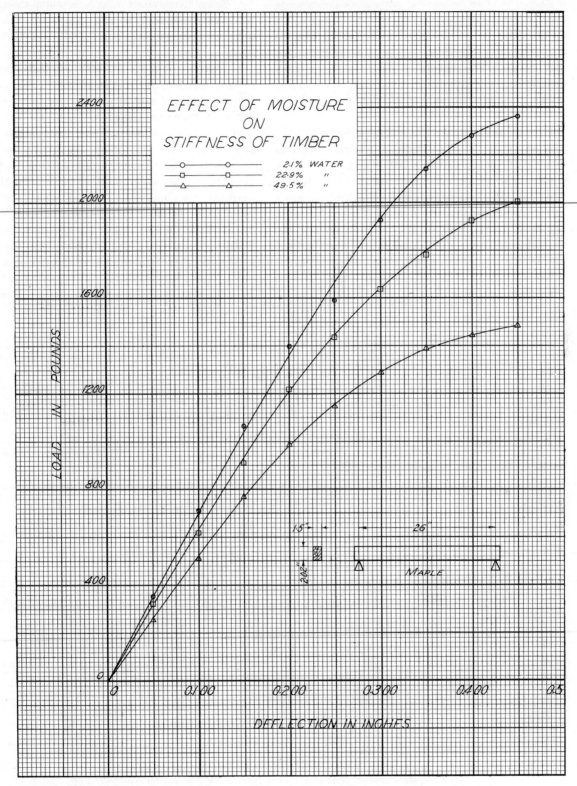

Fig. 20-2. Plane curve.

diameter. If more than one curve is shown on a single chart, squares and triangles may be used for the points on the other curves, as shown in Fig. 20–2. If more curves are needed, solid circles, squares, and triangles may be used. They should be smaller than the open ones. If a curve is to be drawn to represent a mathematical equation, plotted points should not be shown on the finished chart.

e. Drawing the curve. The nature of the curve to be drawn between plotted points will depend upon the data involved. If there is no direct relationship between the variables, as, for example, time and rainfall, straight lines will be drawn from point to point, as shown in Fig. 20–4. When there is a direct relationship, as in Fig. 20–2, a smooth curve will be drawn through the average of the points. The curve should touch but not pass through the circles of the plotted points.

f. Titles. Every chart must have a well thought-out title stating specifically what is represented. This should be placed in an open area to make the total effect a well-balanced sheet.

g. Sketches. If a small sketch will make the chart more intelligible, this may be placed on the sheet but tables of data and extensive explanatory matter should not be placed within the chart.

20.5 Logarithmic charts. These charts are most useful in engineering work where the relationship of the variables is more complex, as, for example, a product, quotient, or exponential form of the variables. In such cases the chart becomes a straight line on logarithmic paper, as illustrated in Fig. 20–5. By the use of logarithmic charts empirical equations to represent test data can frequently be derived, as discussed in Chapter 22. The ruled lines of this type of paper are spaced according to

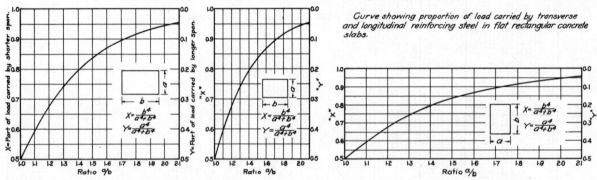

Fig. 20–3. Effect of scale on apparent slope of curve.

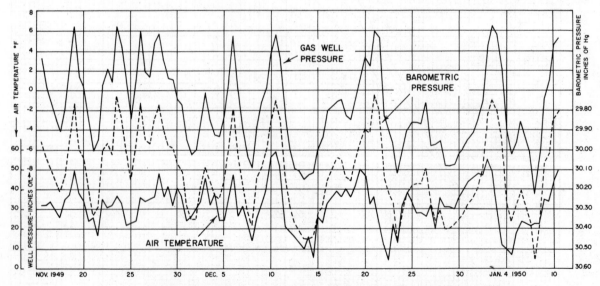

Record of gas-well pressures, barometer readings, and air temperatures during a two-month period, November 1949 to January 1950, for the Alvin Albrecht farm gas well, sec. 34, T. 15 N., R. 9 E., Bureau County.

Fig. 20–4. Gas well pressures. (Courtesy Illinois State Geological Survey.)

the logarithms of numbers. Such paper is commonly available with one, two, or three cycles, in each direction.

20.6 Semilogarithmic charts. When the rate of change in two variables is more important than the quantitative change, semilogarithmic paper is used since the slope of the tangent to the curve at any point gives the rate of change at that point and the whole chart indicates a trend in the rate more accurately than does the same data plotted on rectangular coordinates, as may be seen by comparing the two charts of Fig. 20–6. Semiloga-

rithmic paper has a logarithmic scale in one direction and an arithmetic scale in the other. Equations of the general form $y = a10^{MX}$ will plot as straight lines on this paper. Empirical equations can frequently be determined by plotting data on this type of paper.

20.7 Trilinear charts. Trilinear charts are in the form of an equilateral triangle. The coordinates are ruled parallel to the sides, and the altitude perpendicular to any side represents 100. These charts are useful in comparing properties of chemicals or alloys composed of

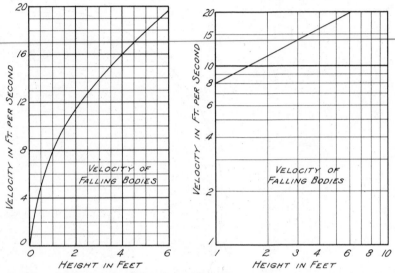

Fig. 20–5. Same curve on rectangular and logarithmic paper.

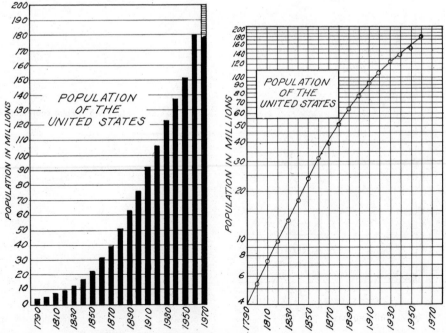

Fig. 20–6. Bargraph and semilog chart of same data.

three substances, as shown in Fig. 20–7. The equilateral triangle has the property that the sum of the perpendiculars to the three sides from any point inside is equal to the altitude of the triangle. It will be noted in Fig. 20–7 that only a portion of the complete triangle has been drawn since the curves lie in one corner and it would be a waste of space to show the remainder of the blank chart.

20.8   Polar charts. These charts are useful when equations are given in polar coordinate form or when quantities radiating from a center are involved, as, for example, illumination charts. They are also used in modified form upon continuous recording devices, as illustrated in Fig. 20–8. The radiating lines are curved in this case because the recording stylus is pivoted at a fixed center.

20.9   Pie diagrams or sector charts. These charts, circular in form, are used to show the relative distribution of the parts of a whole, as illustrated in Fig. 20–9. Other common examples are the distribution of the tax dollar,

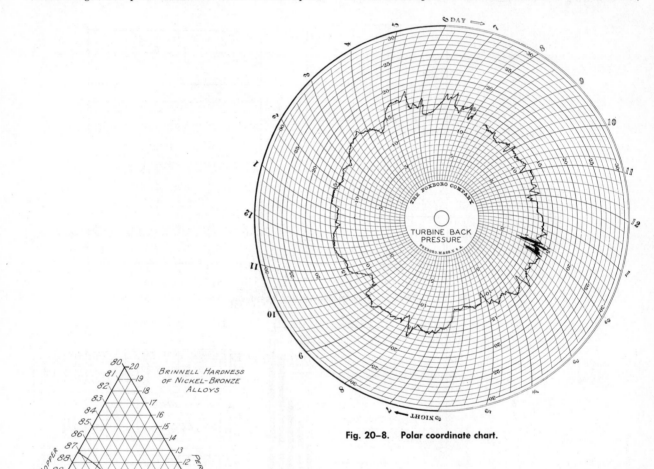

Fig. 20–8.   Polar coordinate chart.

Fig. 20–7.   Trilinear curve.

or the costs of production in an industry. They are quite effective and simple to make. If the sector areas are shaded, Zip-A-Tone may be used.

20.10   Bar charts. Bar charts are more commonly used for the popular presentation of facts since they are easy for the average layman to interpret. Bar charts may have the bars either vertical or horizontal, as shown in Figs. 20–10 and 20–11. They may be additive, as in Fig. 20–12, or comparative, as in Fig. 20–13. The same general rules used for rectangular coordinate charts apply

here with only slight modification. Shading of the bars can be done most economically with Zip-A-Tone, a commercial product available from dealers in art and drafting supplies.

20.11   Flow and organization charts. In the process industries it is often desirable to trace the raw material through the various stages of handling to the finished product. This is readily accomplished by a flow chart, as illustrated in Fig. 20–14.

Charts showing the lines of authority or responsibility

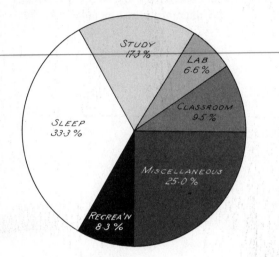

Fig. 20–9.   Pie diagram.

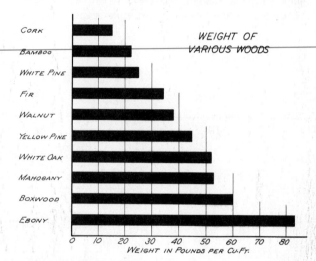

Fig. 20–11.   Horizontal bars.

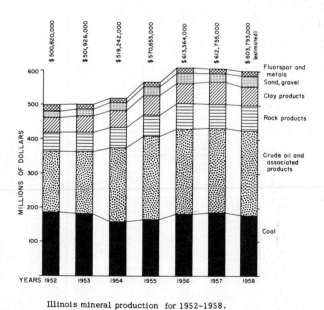

Illinois mineral production for 1952-1958.

Fig. 20–10.   Bar diagram.
(Courtesy Illinois State Geological Survey.)

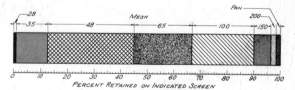

Fig. 20–12.   A 100 per cent bar chart.

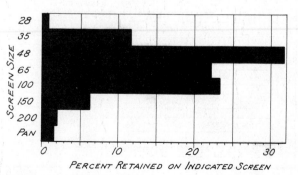

Fig. 20–13.   Histogram.

from chief executive to the minor departments can also be shown in this type of chart, which is then called an organization chart. For formal presentation, the lettering on such charts is usually done mechanically with Wrico or Leroy lettering guides.

20.12 Distribution diagrams. These diagrams usually take the form of maps and may show a wide variety of information useful in business operations, such as distribution of sales, density of population, etc. A good map of the area under consideration is a basic requirement. These are usually traced from existing maps in atlases or the like. A typical example is shown in Fig.

20–15. In addition to location, quantitative values are usually involved. These values are shown by different types of shading.

20.13 Computation charts. Though many of the foregoing charts can be used to simplify calculations, a number of charts are designed specifically for that purpose. Charts of these types are discussed in Part III of this textbook.

20.14 Three-dimensional charts. Three-dimensional charts are based upon one of the pictorial forms of projection discussed in Chapters 17 and 18 of this book. They are useful for illustrating in a popular way the

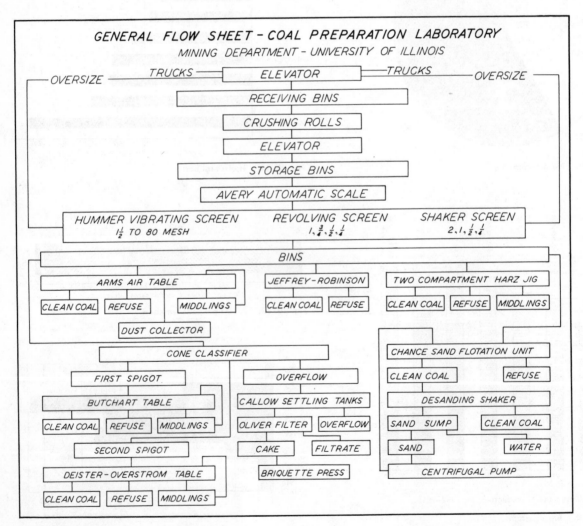

Fig. 20–14. Flow chart.

relationship between three variables. Figure 20–16 shows a chart of this type.

20.15   Charts and diagrams for publication or lantern slides. Many times in teaching or in public discussion it is desirable to have charts prepared for reproduction as lantern slides, as illustrated in Fig. 20–17. For those who have occasion to make drawings for this purpose it is recommended that a copy of American Standards, Y15-1—1959 *Illustrations for Publication and Projection* and Y15-2—1960 *Time Series Charts,* be obtained.

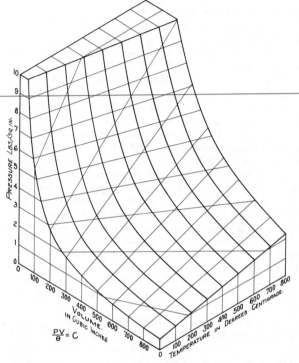

Fig. 20–16.   Three-dimensional chart.

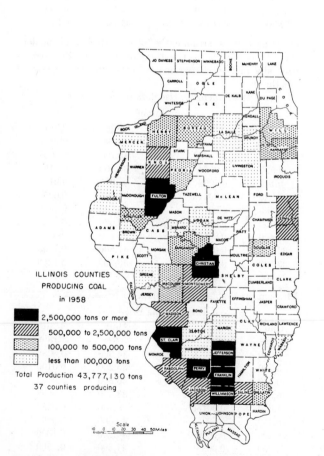

Fig. 20–15.   Distribution chart.
(Courtesy Illinois State Geological Survey.)

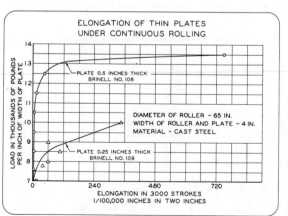

Fig. 20–17.   Lantern slide.

PROBLEMS

The information contained in the following problems should be shown in chart form according to specifications in the book or from the instructor. If these are not given, the student should select the best form of presentation for any particular data.

Each chart should be complete with proper titles, coordinate markings, and any other necessary information. It is recommended that 8½ × 11-inch paper be used for these charts, and commercial coordinate papers should be used when available.

Coordinates are not specified. The student should select his own values to give the best results.

Plane Curves—Rectangular Coordinate Paper

1. Plot a curve for the areas of circles, $A = \pi r^2$, of radii varying from 0 to 14′.

2. Plot a curve for the areas of spheres, $A = 4\pi r^2$, of radii varying from 0 to 14′.

3. Plot a curve for the volume of spheres, $V = .5236d^3$, for diameters from 0 to 10′.

4. Plot a curve for computing the volume of a liquid at different depths in a segment of a hemisphere 20′ in diameter. $V = \pi h(c^2/8 + h^2/6)$, where h = depth of liquid and c = diameter of liquid surface. Show a sketch in your chart to explain the terms in the equation.

5. Plot a curve for computing the volume of a liquid at different depths in a cylindrical tank whose axis is horizontal, and whose diameter is 10′. Carry the curve from zero to a full tank by 1′ intervals. Make a diagram showing the meaning of terms in your equation. Consult a handbook for necessary equations.

6. The equation for the bending moment of a beam is $M = \frac{1}{8}WL^2$, where $M =$ the bending moment in foot-pounds, $W =$ the uniform load in pounds per foot of beam, and $L =$ the span in feet. Compute and plot three curves for these values of W, namely, 100, 200, and 300 pounds per foot, for all spans from 5 to 35′.

7. Plot a curve for wind pressures on a flat surface normal to the wind as given by Marvin's formula, $P = .004V^2$, where P is the pressure in pounds per square foot and V is the velocity of the wind in miles per hour. Use values of V from 0 to 100 miles per hour.

8. Plot a curve showing the growth in population of your state. Data from U. S. Census.

9. Plot a smooth curve showing the maximum rainfall to be expected for any period of time from the following data. *Note:* The curve will pass along the upper boundary of the plotted points. One or two extreme points may be outside of the curve.

Storm Intensity Data

Column *A:* Duration of storm in minutes.
Column *B:* Rainfall in inches per hour.

A	B	A	B	A	B
121	0.78	27	3.52	63	2.06
122	1.18	18	4.31	15	3.10
25	1.21	32	2.70	15	3.62
56	1.26	26	2.92	15	4.51
103	2.10	180	0.90	60	1.20
63	1.32	82	0.70	56	2.20
32	2.11	70	1.10	22	3.93
38	1.82	72	1.77	12	4.88
34	2.80	70	1.90	7	5.92
4	5.92	45	1.30	11	2.30
10	5.10	24	1.61	16	3.87
10	4.15	8	1.46		

10. Draw stress-strain diagram for mild steel from the data given below. Plot strain on the horizontal axis.

Mild Steel

Unit Stress	Unit Strain	Unit Stress	Unit Strain
0	0	32,800	0.0022
4,080	0.00012	33,500	0.0030
7,670	0.00025	34,400	0.0052
11,100	0.00037	37,000	0.0250
15,400	0.00050	47,000	0.0625
18,700	0.00063	52,000	0.1000
23,200	0.00075	53,400	0.1250
26,700	0.00087	54,100	0.1500
30,100	0.0010	54,800	0.1875
32,800	0.00113	55,100	0.2375
33,800	0.00119	54,700	0.2625
32,700	0.0015	47,500	0.3125

11. Draw a stress-strain curve for mild steel from the data above. Plot only as far as the 37,000-pound load. Plot strains horizontally, and select coordinates so that the curve goes well across the sheet.

12. Same as Problem 10. Use data for duralumin.

Duralumin

Unit Stress	Unit Strain	Unit Stress	Unit Strain
0	0	35,700	0.0087
4,520	0.0004	36,300	0.0107
9,100	0.0008	37,300	0.0130
15,820	0.00143	41,300	0.0250
20,300	0.00186	46,100	0.0500
24,900	0.0023	48,000	0.0625
29,400	0.0030	50,100	0.0750
32,000	0.0044	51,500	0.1000
33,500	0.0057	53,300	0.1250
34,500	0.0069	53,500	0.1600

13. Same as Problem 10. Use data for brass.

Free-Cutting Brass

Unit Stress	Unit Strain	Unit Stress	Unit Strain
0	0	34,900	0.0083
5,750	0.00033	35,200	0.0100
10,600	0.00066	36,600	0.0133
16,800	0.00122	37,500	0.0208
21,600	0.00166	39,100	0.0333
26,300	0.0023	40,800	0.0667
29,200	0.0030	44,200	0.1000
32,200	0.0039	47,500	0.1500
32,200	0.0051	49,400	0.2000
34,000	0.0059	50,500	0.2333

Plane Curve—Logarithmic paper

14. Same as Problem 1. Plot on logarithmic paper.
15. Same as Problem 2. Plot on logarithmic paper.
16. Same as Problem 3. Plot on logarithmic paper.
17. Same as Problem 6. Plot on logarithmic paper.
18. Same as Problem 7. Plot on logarithmic paper.

Semilogarithmic Chart

19. Same as Problem 8. Use semilogarithmic paper.

Bar Charts

20. Make a bar chart comparing the loss of weight of various metals in different solutions as given in the table below. Group the three bars for each metal together.

Action of One-Half Liter of 0.2 *N* Salt Solutions, Renewed
Daily for 7 Days, on Metals at 17° to 20° C

Loss in grams per square meter per hour

Metal	MgCl$_2$	CaCl$_2$	NaCl
Zinc	0.57	0.21	0.06
Cast iron	0.51	0.12	0.06
Wrought iron	0.51	0.18	0.15
Aluminum	0.10	0.03	0.00
Lead	0.33	0.24	0.01
Copper	0.15	0.12	0.01
Tin	0.10	0.08	0.00
Nickel	0.03	0.05	0.00

21. Plot the following information in the form of:
a. A barograph.   *b.* A pie diagram.
c. A 100% bar chart.   *d.* A histogram.

Distribution of the Opening Money of a State University

Item	Amount	Per Cent
Instruction	15,200,000	36
Related activities	2,900,00	7
Organized research	8,400,000	20
Extension and public service	4,200,000	10
Libraries	1,300,000	3
Physical plant	5,830,000	14
Administration	3,002,000	7
Retirement, etc.	1,093,000	3

22. Plot the following information in the form of:
a. Plane curve.   *b.* Barograph.
c. 100% Bar.   *d.* Histogram.

Screen Analysis of Medium Sand

Screen	Size of Opening	Amount Passing in Pounds
#100	0.0055	0.75
#50	0.011	3.00
#40	0.015	5.75
#30	0.022	10.00
#20	0.034	14.25
#10	0.073	20.50
⅛ in.	⅛	21.75
³⁄₁₆ in.	³⁄₁₆	23.25
¼ in.	¼	25.00

Trilinear Chart

23. Make a trilinear chart for the data shown in the following table. Let the upper vertex represent 100% volatile matter, the left vertex 100% moisture. Plot a smooth "coalification curve" through the points. A coalification curve shows the changes from peat to anthracite due to geologic forces. The left wing of the curve shows the loss of moisture due to vertical pressure, the right wing the loss of volatile matter due to lateral pressure.

Analysis of Fuel on Ash-Free Basis

Type	Per Cent Moisture	Per Cent Volatile Matter	Per Cent Fixed C
Anthracite	4.1	4.8	91.1
Semianthracite	4.0	11.2	84.8
Bituminous A	2.8	20.2	77.0
Bituminous B	3.2	36.3	60.5
Bituminous C	12.0	39.1	48.9
Bituminous D	19.8	35.7	44.5
Lignite	37.6	29.6	32.8
Peat	81.6	12.4	6.0

Sector Diagrams

24. Make a sector diagram showing the distribution of the various items entering into the cost of government in the island of Puerto Rico.

Items	Per Cent
General government	14.4
Protection	9.6
Education	29.4
Social welfare	9.7
Highways and streets	13.7
Economic development	5.8
Public utilities	10.2
Debt service	7.2

25. Secure data and make a chart showing the distribution of the tax dollar in your community.

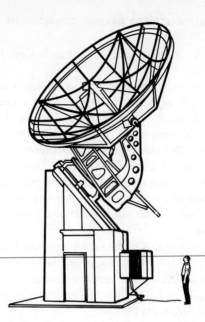

21

Graphic Vector Analysis

21.1 Introduction. Many quantities that are important in engineering work are defined by two properties: direction and magnitude. In addition each has a point of application which locates the line of action and gives the quantity a definite position in space. These factors may be represented graphically by a line called a vector. The direction of the vector line represents the direction of the quantity, and the length of the line represents the magnitude. The vector as such has no relation to the line of action of the original quantity.

Such things as force, velocity, acceleration, displacement, magnetic intensity, and others fall into this class. Therefore, problems involving these factors may be solved graphically by means of a vector diagram. The graphical solution is usually comparatively easy and fast, and it can be made as accurate as necessary by increasing the scale of the drawing. In many cases the graphical solution is satisfactory, but at other times an analytical approach is preferred, in which case the graphical solution may be a valuable check. The graphical solution also frequently helps to visualize the action.

21.2 Definitions. In order to be able to understand the use and applications of vector diagrams, it is necessary to define a few terms.

a. Vector quantity. Any quantity that may be completely described by direction, magnitude, and a definite position in space.

b. Line of action. The line in space along which the vector quantity acts.

c. Point of application. The point on the line of action where the action begins.

d. Vector. A straight line that represents the vector

◀ Close-up of radio telescope used for following sun and recording solar flames (National Bureau of Standards).

quantity in direction and magnitude but not in line of action.

e. Direction. The specification telling which way along the line of action the vector tends to produce results. It is usually specified by an arrow on the vector.

f. Concurrent vectors. When all of the vectors meet in a single point they are called concurrent.

g. Coplanar vectors. When all of the vectors concerned lie in a single plane, they are called coplanar.

h. Resultant. A single vector that can be used to replace *or produce the same result* as a group or system of vectors.

i. Equilibrant. A single vector that will just balance a group or system of vectors. It has the same magnitude as the resultant but the opposite direction.

j. Equilibrium. A condition in a system of vectors where all resultants are zero.

k. Composition of vectors. The process of combining a system of vectors into a smaller number, usually one, which is the resultant.

h. Resolution of vectors. The process of replacing a given system of forces by another system having a larger number of forces. The most common case of resolution is the breaking down of a single force into two or more components.

m. Vector diagram. A continuous polygon of vectors. If the forces are concurrent and the polygon is a closed figure, the system is in equilibrium, provided the vectors all point in a continuous directional pattern around the polygon.

21.3 Composition of two forces. When two vectors act at a point, they form a concurrent coplanar system and the resultant may be obtained by means of a parallelogram. In Fig. 21–1(*a*), a boat started at *A* and is being driven in the direction *AB* at ten miles per hour, and the stream flows in the direction *CG* at four miles per hour. It is desired to determine the actual direction and speed of travel. In Fig. 21–1(*b*), a vector *ab* is drawn parallel to *AB* and the length is made ten units to any convenient scale. An arrow on the vector shows the direction of action. Then the vector *ae* is drawn parallel to *CG* and made four units in length to the same scale as *ab,* with an arrow showing the direction. A parallelogram of forces may be drawn and the diagonal *ad,* with the proper arrow, will represent the direction of travel and the velocity will be the length of *ad* to the same scale used for the original vectors. The usual method of solving this problem is by drawing only half of the parallelogram as shown in Fig. 21–1(*c*). The vector *ab* is constructed and then *bd* is drawn parallel to *CG* and of the proper length to locate *d* and the resultant *ad*. This saves time and is especially convenient when more than two vectors are involved.

Line *AD* in Fig. 21–1(*a*) can be drawn parallel to *ad* to determine the point of landing on the opposite shore. The vector diagram could have been started at *A* to locate *AD* immediately, but this is not always possible or convenient. It is not necessary for the vector diagram to have any definite position with respect to the line of action which is *AD*.

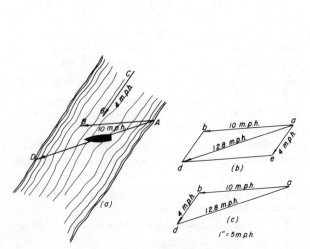

Fig. 21–1.   Composition of concurrent coplanar vectors.

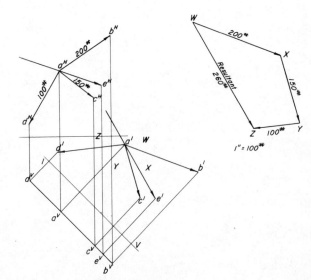

Fig. 21–2.   Composition of concurrent coplanar vectors.

In a coplanar system it is important that the vectors be laid out in the view that shows the true size of all the vectors.

21.4 Composition of concurrent coplanar vectors. In Fig. 21–2, there are three ropes, AB, AC, and AD, pulling at point A, with the magnitude specified on each rope. Since the H and V projections do not show the ropes in true size, it will be necessary to project the system onto auxiliary plane 1 which is set up parallel to the three forces. In this situation it is customary to letter the spaces between the forces, as W, X, Y, and Z. The force AB will then be known as WX, the force AC as XY, and AD as YZ. This makes the lettering of the vector diagram very simple. The forces may be taken in any order, but it is customary to take them either clockwise or counterclockwise. Therefore WX is first laid out parallel to $a'b'$ and of a length of 200 pounds on a scale of 1 inch = 100 pounds. XY is then made parallel to $a'c'$ beginning at point X with a length of 150 pounds, and YZ beginning at Y parallel to $a'd'$ and 100 pounds in length. The resultant or the force that will replace the three will be WZ and the magnitude, *260 pounds, can be determined by measuring the line WZ.* If desired, the line AE may be drawn parallel to WZ and carried back to the H and V projections to locate the line of action of the resultant.

If the original forces are so located that the plane does not show edgewise in either the top or front view, then two auxiliary projections will be necessary to determine the true size of the plane and the true magni-

tude of the forces. This construction is shown in Fig. 21–3.

21.5 Composition of concurrent non-coplanar vectors. When the vectors do not lie in one plane, it is impossible to find the true length of every vector in any one view. Therefore, the vector diagram must be drawn in two views at the same time. In Fig. 21–4(a), it is desired to find the direction and magnitude of the magnetic intensity at point P, due to AB which is a long straight conductor that carries a current (i), and to CD which is a bar magnet having point poles of strength m at each end. The values of H_i, H_c, and H_d represent the magnetic intensities at point P due to the conductor, pole C, and pole D, respectively. These values can be calculated by well-known formulas when the current i, the strength of the magnet, and all distances are known. The lines PE, PC, and PD give the respective lines of action of the forces. The values, H_i, H_c, and H_d, may be placed consecutively in a vector diagram whose resultant is the magnetic intensity acting on point P. Beginning at point W, in Fig. 21.4(b), the magnetic intensity H_i, due to the conductor, is laid out parallel to PE. The vertical projection shows true length. This establishes the vector WX. From X, a vector XF is made parallel to PC, and on its true length in the auxiliary view, the

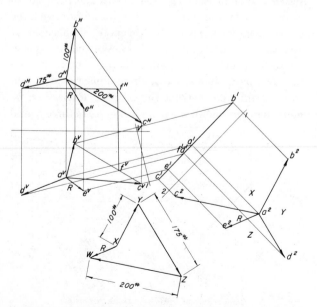

Fig. 21–3. Composition of concurrent coplanar vectors.

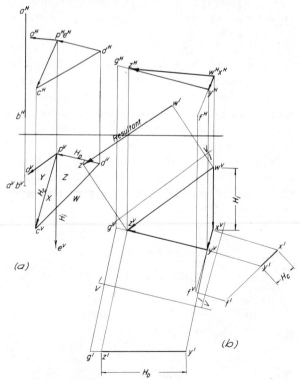

Fig. 21–4. Composition of concurrent non-coplanar vectors.

value H_c is measured to locate point Y. From Y, a vector YG is made parallel to PD and the length H_d measured on its true length to locate point Z. The resultant then will be the vector from W to Z. Its true length must be determined to get the magnitude of the magnetic intensity at point P. By drawing through P in Fig. 21–4(a), a line parallel to WZ, the line PO is established which gives the direction of the magnetic intensity at P.

21.6   Resolution of forces. If it is desired to break a given force down into a number of components, this may be done by considering the known force to be the resultant. From Fig. 21–5 it can be seen that there are any number of sets of components that may be drawn. The only conditions are that their lines of action all pass through a point on the line of action of the original force, and that in the vector diagram the original force shall turn out to be the resultant of all the components.

If the lines of action are given, the number of possible solutions is decreased. When there are only two components and the lines of action are given, there will be only one result. To resolve a known force into a set of components so that the system will be in equilibrium requires that the known force be the equilibrant of all the components instead of the resultant.

21.7   Equilibrium. When a condition exists in a system of vectors in which the resultant is zero, the system is said to be in equilibrium. The vector diagram of a system that is in equilibrium is a closed polygon with the arrows on the vectors all pointing around the polygon in the same direction. In each of the preceding problems an extra vector could have been added which would produce a state of equilibrium in the system. This vector is called the equilibrant and it is equal to the resultant but opposite in direction.

The system of forces in Fig. 21–6 in which a weight is suspended by two ropes is in a state of equilibrium. The vector diagram always considers the forces acting

on a single joint, in this case, point A, and here they are concurrent coplanar forces. In considering the forces acting on this joint there are six factors that must be known. They are the magnitude and direction of each of the three forces. When it is known that the joint is in equilibrium, the problem can be solved if there are no more than two unknowns. If there are more unknowns at any one joint the problem is said to be statically indeterminate. In Fig. 21–6, the magnitude and direction of the load are known, and the direction of each of the other forces, leaving their two magnitudes, unknown. Therefore, the problem can be solved by a vector diagram. In Fig. 21–6(b) the vector XY for the known force is laid out to a scale of 1 inch = 50 pounds. The direction of YZ is known and can be drawn through Y, parallel to AD, but the magnitude is not known. The direction of XZ is known and it can be drawn through X, parallel to AC, but its magnitude is unknown. However, when the two direction lines are constructed it is found that they intersect at a point that can be called Z. The lengths of YZ and ZX can then be measured. Since in equilibrium the arrows must all point around the diagram in the same direction, the direction of the forces is found to be from Y to Z and from Z to X. The arrows indicate the direction in which the forces act on the original joint, and from this it can be seen that each force is pulling away from the joint and therefore they are all in tension. If the arrow is found to be pointing toward the joint, the member is in compression.

21.8   Resolution of vectors in a three-dimensional system. When it becomes necessary to find the loads in a three-dimensional structure, the work of drawing the vector diagram becomes a little more complicated. It has been seen in a plane vector system that it is possible to construct the diagram if there are no more than two unknowns. In a space or three-dimensional system it is possible to construct the diagram if there are no more than three unknowns. In Fig. 21–7(a) a three-legged

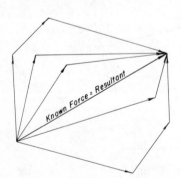

Fig. 21–5.   Resolution of a vector.

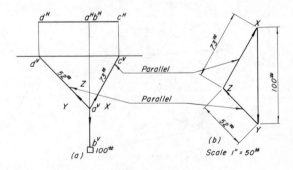

Fig. 21–6.   Resolution of forces in equilibrium.

tripod is supporting two known forces of 100 pounds each. There are ten possible factors in this problem, of which seven are known. They are the direction and magnitude of the known forces and the direction of the three components. The unknowns are the magnitudes of the components, or in other words the load in each leg of the tripod. If the known forces are called *AB* and *BC*, the other three may be called *CD*, *DE*, and *EA*. The vector diagram may be constructed in the usual way. Assume point *A* in both projections of Fig. 21–7(*b*). Draw *AB* in a vertical position and measure the length of 100 pounds in the vertical projection. *BX* can be drawn parallel to the other known force and its true length determined at b^1x^1. On the true length lay out the value of 100 pounds to locate c^1, and project it back to the horizontal and vertical views. Next a line *AZ*, of any length, must be drawn through point *A* parallel to leg *EA* of the tripod. Point *E* will be somewhere on that line. Then through *C*, a line *CY*, of any length, must be drawn parallel to leg *CD* of the tripod. Point *D* will be somewhere on that line. The final step is to construct a line intersecting *AZ* and *CY* and at the same time being parallel to leg *DE* of the tripod. The construction is shown in the figure, but the theory is discussed in detail in Art. 15.48. In this case the point projection of line *MN*, which is parallel to leg *DE*, is found in the second auxiliary projection shown in Fig. 21–7(*c*). This

projection therefore locates the point projection of *DE* at the place where a^2z^2 crosses c^2y^2. When the position of this connecting line has been determined, the location of points *D* and *E* will have been found. The closed vector diagram is lettered *ABCDEA*, and the magnitude of the three unknown forces may be found by obtaining the true length of each line and using the same scale as was used for *AB*. By reference to the arrows it can be seen that *DE* is in tension, whereas the others are all in compression.

21.8.1 *Alternate solution.* A somewhat easier solution for this problem may be obtained by resolving the known force, *AB* shown in Fig. 21–8(*a*), into two components, one *BP*, parallel to one of the legs, in this case *BP* is parallel to leg No. 1, and the second, *PA*, lying in the plane of the other two legs, as shown in Fig. 21–8(*b*). This second component can then be resolved into two components, *PC* and *CA*, which are parallel, respectively, to the other two legs.

The construction is as follows:

a. On the true length projection of the known force a^1x^1 lay off the value as given in some convenient scale. When projected back to the *H* and *V* views this locates the vector *AB*. See Fig. 21–8(*b*).

b. Through *B* construct a line, *BY*, parallel to leg No. 1. Find the point, *P*, where it pierces the plane formed by legs *2* and *3*. (See Art. 15.31 for discussion of

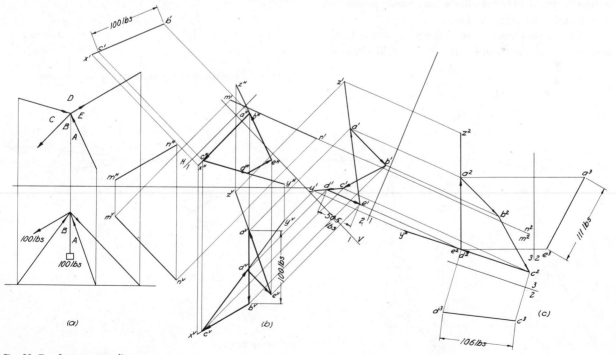

Fig. 21–7. Space vector diagram.

this construction.) Find the true length of *BP*, which will be the load in leg No. *1*.

c. Through point *P*, construct a line parallel to leg No. *3* until it intersects leg No. *2* at point *C*.

d. Find the true lengths of lines *PC* and *AC*, and these will be the loads in the other legs of the tripod.

By reference to the arrows it can be seen that leg *3* is in tension, whereas the other two are in compression.

21.9 Resultant of non-concurrent coplanar vectors. When a series of non-concurrent vectors lie in a single plane, they must intersect in pairs unless they are parallel. Therefore, the resultant can be found by combining two vectors as V^1 and V^2 in Fig. 21–9 to get the resultant R^1. Then V^3 may be combined with R^1 to get resultant R^2. The magnitude and direction of each resultant are found in the vector diagram in Fig. 21–9(*b*) and the line of action in Fig. 21–9(*a*). If the resultant of the first two forces happens to be parallel to the third force but opposite in direction, the resultant will be a couple.

21.10 The string polygon. The same result could be obtained by means of a string polygon or, as it is often called, a funicular polygon. This is a very important method of analysis and should be familiar to every engineer. The illustration in Fig. 21–10 is the same as Fig. 21–9, and although in this case the method of Fig. 21–9 may seem easier, the method of the string polygon can be used in many other problems that would be difficult or impossible by other methods.

To solve a problem by the string polygon method, it is necessary to have some direct relationship between

the original vectors. This is accomplished by resolving each force into two components in such a way that one of the components of the first force in also a component of the second force but opposite in direction. The vector *AB* in Fig. 21–10(*b*) represents the force V^1 of Fig. 21–10(*a*), and by selecting a pole *P* at any convenient place, the vector *AB* can be resolved into two components, *AP*, called string S^1, and *PB* called string S^2. The vector *BC*, representing force V^2, can be resolved into two components *BP*, which is still called S^2, and *PC*, called S^3. From this it can be seen that *PB* and *BP* are equal and opposite and would therefore cancel out, leaving *AP* and *PC* as the components of the resultant R^1. In a similar manner the vector *CD*, representing force V^3 can be resolved into two components *CP*, string S^3, and *PD*, string S^4. Again it can be seen that *PC* and *CP* cancel each other, leaving *AP* and *PD* as the components of the resultant R^2.

Lines of action of these various components can be determined as in Fig. 21–10(*c*) by assuming a starting point, *O*, as any point on the line of action of V^1. The lines of action S^1 and S^2 in Fig. 21–10(*c*) can then be

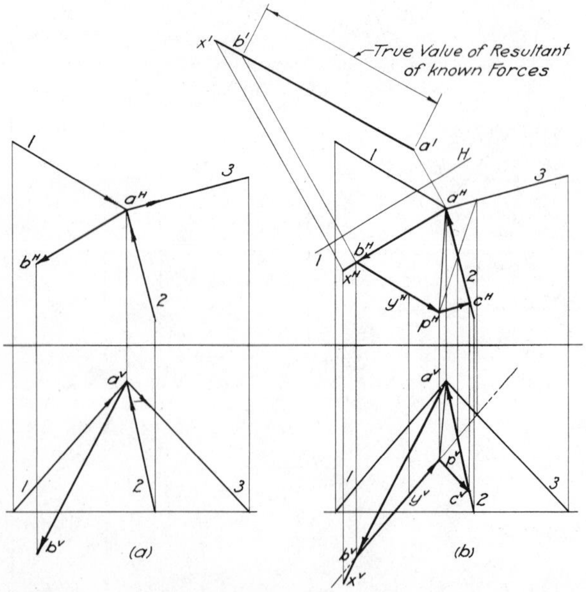

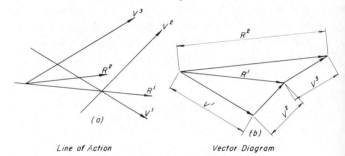

Line of Action   Vector Diagram

Fig. 21–9. Composition of non-concurrent coplanar vectors.

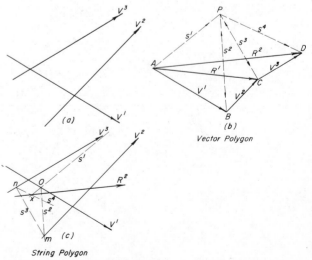

Fig. 21–10. Composition of non-concurrent coplanar vectors—string polygon method.

![Fig. 21-8 space vector diagram]

Fig. 21–8. Space vector diagram.

drawn respectively parallel to the strings S^1 and S^2 in Fig. 21–10(b). Since S^2 is also a component of the force V^2, the point "m" is located at the intersection of S^2 and V^2 in Fig. 21–10(c). From point "m" a line is then drawn parallel to S^3 to locate point "n" on force V^3 and from "n" a line parallel to S^4 gives the line of action of the last component. Since it has already been shown that S^1 and S^4 are the components of R^2, their intersection in Fig. 21–10(c) must be one point on the line of action of R^2 and through this point "x" the line of action of the resultant may be drawn parallel to R^2 in Fig. 21–10(b). The first point "O" can be chosen any place on V^1 since any other locations would merely determine a different point on the line of action of R^2.

21.11 Resultants of vector systems. There are several possibilities that must be investigated when determining the resultant of a set of vectors. If, in each case, the vector polygon and the string polygon are drawn, it is possible to tell immediately what the form of the resultant will be. The three possibilities are as follows:

a. If, as in Fig. 21–10(b), the vector polygon does not close, the resultant must be a force. A vector diagram is said to close when the end of the last vector coincides with the beginning of the first vector. In this case point D would have to fall on point A for closure.

b. If the vector polygon closes with the vectors all pointing around the polygon in the same direction, but the string polygon does not close, the resultant will be a couple. A couple is defined as two forces which are equal and opposite but whose lines of action are parallel and at a definite distance apart. In Fig. 21–11(b) the vector polygon closes, but the string polygon, shown in dashed line, in Fig. 21–11(a) does not close because there are two parallel positions of string S^1. In this case the resultant is a couple whose forces are both S^1 acting at a distance of "a" from each other.

c. If the vector polygon closes with the vectors all pointing around the polygon in the same direction, and the string polygon also closes, the system is in equilibrium. This condition is illustrated in Fig. 21–12.

21.12 Parallel forces. The problem of parallel forces is a special case of non-concurrent forces and may be solved by the same method. Figure 21–13 shows a truss with vertical loads as specified. The appearance of the

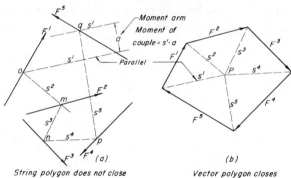

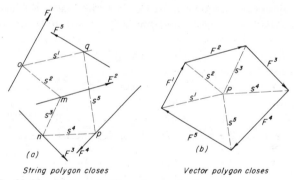

Fig. 21–11. Vector and string polygons of a force system when the resultant is a couple.

Fig. 21–12. Vector and string polygons of a force system in equilibrium. The resultant is zero.

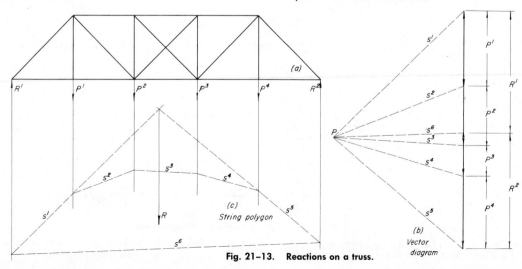

Fig. 21–13. Reactions on a truss.

vector diagram, shown in Fig. 21–13(b), is different because it becomes a straight line with the panel loads all pointing down and the reactions pointing up. When in equilibrium, the sum of the reactions must equal the loads, so the vector diagram will close at the top point of P^1. It will be necessary to determine the value of each reaction. To do this the vector diagram of Fig. 21–13(b) is drawn and pole P chosen at some convenient place. The string diagram Fig. 21–13(c) is then drawn as previously described in paragraph 21.10 beginning at any convenient point on P^1. The strings, S^1 and S^5, if continued to the point where they intersect will locate a point on the resultant of all the forces. A line through this point, parallel to the forces and having a magnitude which can be measured on the vector diagram from the beginning of P^1 to the end of P^4, will be the resultant.

However, the usual problem in this situation is to find the value of each reaction when the beam is in equilibrium. For equilibrium the string polygon must close as well as the vector polygon and the only way that can be done is to connect the point where S^5 crosses R^2, in Fig. 21–13(c), with the point where S^1 crosses R^1. This gives the direction of string S^6, which may be transferred to the vector diagram in Fig. 21–13(b) by draw-

ing parallel to S^6 in Fig. 21–13(c). The value of R^2 may then be scaled between S^5 and S^6, and the value of R^1 between S^6 and S^1, since in each case these forces are the components of the resultants.

21.13   Centroid of an area. The centroid or center of gravity of an area is defined as that point where the area would act if it were concentrated at a point. For simple figures it is usually quite easy to locate the centroid, but for irregular areas the string polygon forms a convenient method. The method given here is general and may be applied to any area, but for regular figures there are usually easier methods. For instance, if there is an axis of symmetry, the centroid must be on that axis.

The irregular figure shown in Fig. 21–14(a) will serve to show the general method. The area will first be divided into fairly small parts by means of vertical lines. It must be remembered that the method is approximate, but the accuracy can be improved by increasing the number of divisions. Next the approximate center of each small area is selected by estimation and judgment, and vertical lines are drawn through each of these centers. In a triangle the centroid will be one-third of the altitude from the base, and for a trapezoid the centroid will be near the center but closer to the larger side. The

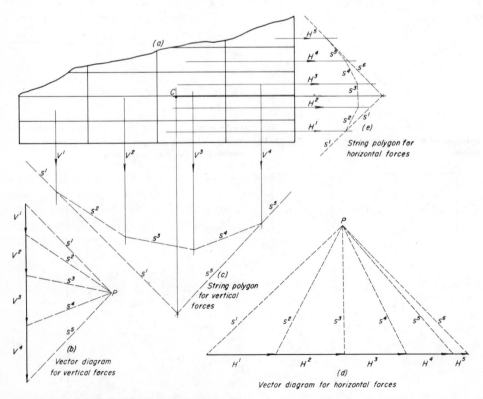

Fig. 21–14.   Graphic method for locating a centroid.

area of each small part is approximated by scaling the average height and multiplying it by the width. These areas can be treated like forces and give the length of the vectors marked V^1, V^2, V^3, and V^4 which are placed on the vertical lines and are to be used as vectors. The vector diagram is then drawn in Fig. 21–14(b), a pole selected, and the strings drawn. The string polygon below the area, Fig. 21–14(c), is then drawn and the intersection of strings S^1 and S^5 determined. A line through this point parallel to the vectors is a locus, and the centroid must lie on this line.

The figure is then divided into horizontal segments and the process repeated in the vector diagram shown in Fig. 21–14(d). When the string polygon to the right of the area, Fig. 21–14(e), is complete, the intersection of strings S^1 and S^6 determines a point on a locus line on which the centroid lies. The intersection, C, of these two locus lines is the centroid.

21.14   Moments of a force about a point. A moment is defined as the product of a force times the distance measured from the line of action of the force to some point about which the moments are to be taken. It is frequently necessary in engineering problems to find the moment of a force about some point. This may be done graphically as shown in Fig. 21–15. To find the moment of force F about point O, a vector diagram with pole P and strings S^1 and S^2 is drawn. See Fig. 21–15(b). This triangle, lettered PDE, is then used to draw the string polygon lettered ABC, by drawing the strings S^1 and S^2 parallel to the components, S^1 and S^2, of the force F. These components are often called rays. The starting point A is at any point on the line of action of the force F.

Since the triangles PDE and ABC are similar,

$$ED : y :: BC : X$$

or $$ED \cdot X = BC \cdot y = m \cdot y$$

Since $ED \cdot X$ is the moment desired, it can be obtained by measuring BC(m) at the scale to which Fig. 21–15(a) was drawn, in this case, 1 inch = 10 feet, and multiply-

ing it by the pole distance (y), measured to the scale at which Fig. 21–15(b) was drawn, in this case, 1 inch = 100 pounds. Therefore, the moment is obtained by scaling m in feet and y in pounds, and multiplying them to get an answer in foot-pounds. If the pole distance can be set at some even number such as 10 or 100, the result is easily obtained.

In Fig. 21–16, the moment of three forces about the line XX is found to be $m \cdot y$ in foot-pounds. In this figure, the vector diagram is drawn to a scale of 1 inch = 1000 pounds and the pole distance, y, is scaled as 1400 pounds. The string polygon is drawn to the scale of 1 inch = 10 feet and the distance between S^4 and S^1 on the line XX, about which the moments are taken, is scaled as 21.2 feet. The moment is therefore 1400 × 21.2 = 29,680 foot-pounds.

21.15   Moments on a beam. One of the most common problems of this kind occurs in finding the moments at various points in a beam. Figure 21–17 shows a beam loaded with a series of concentrated loads. It is desired to find the moment of these forces about the plane XX. First the vector diagram, Fig. 21–17(b), is drawn and the pole selected. The string polygon, Fig. 21–17(c), is then drawn and string S^6 is located from which the values of the reactions can be determined by means of the vector diagram. It was proven in Art. 21.14 that the moment is the product of the pole distance and the intercept of the two strings of a force on the plane about which the moment is to be taken. Therefore, the moment of R^1 about XX is R^1_m in Fig. 21–17(c) times y. In the same manner the moment of W^1 is W^1_m times y, of W^2 is W^2_m times y, and of W^3 is W^3_m times y. However, since the moment of R^1 is clockwise and the other three are counterclockwise, they must be subtracted, leaving the actual moment to be $m^1 \times y$. It will be noted that m^1 is the vertical intercept on the string polygon, so the moment at any point on the beam may be found by taking the vertical intercept on the string polygon at that point and multiplying it by the pole distance. It makes no difference whether S^6 is horizon-

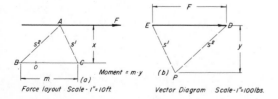

Fig. 21–15.   **Moment of a force about a point.**

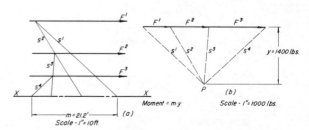

Fig. 21–16.   **Moment of forces about a line.**

tal or not. Either end of the beam may be used and the result will be the same, since the end used may be considered as a free body with the beam broken on plane *XX* and acted on by the reaction and the specified loads. The free body is then held in equilibrium by means of the moment found on plane *XX*.

21.16 Moment of inertia. Moment of inertia is defined as the product of the mass or area times the square of the distance from the center of gravity to the point about which moments are to be taken. The equation for the moment of inertia as given in the textbooks is $I = \Sigma M(r)^2$, where M is the mass and r is the distance from the center of gravity to the point about which moments are to be taken. If the mass, assumed to be acting in a certain direction, is represented by a vector, F, as in Fig. 21-18(a) and the distance r is marked x, it will be necessary to multiply the vector by $(x)^2$, if the moments are taken about point O. In Art. 21.14 the method of multiplying the vector by x was explained. In Fig. 21-18 a method is shown whereby the vector can be multiplied by $(x)^2$.

The first step, Fig. 21-18(a) and Fig. 21-18(b), is exactly the same as explained in Art. 21.14. It has already been shown that $ED \cdot x = BC \cdot y$. Then if a second pole, P^1, is chosen as in Fig. 21-18(c) and BC used as a vector, a second string polygon, GHK, can be drawn as in Fig. 21-18(d). In these figures P^1BC and GHK are similar triangles. Therefore

$$m : y^1 :: m^1 : x$$
or $$mx = m^1 y^1$$
Since $$I = F \cdot (x)^2 = F \cdot x \cdot x$$
and from Art. 21.14 $$F \cdot x = m \cdot y$$
then $$I = m \cdot y \cdot x \quad \text{or} \quad I = m^1 \cdot y^1 \cdot y$$

That is, the moment of inertia is found by multiplying the first pole distance y, measured on the scale to which it was drawn, 1 inch = 100 pounds, by the second pole distance, y^1, measured on the scale to which it was drawn, 1 inch = 10 feet, by the intercept on the last string polygon m^1, measured on the scale to which it was drawn, 1 inch = 10 feet. The answer will therefore be in terms of pounds (foot)^2.

For finding the moment of inertia of an area it is necessary to divide that area into rather small parts and represent each part by means of a vector through the approximate centroid of the area. The method is

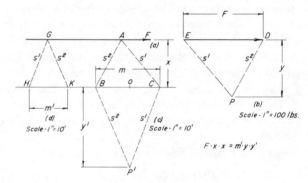

Fig. 21-18.   **Product of a force times the square of a distance.**

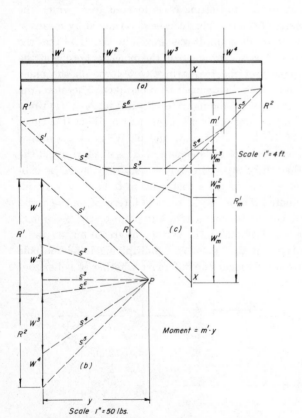

Fig. 21-17.   **Moments in a beam.**

approximate but becomes more accurate as the number of divisions is increased. To illustrate the effect of more divisions on the accuracy, Figs. 21–19 and 21–20 have been drawn. In each case the moment of inertia of a 4×6 rectangle has been found. In Fig. 21–19 the rectangle was divided into two parts and two vectors were used, whereas in Fig. 21–20 four divisions were used and four vectors. It can be seen that two different answers have been obtained, 116 and 126.4, respectively. If an infinite number of divisions could be used, the same result could be obtained as would result from analytical integration and the result would be 128. Therefore, for an approximate answer it seems that, in this case, four divisions should be satisfactory. Actually, the graphical method would not be used for such simple areas. It is particularly valuable for irregular areas that are hard to solve analytically.

21.17 Radius of gyration. The radius of gyration in

Fig. 21–21(a) is the distance "r" from an axis about which moments are to be taken, to a line "R" representing a summation of a series of parallel forces that is so located that the moment of inertia of the summation about the given axis is the same as the total moment of inertia of all the individual forces about that same axis. In Fig. 21–21, R is a summation of all the forces $(F^1 + F^2 + F^3)$, which acts at a distance r from the plane XX, about which moments are being taken. This distance r is by definition the radius of gyration if the moment of inertia of R about XX is the same as sum of the moments of inertia of F^1, F^2, and F^3 about axis XX.

By definition
$$I = R(r)^2$$
or
$$(r)^2 = \frac{I}{R}$$

By the previous paragraph
$$I = m^1 \cdot y^1 \cdot y$$
then
$$(r)^2 = \frac{m^1 \cdot y^1 \cdot y}{R}$$

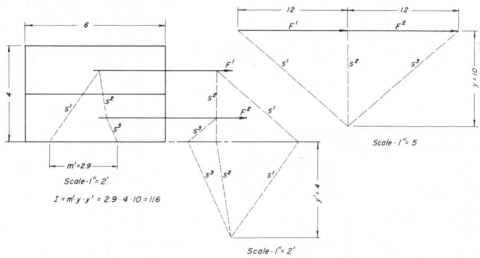

$$I = m' \cdot y \cdot y' = 2.9 \cdot 4 \cdot 10 = 116$$

Fig. 21–19. Moments of inertia of a rectangle about one side—two divisions. Culman's method.

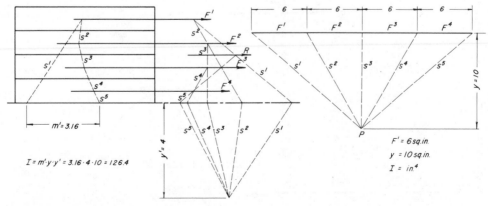

$$I = m' \cdot y \cdot y' = 3.16 \cdot 4 \cdot 10 = 126.4$$

$F' = 6 \, sq.in.$
$y = 10 \, sq.in.$
$I = \quad in.^4$

Fig. 21–20. Moment of inertia of a rectangle about one side—four divisions.

If the distance y is made equal to R as has been done in Fig. 21–21(b), then the equation becomes

$$(r)^2 = m^1 \cdot y^1$$

The length of the radius of gyration may then be found graphically as illustrated in Fig. 21–21(e). To do this, the distance AB is made equal to m^1, and the distance BC is made equal to y^1. A semicircle is then drawn with AC as a diameter and a perpendicular to that diameter erected at B. Then by geometry

$$AB : BD :: BD : BC$$

or

$$(BD)^2 = AB \cdot BC = m^1 \cdot y^1 = (r)^2$$

Therefore the value of r may be scaled at BD on Fig. 21–21(e).

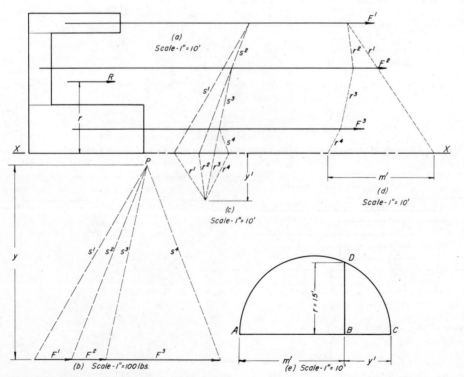

Fig. 21–21.   Radius of gyration.

PROBLEMS

In solving these problems the student should use as large a scale as possible on the sheet of paper that he is using. If a large sheet of paper is used, the scale can be made large and the accuracy will be better. However, with careful work a reasonable answer can be obtained on an 8½ × 11 sheet. Some of the problems require a knowledge of engineering geometry for solution. Although some of the problems may be solved without a formal study of Chapter 15, it is believed that the students will be able to comprehend the work and get more benefit from it if they first have a good knowledge of geometry.

1. A river, 1 mile wide, is flowing due south with a current of 10 miles per hour. A boat traveling 20 miles per hour with respect to the water must land at a point directly opposite the starting point. What direction must it travel and how long will it take to cross?

2. A weight of 100 pounds is suspended by two ropes attached to the ceiling at points 10 feet apart. One rope is 8 feet long and the other is 10 feet long. Find the load in each rope.

3. A derrick picks up a load of 2000 pounds. The boom of the derrick is at an angle of 45° with the horizontal and the cable connecting the end of the boom with the top of the mast is at an angle of 15° with the horizontal. Find the load in the cable and the boom and indicate whether they are in tension or compression.

4. A falling body is acted on by gravity and by a horizontal wind that causes a horizontal acceleration of 2 feet per second per second. What is the magnitude and direction (angle with the horizontal) of the resulting acceleration?

5. A 4-foot cube of stone is resting on a fairly smooth surface. Two of the vertical faces of the cube are in a N-S direction. A force of 2000 pounds pushing due east is applied at the SW corner. Another force of 2500 pounds is applied at the NE corner and is pulling N 45° E. A third force of 1850 pounds is applied at the SE corner and is pulling in a direction S 60° E. These forces are just enough to start motion. What is the direction of the motion? What is the frictional resistance to motion?

6. An equilateral triangle, 6 feet on a side, is horizontal and has the west side in a N-S position. It is acted on by three forces. One at the N corner pulls N 45° E with a magnitude of 50 pounds. One at the east corner acts in a direction S 60° W with a magnitude of 35.4 pounds. The other at the south corner acts in the direction S 15° W with a magnitude of 18.3 pounds. Find the resultant.

7. Four forces acting at a point have magnitudes of 100 pounds, 200 pounds, 300 pounds, and 400 pounds. They act along the edges of a right, regular, rectangular pyramid whose apex is at the point where the three forces act. The altitude of the pyramid is 20 feet and the base is a rectangle 10 feet by 15 feet. Find the resultant of the four forces. Describe it by means of a vertical component and two horizontal components which are parallel respectively to the sides of the base of the pyramid.

8. An airplane must take off in a direction N 30° E to take advantage of a rising air current of 2 miles per hour. The wind is due south at 20 miles per hour. Flying speed of the plane is 75 miles per hour with relation to the air, and the plane is climbing at an angle of 20°. What is the compass bearing of the flight and the speed? How long will it take to reach an altitude of 10,000 feet?

9. A captive balloon is held by three ropes, each 100 feet long. They are fastened to the ground at points A, B, and C. These points are the three corners of an equilateral triangle 75 feet on a side. AB is a N-S line. The balloon has a lift of 1000 pounds and a wind blowing S 45° E causes a horizontal force of 200 pounds exerted by the balloon. Find the load in each of the three ropes.

10. A beam 15 feet long is supported at both ends, and loaded with four concentrated loads. These loads are specified in the table.

Load No.	Magnitude	Distance from the left end
1	1000 pounds	3 feet
2	500	5
3	2000	10
4	300	13

   a. Find the resultant of the loads.

   b. Find the value of each reaction.

   c. Find the moment in the beam at any point specified by the instructor.

11. A beam 12 feet long is supported at both ends and loaded with a uniformly increasing load starting with 160 pounds at the left end and increasing to 400 pounds at the right end. Find the reactions and the moment at any point.

12. A semicircle has its base on the X-axis. The radius is 2 inches.

   a. Find the centroid.

   b. Find the moment of inertia about the base.

   c. Find the radius of gyration about the same axis.

13. A T-section has its top 24″ × 4″ and the stem 14″ × 6″.

   a. Find the centroid.

   b. Find the moment of inertia about an axis through the bottom of the stem.

   c. Find the radius of gyration about the same axis.

14. For the irregular area described below, find the centroid, the moment of inertia, and the radius of gyration about the specified axis.

The axis is a horizontal line. The base of the area is a horizontal line 1 inch above the axis. The coordinates of the points on the outline of the area are listed in the table and are measured to the right from the left edge of the figure and upward from its base.

| Point No. | Distances | |
	Right	Vertical
1	1	1.5
2	2	2
3	3	1
4	4	1
5	5	3
6	6	4
7	7	4

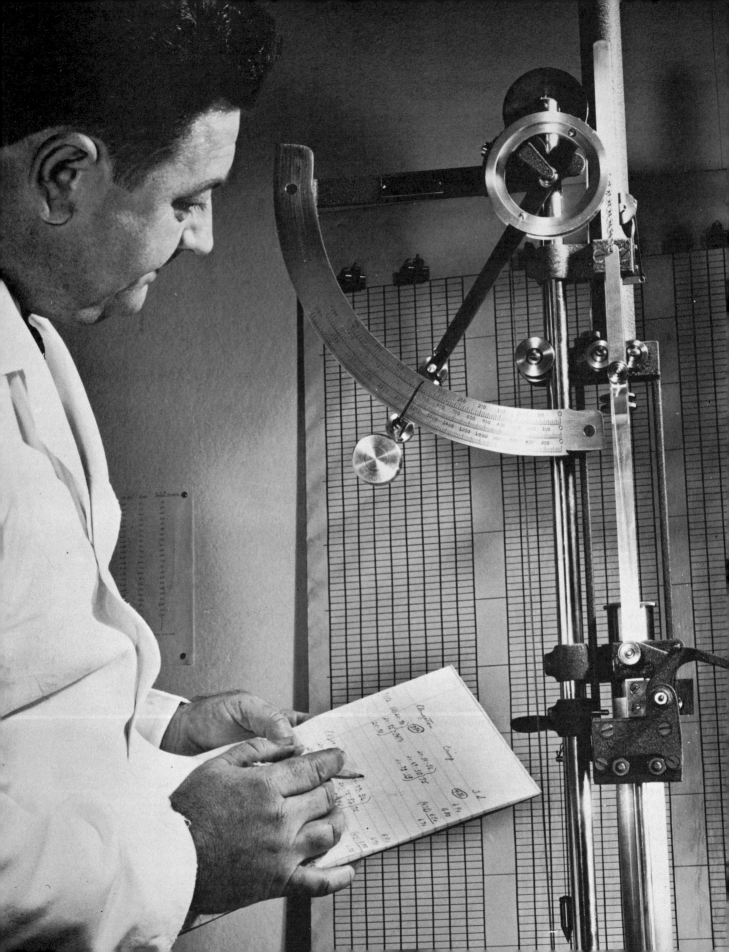

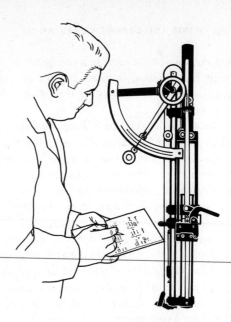

22

Graphic Layouts for Empirical Equations

22.1 Use of empirical equations. Engineers and businessmen deal constantly with equations. Some of these are developed by a logical reasoning process and are called rational equations. Others are developed from observations of natural processes or from data obtained in carefully controlled laboratory experiments. The latter are called empirical equations. These equations are very useful in the design and development of many types of structures, machines, and other equipment. Many natural phenomena follow such equations, and problems relating to them can thus be solved.

22.2 Presentation of data. The purpose of most laboratory experiments is to determine how one variable in a certain situation changes with respect to another, while all other factors are held relatively constant. The controlled variable is usually called the independent variable and the other the dependent variable. The results of the experiment may be presented in three forms:

a. As tabulated data.

b. Graphically by a curve which represents the data as accurately as possible, and

c. By an equation which represents the curve with a minimum deviation.

Of these methods the first is cumbersome and difficult to use for interpolation or extrapolation. The curve, on the other hand, quickly shows trends and the value of one variable corresponding to another can be found quickly and accurately. The curve can easily be extended, if the data upon which it was based warrants such extension. An equation, if reasonably simple, is compact and can be used as easily as the graph. It also permits extension beyond the range of the original data.

An equation can also be used in a computer for rapid solution, if the equation is more difficult or must be used repeatedly. For these reasons, it is often desirable to have an equation.

22.3   Limitations. No matter how carefully the graphical work is done nor how accurately the mathematical equation is determined, it can never be more reliable that the original data from which it was obtained. Even in a well-controlled experiment there are always possibilities of errors of observation in making readings of the instruments. Some of these errors are self-compensating in that some may be too high, whereas others are too low. Generally such errors do not affect the validity and usefulness of the data. If one reading appears to be entirely out of line, when plotted on graph paper, such a point can simply be ignored in drawing the curve.

On the other hand, errors due to faulty instruments, improper calibration, or inaccurate setting and adjustment may cause all readings to be either too high or too low. Nothing can be done in the graphical layout to compensate for such errors. Instruments must be corrected and the work repeated.

22.4   Accuracy of graphical work. Since the derivation of an equation by the methods of this chapter will depend upon the plotting of data and the subsequent drawing of an average straight line or curve through the plotted points, it is obvious that such work must be done with accuracy. To assist in this process the following suggestions are offered.

a. Review Chapter 20 and particularly Art. 20.4 and follow the suggestions therein contained.

b. Make the layout of the chart as large as possible. The customary 8½ × 11-inch printed coordinate papers may be used, but where greater accuracy is desired, it may be advisable to construct large-scale charts.

c. When indicating plotted points make these as sharp and small as possible. Later, if desired, the location can be indicated by a cross mark or a small circle.

d. The average line, whether straight or curved, should have:

1. As many points on the line as possible. Sometimes, of course, none can be on the line.

2. Approximately an equal number of points above and below the line and the summation of ordinate distances above and below the line, within a limited length, equal to zero as shown in Fig. 22–1.

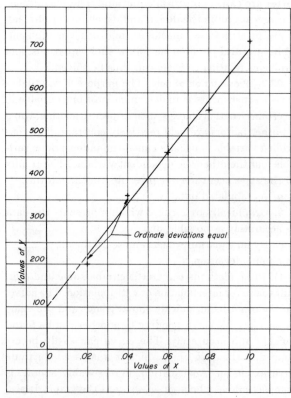

Fig. 22–1.   Drawing an average line.

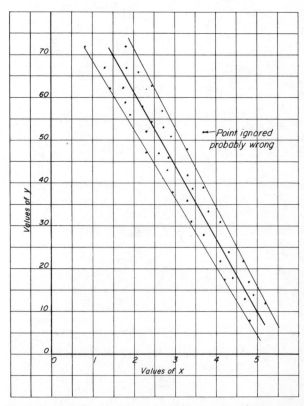

Fig. 22–2.   Drawing an average line through scattered points.

3. When there are dozens of points scattered at random across a rather narrow belt as in Fig. 22.2, it is best to draw very lightly the top and bottom enclosing or enveloping lines, ignoring, of course, any extreme points. Giving consideration to the density of distribution of the points, the average line will be somewhere near the halfway position between the upper and lower boundary lines.

22.5   Selection of the type form of the equation. If an average curve drawn to fit plotted data does not result in a straight line on rectangular coordinate paper it is difficult to select the type of equation which will represent the data accurately. There are no rules for making a selection among the many possible equations. If, however, a convenient working equation, suitable for engineering computations of a practical character, is needed, a few suggestions can be offered. The selection, in this chapter, will be limited to three equations which are relatively simple and can be based upon a straight line. The form of the equation depends on the kind of coordinate paper used for plotting. None of these are too laborious for practical use. Two other equation forms based upon curves on rectangular coordinate paper will

also be given, but these are not so readily applied.

a. $y = mx + c$. This is the familiar equation of a straight line on rectangular coordinate paper.

b. $y = a(10)^{bx}$. If this equation is transformed by taking logarithms of both sides, it becomes

$$\log y = \log a + bx \log 10$$

Since $\log a$ is a constant and $\log 10$ is 1, this is the equation of a straight line on semilog paper with y on the log scale and x on the uniform scale.

c. $y = ax^m$. If this equation is also transformed by taking logarithms of both sides, it becomes

$$\log y = \log a + m \log x$$

This is the equation for a straight line on logarithmic coordinate paper.

Two other straight-line types are possible with a little additional computation. They are

d. $y = a(10)^{mx} + c$; or $y - c = a(10)^{mx}$ which becomes

$$\log (y - c) = \log a + mx$$

thus showing $\log (y - c)$ to be linear with x on semilog paper.

e. $y = ax^m + c$; or $\log (y - c) = \log a + m \log x$
This shows $\log (y - c)$ to be linear with $\log x$ on logarithmic paper.

f. Two other forms which can sometimes be used with curved lines are:

$$y = a + bx + cx^2 \ldots (n + 1) \, x^n \quad \text{and}$$
$$(y + b)(x + a) = c$$

22.6   Rectification of curves. From the foregoing paragraph, with the exception of the last two, it will be noted that the equations are all based upon straight lines upon certain kinds of coordinate paper. Examination of the tabulated data from an experiment usually will not reveal the nature of the curve to be drawn. The customary practice therefore is as follows:

a. Plot the data upon rectangular coordinate paper. If a straight line can be drawn, proceed to the development of the equation.

b. If a straight line does not result upon rectangular coordinate paper, a comparison of the curve obtained, with those shown in Figs. 22–3, 22–4, and 22–6 may give a clue for another plotting upon one of the other two types of coordinate paper. Curves in Fig. 22–3 will develop as straight lines with positive slopes on logarithmic paper, and those in Fig. 22–4 will become straight lines with negative slopes as shown in Fig. 22–5. The curves in Fig. 22–6 will become straight lines if plotted

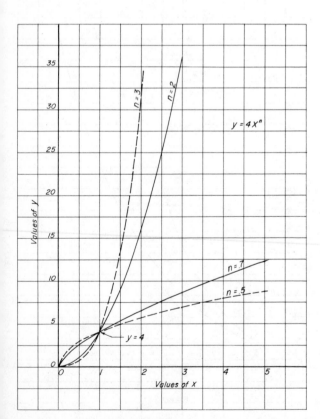

Fig. 22–3.   Curves of parabolic form.

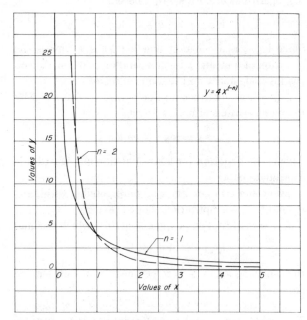

Fig. 22–4. Curves of hyperbolic form.

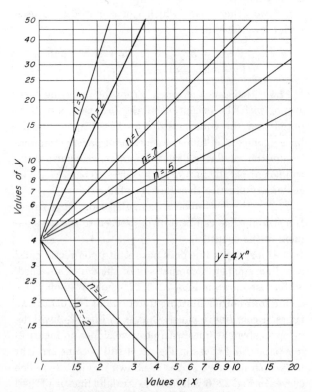

Fig. 22–5. Curves showing as straight lines on logarithmic paper.

on semilog paper as shown in Fig. 22–7. It will be noted that positive exponents give positive slopes and negative exponents give negative slopes.

c. If a second plotting on log or semilog paper does not result in a straight line, then the remaining type of coordinate plotting should be tried. If only a very slight curvature exists on either type of paper, then equations shown in Art. 22.5*d, e,* and *f* may be tried.

Briefly, then the graphical portion of finding empirical equations to fit tabulated data is as follows:

1. Plot first on rectangular coordinate paper. If a straight line does not result, then,

2. Plot on one or both of the remaining types of coordinate paper until an average straight line can be drawn.

3. Having a straight line, derive the equation by one of the methods discussed in the following paragraphs.

22.7 Methods of determining the equation. Four methods for finding the equation for a straight line are listed below. The first two are relatively simple, the third requires more labor, and the fourth, though prob-

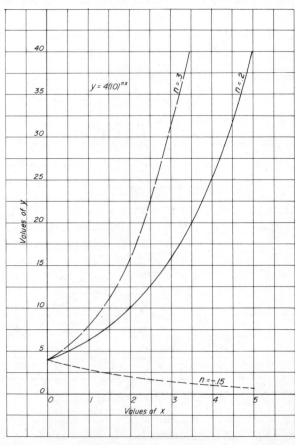

Fig. 22–6. Equations of the form $y = a(10)^{nx}$ show as curves on rectangular coordinate paper.

ably more accurate, is quite laborious. It will not be discussed in this chapter.

1. Slope and intercept method.
2. Method of selected points.
3. Method of averages.
4. Method of least squares.

Each of the first three methods will be illustrated with a typical problem. On the last of these problems, all three methods will be used and their relative reliability checked.

22.8   Straight line on rectangular coordinate paper. *Slope and intercept method.* Equation $y = mx + c$. In Fig. 22–8 the tabulated data in the upper left corner give the collapsing pressure Q of steel tubes compared with the ratio S of the wall thickness of the tube to its outside diameter. The data have been plotted on rectangular coordinate paper with S as the independent variable. The plotted points are well distributed about the selected straight line.

To obtain the equation for the line by the slope and intercept method, two steps are required.

a. Extend the line to the y-axis and read the intercept. This is the constant c in the equation. It will be noted in this problem that when the line was extended it intercepted the y-axis below the x-axis, therefore giving the constant a negative value, namely, -1330.

b. Determine the slope of the line. The slope is expressed as the tangent of the angle which the line makes with the x-axis.

In analytical geometry the slope is usually determined by dividing the difference of the coordinates of the two points as shown for (a) and (b) in Fig. 22–8.

$$m = (y_2 - y_1)/(x_2 - x_1) =$$
$$(5100 - 1500)/(.075 - .033)$$
$$= 3600/.042 = 85,700$$

The equation therefore is $Q = 85,700S - 1330$.

As a check on the accuracy of this equation we may substitute any value of S, say .06 in our equation, and compute the value of Q, which in this case comes out to be 3812. This agrees with the position of the line and is reasonably satisfactory. A further method of check-

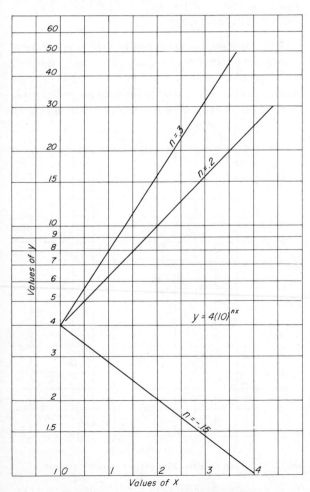

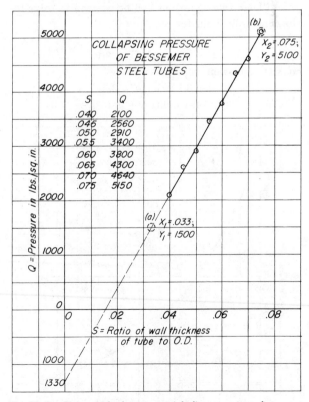

Fig. 22–8.   Data which plot as a straight line on rectangular coordinate paper.

◀ **Fig. 22–7.   Equations of the form $y = a(10)^{nx}$ show as straight lines on semilog coordinate paper.**

ing the reliability of an equation is shown in Art. 22.12.

22.9 Straight line on semilog paper. *Method of selected points.* Equation $y = a(10)^{mx}$. The data for the free swing of a pendulum at given intervals after it was started are shown in the upper right corner of Fig. 22–9 and the plotted rectangular coordinates below. Since an average straight line cannot be drawn through the plotted points, a second trial must be made. A comparison of this curve with Figs. 22–3 and 22–4 shows (1) that it does not pass through the origin $x = 0, y = 0$ and (2) it is not asymptotic with the *x*- and *y*-axes. On the other hand, a comparison with the type curve in Fig. 22–6 shows a similarity in that both curves intersect the *y*-axis and appear to be asymptotic with the *x*-axis.

This suggests that plotting the same data on semilog paper be tried as shown in Fig. 22–10. This does give an excellent straight line. Therefore the equation may be rewritten as $\log y = \log a + mx \log (10)$.

Since there are two constants to determine, two points on the line may be chosen which are not necessarily a part of the data unless by chance the line goes through one point. Then two equations can be written to solve for the constants. Thus for point a

$$x = 3.0 \quad \text{and} \quad y = 3.1$$

gives the equation

or

$$\log 3.1 = \log a + 3m$$
$$.491 = \log a + 3m$$

Point *b*

$$x = 12 \quad \text{and} \quad y = .44$$

gives the equation

or

$$\log .44 = \log a + 12m$$
$$-.357 = \log a + 12m$$

Subtracting the first equation from the second, we obtain

$$-.848 = 9m \quad \text{and} \quad m = -.094$$

Substituting this value in the first equation, gives

$$.491 = \log a - .282$$

Therefore

$$\log a = .773 \quad \text{and} \quad a = 5.93$$

Therefore the equation for the line is

$$y = 5.93(10)^{-.094\,x}$$

As a check, solve this equation for $x = 8$. Then

$$\log y = \log 5.93 + (-.094)(8)(\log 10)$$
$$\log y = .773 - (.094)(8) \quad \text{or} \quad \log y = .021$$

then $y = 1.05$

which is quite satisfactory.

22.10 Straight line on log paper. *Method of averages.* Equation $y = ax^m$. For this illustration, the relationship of the horizontal force H per inch of length of roller bearing on bridges required to produce movement to L, the load per inch of roller is used. The data are shown

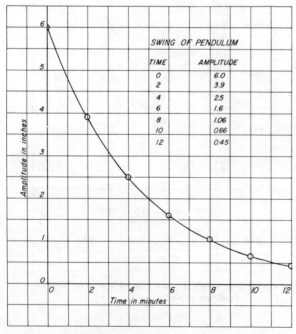

SWING OF PENDULUM	
TIME	AMPLITUDE
0	6.0
2	3.9
4	2.5
6	1.6
8	1.06
10	0.66
12	0.45

Fig. 22–9. Data which plot as a curve on rectangular coordinate paper.

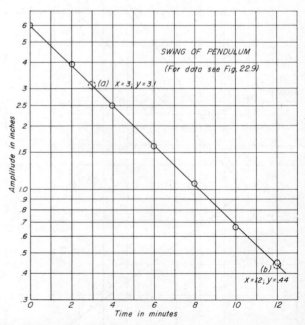

Fig. 22–10. Data from Fig. 22–9 plotted on semilog paper.

in tabular form in Fig. 22-11. When the data were plotted on rectangular coordinates, a straight line could not be drawn through the average of the points as shown in Fig. 22-11.

A comparison with the curves in Figs. 22-3 and 22-6 would seem to point to plotting on semilog paper. This was tried, but a straight line did not result. The data were again plotted on logarithmic paper with the result shown in Fig. 22-12. There is a slight reversal in the curve of the actual plotted points, but the straight line approximates the whole series very well.

The method of averages requires that the data be divided into two equal parts, which has been done in Table 1. The summation of each part is then used to obtain the necessary two equations. Note that, except for the summation of two parts of the data, the method is just like the method of selected points as far as the computations are concerned. There is this difference however, namely, that the straight line is not used at all except to show that the data do seem to fit about such a line. Other than this, the line itself is not used.

For the solution, the logarithmic form of the equation is used. Thus

$$y = ax^m \quad \text{becomes} \quad \log y = \log a + m \log x$$

Substituting the summations from the table in this equation, we obtain

and
$$4.432 = 4 \log a + 2.556\, m$$
$$6.228 = 4 \log a + 3.702\, m$$

Since each logarithm is the summation of four quantities, Log a, which is a constant, must also be multiplied by 4. This coefficient will always be equal to the number of items in the summations. Eliminating 4 Log a between the two equations gives

$$1.796 = 1.146\, m \quad \text{or} \quad m = 1.796/1.146 = 1.567$$

TABLE 1. SUMMATION OF TWO PARTS OF TABULAR DATA

H	$\log H$	L	$\log L$
8.0	.903	3	.477
11.0	1.041	4	.602
15.0	1.176	5	.699
20.5	1.312	6	.778
Summation	4.432		2.556

H	$\log H$	L	$\log L$
26.0	1.415	7	.845
33.5	1.525	8	.903
40.5	1.607	9	.954
48.0	1.681	10	1.000
Summation	6.228		3.702

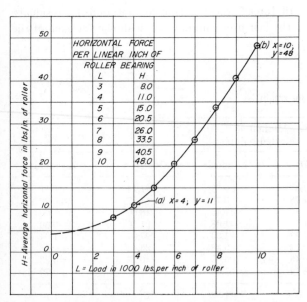

Fig. 22-11.   Data which plot as a curve on rectangular coordinate paper.

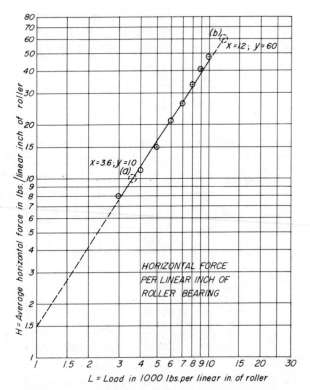

Fig. 22-12.   Data from Fig. 22-11 plotted on logarithmic paper.

This quantity represents the slope of the line. Substituting this value in the second equation above, we get

$$6.228 = 4 \log a + 5.800$$
$$4 \log a = .428 \quad \text{and} \quad \log a = .107$$

Therefore

$$a = 1.28$$

and the equation becomes

$$H = 1.28 \, L^{1.567}$$

22.11   Solution of the problem by the first two methods. In order to show the method for checking the accuracy of the equation and to compare results by the different methods, this problem will be solved by the other two methods.

a. Slope and intercept method. By extending the line in Fig. 22–12 to the y-axis where $x = 1$ or $\log x = 0$ it can be seen that the intercept is 1.5 as nearly as it can be read. Selecting points a and b on the line (not from the data) and writing the equation for the slope,

$$(\log y_2 - \log y_1)/(\log x_2 - \log x_1) =$$
$$(\log 60 - \log 10)/(\log 12 - \log 3.6)$$
or $\quad (1.778 - 1.00)/(1.079 - .556) = 1.489$
Hence $\qquad\qquad m = 1.489$
By this method, therefore, the equation is
$$H = 1.5 \, L^{1.489}$$

b. Method of selected points. Using the same two points a and b on the line in Fig. 22–12 and substituting the values of the coordinates of these points in the equation,

$$\log 10 = \log a + m \log 3.6$$
$$\log 60 = \log a + m \log 12$$

Inserting the values of the logarithms

$$1 = \log a + m \times .556$$
$$1.778 = \log a + m \times 1.079$$

Eliminating Log a between these equations

$$.778 = m \times .523 \quad \text{or} \quad m = .778/.523 = 1.49$$

Substituting the value of m in the first equation, it becomes

and
$$1 + \log a = 1.49 \times .556$$
$$\log a = .173 \quad \text{and} \quad a = 1.492$$

The equation by this method therefore is

$$H = 1.492 \, L^{1.49}$$

22.12   Check on equations by the method of residuals. In Art. 22.8 and 22.9 the accuracy of the equations was checked by solving for a single point, which gives only a partial proof. The following procedure gives a more reliable check over the whole range of the data. The method consists of substituting values of the independent variable in the equation and computing the value of the other variable from the equation. The difference between the computed value and the observed value is called a residual. It is designated as plus when the observed quantity is larger than the calculated quantity and minus when the observed quantity is smaller than the computed one. Thus if the plotted point appears above the line, we might expect a plus residual, if below the line, a minus or negative residual. Ideally the sum of the residuals should be zero.

In Table 2, the results of computations for residuals, in the last problem, have been shown for each of the

TABLE 2. CHECKING RELIABILITY OF EQUATIONS

Data from experiment		Computations for residuals					
L	H	Slope and intercept method		Method of selected points		Method of averages	
		H_c	Residuals	H_c	Residuals	H_c	Residuals
3	8.0	7.66	+0.34	7.67	+0.33	7.14	+0.86
4	11.0	11.70	−0.70	11.78	−0.78	11.27	−0.27
5	15.0	16.50	−1.50	16.45	−1.45	16.00	−1.00
6	20.5	21.75	−1.25	21.58	−1.08	21.30	−0.80
7	26.0	27.00	−1.00	27.23	−1.23	27.04	−1.04
8	33.5	33.20	+0.30	33.12	+0.38	33.42	+0.08
9	40.5	39.50	+1.00	39.45	+0.05	40.27	+0.23
10	48.0	45.20	+2.80	46.14	+1.86	47.21	+0.79
		$\Sigma =$	−0.01	$\Sigma =$	−1.92	$\Sigma =$	−1.15

three methods. The columns marked H_c under each method give the computed values. To get the residuals these values are subtracted from the observed values under Column H. As might be expected from the chart the numbers of plus and minus residuals are equal. The summation for the slope and intercept method comes about as close to the ideal as one could expect. The other two methods, in this particular case, do not give quite as good results. Frequently this works out in the opposite order. It should be noted again that the method of averages makes no use of the plotted line once it has been established that the particular coordinate plotting does result in a good average straight line. It may be observed that the intercepts obtained by the three methods differ by less than .01 for two of them and by .22 for the third. The slopes likewise differ very little. Any one of the equations would be satisfactory.

22.13 Curves other than straight lines. *Rectangular coordinates. Method of selected points.* The method of selected points can be used for curves other than straight lines under certain conditions. For example, the curve in Fig. 22–11 seems to have a parabolic shape, but it does not cross the y-axis at zero. It is, however, horizontal at the intersection with the y-axis. In such cases the general equation

$$y = a + bx + cx^2 \ldots (n + 1)x^n$$

can be applied with considerable success.

Thus, if the curve in Fig. 22–11 is extended as shown by the dash line, it crosses the y-axis at $y = 4$, thus giving the constant a in the equation. In order to have an equation that is simple to use, the second power of x is about as far as one should go. If greater accuracy is re-

quired and machine computations can be used, higher powers could be found.

If it is decided to use only the second power of x, then it is necessary to determine only two more constants, namely, b and c in the general equation. Therefore, if points a $(x = 4; y = 11)$ and b $(x = 10; y = 48)$ are selected, and these values are substituted in the equation

$$11 = 4.0 + 4b + 16c$$
$$48 = 4.0 + 10b + 100c$$

Eliminating b between the two equations

$$c = .4417$$

Substituting this value in the first equation

$$b = -.017$$

The equation therefore is

$$y = 4.0 - .017x + .4417x^2$$

The computation of residuals shown in Table 3 indicates that this equation is reasonably close. Since it does not involve logarithms, it is just as easy to use as the straight-line equation. However, if higher powers of x must be used to get a close-fitting curve, the equation becomes somewhat cumbersome.

As a second illustration of the use of the method of selected points to curves other than straight lines, let it be assumed that the curve in Fig. 22–9 is used only from $x = 2$ to $x = 12$. This portion of the curve appears to be hyperbolic in form with the asymptotes somewhere near the x- and y-axes. This type of curve might conform to the equation

$$(x + a)(y + b) = c$$

TABLE 3. CHECKING RELIABILITY OF EQUATIONS

$y = a + bx + cx^2$
$y = 4 - .017x + .4417x^2$

Data from experiment		Computations of residuals				
x	y	a	$-.017x$	$.4417x^2$	y_c	Residual
3	8	4	−.051	3.975	7.924	+ .076
4	11	4	−.068	7.067	10.999	+ .001
5	15	4	−.085	11.043	14.958	+ .042
6	20	4	−.102	15.901	19.799	+ .201
7	26	4	−.119	21.643	25.524	+ .476
8	33.5	4	−.136	28.269	32.133	+1.367
9	40.5	4	−.153	35.778	39.625	+ .875
10	48	4	−.170	44.170	48.000	+ .000

$$\Sigma = +3.038$$

TABLE 4. CHECKING RELIABILITY OF EQUATIONS

Equation $(x + 3)(y + 1.275) = 25.875$

Data from experiment		Computation of residuals	
Time (x)	Amplitude (y)	Y_c	Residuals
2	3.9	3.900	0.000
4	2.5	2.420	+0.080
6	1.6	1.600	0.000
8	1.06	1.075	−0.015
10	0.66	0.715	−0.055
12	0.45	0.450	0.000

Summation $\Sigma = +0.01$

With three constants to determine it will be necessary to select the two end points $x = 2$ and $x = 12$ and one near the middle $x = 6$ with their corresponding values of y. Three equations can then be written as follows:

$$(2 + a)(3.9 + b) = c$$
$$(6 + a)(1.6 + b) = c$$
$$(12 + a)(.45 + b) = c$$

Solving these three simultaneous equations gives

$$a = 3; \quad b = 1.275 \quad \text{and} \quad c = 25.875$$

Hence the equation is

$$(x + 3)(y + 1.275) = 25.875$$

If this equation is checked for residuals between points $x = 2$ and $x = 12$ as shown in Table 4, the summation of residuals is $+.01$, which is as close as one could expect to get.

When $x = 0$, the solution of the equation gives $y = 7.35$, which obviously does not fit the curve, hence it is good only between the values of $x = 2$ to 12.

PROBLEMS

In the following problems find the equation which fits the data by the method specified. In each case check your equation by the summation of residuals. Plot the data on 8½ × 11 coordinate paper of the proper type.

1. Use data from Fig. 22–8 and solve by the method of selected points.

2. Use data from Fig. 22–8 and solve by the method of averages. Omit middle point in your summation for averages and residuals.

3. Use data from Fig. 22–9 and solve by the slope and intercept method.

4. Use data from Fig. 22–9 and solve by the method of averages.

5. Plot the data of Table 1 on 2 cycle semilogarithmic paper. Draw an average straight line through the points and determine the equation of the line by the slope and intercept method.

Table 1

x	y
10	20
20	36
30	56
40	105
50	170
60	300

Table 2

x	y
5	110
15	84
25	62
35	43
45	31
55	23

6. Plot the data of Table 1 as in Problem 5 and determine the equation of the average straight line by the method of selected points.

7. Plot the data of Table 2 on 2 cycle semilogarithmic paper. Draw an average straight line through the points and determine the equation of the line by the slope and intercept method.

8. Same as Problem 7 using the method of selected points.

9. Plot the data of Table 3 on rectangular coordinate paper and draw a smooth curve through the points. Extend the curve to the X-axis and then determine an equation to fit the curve as nearly as possible by the method of selected points using the general form of equation $x = a + by + cy^2$.

10. Plot the data of Table 3 on 2 cycle log-log paper and draw an average straight line through the points. Determine an equation for the line by the slope and intercept method.

Table 3

x	y
2	30
6	54
10	74
20	110
30	136
40	155
50	182
60	200

Table 4

x	y
40	170
60	105
80	76
100	55
150	36
200	24

11. Same as Problem 10. Solve by the method of selected points.

12. Plot the data of Table 4 on rectangular coordinate paper and find an equation of the general form $(x + a)(y + b) = c$ which will fit a smooth curve drawn through the points as nearly as possible. Assume three points on the curve, one near each end and one near the middle. These points should be on the curve and not necessarily a part of the plotted data unless the curve actually passes through the points.

13. Plot the data of Table 4 on 2 cycle semilogarithmic and/or 2 cycle log-log paper until an average straight line can be drawn through the points. Determine the equation for the line by the slope and intercept method.

14. Same as Problem 13 using the method of selected points.

15. Solve Problem 6, 7, 10, or 13 as assigned by the instructor by the method of averages.

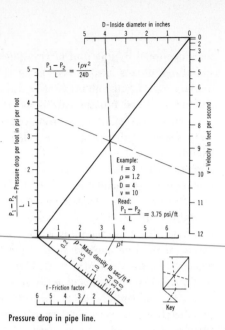

Pressure drop in pipe line.

D—Inside diameter in inches

$$\frac{P_1 - P_2}{L} = \frac{f \rho v^2}{24D}$$

$P_1 - P_2$—Pressure drop per foot in psi per foot

v—Velocity in feet per second

Example:
f = 3
ρ = 1.2
D = 4
v = 10
Read:
$\frac{P_1 - P_2}{L}$ = 3.75 psi/ft

ρ—Mass density lb sec/ft 4

f—Friction factor

Key

Chemical process piping design.

23

Construction and Use of Nomographs

23.1 The Nomograph. The nomograph or alignment chart, as it is sometimes called, is a graphical device for solving equations by means of a straight line, called an isopleth, laid across three or more calibrated scales which represent the variables in an equation. Nomographs make it possible to save considerable time when it is necessary to solve an equation repeatedly. They can be used by persons who may not have the mathematical skill to solve the equation. These charts have a built-in safety device in that the range of the scales can be limited to values for which the equation is valid. This prevents using them where the equation would not apply.

Nomographs can be designed by means of plane geometry as will be done in this chapter, or by means of matrix algebra as explained in more advanced texts. The number of variables and forms of equations which can be handled in an alignment chart depends largely upon the skill and ingenuity of the designer. Here we shall limit our discussion to the more common types of charts and equations which will give an adequate basis for further study and development of the subject.

a. Two variables. Two parallel scales in contact or with a turning point between them.

$$f(x) = f(y)$$

b. Three variables. Three parallel scales.

$$\left.\begin{array}{l} f(x) + f(y) = f(z) \\ f(x) - f(y) = f(z) \end{array}\right\} \text{ natural scales}$$

$$\left.\begin{array}{l} f(x) \cdot f(y) = f(z) \\ \dfrac{f(x)}{f(y)} = f(z) \end{array}\right\} \text{ logarithmic scales}$$

23—01

c. Three variables. N or Z charts.

$$\frac{f(x)}{f(y)} = f(z) \qquad \text{natural scales}$$

d. Four variables. Four parallel scales.

$$f(x) \pm f(y) \pm f(v) = f(z) \qquad \text{natural scales}$$
$$f(x) \cdot f(y) \cdot f(v) = f(z) \qquad \text{logarithmic scales}$$

e. Four variable proportionality charts. Parallel scales.

$$\frac{f(x)}{f(y)} = \frac{f(v)}{f(z)}$$

f. Four variable combination parallel scale and N-chart.

$$f(x) \pm f(y) = \frac{f(v)}{f(z)}$$

23.2 Definitions. It is assumed that the student has studied algebra and is familiar with the following terms which are briefly defined for review purposes.

a. Constant. A constant is a term in an equation which always has the same value. Thus in the equation $M = \frac{1}{8}wl^2$, $\frac{1}{8}$ is a constant and has this value regardless of values assigned to all other terms.

b. Variable. A variable is a term in an equation which may have different values. For practical purposes these values usually lie between specified limits. If the variable may have all values between the limits, it is said to be continuous over this range.

c. Function of a variable. A function of a variable is any expression involving that variable, as for example, a function of x may be $(2x + 1)$, x^3, $1/x^2$, $\sin x$, $\log x$, and the like.

d. Functional modulus. A functional modulus is a proportionality or multiplying factor used to design a functional scale. It is the distance on the functional scale occupied by one unit of the function. The functional modulus is used in laying out the values in the line marked $2x^3$ in Table 1. For example, when $x = 3$, the value of the function $2x^3$ is 54. If the functional modulus were .1, the distance from the zero point on the scale, which is always the zero value of the function, would be $54 \times .1 = 5.4$ inches. The functional modulus is represented by a lower case m; in this case, the functional modulus is called m_x.

e. Scale modulus. The scale modulus is the functional modulus multiplied by any constant coefficient in the function. The scale modulus is used in laying out the values in the line marked x^3 in Table 1. For example, when $x = 3$, the value of x^3 is 27. If the functional modulus were .1, then in this case the scale modulus would be .2. By multiplying $27 \times .2 = 5.4$ inches, the same distance from the zero point is obtained as though the functional modulus had been used. The use of the scale modulus will save some time in the layout of the chart. The scale modulus is represented by capital M or in this case M_x.

23.3 Functional scales. Any function may be represented by a scale, called a functional scale. The method of constructing such scales is illustrated by two examples. In practical work the range of the variables is always limited. The limits are established either by experience and usage or by experimental procedures which indicate the range over which the equation is valid.

The steps in making a functional scale are as follows:

1. Make a table of the values of the variable which it is desired to have shown on the scale.

2. Compute the corresponding values of the function.

3. Determine the length of the scale to accommodate:
   a. the range of the function
   b. the size of the paper it is convenient to use.

TABLE 1. CALCULATIONS OF THE VALUES OF THE FUNCTION OF A VARIABLE

Values of the variable x	0	1	2	3	4	5	6	7	8
x^3	0	1	8	27	64	125	216	343	512
Values of the function $2x^3$	0	2	16	54	128	250	432	686	1024

TABLE 2. CALCULATIONS OF DISTANCES TO BE LAID OUT TO OBTAIN A FUNCTIONAL SCALE

Values of x	0	1	2	3	4	5	6	7	8
Values of the function $2x^3$	0	2	16	54	128	250	432	686	1024
.01 by $2x^3$	0	.02	.16	.54	1.28	2.50	4.32	6.86	10.24

4. Choose a modulus or multiplying factor to give the desired length.

5. Layout the values of the function of the variable using the selected functional modulus as a unit.

6. Mark the division points with the value of the variable.

Thus, if L equals the length of scale, and m is the modulus, then

$$L = m_z[f(x_2) - f(x_1)] \qquad (1)$$

where $f(x_2)$ is the upper limit of the function and $f(x_1)$ is the lower limit.

Example 1. Let $f(x) = 2x^3$ and the range be from 3 to 8. Let it be required to show only the integral values on the scale. Steps 1 and 2 are shown in Table 1.

Using equation 1 the length of the functional scale can be determined. It is possible to proceed in either one of two ways. The length of the scale may be chosen, from which the modulus can be computed, or by reversing the process, the modulus can be chosen and the length computed. The exact length of the scale is rarely important. But it is very convenient to have the modulus an integer or whole number which will permit using commercially available scales for the work. In the given example,

$$L_x = m_x(1024 - 54) = 970m_x$$

If it is desired to have a length suitable for 8½ × 11-inch paper, a functional modulus $m_x = .01$ may be chosen. This will give a scale length of 9.70 inches and permit the use of the engineer's 10-scale. Each value shown in the lower row of Table 1 may be multiplied by the modulus .01 to obtain the length in inches shown below in Table 2 for each value of the variable.

The scale can now be constructed as shown in Fig. 23–1. If further subdivisions are needed, they can be computed and plotted or a fan chart, as shown in Fig. 23–2, can be used for approximate results, provided the plotted points are not too far apart and the change in spacing between successive points does not vary too greatly. The chart can be used to subdivide two adjacent spaces into five parts each. It can be used as an underlay with a light table or as an overlay and punch the points through with a pin. With one division point on the first line, the next on the middle line of the fan chart, and the third on the last line and having the angle of the line in the proper direction, the points may be marked. However, it should be remembered that this method is approximate.

The construction of the preceding functional scale could have been shortened somewhat if a scale modulus had been used instead of the functional modulus. Whenever a function has a constant coefficient it is possible to multiply the functional modulus by the coefficient to obtain a scale modulus, in which case the coefficient appears in the modulus rather than in the values to be plotted. Thus in Table 1 the last step could be omitted and a scale modulus of .02 used to give exactly the same result. This is often very convenient. It should be noted in Fig. 23–1 that the divisions on the scale are marked with the values of the variable, not those of the function. This is always true of functional scales. Other illustrations of functional scales can be seen on the student's slide rule on which many functional scales have been plotted; for example, the C, D, and trigonometric scales.

23.4 Conversion chart. Equation $f(x) = f(y)$. The conversion chart is a graphical device for relating one variable to another in an equation which involves only two variables. This can be done by placing the two functional scales on opposite sides of the same line as in Fig. 23–3. In this case both scales must have the same

Fig. 23–1.   Construction of a functional scale for $F(x) = 2x^3$.

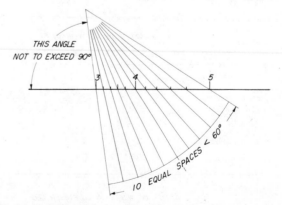

Fig. 23–2.   Use of fan chart to subdivide two unequal spaces.

modulus, they must run in the same direction, and the zero values of both functions must be at the same point. On the other hand, if it is more convenient to have different moduli for the two functional scales these scales may be on two different parallel lines, run in opposite directions, and be related to each other through a turning point, or pole, as in Fig. 23–4.

Both scale arrangements are illustrated in the following examples.

Example 1. Let it be required to make a conversion chart on a single line for the area of a circle in terms of the radius, $A = \pi r^2$, and let the range of r be from 0 to 10 feet. See Fig. 23–3. The standard equation is $f(A) = f(r)$. The computations are shown in Table 3.

Using equation 1 for length of scale,

$$L_r = m_r[f(r_2) - f(r_1)]$$

$L_r = m_r(314 - 0) = 314\, m_r$. If m_r is chosen as $\frac{1}{60}$, then $L_r = 314 \times \frac{1}{60} = 5.23$ inches, which is a convenient length. When we apply the same modulus to the A-scale, $L_A = 320 \times \frac{1}{60} = 5.33$ inches. The scales may then be plotted with the engineer's 60-scale as shown in Fig. 23–3 by beginning each scale at a common point which is the zero value of both functions, and using the values of $f(r)$ and $f(A)$.

Example 2. Let it be required to make a conversion chart with two parallel scales and a turning point for the equation for the discharge of water over a sharp-crested weir, as illustrated in Fig. 23–4. The equation is $Q = 3.34 \cdot H^{1.47}$ where Q is the quantity of water in cubic feet per second and H is the height of the water above the weir in feet with a range from 0 to 4 feet. The standard equation is $f(Q) = f(H)$. The computation of the necessary data for the functions is shown in Table 4. The moduli $m_H = \frac{1}{5}$ and $m_Q = \frac{1}{6}$ are assumed to give the desired length of scale as explained in Art. 23.3 The scales may be placed at any convenient distance apart, but must run in opposite directions. The diagonal connecting the zero points should have a convenient length. The location of the turning point can be determined graphically by drawing lines between two sets of related values of the functions. Thus when $H = 0$, $Q = 0$, and when $H = 4$, $Q = 25.65$. The location of the turning point may also be computed from the ratio of the functional moduli.

By similar triangles in Fig. 23–4,

$$\frac{AB}{BC} = \frac{DE}{DC} \quad \text{or} \quad \frac{AB}{DE} = \frac{BC}{CD}$$

If $BC = a$ and the diagonal $L = 6$ inches,

$$\frac{m_H f(H)}{m_Q f(Q)} = \frac{a}{L - a}$$

Since $f(Q) = f(H)$, then

$$\frac{m_H}{m_Q} = \frac{a}{L - a} \quad \text{or} \quad \frac{\frac{1}{5}}{\frac{1}{6}} = \frac{a}{6 - a}$$

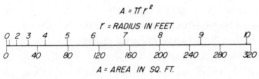

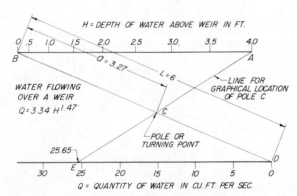

Fig. 23–3. Conversion chart.

Fig. 23–4. Conversion chart with pole.

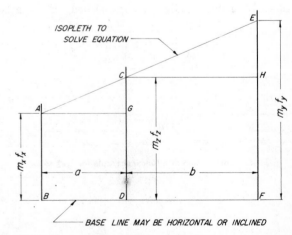

Fig. 23–5. Three variable parallel scale chart.

Solving this equation "a" equals 3.27 inches measured on the diagonal from the zero point of the H-scale. See Fig. 23–4.

23.5 Three variable parallel scale chart. Equation $f(x) + f(y) = f(z)$. If a three variable parallel scale chart or nomograph is to be constructed as shown in Fig. 23–5, the relationship between the scale spacing and the functional moduli can be determined by the principles of plane geometry. In Fig. 23–5, AG and CH are drawn parallel to BF, thus giving two similar triangles ACG and CEH. Therefore

$$\frac{EH}{b} = \frac{CG}{a} \quad \text{or} \quad \frac{EF - HF}{b} = \frac{CD - GD}{a}$$

or $\qquad a \cdot (EF - HF) = b \cdot (CD - GD)$

When we substitute the functional scale lengths for EF, HF, etc., the equation becomes

$$am_y f(y) - am_z f(z) = bm_z f(z) - bm_x f(x),$$

When we collect terms,

$$bm_x f(x) + am_y f(y) = (a + b) m_z f(z)$$

If this equation is to reduce to $f(x) + f(y) = f(z)$, then the coefficients must be equal or

$$bm_x = am_y = (a + b)m_z$$

Hence $\qquad \dfrac{m_x}{m_y} = \dfrac{a}{b}$ $\qquad\qquad$ (2)

This equation gives the relationship between the moduli of the outside scales and the scale spacing.

Also from the equation

$$am_y = (a + b)m_z$$

$$m_y = \left[\frac{a + b}{a}\right] m_z = \left[1 + \frac{b}{a}\right] m_z$$

But $\qquad \dfrac{b}{a} = \dfrac{m_y}{m_x}$ so $\left[1 + \dfrac{m_y}{m_x}\right] m_z = m_y$

TABLE 3. CALCULATIONS OF THE VALUES OF THE FUNCTION OF THE VARIABLES

Variable r

Values of r	0	1	2	3	4	5	6	7	8	9	10
r^2	0	1	4	9	16	25	36	49	64	81	100
$f(r) = \pi r^2$	0	3.14	12.6	28.3	50.3	78.5	113	154	201	254	314

Variable A

Values of A	0	40	80	120	160	200	240	280	320	Values selected as desired
$F(A) = A$	0	40	80	120	160	200	240	280	320	

TABLE 4. CALCULATIONS OF THE DISTANCES TO BE PLOTTED TO OBTAIN THE FUNCTIONAL SCALES

Variable H

H	0.0	0.5	1.0	1.5	2.0	2.5	3.0	3.5	4.0
$H^{1.47}$	0.0	0.36	1.0	1.82	2.77	3.85	5.03	6.30	7.68
$f(H) = 3.34\,H^{1.47}$	0.0	1.21	3.34	6.08	9.25	12.84	16.78	21.03	25.65
$m_H f(H) = \tfrac{1}{5} \cdot 3.34 \cdot H^{1.47}$	0.0	0.24	0.67	1.22	1.85	2.57	3.36	4.21	5.13

Variable Q

Q	0	5	10	15	20	25	30
$f(Q) = Q$	0	5	10	15	20	25	30
$m_Q f(Q) = \tfrac{1}{6}Q$	0	0.83	1.66	2.5	3.33	4.16	5.00

Therefore

$$\left[\frac{m_x + m_y}{m_x}\right] m_z = m_y \quad \text{or} \quad m_z = \frac{m_x m_y}{m_x + m_y} \qquad (3)$$

This equation gives the functional modulus for the scale in the middle, in terms of the moduli for the two outer scales. These calculations must always be made with the functional modulus not the scale modulus. The equation must be arranged so that the scale which is to be the center scale of the chart is the only variable on that side of the equation.

Example 1. Let it be required to make a nomograph for the equation $E = RI$ which gives the relationship between voltage, resistance, and current in an electric circuit. The range for R is to be from 1 to 20 ohms and the amperage I from 10 to 100 amperes. The following

steps can generally be used as a guide in the construction of charts.

Step 1. Write the equation in proper form. $f(x) + f(y) = f(z)$. To get the equation $E = RI$ into the proper form, it is necessary to take logarithms of both sides. The equation then becomes Log $E = $ Log $R + $ Log I, and E will be the center scale.

Step 2. Select the moduli to give suitable lengths for the outside scales.

$$L_R = m_R (\log 20 - \log 1) = m_R (1.301 - 0) = 1.301 m_R$$

For an 8½ × 11-inch page, approximately 8 inches will make a suitable length; hence, if m_R is assumed as 6, the length will be 7.8 inches.

$$L_I = m_I (\log 100 - \log 10) = m_I (2 - 1) = 1\, m_I$$

TABLE 5. DATA NECESSARY FOR LAYOUT OF CHART

Var.	Range of variable	Function	m	M	L	Direction	Spacing from center scale
R	1 to 20	Log R	6	6	7.8	↑	3
E	10 to 2000	Log E	3.43	3.43	7.9	↑	0
I	10 to 100	Log I	8	8	8	↑	4

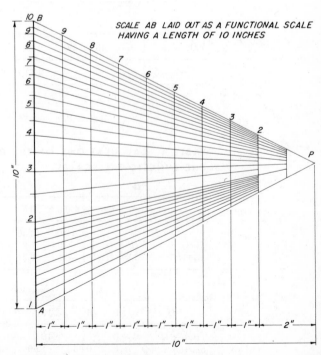

Fig. 23–6. **Chart to obtain logarithmic scales.**

For this scale the modulus may be chosen as 8 which will make $L_I = 8$ inches.

Step 3. Determine the modulus for the center scale. From equation 3

$$m_E = \frac{m_R m_I}{m_R + m_I} = \frac{6 \cdot 8}{6 + 8} = \frac{48}{14} = 3.43$$

Step 4. Determine the scale spacing. From equation 2, $m_R/m_I = a/b = 6/8 = 3/4$. The scales may therefore be spaced so that the distance from the R-scale to the E-scale is ¾ of the distance from the I scale to the E scale. The ¾ is only a ratio and any suitable numbers having that ratio may be used. In this case the distance from the R-scale to the E-scale may be chosen as three inches and therefore the distance from the I-scale to the E-scale will be 4 inches. Table 5 shows all the information necessary for laying out the chart in a convenient form that is easy to check.

Step 5. Lay out the scales. All the scales must be logarithmic, and it is necessary to construct three scales, one having a 6 inch cycle, one having an 8 inch cycle and the third having a cycle 3.43 inches long for the center scale. To obtain these functional scales of the desired lengths (6, 8, and 3.43 inches), the construction shown in Fig. 23–6 may be used, and the chart folded at the cycle whose length is M. To construct this chart pick out the logarithms of the desired numbers from a slide rule or a table of logarithms, multiply them by 10, and plot them in inches to obtain the 10 inch scale shown in Fig. 23–6. Approximately opposite the middle of the scale and 10 inches away, select a pole P. From each of the divisions on scale AB, draw a line to the pole P. Then draw lines parallel to scale AB at 1-inch intervals until 1 inch from P. Number these lines successively 9, 8, etc., beginning with the first from the 10-inch scale. This chart can now be folded at any one of the lines or between them at the proper place to give a logarithmic scale of any length from 1 to 10 inches.

The 8- and 6-inch scales can now be used to construct the outside scales of the chart in Fig. 23–7 and by folding the chart made similar to Fig. 23–6 at 3.43, the center scale of the chart in Fig. 23–7 can be laid out as shown in Fig. 23–7. A base line must be established to give a starting point for each scale. This is frequently the line through the zero point of each scale and is usually horizontal. However, it may be any line that

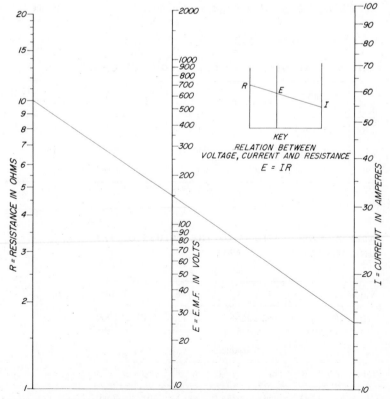

Fig. 23–7. Three variable parallel scale nomograph—logarithmic scales.

goes through points that give a solution of the equation. In this case, the base line is horizontal and goes through the points $R = 1$, $I = 10$, and $E = 10$. See Fig. 23–7. These points are obtained by assuming $R = 1$, $I = 10$, and substituting in the equation to obtain $E = 10$. These points are also the assumed lower limits for the chart.

Step 6. Check the chart. Each chart should always be checked for accuracy by solving the equation for selected values of two of the variables and then testing the chart with an isopleth connecting these values to see if the same answer is obtained. It is important that the check be made on an inclined line to catch any error in spacing.

Example 2. Let it be required to construct a nomograph for the equation for the moment of inertia of a hollow square,

$$I = \frac{(B^4 - b^4)}{12}$$

as illustrated in Fig. 23–8. The outside dimension "B" is to have a range from 4 to 10 inches and the inside dimension "b" from 3 to 8 inches.

Step 1. Write the equation in proper form.

$12\,I = B^4 - b^4$ is perhaps most convenient.

Step 2. Select the moduli to give suitable scale lengths.

$$L_B = m_B(10^4 - 4^4) = (10{,}000 - 256)m_B = 9744\,m_B$$

If $m_B = \dfrac{1}{1000}$, then $L_B = 9.744$ inches.

$$L_b = m_b(8^4 - 3^4) = (4096 - 81)m_b = 4015\,m_b$$

If $m_b = \dfrac{1}{500}$, then $L_b = 8.03$.

Step 3. Determine the modulus for the middle scale. From equation 3, it can be seen that $m_I = m_B m_b / m_B + m_b$.

When we substitute the known values of m_B and m_b

$$m_I = \frac{.001 \cdot .002}{.001 + .002} = .000667$$

By solving the original equation using the maximum value of B and the minimum value of b (since b is negative), the maximum value of $12I$ is found to be 9919. In this case, the effect of the small b value is insignificant, so the I scale would probably be carried to the point where $12I = 10{,}000$. The minimum value of I will be zero when B and b are equal. Then $L_I = m_I(10{,}000 - 0)$ $= .000667 \cdot 10000 = 6.67$ inches.

Since this modulus is uneven, it will be necessary to

TABLE 6. DATA NECESSARY FOR LAYOUT OF CHART

Var.	Range of variable	Function	m	M	L	Direction	Spacing from center scale
B	4–10	B^4	.001	...	9.744	↑	2³⁄₁₆
I	0–833	$12\,I$	.000667	.008	6.67	↑	0
b	3–8	b^4	.002	...	8.03	↓	4³⁄₈

TABLE 7. CALCULATIONS OF THE VALUES OF THE FUNCTION OF THE VARIABLE

Variable B

Values of B	4	5	6	7	8	9	10
$f(B) = B^4$	256	625	1296	2401	4096	6561	10,000

Variable b

Values of b	3	4	5	6	7	8
$f(b) = b^4$	81	256	625	1296	2401	4096

multiply all the values of the function by the modulus, to get values to plot. However, it will be easier to multiply the modulus by 12 to get a scale modulus rather than to multiply each value of the function by 12.

Hence the scale modulus will be $.000667 \times 12 = .008$. All of the information necessary to lay out the chart is shown in Table 6 in a convenient form that is easy to check. When the desired values of I are multiplied by .008, they may be plotted in inches. The dimensions on this scale may also be laid out by geometrical construction as shown in Fig. 23–8.

Step 4. Scale spacing. Using equation 2

$$\frac{a}{b} = \frac{m_B}{m_b} = \frac{.001}{.002} \quad \text{or} \quad \frac{2}{4}$$

which indicates that the distance from the b-scale to the

I-scale must be two times as great as the distance from the B-scale to the I-scale.

Step 5. Layout the scales. Since the inside dimension b of the hollow square is negative, the scale must run downward. The middle scale must begin on a line joining the zero values of the outside scales even though these may not be included in the final chart, or upon a set of simultaneous values obtained by solving the equation. See Fig. 23–8. Computations for the two outside scales are shown in Table 7.

The scale for B may be laid out with the engineer's 10-scale using one hundred times the values on the scale since $\frac{1}{1000} = \frac{1}{10} \times \frac{1}{100}$. The first fraction indicates the scale and the second the multiplier. The values opposite B^4 are plotted, but as usual are marked with the values of the variable as shown in Fig. 23–8. For the b-scale the

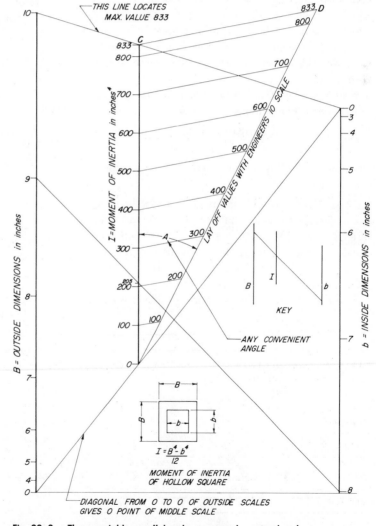

Fig. 23–8.   Three variable parallel scale nomograph—natural scales.

engineer's 50-scale may be used since the modulus for b is $\frac{1}{500}$ which is equal to $\frac{1}{5} \times \frac{1}{100}$. The values opposite b^4 in Table 7 are used and plotted using one hundred times the values on the 50-scale. For the I-scale the modulus is .000667, but since the function is $12I$ the scale modulus is $12 \times .000667 = .008$. The values of I may be multiplied by .008 to obtain distances that may be laid out in inches to obtain the divisions.

Since there is no convenient scale for this modulus, another procedure is possible. Draw the diagonal connecting the zero points of the functions of the two outside scales, which are $6\frac{5}{16}$ inches apart. Draw a vertical line $2\frac{3}{16}$ inches from the B-scale. Beginning where this line crosses the diagonal lay off a distance of 6.67 inches, which is the computed length of the I-scale. From the zero point of the I-scale draw an inclined line at any convenient angle A and with the 10-scale, lay off the equal divisions for the values of I ending with 833 which corresponds to the maximum scale length. From this point lettered D, draw a line to point C and then subdivide the I-scale by parallel lines as shown in Fig. 23–8.

Step 6. Check the nomograph by computing the value of I for one set of values for B and b.

Thus $\quad I = \dfrac{9^4 - 8^4}{12} = \dfrac{(6561 - 4096)}{12} = 205$

The line connecting 9 and 8 shows this value on the center scale.

23.6 *Z or N-Chart.* Equation $f(x)/f(y) = f(z)$. *Natural scales.* This type of chart can be made in the form of a letter Z or N. The first shape has been chosen for the derivation of the equations to be used in the layout of the chart. If the Z of Fig. 23–9 were revolved 90 degrees clockwise, it would be a letter N.

The variable that is by itself on one side of the equa-

tion will be plotted on the diagonal line. By shifting terms in the equation any one of the variables can be placed by itself. If all other considerations are equal, the most complicated function is usually plotted on the diagonal because this makes the layout easier.

From the similar triangles ABC and CDE in Fig. 23–9, it can be seen that

$$\frac{m_x f(x)}{P} = \frac{m_y f(y)}{L - P}$$

then

$$\frac{m_x f(x)}{m_y f(y)} = \frac{P}{L - P}$$

But from the given equation

$$\frac{f(x)}{f(y)} = f(z)$$

Therefore

$$\frac{m_x}{m_y} f(z) = \frac{P}{L - P}$$

and $\quad m_x f(z) L - m_x f(z) P = m_y P$

$$m_x f(z) L = P[m_x f(z) + m_y]$$

and $\qquad P = \dfrac{L m_x f(z)}{m_x f(z) + m_y}$

Divide both the numerator and denominator of this fraction by m_x,

then $\qquad P = \dfrac{L f(z)}{f(z) + \dfrac{m_y}{m_x}} \qquad\qquad (4)$

The length of the diagonal and the moduli for the outside scales m_x and m_y can be arbitrarily chosen to give

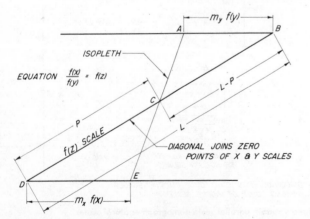

Fig. 23–9. Z or N nomograph—three variables.

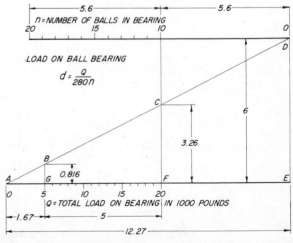

Fig. 23–10. Location of the diagonal scale for a Z chart.

a convenient scale layout. Then for any length L the value of P in equation 4 can be computed for any chosen value of $f(z)$. With these computations a diagonal scale can be constructed. The diagonal scale can also be constructed graphically with somewhat less labor. This method, illustrated in the following examples, is recommended.

Example 1. Let it be required to make a Z-chart for the following equation for bearing sizes

$$d = \frac{Q}{280\,n}$$

where d equals the diameter of the bearing, Q equals the total load, and n equals the number of balls in the bearing. Let Q vary from 5000 to 20,000 pounds and n from 10 to 20 balls.

Step 1. The equation is in satisfactory form.

Step 2. Select moduli for the outside scales to give a reasonable chart size. It should be noted that although the diagonal scale must connect the zero values of the functions of the outside scales, which run in opposite directions, these points do not have to be included in the chart, as the example in Fig. 23–10 will show.

$$LQ = m_Q(20{,}000 - 5000) = 15{,}000\,m_Q$$

If $m_Q = \dfrac{1}{3000}$, $L_Q = 5.0$ inches

$$L_n = m_n\,(280 \times 20 - 280 \times 10) = 2800\,m_n$$

If $m_n = \dfrac{1}{500}$, $L_n = 5.6$ inches

$$\frac{m_n}{m_Q} = \frac{\dfrac{1}{500}}{\dfrac{1}{3000}} = 6$$

This value is used in equation 4.

In order to lay out the chart shown in Fig. 23–10, it is necessary to compute the length of each outside scale from zero to the minimum value to be used in order to get the overall length of the chart. For the Q-scale the minimum value is 5000 pounds, therefore

$$L_Q = m_Q\,(5000 - 0) = 5000 \times \frac{1}{3000} = 1.67 \text{ inches}$$

For the n-scale the minimum value is 10; therefore

$$L_n = m_n(2800 - 0) = 2800 \times \frac{1}{500} = 5.6 \text{ inches}$$

From the Fig. 23–10, it can be seen that the overall length, including the zero points, is 12.27 inches. If the zero points had to be included, this would be much too large. By making the width of the chart 6 inches, the location of points B and C on the diagonal can be computed, and the diagonal laid out so that if it were extended, it would pass through the zero values of the functions that are plotted on the parallel scales. A freehand sketch of the entire chart including the zero points should be made to assist in the calculations. The diagonal may be found graphically if the distant zero point can be temporarily located on the table. From similar triangles in Fig. 23–10, ADE and ACF, it can be seen that

$$\frac{DE}{EA} = \frac{CF}{FA} \quad \text{or} \quad \frac{6}{12.27} = \frac{CF}{6.67} \quad \text{and} \quad CF = 3.26 \text{ inches.}$$

Also $\dfrac{DE}{EA} = \dfrac{BG}{AG}$ or $\dfrac{6}{12.27} = \dfrac{BG}{1.67}$ and $BG = .816$ inch.

The scales are now laid out as in Figs. 23–10 and 23–11.

Step 3. The division points of the diagonal scale may be located by computing the distance of each from the zero point by the use of equation 4. The computations for such spacing are shown in Table 8 and the plotting

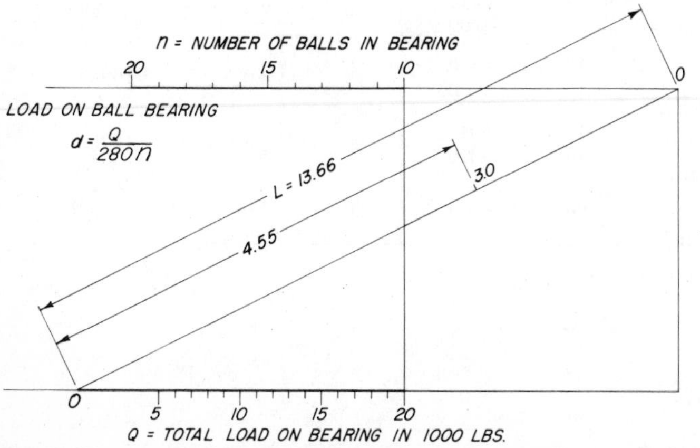

n = NUMBER OF BALLS IN BEARING

LOAD ON BALL BEARING

$d = \dfrac{Q}{280\,n}$

$L = 13.66$

Q = TOTAL LOAD ON BEARING IN 1000 LBS.

Fig. 23–11.   Layout of diagonal scale by direct measurement.

TABLE 8. CALCULATIONS FOR DIRECT MEASUREMENT ON Z CHART

Direct measurement $L = 13.66$		$P = \dfrac{Lf(d)}{f(d) + m_n/m_Q}$	
$f(d)$	$f(d) + m_n/m_Q$	$Lf(d)$	$\dfrac{Lf(d)}{f(d) + m_n/m_Q}$
1.5	7.5	20.5	2.73
2.0	8.0	27.3	3.42
2.5	8.5	34.2	4.02
3.0	9.0	41.0	4.55
3.5	9.5	47.9	5.05
4.0	10.0	54.6	5.46

illustrated for one point, $d = 3.0$ in Fig. 23–11. These distances when calculated in this manner will always be measured from the zero point of the function which shows as the numerator of the equation.

Step 4. Scale spacing. The scale spacing and arrangement in this case have been accomplished in Step 2.

Step 5. Layout the scales. Beginning with the n-scale, it may be seen that the function of n is $280n$. These values are shown in Table 9. Since the modulus is $\frac{1}{500}$, the engineer's 50-scale may be used. Thus $\frac{1}{500} = \frac{1}{5} \times \frac{1}{100}$. It is therefore possible to use one hundred times the values printed on the scale. The beginning point for $n = 10$ is therefore at 28 on the 50-scale and the end is at 56. Note that on the chart these points are labeled 10 and 20, not 2800 and 5600.

For the Q-scale the modulus is $\frac{1}{3000}$ and the engineer's 30-scale may be used. Again $\frac{1}{3000} = \frac{1}{3} \times \frac{1}{1000}$ so use one thousand times the values on the scale, and begin at 5000, which is 1.67 inches from the zero point as required.

One method for locating the division points on the diagonal scale has already been described in Step 3. A somewhat easier method is described in the following paragraph.

For the diagonal scale which carries the values for d, it is necessary to choose the major divisions which are to be shown and arrange them as shown in Table 9. Then selecting one convenient value for n, the corresponding values of Q are computed from the original equation for each value of d. In this case, n was chosen equal to 20. It is best to choose this pole in such a place that the rays will intersect the diagonal line as nearly perpendicularly as possible. Having the Q-values, isopleths may be drawn from $n = 20$ to the corresponding points on the Q-scale. The intersection of these lines with the diagonal locates points on the d-scale, as shown in Fig. 23–12.

Step 6. Check the scale. Since the layout was made graphically, the check must be made by computing one or two points for direct measurement or by using some point other than $n = 20$. If the direct method had been used to layout the scale, the check should be made graphically in the usual way.

23.7 Four variable parallel scale chart. The standard form of the equation is:

$$f(v) + f(x) + f(y) = f(z) \quad \text{natural scales}$$
$$f(v) \cdot f(x) \cdot f(y) = f(z) \quad \text{logarithmic scales}$$

This type of chart is based upon the three variable charts; hence, no new derivations are required. The equation is simply divided into two parts, each of which is set equal to a new term. Thus

$$f(v) + f(x) = f(p) = f(z) - f(y)$$

A three variable parallel scale chart can be made for each equation and they will have a common scale for $f(p)$ which will be a pivot scale and need not be calibrated. This scale must

1. have the same modulus in both charts.
2. run in the same direction in both charts.
3. have the same zero point for $f(p)$ for both charts.

It is often convenient to have the pivot scale in the same position in both equations. In many cases, placing the pivot scale in the center will reduce the width of the chart and make the lengths of the scales more uniform.

Example 1. As an illustration we shall use the equation for the weight of steel plates such as may be used for beam or column bearings, as shown in Fig. 23–13.

$$W = 0.282 \, LBT \quad \text{where}$$

TABLE 9

Computations for layout of n scale		Computations for graphical layout of d scale $Q = 280nd$		
n	$f(n) = 280 \, n$	Pole n	d	Values of Q with $n = 20$
10	2800	20	1.5	8,400
11	3080			
12	3360	20	2.0	11,200
13	3640			
14	3920	20	2.5	14,000
15	4200			
16	4480	20	3.0	16,800
17	4760			
18	5040	20	3.5	19,600
19	5320			
20	5600	20	4.0	22,400

L = the length with a range from 18 to 36 inches
B = breadth with a range from 12 to 30 inches, and
T = thickness with a range from ½ to 2.0 inches.

Step 1. Rewrite the equation in proper form.

$$\log W = \log .282 + \log L + \log B + \log T$$

For the time being, it is possible to ignore the log of the constant and take care of it when placing the last scale because the effect of the constant is merely to move the last scale up or down. Therefore, the equation may be written:

$$\log W - \log L = \log p = \log B + \log T$$

or making two equations

$$\log W - \log L = \log p$$
and $\quad \log B + \log T = \log p$

Step 2. Determine the moduli for the outside scales of the first chart. For the W-scale it is first necessary to

compute the range of the function corresponding to the other functions.

$$W \text{ min.} = .282 \times 12 \times 18 \times .5 = 30.45$$
$$W \text{ max.} = .282 \times 30 \times 36 \times 2.0 = 609.12$$
$$L_W = m_W (\log 609.12 - \log 30.45)$$
$$= m_W (2.7847 - 1.4835) = 1.3012 \, m_W$$
If $m_W = 5$, then $L_W = 6.506$ inches.
$$L_L = m_L (\log 36 - \log 18)$$
$$= m_L (1.5563 - 1.2553) = .3010 \, m_L$$
If $m_L = 20$, then $L_L = 6.02$.

Step 3. Since we have the moduli for the outside scales, then by equation (3) the modulus for the middle scale p is

$$m_p = \frac{(m_W \times m_L)}{(m_W + m_L)} = \frac{(5 \times 20)}{(5 + 20)} = 4$$

The length of the p-scale need not be computed since it is a pivot scale only and is not calibrated.

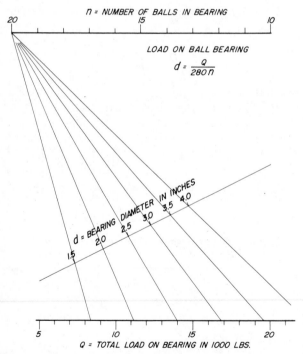

Fig. 23-12. Layout of diagonal scale by graphical method.

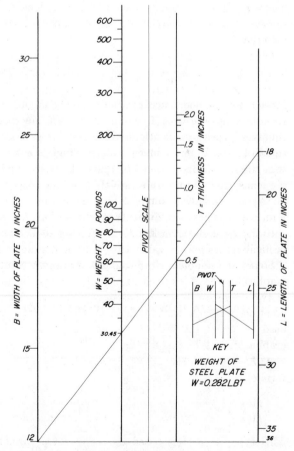

Fig. 23-13. Four variable parallel scale chart.

For the second equation the moduli must be worked out in somewhat different order.

$$L_B = m_B \, (\log 30 - \log 12) = m_B \, (1.477 - 1.079) =$$
$$.398 \, m_B$$

If $m_B = 20$, then $L_B = 7.96$ inches.

Since m_p must be the same for this chart as the preceding one it is necessary to compute the modulus for the scale of function T which is an outside scale by means of equation 3 on page 23-06.

$$m_p = \frac{(m_B \times m_T)}{(m_B + m_T)} \quad \text{or} \quad 4 = \frac{(20 \times m_T)}{(20 + m_T)}$$

By solving the above equation, it is found that $m_T = 5$. Therefore $L_T = 5\,[.301 - (-.301)] = 5 \times .602 = 3.01$ inches.

The fulfillment of the conditions for this chart can best be checked by arrangement in tabular form as shown in Table 10. Note that the term L is negative in the equation and the direction of the scale is therefore downward. All others are positive and therefore upward. The scale for p is in the middle for both equations.

Step 4. Scale spacing. From equation 2 it may be seen that

$$\frac{m_W}{m_L} = \frac{5}{20} = \frac{1}{4}$$

Since the same moduli occur in the second equation, the spacing is also the same. In making the chart, however, it makes a very good solution to reverse them as shown in Fig. 23-13. In order to get a chart which is not too wide, we shall choose as our 1 to 4 ratio the terms .6 and 2.4 which gives a total chart width of 4.8 inches.

Step 5. Layout the scales. Using logarithmic scales 4 inches, 5 inches, and 20 inches long, the chart can be constructed as shown in Fig. 23-13. For the 20-inch log-scale distances may be taken from a 10 inch-scale with dividers and doubled. Note that the minimum values

are aligned along the diagonal which is used as a base line. Since this is a correct solution of the equation, this alignment takes care of the constant. The spacing of the scales is such that they could all have been plotted on two lines, but by reversing the distances and using four lines, the danger of mixing up the variable was reduced. Spacing of the scales could be in a variety of forms as shown in Fig. 23-14.

Step 6. Check the chart. The equation can be solved by choosing values of three variables and solving for the fourth. The chart should give the same answer.

23.8 **Proportionality chart.** *Four variables.* Equation $f(v)/f(x) = f(y)/f(z)$. From Fig. 23-15 by similar triangles

$$\frac{m_v f(v)}{m_x f(x)} = \frac{a}{b} = \frac{m_y f(y)}{m_x f(z)}.$$

If the original equation is to hold true, then

$$\frac{m_v}{m_x} = \frac{a}{b} = \frac{m_y}{m_x} \tag{5}$$

Example 1. Let it be required to construct a chart for the equation

$$D = \frac{WS^2}{8H}$$

which is used in computing the sag of a cable. See Fig. 23-16. Where D = the sag of cable in feet,

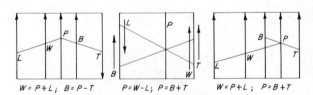

$$W = P + L; \quad B = P - T \qquad P = W - L; \quad P = B + T \qquad W = P + L; \quad P = B + T$$

Fig. 23-14. **Other arrangements of four variable parallel scale charts.**

TABLE 10. DATA NECESSARY FOR LAYOUT OF CHART

Var.	Function	Range	m	L	Direction	Spacing from pivot scale
W	Log W	609.1 to 30.45	5	6.505	↑	.6
L	Log L	36 to 18	20	6.02	↓	2.4
p	Log p		4		↑	0
B	Log B	30 to 12	20	7.96	↑	2.4
T	Log T	2.0 to 0.5	5	3.01	↑	.6

W = weight of cable from 0 to 2.0 pounds/feet
S = span of cable from 0 to 900 feet
H = horizontal tension from 0 to 10,000 pounds

Step 1. Write the equation in proper form $D/S^2 = W/8H$.

Step 2. Select moduli to give suitable scale lengths and spacing. Any three moduli may be chosen arbitrarily and the fourth computed from equation (5) above. Since this will be an N-shaped chart, the zero values of the functions of the variables represented on the four scales must be at the ends of the diagonals. The zero points need not necessarily be included in the chart, but the diagonal must be positioned so it would join them.

$L_W = m_W (2.0 - 0) = 2\, m_W$
If $m_W = 2$, then $L_W = 4$ inches.
$L_H = m_H (80{,}000 - 0) = 80{,}000\, m_H$
If $m_H = \dfrac{1}{20{,}000}$, then $L_H = 4$ inches.
$L_S = m_S (810{,}000 - 0) = 810{,}000\, m_S$
If $m_S = \dfrac{1}{200{,}000}$, then $L_S = 4.05$.

Step 3. Determine the modulus and length of the last scale. By solving the original equation for maximum and minimum values, the range for D is found to be $0 - 20.25$. Greater theoretical range could be obtained by making H a minimum when W and S are maximum.

However, this would be an impossible condition since the horizontal force could not be a minimum when the weight and span are maximum. Since

$$\frac{m_D}{m_S} = \frac{m_W}{m_H},$$

then
$$m_D = \frac{(m_W m_S)}{m_H} = \frac{2 \times \dfrac{1}{200{,}000}}{\dfrac{1}{20{,}000}} = \frac{1}{5}$$

$$L_D = m_D (20.25 - 0) = \frac{1}{5} \times 20.25 = 4.05$$

Step 4. Scale spacing. Since the middle scale is a diagonal, uncalibrated, and merely a pivot, axis spacing is not involved except that the diagonal must connect the zero points of the other scales.

Step 5. Layout the scales. As will be noted from Fig. 23-16 the terms of the first half of the equation are on the inside of the scales and run in opposite directions. The terms on the other side of the equations are on the outside and in the same order. Considerable variation in the position of the scales is allowable as long as the key shows clearly how the chart shall be read.

Step 6. Check the chart. Assume $W = 2.0$, $S = 500$, and $H = 8000$, then

$$D = \frac{(2.0 \times 250{,}000)}{(8 \times 8000)} = \frac{500{,}000}{64{,}000} = 7.8 \text{ feet}$$

The same answer may be obtained from the chart. As

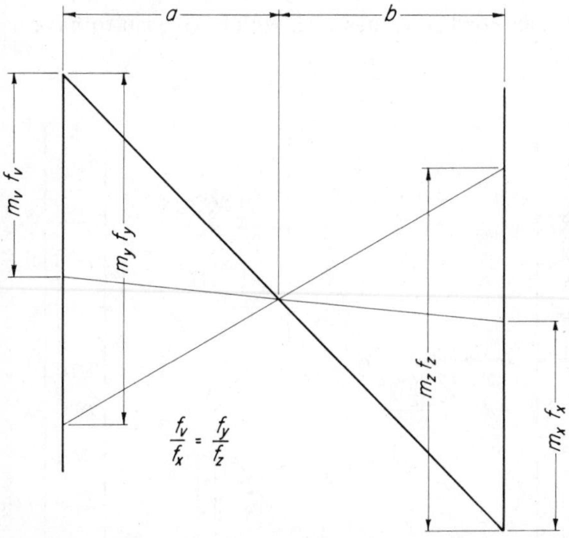

Fig. 23-15.   Geometry for proportionality chart.

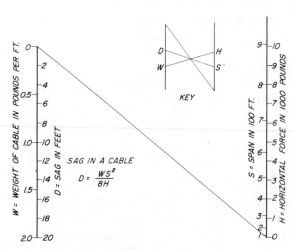

Fig. 23-16.   Proportionality chart.

stated above, these charts can be made in a variety of forms as illustrated in Fig. 23–17.

23.9 Combination chart. Four variables. Equation $f(v) + f(x) = f(y)/f(z)$. This equation can be divided into two parts with a new term p set equal to each.

$$f(v) + f(x) = f(p) = \frac{f(y)}{f(z)}$$

These two equations can be solved by two charts having a common scale for $f(p)$. The first equation $f(v) + f(x) = f(p)$ can be solved by a three variable parallel scale chart, and the second $f(p) = f(y)/f(z)$ by an N-chart. The scale or axis common to both charts must have the same modulus and run in the same direction in both charts.

Example. Let it be required to make a chart for the equation for train resistance due to grade

$$R = \frac{2000\,(B - E)}{L}$$

with the following ranges for the various terms, as shown in Fig. 23–18.

$B =$ Elevation at high end of section.   Range 0 to 20 feet.

$E =$ Elevation at low end of section.   Range 0 to 20 feet.

$L = 1000$ to 3000 feet length of section

$R =$ Resistance 0 to 40 pounds per ton.

Step 1. Rewrite the equation in the proper form.

$$\frac{RL}{2000} = p = (B - E)$$

For the first equation $B - E = p$ the term p becomes the middle scale and is positive upward. In order to have the p-scale on the outside of the N-chart and also the same direction as in the parallel scale chart, the other equation must be written $L/2000 = p/R$.

Step 2. Choose moduli to give suitable scale lengths.

$$L_B = m_B\,(20 - 0) = 20\,m_B$$
If $m_B = \frac{1}{4}$, then $L_B = 5$ inches.
$$L_E = m_E\,(20 - 0) = 20 m_E$$
If $m_E = \frac{1}{4}$, then $L_E = 5$ inches.

Step 3. Compute modulus for the middle scale.

$$m_p = \frac{m_B \times m_E}{m_B + m_E} = \frac{\frac{1}{4} \cdot \frac{1}{4}}{\frac{1}{4} + \frac{1}{4}} = \frac{1}{8}$$

Then $\qquad L_p = \frac{1}{8}(20 - 0) = 2\frac{1}{2}$ inches

For the N-chart, the graphical method for calibrating the diagonal scale for L is used and it is therefore only necessary to choose a modulus for the R-scale.

$$L_R = m_R\,(40 - 0) = 40\,m_R$$
If $m_R = \frac{1}{8}$, then $L_R = 5$ inches.

For the N-chart, it will be convenient to keep it inside the parallel scale chart. We shall therefore choose a width of 2 inches and let the diagonal be what it will. The scales may now be laid out as shown in Fig. 23–18. Since the R-, B-, and E-scales are natural scales and should give no trouble, only the calibration of the L-scale will be discussed.

It will be necessary to solve the equation $p/R = L/2000$ for the values of L which we wish to have on

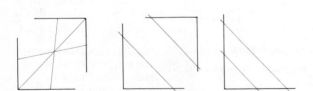

Fig. 23–17. Other arrangements for proportionality charts.

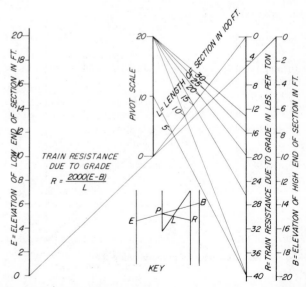

Fig. 23–18. Combination chart.

the diagonal scale. One or more poles may be used on the p-scale. They are taken on the p-scale because it will then be unnecessary to plot any other points on that scale.

In the table of computations below, 10 and 20 on the p-scale have been used for the poles. By drawing an isopleth from the pole to the corresponding value of R, the location of the corresponding point on the L-scale is located. The computations are shown in Table 11.

TABLE 11. COMPUTATIONS FOR SOLUTION BY POLE METHOD $\dfrac{p}{R} = \dfrac{L}{2000}$

L	p	R
500	10	40
1000	20	40
1500	20	26.7
2000	20	20
2500	20	16
3000	20	13.3

PROBLEMS

The problems below have been grouped according to the number of variables involved. The instructor may assign the type of chart he wishes the student to make, or if no specification is made the student may select the type which fits the situation.

The range of variables given is for general guidance only and may be altered if a better nomograph will result. Unless otherwise specified by your instructor only the major scale markings shall be shown. Each scale must be given a name or legend describing it and the entire chart should be given a title. Those charts with three or more variables will have a key showing how to use the nomograph.

Functional Scales

Make a single functional scale for one of the functions assigned from the problems in the following group. Make the scale 6 inches long or if drawn lengthwise of the sheet ($8\frac{1}{2} \times 11$) make it 8 inches long.

1. $f(x) = \sin x$ from $x = 10°$ to $60°$
2. $f(x) = (x^2 + 2)$ from $x = 2$ to 10
3. $f(x) = 1/x$ from $x = 1$ to 20
4. $f(x) = \tan x$ from $x = 10°$ to $45°$
5. $f(x) = \text{Log } x$ from $x = 1$ to 10
6. $f(x) = \text{Log } x$ from $x = 2$ to 20

Two Variable Charts

Make an adjacent scale chart, or two scales with a pole or turning point between them, from the following group as assigned by your instructor.

7. $Y = \dfrac{D}{\pi}$

$Y =$ distance of the centroid of a semicircular arc of wire from the diameter.
$D =$ diameter, 2 to 20 inches.

8. $t = 2\pi\sqrt{\dfrac{l}{g}}$

$t =$ time in seconds for complete oscillation of a pendulum.
$l =$ length of pendulum, 3 to 6 feet.
$g =$ acceleration due to gravity (32.2).

9. $P = .0036V^2$

$P =$ pressure on an area perpendicular to the direction of the wind in pounds per square feet.
$V =$ velocity of the wind, 10 to 100 miles per hour.

Three Variable Charts

10. $A = \pi rh$

$A =$ area of the surface of a cone in square feet.
$r =$ radius of the base, 1 to 10 feet.
$h =$ slant height, 5 to 50 feet.

11. $V = \dfrac{\pi}{6}(D^3 - d^3)$

$V =$ volume of a hollow sphere in cubic inches.
$D =$ outside diameter, 2 to 20 inches.
$d =$ inside diameter, 1 to 18 inches.

12. $I = \dfrac{\pi}{64}(D^4 - d^4)$

$I =$ moment of inertia of an open circular area about a centroidal axis.
$D =$ outside diameter, 6 to 10 inches.
$d =$ inside diameter, 4 to 8 inches.

13. $I = \dfrac{\pi}{64}Dd^3$

$I =$ moment of inertia of an elliptical disk about its major axis.
$D =$ length of major axis, 5 to 20 inches.
$d =$ length of minor axis, 4 to 16 inches.

14. $F = \mu N^{0.97}$

$F =$ frictional resistance in pounds.
$\mu =$ coefficient of friction, 0.20 to 0.60.
$N =$ normal force, 10 to 100 pounds.

15. $Q = .385BH\sqrt{2gH}$

$Q =$ cubic feet of water passing over a rectangular weir per second.
$B =$ width of weir, 2 to 20 ft.
$H =$ depth of water above bottom of weir, 1 to 10 ft.

Four Variable Charts

16. $p = \dfrac{2tf}{D}$

    $p =$ internal pressure in cylindrical tank in pounds per square inch.

    $t =$ thickness of plate, ¼ to 1½ in.

    $f =$ tensile stress, 10,000 to 20,000 lbs. per sq. in.

    $D =$ internal diameter of cylinder, 48 to 120 inches.

17. $W = .286\, LBT$

    $W =$ weight of cast iron base plate in lbs.

    $L =$ length in inches, 12 to 24.

    $B =$ width in inches, 8 to 20.

    $T =$ thickness, ½ to 2½ inches.

18. $E = \dfrac{\mu W \pi D N}{12}$

    $E =$ work absorbed in revolving bearing in foot pounds per minute.

    $\mu =$ coefficient of friction, .15 to .30.

    $W =$ total load on bearing, 100 to 1000 pounds.

    $D =$ diameter of bearing, .75 to 2.50 inches.

    $N =$ number of revolutions per minute, 400 to 2000.

Five Variable Charts

19. $I = \dfrac{BD^3 - bd^3}{12}$

    $I =$ moment of inertia of a hollow rectangle about a centroidal axis perpendicular to the depth.

    $B =$ outside width, 6 to 16 inches.

    $b =$ inside width, 4 to 14 inches.

    $D =$ outside depth, 8 to 18 inches.

    $d =$ inside depth, 6 to 16 inches.

20. $HP = \dfrac{.786 P L D^2 N}{33,000}$

    $HP =$ horse power of a reciprocating steam engine.

    $P =$ steam pressure, 50 to 150 pounds per square inch.

    $L =$ length of stroke, 8 to 24 inches.

    $D =$ diameter of cylinder, 6 to 16 inches.

    $N =$ number of strokes per minute, 40 to 240.

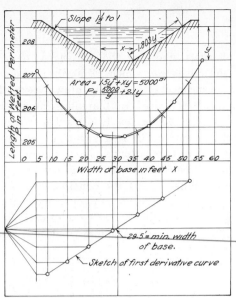

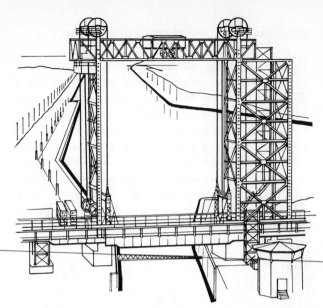

Minimum width of base determined by graphical differentiation.

24

Graphical Mathematics

24.1 Introduction. Graphical solutions to mathematical problems have some advantages and some disadvantages that must be considered carefully when they are to be used. One of the principal advantages is speed, and as a general rule graphical solutions are not used unless they save time, or provide a necessary check on the analytical method. When the analytical solution is complicated and time-consuming or impossible, the engineer should look for a convenient graphical device. If a highly accurate result is desired, the analytical solution should be used. However, fair accuracy can be obtained by graphical methods if a large scale is used.

Graphical solutions are available for many problems in arithmetic, algebra, trigonometry, calculus, and differential equations. The engineer should be familiar with all of them so that he can use them when conditions are suitable.

24.2 Arithmetic. The best known and most used graphical method for solving arithmetical problems is the slide rule. Other methods, such as network charts and proportional charts and nomographs, are available for such operations as addition, subtraction, multiplication and division. The desirability of their use as tools depends on the condition of the problem.

24.2.1 *Addition.* The network chart shown in Fig. 24-1(*a*) is based on the equation of a straight line, $y = mx + b$. In this equation the term "*m*" represents the slope of the line. If the slope (the tangent of the angle with the X-axis) is made equal to -1, the equation becomes $y = -x + b$ or $y + x = b$. A series of straight lines for various values of *b,* which is usually the *y* intercept of the line, can be plotted as shown in

24–01

Fig. 24–1(a). Since the chart is composed entirely of straight lines, interpolation is very easy. The values of all inclined lines can be read on the Y-axis at the point where they intersect it. Thus the values $x = 5.2$ and $y = 3.3$ locate the point c from which the diagonal line can be drawn and the answer read on the Y-axis as 8.5. Figure 24–1(b) shows a practical use of this network chart for finding the summation of the components of two forces. In the illustration, the equation is $\Sigma F = F_1 \cos 45° + F_2 \sin 30°$. The network is plotted in the same manner as the one shown in Fig. 24–1(a), using $.5\ F_2$ for x and $.707\ F_1$ for y. In the example F_1 is 16 and F_2 is 23 and, in

this particular case, the answer may be read on an inclined scale from which ΣF may be read directly as 22.8. The inclined scale may be drawn inside the figure or outside as desired. Both are illustrated in Fig. 24–1(b).

24.2.2   Subtraction. It is possible to use the network chart shown in Fig. 24–1 for subtraction, but a more convenient one can be found as shown in Fig. 24–2(a). In this figure, the equation of the straight line $y = mx + b$ is used. When $m = 1$ the equation becomes $y - x = b$. Using this equation a series of straight lines are plotted for various values of b. The solution is shown for $y = 16.5$ and $x = 8.75$. The interpolation is made by draw-

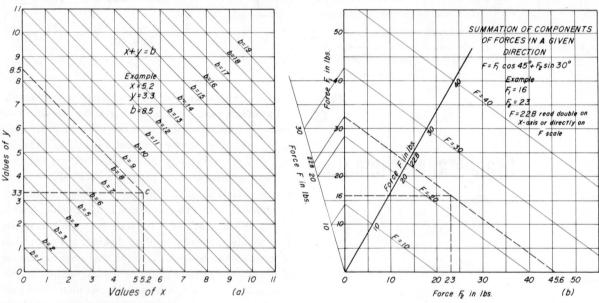

Fig. 24–1.   Network chart for addition.

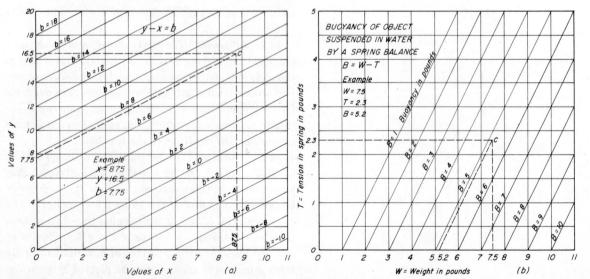

Fig. 24–2.   Network chart for subtraction.

ing an extra line through point C, located from the values of x and y, and reading the answer, 7.75, on the Y-axis.

An example of the use of this network is shown in Fig. 24–2(b) which gives the solution of the equation $B = W - T$ for the buoyancy of an object suspended in water. In this case $W = 7.5$, $T = 2.3$, which locate point C from which the B line may be drawn parallel to the others and the answer, 5.2, read on the W-scale. It should be observed that the inclined lines in this chart would be 45° only if the horizontal and vertical scales were the same.

The use of these charts is limited since the analytical solution is usually easier and faster. They are valuable when similar operations of some complexity are to be repeated many times or for a quick check on the analytical solution.

24.2.3 Addition and subtraction of three numbers. A network chart seems to be of very limited usefulness for

an equation such as $x = a + b + c$. It can be made by combining two charts such as those shown in Figs. 24–1(a) and 24–2(a). It is best to divide the equation into two parts by letting $y = a + b$, then by substitution $x = y + c$. For convenience these two equations may be written $b = y - a$ and $c = x - y$. If the Y-axes are made coincident, two charts can be placed side by side to solve the equation. The values do not need to be placed on the Y-axis since the term "y" does not appear in the original equation unless the final answer is to be read on that scale. The solution of the equation is given for $a = 3$, $b = 4$, and $c = -2$ as shown in Fig. 24–3(a). The answer, 5, is read on the X-scale.

The equation $Q = U_2 - U_1 + W$, which is the first law of thermodynamics, is solved in Fig. 24–3(b). The first step is to divide the equation into two parts: $Q - W = Y = U_2 - U_1$. These may again be changed to give the equations $Q = W + Y$ and $U_2 = Y + U_1$. In

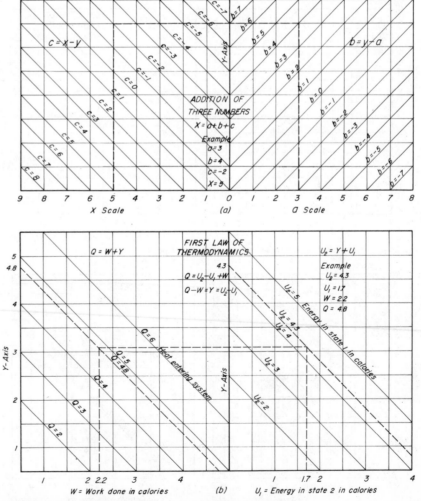

Fig. 24–3. Network chart for adding or subtracting three numbers.

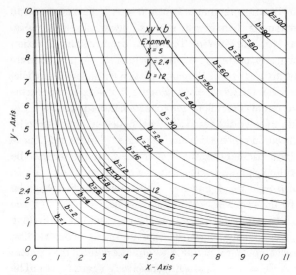

Fig. 24-4.   Network chart for multiplication—rectangular coordinate paper.

this form the vertical scale can be made the Y-axis of both charts. An example is shown for the values $U_2 = 4.3$, $U_1 = 1.7$, $W = 2.2$, and the answer, $Q = 4.8$, is read on the vertical scale at the extreme left.

24.2.4   *Multiplication.* A network chart for multiplication can be formed by plotting curves for various values of the equation $xy = c$. If these curves are plotted on rectangular coordinate paper, they form a series of hyperbolas as shown in Fig. 24-4. This chart is not very practical since the curves require considerable time to plot and interpolation is not easy. However, if logarithms are taken of both sides, the equation becomes $\log x + \log y = \log c$ or $\log x = \log c - \log y$, which is in the form of the equation of a straight line, $y = mx + b$. Therefore, if the equation is plotted on logarithmic paper, as in Fig. 24-5(a), the curves become straight lines and solutions are easily obtained. Interpolation is easy as shown in the figure for values of $x = 1.6$ and

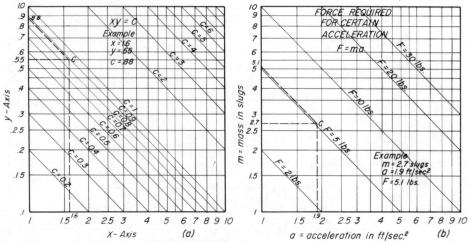

Fig. 24-5.   Network chart for multiplication—logarithmic paper.

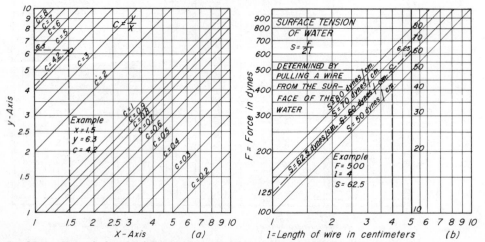

Fig. 24-6.   Network chart for division.

$y = .55$, where a new line is constructed through point C, as determined by the values of x and y. The answer is read on the Y-axis as .88. The network chart to solve the equation $F = ma$ for finding the force necessary to cause acceleration "a" in a mass "m" is shown in Fig. 24–5(b). In the example $m = 2.7$ slugs and $a = 1.9$ feet/second^2 locate point C. From C a line is drawn parallel to the F lines and the answer is read as 5.1 pounds on the Y-axis.

24.2.5 Division. The same principles apply for division as for multiplication. When the equation $y/x = c$ is plotted on logarithmic paper, the chart shown in Fig. 24–6(a) is obtained. Interpolation is easy by drawing an inclined line through the point O, obtained from the coordinates, and reading the answer at the point of intersection of the Y-axis with the inclined line. The solution is given for $x = 1.5$ and $y = 6.3$. The answer shows $C = 4.2$.

The network chart to solve the equation $S = F/2l$, to determine the surface tension of water, is shown in Fig. 24–6(b). The example shows the solution for $l = 4$ centimeters and $F = 500$ dynes. These two values locate the point C from which the diagonal is drawn parallel to the S lines until it intersects the axis at 125. The correct answer for S in this case is found by dividing 125 by 2 to get 62.5 dynes per centimeter, or by reading the answer directly on the vertical scale through $l = 5$. These divisions must be marked as one-tenth of the values on the F scale.

24.2.6 Combinations. Continuous operations may be performed by combining two or more charts. In the equation $x = ab/c$, a regrouping may be done by making $y = a/c$. Then by substitution $x = by$. By constructing these two charts with the y-axes coincident, the original equation may be solved as shown in Fig. 24–7(a). The solution is given for $c = 5$, $a = 20$, and $b = .6$, where it

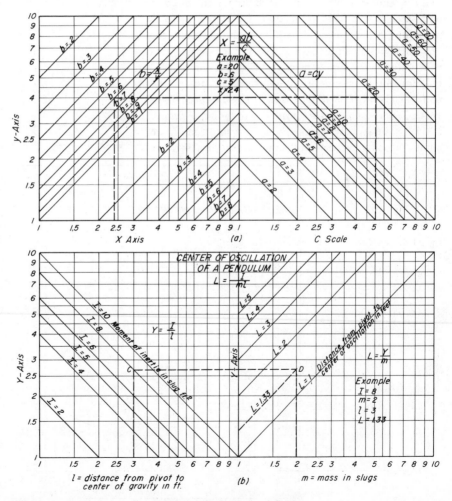

Fig. 24–7. Network chart for combined multiplication and division.

is shown that $x = 2.4$.

To find the center of oscillation of a pendulum the equation is $L = I/ml$. The network chart to solve this equation is shown in Fig. 24-7(b). In this case, the equation is divided into two equations, $y = I/c$ and $L = y/m$. In the example, the terms $I = 8$ and $l = 3$ locate the point C. From point C and the term $m = 2$, the point D may be located from which an L line may be drawn parallel to the other and the value of L may be read from the vertical axis at 1.33 feet.

24.2.7   Proportion. Problems in proportion can be easily solved by nomographs as explained in Art. 23.8. These may be arranged for very complicated functions of four variables, or they may be as simple as two uniform scales at right angles to each other when only a simple arithmetical proportion is involved. Fig. 24-8 shows this method of solving a proportion when a, b, and c are known by plotting the numerators on one scale and the denominators on the other scale. Thus if $b = 6.8$ and $c = 3.5$ the diagonal line joining these points can be drawn as in Fig. 24-8. Then by constructing a line through $a = 2.2$ parallel to the diagonal, the answer $y = 4.3$ can be read on the vertical scale. This is actually a very simple nomograph, but it can be used only for simple arithmetical proportions. In fact, all the charts that have been discussed in this chapter up to this point are sometimes considered to be nomographs.

24.3   Algebra. When the analytical solution of two simultaneous equations is difficult, the graphical solution may save time. If each curve be plotted on rectangular coordinates, the points of intersections of the two curves will locate points that satisfy both equations. Those points are therefore the required values. This is shown in Fig. 24-9.

The graphical solution may also be used to find the roots of a complicated equation like $y^3 - 4y^2 + y - 10 = 0$.

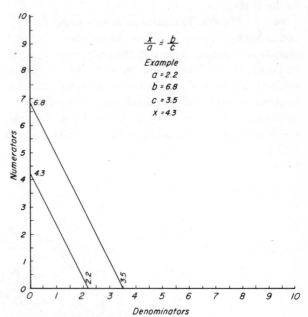

Fig. 24-8.   Proportion chart.

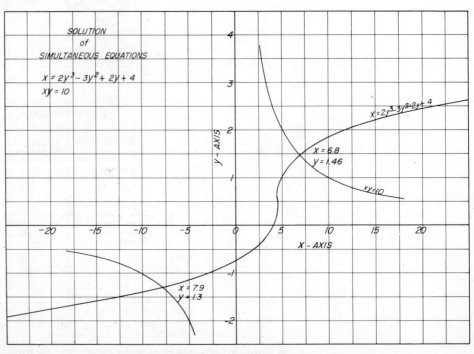

Fig. 24-9.   Solution of simultaneous equations.

By our plotting the curve on a rectangular coordinate paper, with the $f(y)$ on the X-axis the roots are found at the points where the curve crosses the Y-axis where $f(y) = 0$. This is illustrated in Fig. 24–10. Sometimes it is more convenient to form two simultaneous equations and plot both curves. The point or points where the curves cross will then be the answer. Thus if $x = y - 10$, then by substitution $y^3 - 4y^2 + x = 0$. Figure 24–11 shows that by plotting the two curves the point of intersection gives the same point that was obtained in Fig. 24–10. This method is very useful in the solution of transcendental equations in which there is

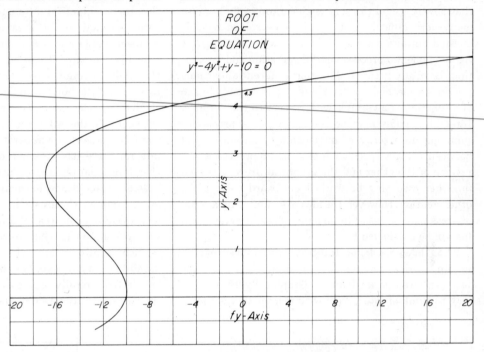

Fig. 24–10.   Roots of an equation.

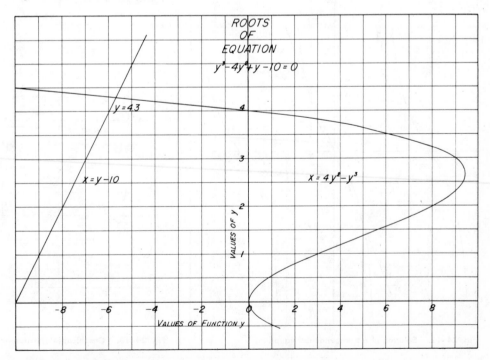

Fig. 24–11.   Roots of an equation.

only one variable which appears in two different forms. In the equation $\tan \alpha = 1.5\alpha$ it is necessary to form two equations $\tan \alpha = y$ and $y = 1.5\alpha$. Figure 24–12 shows the solution of this equation as the intersection of the two curves.

24.4 Graphical calculus. Graphical calculus is a tool that is very useful to every engineer, not only because many very difficult problems may be solved by this method but also because it gives a graphical picture of the fundamental processes of differentation and integration. Basically it can be said that differential calculus provides a method for determining the rate of change of a function of a variable with respect to the variable. Integral calculus may be thought of as a process of summing up a series of increments to obtain a total between certain specified limits. Each process is the reverse of the other and the graphical procedure used in either case may be worked backward to give the other solution. However, the idea of summing up a series of areas may be easier to understand, so integral calculus will be considered first.

24.5 Integral calculus. Integration is a process of adding up a series of increments to obtain the total value between two specified limits. Graphically the easiest way to think of integration with respect to x is that it

is a method of obtaining the area between a curve and the X-axis, between certain values of x. This is done by dividing the area under the curve into small segments and adding these segments together, either graphically or analytically, to obtain the total area. By the graphical method, this involves drawing another curve so that the arithmetical difference between any two ordinates is equal to the area under the original curve between those same two ordinates.

In Fig. 24–13(a) it can be seen that the area under the original curve between the points A and B is equal to 8.8×1 if the horizontal line is placed so that the two shaded triangles are equal. In Fig. 24–13(b) the difference between the ordinates A and B is also 8.8, and this curve is therefore the integral of the original curve. The integral curve has an equation of a higher order and therefore is plotted above the original curve.

24.6 Integration by the area method. The best method for determining the area of a segment under a curve is to find an equivalent area by drawing a horizontal line in such a position that the two small shaded areas of each segment shown in Fig. 24–13(a) are equal. This can usually be done by eye, but the original segments must be selected carefully to give the proper accuracy. Where the curve is fairly straight, the segments can be rather

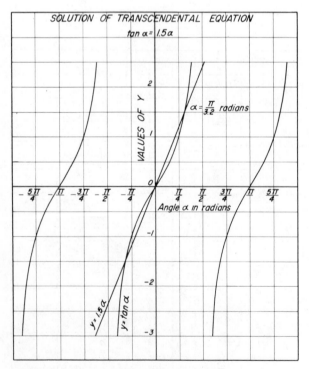

Fig. 24–12. Solution of a transcendental equation.

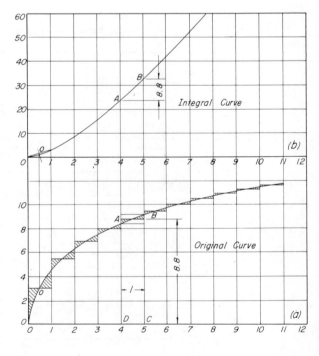

Fig. 24–13. Graphical integration—area method.

large, but when the curve is changing direction rapidly, the division points must be taken closer together. As a check on the work or for using this method for differentiation, it can be seen that the point where the perpendicular bisector of the chord in Fig. 24–13(b) crosses the curve, may be projected to Fig. 24–13(a) to locate the point on the curve where the horizontal line crosses. This is illustrated by point O in Fig. 24–13. If this does not work out, smaller divisions should be taken. When the horizontal line has been drawn properly, the area under the curve will be equal to the area of the rectangle $ABCD$ in Fig. 24–13.

It is then possible to calculate the area of each small increment and plot the integral curve by making the difference between two ordinates of the integral curve equal to the area under the original curve between those ordinates. This is illustrated in Fig. 24–14. Since the integral curve is always taller than the original curve, the scale on the vertical axis of the integral curve is usually made smaller as shown in Fig. 24–14(b).

To solve this problem analytically, it is necessary to take a small vertical segment of width dx and height y. The area of this segment is ydx and the summation of these segments between certain limits such as $x = 0$ and $x = 40$ will give the area under the curve. The orig-

inal equation $x = 3y^2$ may be changed to $y = x^{1/2}/3^{1/2}$. Then if each side be multiplied by dx, the equation becomes $ydx = x^{1/2}/3^{1/2}\ dx$. But $ydx = A$, so $A = x^{1/2}/3^{1/2}\ dx$. The integral of this expression is $A = 1/3^{1/2}[\frac{2}{3}x^{3/2}] + C$. When $C = 0$ the curve goes through the origin and the equation becomes $A = .385x^{3/2}$. This is the equation of the curve shown in Fig. 24–14(b) and plotting the equation will give practically the same results obtained by adding the increments arithmetically.

24.6   Integration by the area method using a string polygon. A method of integration that is all graphical and involves the use of a string polygon is illustrated in Fig. 24–15. The problem in this case is to integrate the area under the curve in Fig. 24–15(a). The procedure is as follows:

a. Divide the area under the curve into vertical segments making them narrow enough so that it is possible to set up a comparatively accurate equivalent area rectangle for each segment as shown in Fig. 24–15(a). In this case it would have been better to subdivide the first space between $x = 0$ and $x = 2$, but this would have made the construction so small that it would be hard to follow. For this reason there is some error in this portion of the curve.

b. Establish the equivalent area rectangle for each

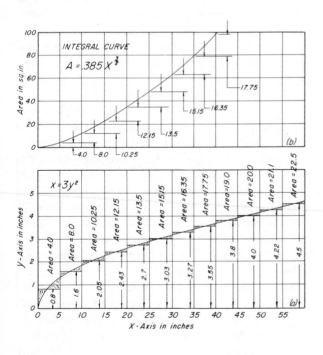

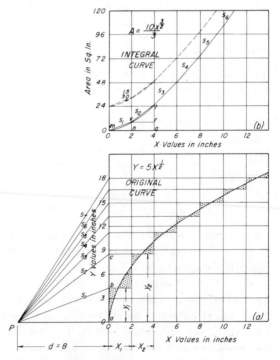

Fig. 24–14.   Graphical integration—equivalent areas.   **Fig. 24–15.   Graphical integration—string polygon method.**

segment. These are shown shaded in Fig. 24–15(*a*).

c. Project the top of each rectangle to the *Y*-axis.

d. Establish a pole on the *X*-axis at some convenient distance from the *Y*-axis. This distance, *d* in Fig. 24–15(*a*), should usually be some multiple of the unit value on the *X*-axis. In Fig. 24–15(*a*), it is made eight times this unit distance.

e. Draw rays from the pole to each of the points on the *Y*-axis. See Fig. 24–15(*a*).

f. Beginning at the origin in Fig. 24–15(*b*) construct a string, s_1, parallel to the first ray, s_1, until it crosses the division line between the first and second segments at *v*.

g. From *v* in Fig. 24–15(*b*) construct string s_2 parallel to ray s_2 and extend it until it crosses the division line between the second and third segments at *t*. Continue in this manner for the rest of the strings.

h. Draw a smooth curve through these points. Notice that the strings become chords of the curve, which gives rise to the name the "chord method" by which it is known.

i. Determine the vertical scale for Fig. 24–15(*b*) by the following method:

Area of the first strip $= x_1 y_1$. By definition of the integral curve $vn = x_1 y_1$ to some scale that can be determined. *Pab* is similar to *mnv*

then $\qquad$ $Pa : ab :: mn : nv$

or $\qquad$ $d : y_1 :: x_1 : nv$

$$x_1 y_1 = nv \cdot d$$

$d = 8$ units on the *X*-scale

Then the scale on the *Y*-axis will be ⅛ of the scale on the *Y*-axis of the original curve. In other words, where one division represented 3 on the original, the same division will represent 24 on the integral curve. *Pac* is similar to *vrt*

then $\qquad$ $Pa : ac :: vr : rt$

or $\qquad$ $d : y_2 :: x_2 : rt$

$$x_2 y_2 = d \cdot rt$$

$$x_1 y_1 + x_2 y_2 = nv \cdot d + rt \cdot d = tq \cdot d$$

Thus it can be seen that the vertical intercept at any point on the integral curve represents the entire area under the original curve to the left of that point.

24.7 **Constant of integration.** In the previous examples it has been assumed that the integral curve began at the origin, but this is not always true. By the original statement, the difference between two ordinates on the integral curve gives the area under the original curve between those two ordinates, but this does not place the integral curve at any particular height on the axis. It could be raised or lowered by any amount and the difference in the ordinates could still be the same value. Some other information must be known to give the integral curve a definite position. One method of locating this curve would be to say that it has to pass through a certain point, and from this information the value of the constant can be determined.

In Fig. 24–15(*b*) the integral curve has been drawn through the origin which makes the constant zero. If it is desired to have the curve go through a point whose coordinates are $x = 1.5$ and $A = 30$, the coefficient may be determined as follows:

Substitute the values in the equation $A = 10x^{3/2}/3 + C$ to obtain $30 = 10 \cdot 1.5^{3/2}/3 + C$.

Then $C = 23.9$ and the integral curve may be started at a point on the area axis where the value is 23.9. The dashed line shows this curve.

The same thing could have been accomplished graphically by making a vertical segment in the original curve, end on the place where $x = 1.5$, then by following the usual procedure the curve could have been started at the required point and appropriate strings drawn forward and backward through that point.

24.8 **Integration of irregular curves.** All the examples used up to this point have been such that they can be solved easier by analytical methods than by graphical. Their purpose has been to develop a method. It is usually well for the beginner to start with a simple case that can be checked analytically. There are two reasons for this: first, to give confidence in the method and second, to show the degree of drafting accuracy that is necessary to obtain a reasonable answer. The graphical method is most useful when the curve is of such a shape that it is very difficult or impossible to write the equation. This frequently occurs with observed data. In Fig. 24–16(*a*), the plotted curve shows the speed of a boat in cruising through a chain of lakes. The speeds were read every five minutes on a Pitot tube speedometer. To find the distance traveled, it is necessary to integrate the area under the original curve. This has been done in Fig. 24–16(*b*) which shows that the boat traveled 9 miles in the first 30 minutes.

24.9 **Differential calculus.** Differentiation is the process which the derivative of a function of a variable with respect to the variable is obtained. A derivative is defined as the limit of the ratio of an increment of a function of a variable to the increment of the variable when the increment of the variable approaches zero as a limit. In the equation $x = y^2$, y^2 is a function of *x* and the curve in Fig. 24–17 shows the relationship between the two variables. If a very small increment of x called $\triangle x$ be considered, then there will be a corresponding increment of y called $\triangle y$. As the $\triangle x$ becomes smaller, that is, as it approaches zero as a limit, the $\triangle y$ also becomes smaller and the ratio $\triangle y/\triangle x$ approaches the tangent of the angle that the curve makes with the X-axis at that point, as a limit. The limit of the ratio $\triangle y/\triangle x$ is therefore the derivative of the function at that point with respect to x or, in other words, the tangent of the angle that the curve makes with the X-axis is the derivative of the curve at that point. It is therefore possible to construct another curve using the same abscissae but with ordinates at each point representing the value of the tangent of the curve at that point. This tangent represents the slope of the original curve or the rate of change of the function of the variable with respect to the variable at that point. The ordinate of the new curve will be the derivative of the original curve at each corresponding point. Fig. 24–18(a) shows a curve where the function of x is $x^3 - x^2/50$. At point A the tangent of the curve has been determined graphically to be 13.3/5 or 2.66/1. By making a new curve, Fig. 24–18(b), whose ordinate at a corresponding point on the X-axis is 2.66, a point on the derivative curve is obtained. Other points may be plotted in a similar manner. The derivative curve is placed below the original curve because the function is of a lower order. The scale used should be as large as possible for accuracy. This is particularly true when the angles become large. For very large angles, it is frequently better to use the reverse of the area method as explained for integration.

24.10 Differentiation by the tangent method. For practical purposes some convenient method must be found to determine the tangent of the curve at various points. If a series of points on the original curve are selected

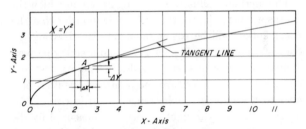

Fig. 24–17. Graphical differentiation—tangent method.

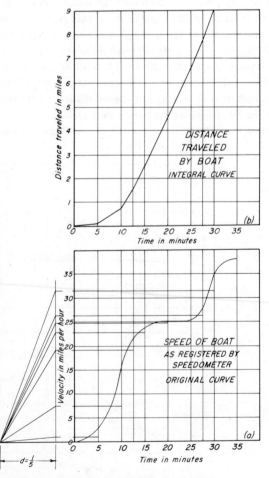

Fig. 24–16. Application of graphical integration.

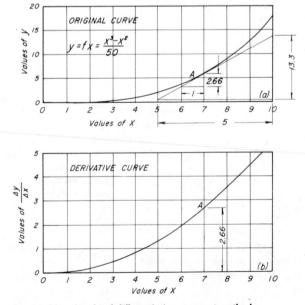

Fig. 24–18. Graphical differentiation—tangent method.

and the chords drawn between them, the tangent will be parallel to the chord if the curve is a circle or a parabola between two adjacent points. If the points are taken sufficiently close together, it is usually possible to find a center which will make that particular part of the curve a circle; in which case the tangent will be parallel to the chord at a point on a perpendicular bisector of the chord as in Fig. 24-19(a). If the curve cannot be considered as a circle, it can usually be fitted as a parabola with the axis either horizontal or vertical. If the axis is horizontal, the tangent will be parallel to the chord at a point that may be formed by drawing a horizontal line from the midpoint of the chord until it intersects the curve as in Fig. 24-19(b). When the axis of the parabola is vertical, the tangent is parallel to the chord at a point that is formed by constructing a vertical line through the midpoint of the chord until it crosses the curve as in Fig. 24-19(c). The circle is best and should be used whenever possible.

The method is illustrated in Fig. 24-20, in which the chords are made longer than desirable in order that the construction will be easier to follow. By drawing the chords mn and np in Fig. 24-20(a) and erecting perpendicular bisectors of these chords, the points "a" and "b" are located. These are the points where lines parallel to the chords will be tangent to the curve. The slope of the line through "a" may be measured by the tangent of the angle, which for this will be 1.15/3 = .38.

This is plotted in Fig. 24-20(b) directly below "a". Likewise the tangent of the angle that the line through "b" makes with the horizontal is 6-1.15/3 = 4.85/3 = 1.62. This is plotted directly below "b" on Fig. 24-20(b). The derivative curve can then be drawn through those points. For the sake of accuracy, the derivative curve should usually be plotted to a larger vertical scale than the original curve.

One very common use of differential calculus is to find the velocity of a moving body when the conditions of its motion are known. Thus, the velocity is the differential of distances with respect to time. It is then possible to find the differential of the velocity with respect to time to determine the acceleration.

This is illustrated in Fig. 24-21 where it is assumed that a body is moving according to the equation $S = t^3 + t^2$ where S is the distance traveled in feet and t the time in seconds. In this equation, t is the independent variable and S is the dependent, so the slope of the curve at any point will be ds/dt. To determine a convenient measure of the tangent at certain points, equal divisions are taken along the X-axis close enough together so that the curves between adjacent points will approximate an arc of a circle. Then a line parallel to the chord will be tangent to the curve at a point where the perpendicular bisector of the chord intersects the circle. In Fig. 24-21(a) the points were chosen at 1, 2, 3, 4, and 5 seconds and the chords drawn between the

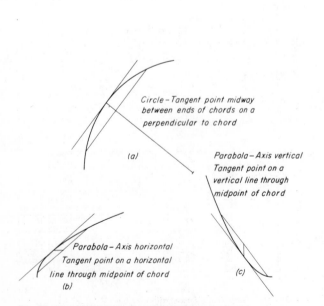

Fig. 24-19.   Location of the point of tangency on a curve.

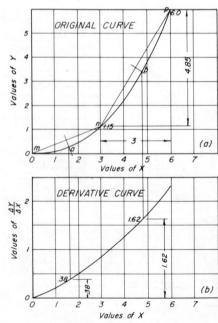

Fig. 24-20.   Graphical differentiation.

points. The tangents have not been drawn, but the perpendicular bisectors of the chords are shown to locate the points of tangency.

The values of S for each of the chosen points are given on the curve in Fig. 24-21(a). The tangent of the angle that the first chord makes with the horizontal axis is 2/1. This value is plotted as shown in Fig. 24-21(b).

The tangent of the second chord will be $12 - 2/1 = 10$, the third $36 - 12/1 = 24$, the fourth $80 - 36/1 = 44$, and the fifth $150 - 80/1 = 70$. These values are plotted directly below the points of tangency to obtain the curve shown in Fig. 24-21(b).

By using the curve found in Fig. 24-21(b), the same process may be used to get the second derivative shown in Fig. 24-21(c). The first derivative gives the velocity time curve and the second derivative gives the acceleration time curve.

24.11   Use of the string polygon for differentiation. A method that is somewhat easier and entirely graphical,

is illustrated in Fig. 24-22. This method involves the use of the funicular polygon or string polygon that was explained in Art. 21.10.

The method of procedure may be divided into the following steps:

a. Divide the original curve into segments that are small enough so that they are approximately arcs of circles. See Fig. 24-22(a).

b. Draw the chords between these points. See Fig. 24-22(a). Mark the chords S_1, S_2, and S_3. Erect perpendicular bisectors of the chords.

c. Below the original curve, lay out another set of coordinates using the same values on the horizontal axis. See Fig. 24-22(b).

d. Assume a pole, P so that the pole distance "d" is equal to 2 units on the horizontal axis. Draw rays S_1, S_2, S_3 parallel respectively to the chords S_1, S_2, and S_3.

e. From the points where the rays cross the vertical axis, draw horizontal lines.

f. From points where the perpendicular bisectors

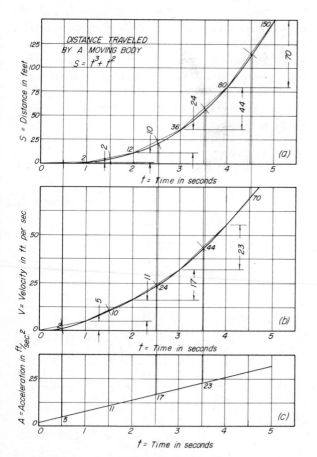

Fig. 24-21.   Application of graphical differentiation.

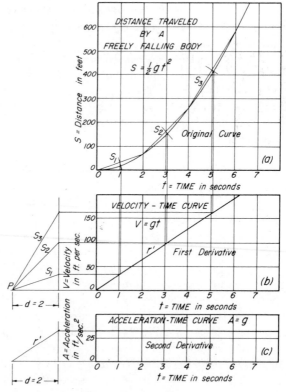

Fig. 24-22.   Graphical differentiation by the string polygon method.

cross the curve in Fig. 24-22(a) project vertically till they intersect the horizontal lines in Fig. 24-22(b) that were drawn in part e. Care must be taken to intersect the corresponding horizontal lines.

g. Through these points of intersection, construct the first derivative curve. In this case the curve is a straight line as shown in Fig. 24-22(b). This means that the velocity increases uniformly.

A second derivative may be found by using Fig. 24-22(b) as the original curve and repeating the process to obtain Fig. 24-22(c). In this case the second derivative is a horizontal line which means that the acceleration is constant.

An important part of this solution is the determination of the scale on the vertical axis of the derivative curve. If the pole distance "d" in Fig. 24-22(b) is made equal to the values of one unit on the horizontal axis, the vertical scale of the derivative curve will be the same as the vertical scale on the original curve. However, in this case, the pole distance has been made equal to two times the value of one unit so that the scale on the derivative curve will be twice as large as the original curve. This is shown in Figs. 24-22(a) and 24-22(b). In Fig. 24-22(c) the pole distance is again equal to two units on the horizontal scale so that the vertical scale in Fig. 24-22(c) is twice as large as the vertical scale in Fig. 24-22(b).

24.12   Derivative of an irregular curve. As in the study of integration, the preliminary problems have been simple ones that can be checked analytically. However, the most important use for graphical differentiation is when it is difficult or impossible to determine the equation of the curve.

It should be remembered that the derivative curve gives the rate of change of one variable with respect to the other variable. Maximum or minimum values of the rate of change will occur when the tangent to the derivative curve is horizontal or, in other words, at the high and low points on the derivative curve. For instance, in Fig. 24-23(a), the population of a certain town has been plotted by years. Certain factors, such as the building of a railroad or the development of new industries, affected the growth of the town. It is desired to know when the greatest rate of growth occurred. The derivative curve as shown in Fig. 24-23(b) was plotted as previously described. It can be seen at a glance that the highest point on the derivative curve is at the year 1950. Therefore the greatest rate of growth was at that time. There was another high point in the rate of growth about 1915.

There was a high point in the population about 1931 and a low point about 1938. These points are indicated on the population curve in Fig. 24-23(a) by high and low points, and on the derivative curve in Fig. 24-23(b), by points where the ordinate is zero.

24.13   Differentiation by the area method. Since the processes of integration and differentiation are reversible, it is possible to use either the area method or the slope method for either process. In most cases the area method is best for integration and the slope method for differentiation. However, the area method is also quite usable for differentiation, particularly for the steep parts of the original curve. The slope method can be used for integration but is not so convenient and its use will not be discussed here.

The procedures in the area method for differentiation are the same as for integration but taken in the reverse order. The principal difference is that the equivalent areas for integrations are estimated so that the area of the equivalent rectangle is equal to the area under the curve, whereas for differentiation the curve is drawn so that the area under the curve is equal to the area of the equivalent rectangle. Figure 24-24 gives an example where both integration and differentiation were performed on the same curve. The original observed data are plotted in Fig. 24-24(a) and the equivalent areas established in that figure. Then by taking a pole at P the rays can be drawn as shown in Fig. 24-24(a). The strings in Fig. 24-24(b) are made parallel to the respec-

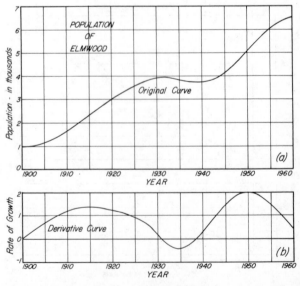

Fig. 24-23.   Application of graphical differentiation.

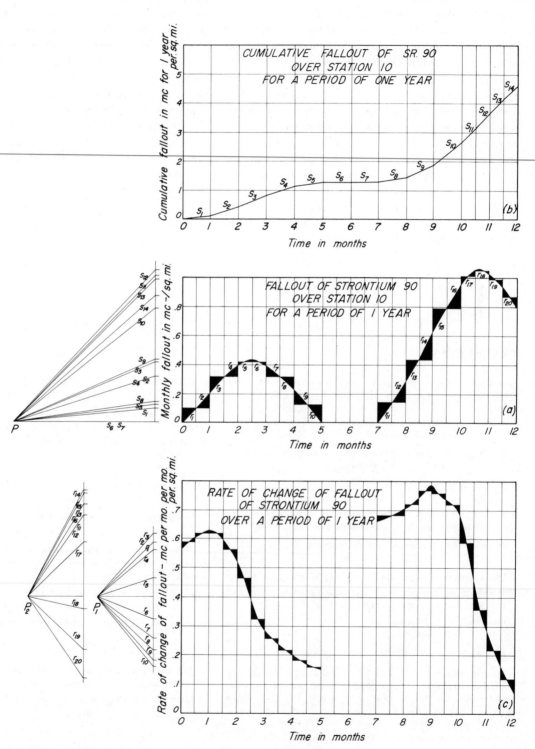

Fig. 24–24.   Graphical integration and differentiation by the area method.

tive rays to give the integral curve in Fig. 24–24(b). Thus the daily fallout of strontium 90 has been added to give the cumulative fallout.

To differentiate the curve shown in Fig. 24–24(a), the first step is to draw the chords so that the curve between the points will be either circles or parabolas. Then the pole P_1 is selected for the left half of the curve and P_2 for the second half. The pole distances are the same, but two poles were used for the sake of clarity to give the desired vertical scale. In Fig. 24–24(a), the pole distance was selected as five times the unit value on the X-axis, whereas in Fig. 24–24(c), the pole distance is two times the unit distance. The rays are then drawn from the pole parallel to the corresponding chords. The intersec-

tions of the rays with the vertical axis give the heights of the various equivalent rectangles. The curve can then be drawn so that the small black triangles in each segment are equal. It is also necessary to keep in mind that the perpendicular bisector of the chords in Fig. 24–24(a) will intersect the arc at a point directly above the place where the curve in Fig. 24–24(c) crosses the top of the equivalent rectangle. It should also be remembered that the points of greatest slope in Fig. 24–24(a) will be in projection with the high or low points of the curve in Fig. 24–24(c), and that the high and low points in the curve of Fig. 24–24(a) will be in projection with the points where the curve in Fig. 24–24(c) cross the horizontal axis.

PROBLEMS

In the solution of these problems, the student must select the proper kind of coordinate paper and choose scales that will enable the problem to be solved on the sheet. Careful plotting is essential and all work must be accurately done if a reasonable answer is to be obtained.

1. Design a network chart to solve the following equation.

$$W = 75 E + 150 C$$

This equation gives the total weight, W in pounds, of a filled abutment where E is the number of cubic feet of earth and C is the number of cubic feet of concrete. W is the total weight. Use the following limits: $E = 0$ to 2000 and $C = 0$ to 400.

2. Design a network chart for the equation

$$W = Q_2 - Q_1$$

This equation gives the amount of heat W in calories that is converted to mechanical work in an engine. Q_2 gives the amount of heat supplied in calories and Q_1 is the heat rejected.

   Limits $Q_2 = 0$ to 1000 calories.
       $Q_1 = 0$ to 500 calories.

3. Design a network chart to solve the equation

$$A = 3/4X + 10/3Y + 12Z$$

This equation gives the square feet of window area in a building when X = the number of $9'' \times 12''$-panes, Y = the number of $20'' \times 24''$ panes, and Z = the number of $36'' \times 48''$-panes.

   Limits $X = 0$ to 100
       $Y = 0$ to 20
       $Z = 0$ to 10

4. Design a network chart for the equation

$$V = 1.3C + 0.5L + 2T$$

This equation gives the approximate cost of floor covering when C = the number of square feet of carpet, L = the number of square feet of linoleum, and T = the number of square feet of tile.

   Limits $C = 0$ to 1500
       $L = 0$ to 400
       $T = 0$ to 200

5. Design a network chart for the equation

$$F = pA$$

This equation gives the total force, in pounds, exerted by a liquid on an area A in square inches when p is the pressure in pounds per unit of area.

   Limits $A = 0$ to 20 square inches
       $p = 0$ to 200 pounds per square inch

6. Design a network chart for the equation

$$I = \frac{E}{R}$$

This equation gives the current I in amperes when E equals the potential difference in volts and R is the resistance in ohms.

   Limits $E = 1/10$ to 10 volts
       $R = 1$ to 10 ohms

7. Design a network chart for the equation

$$P = i^2 R$$

This is the equation for the power absorbed as heat when the circuit is pure resistance R and the current i.

Limits $i = 1$ to 10 amperes
$R = 1$ to 10 volts

8. Design a network chart for the equation

$$w = \frac{300\ \mathrm{HP}}{V}$$

This equation gives the width of single ply belting necessary to transmit a specified horsepower with a certain velocity.

Limits HP = .1 to 6.7 horsepower
$V = 10$ to 200 feet per minute

9. Design a network chart for the equation

$$X = \frac{M \cdot P}{N}$$

This equation determines the resistance of a circuit by means of a Wheatstone bridge.

Limits M = resistance in ohms   1 to 10
        N = resistance in ohms   1 to 10
        P = resistance in ohms   1 to 10
        X = resistance in ohms

10. Design a network chart for the equation

$$p - p_a = \frac{4S}{R}$$

This equation gives the difference in the pressure on the inside and outside of a soap bubble.

Limits R = radius of the bubble in centimeters   1 to 6
        S = surface tension in dynes/centimeter   1 to 100
        p_a = pressure of the atmosphere in dynes/cm².
                                      100,000 to 1,000,000

11. Design a proportion chart for the equation

$$\frac{f}{a} = \frac{F}{A}$$

This equation gives the ratio of hydrostatic pressure to area.

    $F = 1250$ pounds $A = 23.5$ square inches

Find the corresponding values of pressure, p, when area, a, varies from 1 to 10 by single units.

12. Solve the two given simultaneous equations graphically.

$$xy^2 = 43$$
$$\frac{x^2}{2} + \frac{y^3}{3} = 22$$

13. Solve the two given simultaneous equations graphically.

$$3x + 4y = 18$$
$$x^2 + y^2 = 20$$

14. Find the roots of the given equation graphically.

$$x^3 + 5x^2 - 7x - 18 = 0$$

15. Find the roots of the given equation graphically.

$$3x^2 + 4x - 16 = 0$$

16. Find the solution for the given equation graphically.

$$2x - 4 = \log x$$

17. Find the area of the irregular plot of land by graphical integration. The north and west lines are on the section lines which are at right angles to each other and the south line is on the shore of a lake. Measuring from the section corner the following points are located on the shore of the lake.

Point No.	Distance East	Distance South
1	0	650
2	200	660
3	400	547
4	500	530
5	600	583
6	700	630
7	800	600
8	1000	300

18. The monthly fallout in micro-curies per square mile of Strontium 90 over Pittsburgh is listed in the table. Plot the fallout curve and find the cumulative fallout by graphical integration.

Date	Fallout	Date	Fallout	Date	Fallout
Jan.	0.3	May	0.6	Sept.	0.3
Feb.	0.2	June	1.0	Oct.	0.5
Mar.	0.2	July	0.4	Nov.	0.7
Apr.	0.4	Aug.	0.3	Dec.	0.4

19. A certain city pumping station tabulates the rate of pumping each hour as follows:

Time	Rate gallons per minute	Time	Rate gallons per minute
6:00 A.M.	50,000	1:00 P.M.	50,000
7:00 A.M.	60,000	2:00 P.M.	20,000
8:00 A.M.	90,000	3:00 P.M.	25,000
9:00 A.M.	70,000	4:00 P.M.	40,000
10:00 A.M.	30,000	5:00 P.M.	70,000
11:00 A.M.	35,000	6:00 P.M.	60,000
12:00 Noon	60,000		

Find the total water used during the 12-hour period by graphical integration.

20. With the equation $xy = 8$, find the area above the X-axis and below the curve between the values of $x = 1$ and $x = 8$ by graphical integration.

21. With the equation $x = .5y^2$, find the area between the X-axis and the curve between the values of $x = 0$ and $x = 8$ by graphical integration. The integral curve shall go through the point $x = 2$ and $y = 4$.

22. A moving object travels according to the equation $d = t^2/3$. Plot the time distance curve and find the time velocity curve and the time acceleration curve from $t = 0$ to $t = 5$.

23. The population data for Mayview is listed below.

Date	Population	Date	Population
1900	2420	1940	7228
1910	2100	1950	7300
1920	4032	1960	6000
1930	6150		

Plot the population curve and find the time of greatest growth by graphical differentiation.

24. The cam follower on a rotating cam is at the following distances from the center at intervals of one second.

Time in Seconds	Distance in Inches	Time in Seconds	Distance in Inches
0	1.50	9	2.64
1	1.64	10	2.64
2	1.85	11	2.64
3	1.88	12	2.34
4	1.88	13	1.97
5	1.88	14	1.60
6	2.00	15	1.50
7	2.24	16	1.50
8	2.48		

These figures make one complete revolution of the cam. Plot the time distance curve and find the time velocity curve and the time acceleration curve.

Part Four
Professional Applications

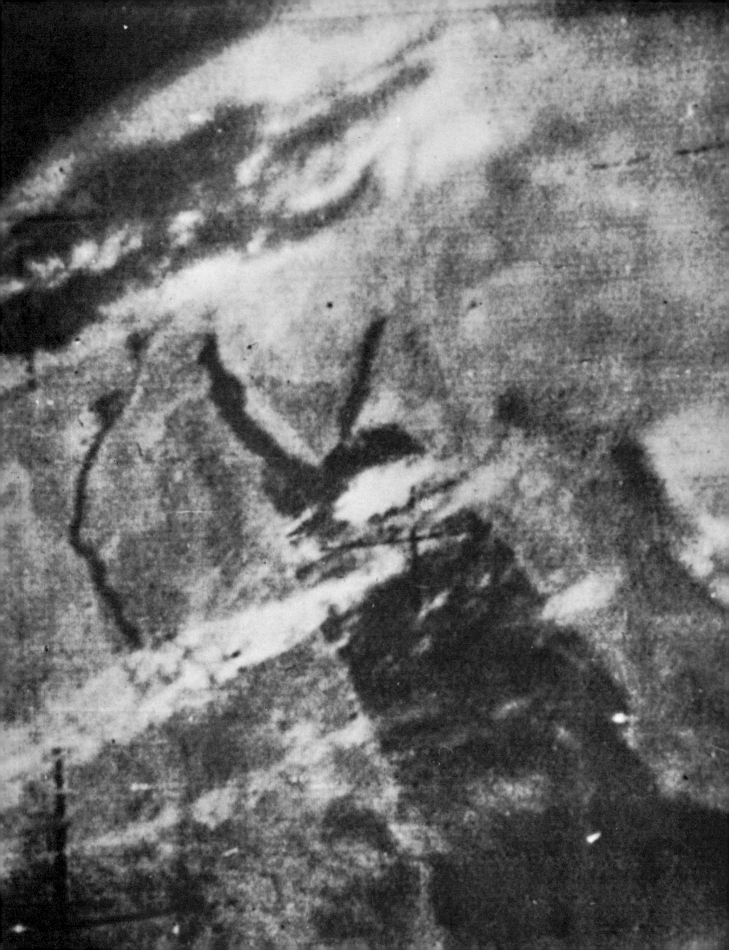

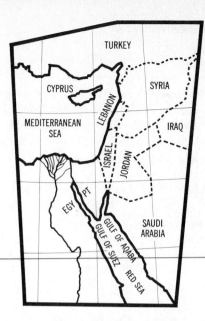

25

Map Drawing

25.1 For the planning and construction of many engineering undertakings, it is necessary to have representations of the earth's surface. Such representations are called maps. When the area to be shown is small, a map is essentially a one-view orthographic projection, and hence only two dimensions can be shown. This is frequently sufficient. Where the third dimension, namely, the difference in elevation of the earth's surface, is essential, symbols are used to give this information. If the area to be shown is large or if extreme accuracy is desired, then other types of projection are used. Such projections are beyond the scope of this book.

25.2 Classification of maps. Maps are conveniently classified upon the basis of their purpose or intended use. On this basis, maps may be divided into four classes which are: geographic, topographic, cadastral, and engineering. Although no hard and fast lines can be drawn between the various classes of maps, the distinctions are usually quite clear, as may be noted from the descriptions in the following paragraphs.

25.3 Geographic maps. Maps of this group show a comparatively large area, and must, therefore, be drawn to very small scales, which means, of course, that only the more important features of the earth's surface can be shown, such as the larger rivers and lakes, mountains, cities, and railroads. On these maps, the cities are located by small circles, and only the larger curves in streams and the principal changes of direction of the railroads are shown. Examples of such maps are to be found in any atlas or geography textbook, and hence are familiar to everyone. The scales vary from a few miles to the inch to several hundred miles to the inch. Relief,

◄ Middle East photographed from an altitude of 450 miles by satellite Tiros I. Gulf of Aqaba near Red Sea is at top. Mediterranean Sea is at upper left (Wide World).

or difference of elevation, is shown in a very general way, usually by hachures or shading.

25.4 Topographic maps. The term topography means the configuration or shape of the land surface of any area. Because of the details which must be shown, the area covered by such maps is quite small as compared to geographic maps. The most widely known maps of this class are those prepared by the United State Geological Survey. A small portion of such a map is shown in Fig. 25–1. Figure 25–1 is taken from the Urbana Quadrangle in Illinois in flat country.

U. S. Geological maps are made to the following scales, determined by the needs in the economic development of the area shown. These maps are always bounded by meridians of longitude and parallels of latitude.

The larger scales shown below are used in the more highly developed areas and the smaller ones in more sparsely settled or desert regions. The arc of latitude and longitude covered is the same in both directions. A scale of $1:24,000$, $1'' = 2000$ feet, covers 7½ minutes of latitude and longitude.

$1:62,500$, $1'' =$ nearly 1 mile.
$1:125,000$, $1'' =$ nearly 2 miles.
$1:250,000$, $1'' =$ nearly 4 miles.

Index maps and circulars of each state and Puerto Rico showing the areas covered by topographic and planimetric maps are available without charge from the United States Geological Survey, Washington 25, D. C. The charge for individual maps is given in the circulars.

The large-scale maps show all the natural features down to little streams which run dry in the summer. City streets, country roads and trails, tunnels, aqueducts, pipelines underground, bridges, houses, and all the works of man together with permanent vegetation such as forest areas are shown. A portion of a privately made topographic map is shown in Fig. 25–2.

25.5 Cadastral maps. Maps of this class are used primarily for showing political and civil boundaries, together with property lines, and are used for the purposes of taxation and the transfer of property. Hence, because of the accuracy required, such maps must be drawn on a still larger scale than either of the preceding classes.

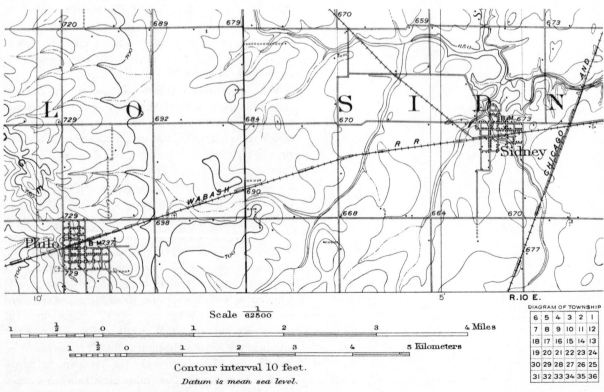

Scale $\frac{1}{62500}$

Contour interval 10 feet.
Datum is mean sea level.

Fig. 25–1. Topographic map. Part of Urbana, Illinois, Quadrangle.

They contain, besides the property lines, only enough of the natural features, such as streams and roads, to enable one to locate the corresponding lines on the ground. Plats of city additions, mineral rights, farm surveys, and the like fall in this group. The scale for such maps is usually greater than 6 inches to 1 mile.

25.6 Engineering maps. Maps drawn for reconnaissance, construction, or maintenance purposes are called engineering maps. The scale is seldom smaller than 1 inch equals 400 feet, and it may approach the architectural scales as the other limit, as for example, ⅛ inch equals 1 foot. Maps for railroad, highway, canal, or hydroelectric construction are excellent examples of this class of maps. Such maps frequently have the character of topographic maps in that they include the contour lines, the natural features, and works of man. Being on a larger scale, they are, of course, much more accurate in detail than the usual topographic map. A portion of a highway construction map is shown in Fig. 25-3.

Public utility companies use what are in effect large-scale cadastral maps to show the location of their lines and connections thereto. Figure 25-4 is a portion of a water company map showing the location of the water mains, fire hydrants, and connections to private property.

Contour maps, showing principally the elevation of the land, are used for location, estimating costs, and construction. A map of this type is shown in Fig. 25-5. Further details concerning the use of contour maps are discussed in Arts. 25.26 and 25.27.

25.7 Military maps. This book is concerned primarily with engineering maps for civilian use, but there is a close connection between topographic maps for this use and military maps. Military maps may be classified according to the scale, which definitely determines the area that can be represented and the use of the map.

Small scale maps with scales ranging from 1:1,000,000 to 1:7,000,000 are used for strategical planning by commanders of large forces.

Intermediate scale maps with scales varying from 1:200,000 to 1:500,000 are used for planning operations, troop movements, concentrations, and supply.

Medium scale maps with scales running from 1:50,000 to 1:125,000 are required for tactical and administra-

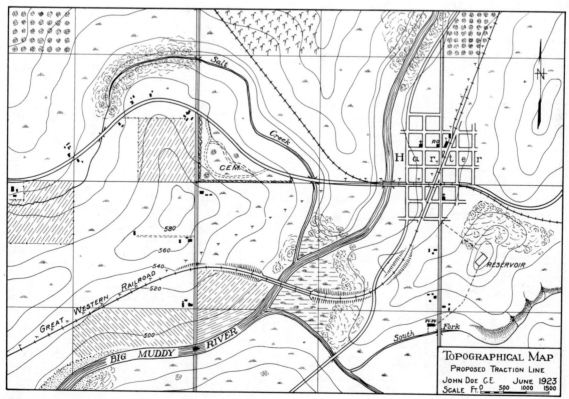

Fig. 25-2. Topographic map.

tive studies for units of the size of regiments. U. S. Geological maps (1:62,500) are suitable for this purpose.

Large scale maps of about 1:20,000 are used for tactical and technical battle needs.

Symbols for military maps are quite extensive and may be found in a booklet called *Military Symbols*.

25.8 Map scales. From the foregoing classification of maps, it will be noted that scales are used ranging from .1 inch equals 1 foot as the largest to 1 inch equals several hundred miles as the smallest. The scale of a map is shown both graphically and numerically at some place near the title or as a part of it, as shown in Fig.

25–1. Sometimes the numerical scale is stated as a ratio. Thus, a scale of 1 inch to the mile is expressed as 1:63,360.

Survey measurements are made in feet and fractions of feet, which are expressed in feet and decimals of a foot instead of in feet and inches; hence the engineer's scales on the boxwood rules are in the decimal system, and have 10, 20, 30, etc., divisions to the inch. These units may also represent 1, 2, or 3 feet to the inch, 10, 20, or 30 feet to the inch, or 100, 200, or 300 feet to the inch. All these scales occur frequently in engineering work.

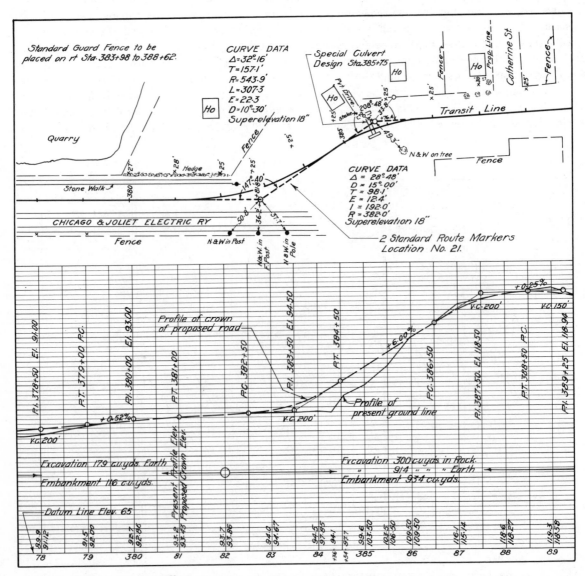

Fig. 25–3. Highway map and profile.

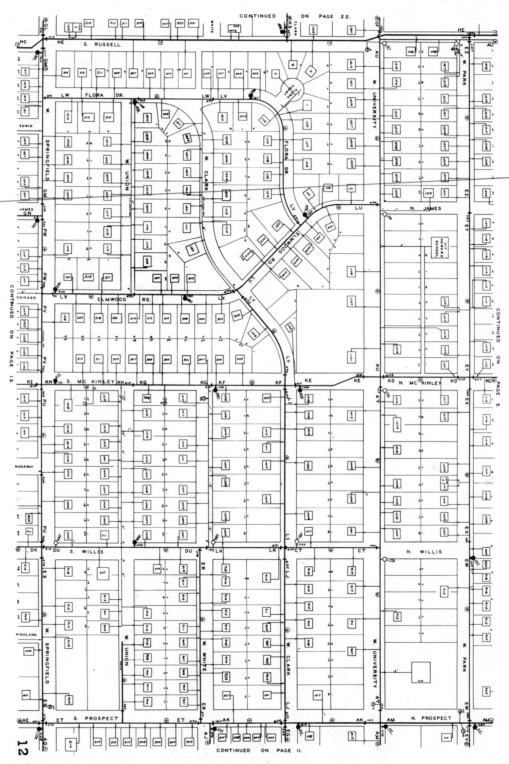

Fig. 25-4. Map of city water supply system. (Courtesy Northern Illinois Water Corp.)

The selection of a scale for a map will be influenced by many factors, chief among which are: the size and character of the area to be shown, the form in which the map is to be presented, and the purpose for which it is to be used. Cost of preparation and length of service must sometimes be considered.

25.9   Map symbols. Since the scale of any map is small, relatively speaking, the representation of objects upon it must be highly conventionalized. Upon all but the largest scale engineering maps, even the largest objects must be shown by symbols rather than by plan views of them. The purpose of a map is, after all, not to show the exact appearance from above, but, rather, to show the comparative size of objects and their position relative to one another. Hence, conventional symbols have been devised which bear some resemblance, where possible, to the objects themselves. The purpose of having this resemblance is for convenience in interpretation.

A well-standardized system of symbols, used by practically all map-making departments of the government, is published in a small booklet called *Military Symbols* published by the Departments of the Army and the Air Force.

25.10   Size and prominence of symbols. The size of symbols should vary only slightly with the scale of the map, since, to almost any scale, most symbols are exaggerations, no matter how small they are made. The symbols shown in Figs. 25–6 to 25–17 are the proper size for the usual engineering maps.

Since the variation in size of symbols is quite limited, prominence may be secured by a variation in the weight of lines used. The purpose of the map will determine which symbols are to be made most prominent. On an oil property map, for example, flowing wells, dry wells, railroads, roads, and property lines are the important features. In practically all cases, the vegetable symbols are least important (military maps excepted) and therefore should be drawn lightly and not too closely together.

25.11   How to draw symbols. There are two distinct steps in learning how to draw symbols, the first of which is a careful examination of a correct model or sample of the symbol, and the second, an endeavor to reproduce it. The more important of these steps is the examination of the sample, for upon the keenness and accuracy of the observation depend the effort at reproduction. For example, an examination of the water lin-

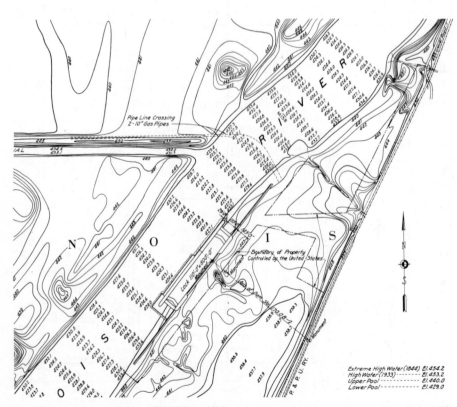

Fig. 25–5.   Contour map for construction.

ing at the right in Fig. 25–6 will make clear that the first lines are drawn very near the shore-line and follow it around very closely, whereas the lines become farther apart and less irregular as we approach the center of the body of water. Examples of both correct and incorrect water lining are shown in Fig. 25–6.

Similarly, a careful examination of the symbol for grass in Fig. 25–7 will show that it consists of about seven short strokes, ranging in length from almost a dot at the ends to about $\frac{3}{32}$ inch at the center. It will also be observed that these strokes are slightly curved and seem to meet in a common center. The individual symbols are arranged at random and not in rows. The careless observer would fail to note many of these essential points, and consequently his attempts at imitation would lack the things which he overlooked. Common errors in making the symbols for grass are shown in Fig. 25–7, in contrast with a correct execution. Likewise, the result of poor observation of the tree symbol is shown in Fig. 25–8.

A large variety of map symbols, printed on cellophane for pasting on a drawing, may be obtained from the trade.

25.12   Colors of symbols. On a finished map, the symbols should be shown in colors. The color for each symbol in Figs. 25–10 to 25–17 is indicated in the figure title. These colors may be readily remembered by four simple groupings, thus: the artificial features, or works of man, are made in black; water features in blue; contours, sand, washes, etc., in brown; and vegetation in green. In printing maps, each color requires a separate printing; therefore a reduction in the number of colors used reduces the cost. Since vegetation, except very large forests, is not permanent, the green is usually omitted.

25.13   Spacing of symbols. One of the greatest difficulties in drawing symbols is to learn how to space those which do not have plotted locations. The general tendency is to cover the sheet too thickly. The draftsman must constantly be on his guard against this practice for two reasons. First, the more symbols drawn the longer it takes and the more it costs to produce the map. Second, it is more difficult to produce uniformity of texture when the symbols are crowded. The heavy and light areas on the map are disagreeably noticeable when symbols are placed too closely together. When there are large areas to be covered with symbols involving the use of parallel lines, as for example in the case of marshlands, a section liner should be used.

25.14   Position of symbols. Another very important point is the position of the symbols on the sheet. All symbols which have a definite base, as for example, grass, marsh, palm trees, and corn, should be drawn with the base parallel to the bottom of the sheet so that the symbols appear in a natural upright position. They should never be placed with their bases parallel to roadways or property lines which run diagonally across the sheet. An illustration of this point is shown in Fig. 25–9. Symbols for vegetation which occur in rows, however, may have the rows running in any direction.

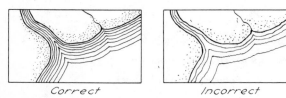

Correct   Incorrect

Fig. 25–6.   Symbol for water lining.

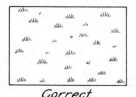
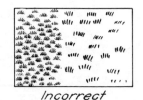

Correct   Incorrect

Fig. 25–7.   Grass.

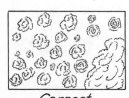
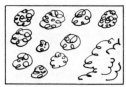

Correct   Incorrect

Fig. 25–8.   Deciduous trees.

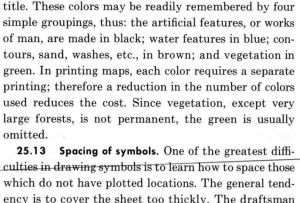

Correct   Incorrect

Fig. 25–9.   Palm trees and tropical grass.

25.15   Special symbols. For some purposes, special symbols must be devised. Thus, for purposes of aerial navigation, a map must show clearly the landing fields of various kinds, beacon, and other aids to navigation, as well as those objects which project up into the air and may be obstructions to flight. Some of these symbols are shown in Fig. 25-16. Such objects as roads, railroads, railway stations, rivers, lakes, woods, and telegraph lines, which will not interfere with flight, are shown by the usual symbols.

Property maps of various industries may also require the engineer to devise symbols to show certain features which are not included among the standard symbols. It should be the engineer's purpose always to make such symbols unmistakable as to meaning and easy to interpret.

25.16   Definition of terms. The following terms are commonly used in surveying and map drafting.

a. Azimuth. The azimuth of a line is the angle the lines makes with a north and south line measured clockwise from the north. See Fig. 25-18. In older survey notes the azimuth angle is frequently given from the south. See problems at the end of this chapter.

b. Back azimuth. The angle measured to the line running in the opposite direction from the azimuth measurement. The back azimuth is therefore equal to the azimuth plus or minus 180°. See Fig. 25-18.

c. Bearing. The angle which a line makes with a north

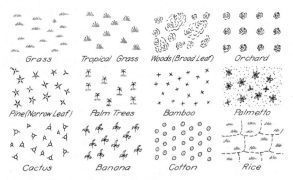

Fig. 25-10.   Vegetation symbols (green).

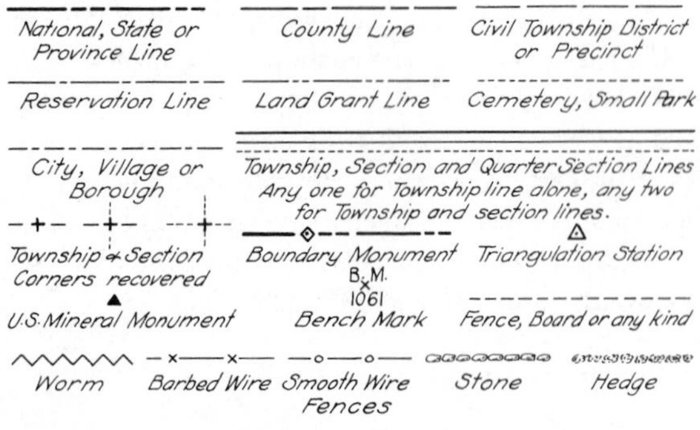

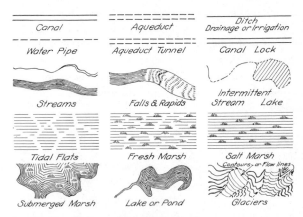

Fig. 25-13.   Hydrographic symbols (blue).

Fig. 25-11. Civil boundaries (black).

National, State or Province Line — County Line — Civil Township District or Precinct

Reservation Line — Land Grant Line — Cemetery, Small Park

City, Village or Borough — Township, Section and Quarter Section Lines. Any one for Township line alone, any two for Township and section lines.

Township & Section Corners recovered — Boundary Monument — Triangulation Station

U.S.Mineral Monument — B.M. 1061 Bench Mark — Fence, Board or any kind

Worm — Barbed Wire — Smooth Wire — Stone — Hedge
Fences

Fig. 25-11.   Civil boundaries (black).

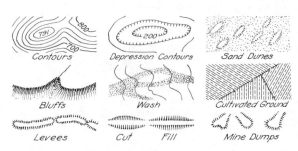

Fig. 25-14.   Relief symbols (brown).

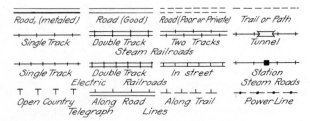

Fig. 25-12.   Roads and communication symbols (black).

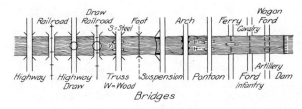

Fig. 25-15.   Bridges and fords (black).

and south line measured either from the north or south. It is always less than 90°. The bearing of a line making 57° to the east of north would be specified as North 57° East or N 57° E. See Fig. 25–18.

d. Backsight. A sight looking back to the last point or station previously occupied. It is 180° from the foresight. See Fig. 25–19.

e. Foresight. In occupying a new point the surveyor orients his transit by sighting back on the point previously occupied. This is the backsight. The telescope of the transit is then plunged 180° to give the foresight. See Fig. 25–19.

f. Deflection angle. The angle of a line in a survey measured to the right or left of the foresight. See Fig. 25–19.

g. Magnetic north. The north point as indicated by the needle of a magnetic compass which points toward the magnetic North Pole. This varies from place to place.

h. True north. A north line established by observations on Polaris, the North Star.

i. Traverse. A broken line measured by observation of angles and distances in the field. In property surveys it is usually the boundary line. A traverse may be open or closed. See Fig. 25–19. It is said to be closed when it ends upon the point of beginning or upon a point whose location has been previously determined.

j. Stations. The turning points of a traverse. In railroad and highway surveys points on the center line at 100-foot intervals are also called stations and are identified during the survey and construction by stakes with the station numbers on them. Points between stations are given the last station number with the distance from that station as a plus quantity.

The following abbreviations are commonly used on maps and map notes:

P.C. Point of curvature: the point at which the tangent ends and the curve begins on a highway or railroad.

Fig. 25–16. Aeronautical symbols, Departments of the Army and Air Force (black—friendly, single line; enemy, double line) (color—friendly, blue; enemy, red).

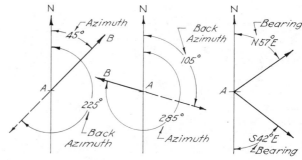

Fig. 25–18. Azimuth and bearing of a line.

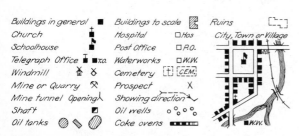

Fig. 25–17. Building symbols (black).

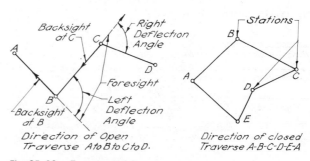

Fig. 25–19. Traverse stations.

P.T. Point of tangency: the point where the curve ends and the tangent begins.

P.I. Point of intersection: the point where the tangents to a curve intersect.

P.S. Point of switch: the point at which a switch diverges from the main line of a railroad.

P.R.C. Point of reverse curve: the point at which one curve ends and another of opposite curvature begins.

25.17   Plotting a map traverse. The method of plotting map notes depends upon that of making the survey and upon the accuracy required. In general, the plotting on a map indicates or duplicates in miniature the work carried out in the field. Thus, an angle measured in the field with a transit may be measured on the map with a protractor, and a distance measured by tape or stadia in the field is measured on the map with a boxwood scale.

℄ of R.R. bridge			79°40′L	603′
℄ of Park Road bridge			138°50′L	231′
Shore of island	at fork		171°20′L	220′
⊙ 3			59°40 R	652′
℄ of Park Road	No/. on curve		151°45 R	119′
North corner of boat house			121°25 R	575′
⊙ 2				

Fig. 25–20.   Survey notes.

The three most common methods of plotting transit surveys, in an ascending order of accuracy, are: (1) protractor and scale method; (2) tangent method; and (3) rectangular coordinate method.

25.18   Protractor and scale method. Where great accuracy is not required, the survey notes may be plotted by means of the protractor and scale. The degree of accuracy depends both upon the kind of instruments used and upon the skill of the draftsman. Any errors made are, of course, carried forward, but are not necessarily cumulative, since the possibility of error in either direction is the same, and in a large number of measurements these errors will to some extent balance each other, unless the errors are due to a personal and constant tendency of the draftsman to overestimate or to underestimate in plotting angles or distances.

For ordinary work, nothing less than a 6-inch celluloid protractor should be used, and this should be tested to see that the 180- and 90-degree angles, at least, are correct. Steel protractors, with straight edge and vernier attached, are, of course, much more desirable.

A portion of a page of survey notes is shown in Fig. 25–20. Let it be required to lay out the angle at Sta. *2* to locate Sta. *3* from these notes. Assume the point *B* in Fig. 25–21 to be Sta. *2* and the line *BA* the "backsight." The first step, then, in laying out the angle is to extend the line *AB* so far past *B* that both ends of the protractor may be on the line when the center is at *B*. Deflection angles are measured to the right and left of the sight line produced; that is, a deflection angle marked right should be laid off to the right of the ex-

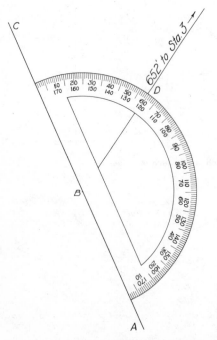

Fig. 25–21.   Plotting angles by the protractor method.

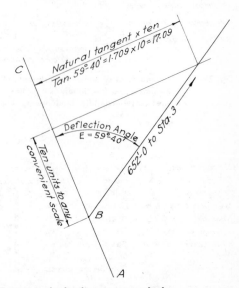

Fig. 25–22.   Plotting angles by the tangent method.

tended line AB when looking forward along that line in the direction C. Hence, the protractor must be laid on the right or left side of the line from which the angle is measured, according as the notes describe the angle, as measured in the field, to the right or left of the line. Having the protractor set as described above, mark off the angle of 59°-40' as accurately as possible, with a very sharp pencil, at the point D. With a straight edge and pencil, draw the line through the point B and the new point just located, and on this line scale off the proper length, namely, 652 feet to locate Sta. 3.

25.19 Tangent method. This method is more accurate for the plotting of angles, but requires more time; hence, it is generally used for plotting traverses; the protractor method may be used for plotting in the details. The tangent method requires a table of natural tangents and is, in brief, simply the plotting of an angle on the basis of the definition of the tangent. Again assuming the same angle as in the previous case, draw the line AB (see Fig. 25-22), extend it beyond B, and lay off on it ten units with any one of the engineer's scales. The larger the scale the greater the accuracy. At the end of these ten units, erect a perpendicular to the right of the line, since the deflection is marked right, and on it scale off the natural tangent of the angle multiplied by 10, which is 17.0901. Then through the point thus located and the point B, draw the line required, and on it scale off the distance 652 feet.

If the deflection angle is much greater than 45°, greater accuracy may be obtained by first erecting a perpendicular at B and laying off on it ten units, and then at the end of this ten-unit line erecting another perpendicular on which may be laid off a distance equal to ten times the tangent of the complement of the angle, as shown in Fig. 25-23.

If the deflection angle is greater than 135°, the ten-unit line should be laid off between B and E, as shown in Fig. 25-24, and the tangent of the supplementary angle must be used.

25.20 Rectangular coordinate method. Inasmuch as this method requires considerable trigonometric calculation and is used only when great accuracy is required, it will not be discussed in this book. Complete information concerning this method may be found in surveying texts.

25.21 Representation of elevation on maps. A one-plane projection can show only two dimensions, but for many purposes it is highly desirable that a map shall show three dimensions, namely, length, breadth, and difference of elevation. This object may be attained by two conventional schemes, that is, by the use of hachures or contours.

25.22 Hachures. If only a general idea of the elevation of the country is desired, the method of hachures is satisfactory, since it gives the effect of relief and is readily understood by the average person. Differences in elevation between any two points, however, can be shown only in a very relative manner. An example of this method of representation is shown in Fig. 25-25, from an examination of which it will be noted that the strokes are short, heavy, and close together where the slope is steep, becoming gradually longer, lighter, and

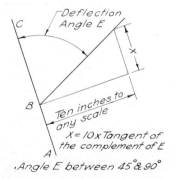

Fig. 25-23. Plotting angles from 45 to 90° by the tangent method.

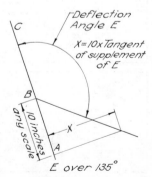

Fig. 25-24. Plotting large angles by the tangent method.

farther apart as the slope becomes more gentle and approaches the horizontal. The direction of the stroke should be the same as that in which water would flow on the slope. Care should be exercised not to have a continuous white line between the several rows of short strokes.

25.23   Contour lines. A contour line on a map is the projection of an imaginary line on the earth's surface which passes through all points of the same elevation. The meaning of a contour line may perhaps become a little clearer from an examination of Fig. 25–26, the lower part of which shows a landscape in perspective, and the upper part of which shows the same landscape in map form with elevations indicated by contour lines at intervals of 20 feet. The shoreline is in reality a contour line. The first contour line above the shore represents what the shoreline would be if the water rose vertically 20 feet. To put it in other words, if a man could walk along such a line on the ground, he would go neither up nor down but proceed always on a level and

eventually he would return to the place from which he started.

With a little reflection the following rules will be observed to be true, both of imaginary contour lines on the ground and of their projection on a map. The rules are stated as applied to a map.

a. Every contour line must either close upon itself or extend to the edge of the map.

b. When a contour line closes, it usually indicates a summit but it may indicate a depression. When it indicates a depression, this is made clear by the symbol shown in Figs. 25–14 and 25–27.

c. Contour lines never cross.

d. Where contour lines are close together the surface is steep, and where they are far apart the surface is gently sloping.

e. When contour lines are close together, they are in a sense parallel to each other (not parallel in a strictly mathematical sense). When they are far apart they need not necessarily be parallel.

f. Contour lines approaching a stream go upstream before reaching the water's edge, where they stop at points directly opposite each other at right angles to the stream. If the stream is shown by a single line they cross it at right angles; if shown by two lines, they do not cross.

g. Contour lines cannot run into the shore of a lake or other still body of water, since the water surface is at the same level at all points.

h. The first contour lines from the water's edge, on opposite sides of a still body of water, must be of the same number or elevation.

i. It is customary to make every fifth contour line

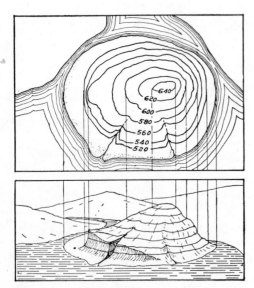

Fig. 25–25.   Hachures.

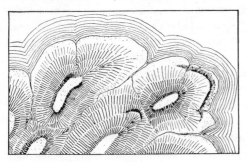

Fig. 25–26.   Meaning of contour lines.

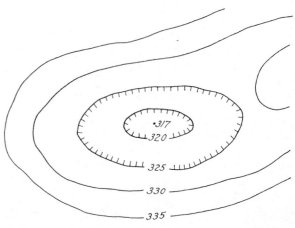

Fig. 25–27.   Depression contours.

heavier than the rest. This line is broken at some convenient place, and the number representing its elevation is inserted in the break in ink of the same color as the line. Where the contour lines are far apart each one may be numbered.

The numbers indicating the elevation of the contour lines are lettered parallel to the contour line, and, where possible, the numbers for consecutive lines are placed in rows, as shown in Fig. 25–26. If it is possible, these numbers should read from the bottom of the sheet. Contour lines may be drawn with a lettering pen or with a pen designed especially for the purpose and called a contour pen. The point of this pen is on a swivel which allows it to turn freely in any direction.

The contour interval may be any desired value, from 1 foot in very flat country up to 200 feet in rough mountainous country. By contour interval is meant the vertical distance between the planes of consecutive contour lines; 5, 10, 20, 100, and 200 feet are the intervals most frequently used.

On a summit or depression, the last contour line is numbered, or the elevation of the high or low point within the contour is given. See Figs. 25–26 and 25–27.

25.24 Plotting contour lines. The data for making a contour map may be obtained in the field by obtaining the horizontal location and the elevation of a series of points sufficiently close together so that reasonable interpolations may be made between them. These points may be taken in a rectangular pattern at intervals suitable to the terrain. They may also be taken in radial patterns from traverse points. In the latter case is is usual to choose points on the surface where there is a change in slope. Thus, in Fig. 25–28, elevations were ob-

tained at four points as indicated at the top of the figure. A sectional view shows the slope of the ground surface, and the light horizontal lines are contour planes at 1-foot intervals. A sectional view, of course, is not necessary since the horizontal distance between points can be divided proportionately. Thus in Fig. 25–28 the 605 contour is two-thirds the distance from 603 to 606.

With this explanation, the actual work of plotting contour lines from survey data is illustrated in Fig. 25–29. Here the traverse stations *1, 2,* and *3* have been shown with the observations of elevations on the earth's surface plotted from each station in the usual radial pattern. Assuming the ground slope to be uniform between plotted points, the space between points can be divided into a number of spaces equal to the difference in elevation between points as indicated for a number of spaces in Fig. 25–29.

In the upper portion of the map completed contours have been shown, and in the other portions the lines are sketched in only between plotted elevations. In general, it will be noted that between the radial lines of plotted points the contour lines follow the stream pattern.

25.25 Use of contour maps. Contour maps are used in engineering work to make preliminary estimates of excavations for structures, in locating dams and computing the volumes of water stored behind them, in computing the area of watersheds, and in many other kinds of work. Figure 25–1 shows a portion of a topographic map taken from a United States Geological map of the Urbana Quadrangle in Illinois.

25.26 Outcrop from contour maps. Contour maps also are used extensively in geology and mining. Figure 25–30

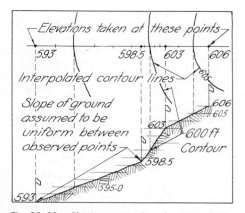

Fig. 25–28. Plotting contour lines by interpolation.

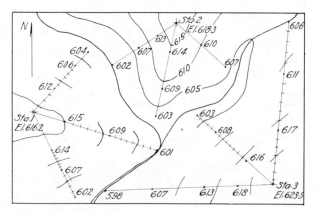

Fig. 25–29. Plotting contours.

illustrates the use of a contour map to determine data concerning a stratum of limestone. The upper surface of the layer was observed to outcrop on the 500-foot contour at point A. At other places the stratum was covered by overlying material. Borings were made at B and C at elevations shown on the map. At B the top surface was encountered at elevation 580 and the bottom at 465. At C these values were, respectively, 420 and 305.

Using the map, an elevation view was made of the three points a^V, b^V, and c^V at the known elevations of the top surface of the stratum. A horizontal line drawn across this triangle from a^V to d^V determines the strike line $a^H d^H$ which upon measurement from the North line shows the strike to be S 52 E. By making an endwise view of the strike line and again plotting the known points as at (b) the stratum is shown edgewise and its thickness and slope or dip can be determined as shown in Fig. 25–30(b). The dip is shown on the map by drawing an arrow perpendicular to the strike line pointing in the downward direction with the value of the dip lettered on it.

Having the edgewise view of the stratum the outcrop can be determined by finding where the top and bottom surfaces of the limestone bed cross the 400–700-foot contour planes in the edge view and projecting these back to the corresponding contour lines. These are shown by the small circles at the edge of the shaded area for the top surface and the black dots for the bottom.

If, on the other hand, an outcrop of a bed is shown on a contour map, the strike can be determined at once by connecting the points where any one contour line crosses the upper line of the outcrop. Having the strike line, an edge view of the bed or layer may be obtained

and from this the dip and thickness.

25.27 Cut and fill from contour maps. Contour maps are also used to determine the cut and fill required in the construction of a railroad or highway, as illustrated in Figs. 25–31 and 25–32. Since the sides of a cut or fill are plane surfaces, contour lines on them will be parallel and equally spaced. Finding the outline of a cut or fill therefore is simply a problem in the intersection of surfaces. Having the contours on the map, it is only necessary to draw the contours in the cut or fill at the same levels as the map contours and find where these lines intersect.

If the road bed is level, the contour lines in cut or fill are parallel to the edge of the road bed. The spacing of these contour lines depends upon the slope of the cut or fill. If the slope is 45° or 1:1 the spacing will be the same as the contour interval of the map whereas if it is 1½:1, the spacing will be 1½ times the contour interval. The solution of a problem of this type is shown in Fig. 25–31(a).

In hilly country, however, level road beds seldom occur. There is usually a definite slope, and this slope or grade is expressed in per cent. Thus a slope or rise of 1 foot in 100 feet of horizontal distance is called a 1% grade. A rise of 2 feet in 100 feet is a 2% grade, and so on. An ascending grade is marked plus and a descending grade minus.

When the road bed is on a grade, the contour lines of the cut and fill are not parallel to the edge of the road bed, as can be seen in Fig. 25–31(b). On an up grade, the contour lines in a cut converge toward the edge of the road bed and those on a fill diverge. The rate of divergence depends upon the grade and the slope of the cut.

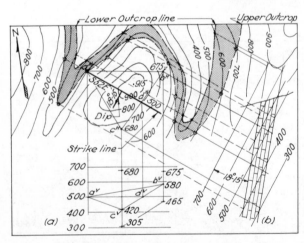

Fig. 25–30. Finding strike and dip from an outcrop.

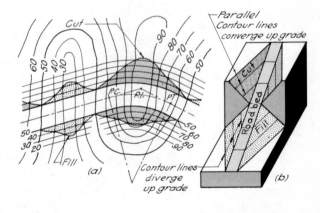

Fig. 25–31. Cut and fill on (a) level grade, (b) inclined grade.

On a 1:1 slope the divergence will be equal to the grade. Thus in a 1% grade and a 1:1 slope the contour line will diverge 10 feet from the edge of the road bed in 1000 feet. With the same grade and a 1½:1 slope the divergence in 1000 feet would be 15 feet. On curves, the divergence must be plotted at each station and a smooth curve drawn. This has been done on one side of the line shown in Fig. 25–32. Theoretically cut and fill will meet at the edge of the road bed on each side. In order not to complicate the illustration, the culvert necessary for drainage was omitted.

Where necessary, additional contours may be interpolated on the map as well as on cut and fill.

A more customary method for determining the outline of the cut and fill is by taking cross sections in the field. This is done by establishing a line perpendicular to the center line at each station and obtaining elevations at selected points on this perpendicular line. These cross sections are then plotted on paper and the roadway placed in its proper position, as shown for the two sections in Fig. 25–32. These sections can be used to determine the edge of the cut or fill and to calculate the quantities of earth to be moved.

25.28   Profiles. A profile is a line showing the elevations of the ground along some one particular line on the earth's surface. Although a profile represents something entirely different from a contour, yet the two are related in such a manner that one may be obtained from the other. A profile usually accompanies a map showing a road, railroad, sewer, water-supply line, or canal location. If the profile is to be made very accurately, the elevation of points on the line should be obtained by means of a level in the field. However, a profile for preliminary purposes may be obtained from a contour map as shown in Fig. 25–33.

When elevations are obtained with an instrument in

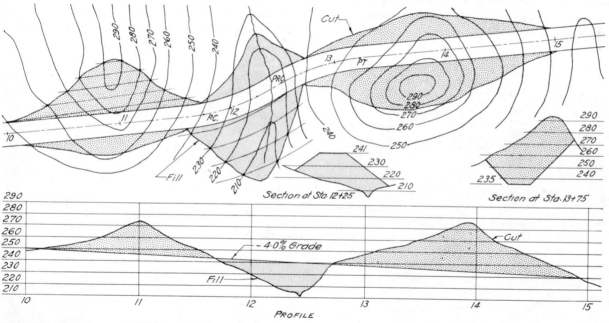

Fig. 25-32.   Plotting cut and fill on an inclined grade line.

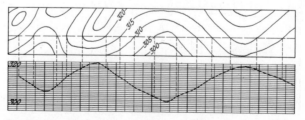

Fig. 25-33.   Profile determined from a contour map.

the field, readings are taken every 100 feet in flat country, and at closer intervals of 50, 25, or 10 feet in rough country, depending upon the ruggedness of the slope. These readings are then plotted on a special coordinate paper called profile paper, in which the spacing of coordinates is different in the two directions.

When the elevations are obtained from a contour map, the proposed line is drawn on the map and the intersections of this line with the contour lines give the elevations of points whose distances apart are obtained by scaling the map. These points are then plotted on the profile paper.

Profiles, as indicated in a preceding paragraph, are usually plotted to two different scales, the larger of which is used on the vertical axis. The purpose of the two scales is to show the variations of elevation more clearly. Since a profile is usually thousands of feet or several miles in length, whereas the difference of elevation varies only over a few hundred feet, the scale which would bring the horizontal length within workable limits would make the vertical distances so small

as to be insignificant.

25.29   Profile on curves. When a profile is made of a line, a portion of which is curved, like a railroad line, for example, the developed length of the curve is shown in profile and not the projected length. In other words, the length of the profile is the same as the true length of the line. The beginning and ending of the curve are shown, and the degree of curvature is indicated, as in Fig. 25–34.

25.30   Grade lines. In engineering work, where maps are used, a profile is seldom drawn except for the purpose of establishing the grade line of some such structure as a railroad, highway, sewer, or other engineering project. The grade line is the controlling line in construction of the types of structures mentioned. It establishes the slope or deviation from the horizontal. The grades of lines are specified in percentages, and represent the number of feet of vertical rise or fall in 100 feet horizontal distance. Grades are specified as plus when the slope is upward, and minus when the slope is downward, in the direction in which the line is laid out. See Fig.

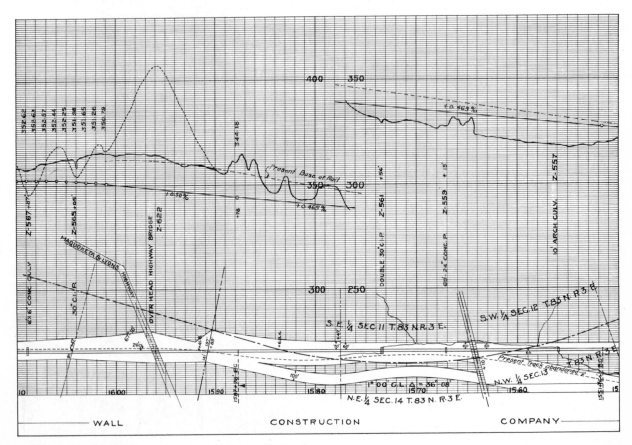

Fig. 25-34.   Railway profile.

25–32. Thus a +5% grade means a rise of 5 feet in 100 feet horizontal distance.

25.31 **Vertical curves.** In lines of any considerable length a uniform grade cannot be maintained from end to end. Although two grade lines of different slope will intersect in a point, in actual construction they must be joined by a vertical curve in order to smooth out the otherwise abrupt change of direction which would be disastrous on highways and railroads. These vertical curves are usually laid out as parabolas in the following manner, and as indicated in Fig. 25–35. Lay out on opposite sides of the point of intersection of the grade lines the same number of 10-, 25-, or 50-foot spaces. In practice both the length and number of these spaces are arbitrarily selected to suit the length of the curve and the nature of the work. The elevation of the end points E and D of the curve, Fig. 25–35, may be determined from the grade lines, and the elevation of the mid-point C of the line ED computed. The parabola passes halfway between A and C at B. With this point established, other points on the parabola may be determined by the fact that the offset from the tangent to a parabola varies as the square of the distance along the tangent. The value of the offset at B being known, offsets at the other points may be computed as shown in Fig. 25–35.

25.32 **Horizontal curves.** When railroads and highways change direction, the change is accomplished by means of circular curves that join the straight parts of the line which are called tangents. The curvature is specified in degrees, as for example, a 3-degree curve. A 3-degree curve is one on which a chord of 100 feet subtends an angle of 3 degrees at the center. Circular curves are joined to the tangent by an easement or spiral curve, but this spiral portion is not shown in the usual map. The radii of curves for various degrees is given in the Appendix.

25.33 **Lettering.** Engineering maps, particularly those drawn to a large scale for the purpose of construction, are usually lettered in single-stroke Reinhardt letters, either slant or vertical, except the titles, which may be made in a more ornamental style. On Geographic and United States Government maps, the lettering is in modern roman with certain variations designed for special purposes. A competent map draftsman must be a master of this style of lettering.

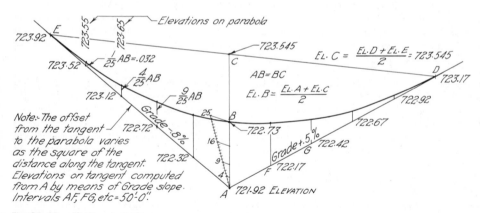

Fig. 25–35. **Plotting vertical curves.**

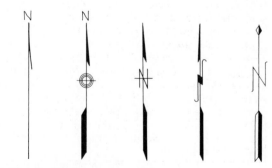

Fig. 25–36. **North points.**

Although the lettering is about the last thing to be inked on a map, the placing of it must receive attention during the preliminary pencil work; otherwise, there will often be no place to put some very essential information when the work is nearing completion. As in all other types of drawing, lettering should be placed, as far as conditions will permit, so that it may be readable from the bottom and right-hand side of a drawing.

25.34 Titles. The title of a map is usually placed in the lower right-hand corner, if possible. It should contain a statement of what the map is, that is, Plat of Jones Subdivision, the location of the ground, the name of the person or company for whom the map was made, the date of the survey, the scale, the north point, and the name or initials of the draftsman. The name of the surveyor may be in the title or it may occur only in a statement which certifies that the survey and map are correct. This statement and signature must be written. They are usually placed near the title but are not a part of it. The scale is frequently represented graphically below the title. In no case should the title be enclosed in a box.

On engineering maps Gothic letters are used; on the more highly finished maps the roman style is preferred.

25.35 North points. Every map should have the direction of the meridian indicated by means of a suitable arrow. Unless otherwise specified, this arrow points true north. The south portion of the arrow should be somewhat longer than the north portion to give it a balanced appearance. The barb and tail should be narrow and graceful, thus avoiding an arrow that is too bold or conspicuous. Sample arrows are shown in Fig. 25–36, page 25–17.

PROBLEMS

In the following problems which have been selected to fit 8½ × 11 and 11 × 17 inch-paper, great care should be exercised in the layout of traverses and in plotting the artificial features and contour lines. With few exceptions, all plotted points fall within the borderlines of the sheets specified. Since these are from older maps the azimuth, when used, has been plotted from the south instead of north as is the case in more recent practice.

Without being specified it is assumed that the student will put in all necessary lettering in the proper size and style. Notes and dimensions given in the sketches are not to appear on the finished map except the size of city lots. Symbols of proper size and color are to be used in all cases.

1. From the survey notes of Figs. 25–37 and 25–38, plot Map A. (Notes in these two figures read up the page.) Plot the traverse by the tangent method, and have it checked by your instructor. When approved, plot the details by the protractor and scale method, using all information given in the sketches.

Plot the data for the contours from Figs. 25–39 and 25–40. (Note that these read down the page.) Draw the contour lines, interpolating where necessary. After the map has been checked, ink it in the proper colors. Scale 1″ = 200′ on 11 × 17 sheet.

2. Same as Problem 1. Use Figs. 25–41 to 25–44 for Map B. Scale, 1″ = 400′.

3. On an A-size sheet (8½ × 11 or 9 × 12), draw a map from the notes and sketches in Fig. 25–45. Observe again that the notes read up the page and that the azimuths are plotted from the south instead of north. Scale, 1″ = 400′.

4. On an A-size sheet (8½ × 11 or 9 × 12), draw the contour map from Fig. 25–46. The elevations have been given on a large grid for rapid plotting. Parts of a few contour lines have been sketched in as an aid. This contour map may be plotted on the map of Fig. 25–45 by properly locating the grid with reference to the section corner at the left in this figure.

5. On an A-size sheet, draw the map from the notes and sketch of Fig. 25–47. Azimuths are again given from the south. Scale, 1″ = 400′.

6. On an A-size sheet, draw a topographic map from the data given in Fig. 25–48. Parts of a few contour lines have been shown as an aid in beginning. These contours may be plotted on the map of Fig. 25–47 by properly aligning the section corners at the right of the figure.

7. From the contour map of Problem 1, Map A, draw the profile along the railroad or highway center line as specified by your instructor. Use a piece of profile paper 5 inches wide and 15 inches long. Rule a border ¾ inch from the narrow left-hand end and ½ inch from the other three edges. Horizontal scale same as map scale. Vertical scale to be selected by the student. This scale should be in units such as 5, 10 or 20 feet to the inch. Make the intersection of the left end of the railroad or highway line with the borderline of your sheet Station No. 1. Stations are marked at 100-foot intervals.

8. Same as Problem 7, using Map B, Figs. 25–41 to 25–44.

9. Same as Problem 7, using Map C, Figs. 25–45 and 25–46. The length of profile paper required is 5 × 12 inches.

10. Same as Problem 7, using Map D, Figs. 25–47 and 25–48. Size of profile paper required 5 × 12 inches.

11. On the profile made as assigned from Problems 7 to 10, draw a grade line that will balance cut and fill as nearly as possible.

12. On an A-size sheet (8½ × 11 or 9 × 12) make a study of six assigned map symbols from Figs. 25–6 to 25–17. Enclose them in neatly balanced rectangles, and letter under each the name of the symbol.

Station			Defl. ∠s	Distance
₵ of east bridge on				
Washington St.			122°00L	675'
North bank of stream				
(average width 15 feet)			127°00L	420'
North bank of stream			148°30L	340'
₵ of bridge on Cherry St.			175°50L	380'
North bank of stream			156°00R	535'
₵ of bridge on Gum St.			138°00R	687'
O2			44°05L	1618'
East bank of stream			144°00L	1055'
Northeast corner of barn			134°30L	758'
South end of 100'bridge on ₵			130°20L	1160'
Northwest corner of house			125°30L	910'
P.T. on switch 6°curve				
(955'radius)			85°55L	830'
P.S. (=Point of switch)			61°40L	395'
P.T. on R.R. Main line 3°				
curve(1910'radius)			48°10L	354'
P.C. on R.R. Main line			24°45R	1032'
Intersection Washington &				
Walnut St. ₵.s. (₵=center line)			41°20R	665'

Locate Station No.1 780' from right border
line and 1200' from upper border line of
12"x18" sheet. Foresight due North along St.
₵. These notes read up the page.

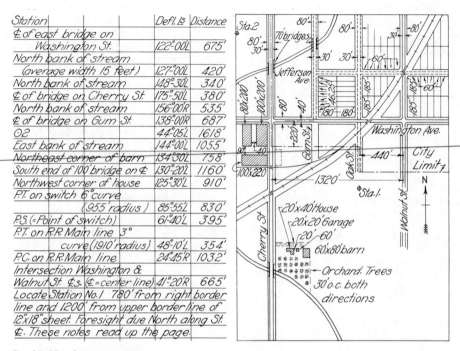

Fig. 25–37.   Survey notes, Map A.

Station			Defl. ∠s	Distance
	Scale of map 1"=200'			
O1			126°30L	1898'
West bank of stream			180°00L	775'
End of R.R. Switch			161°00L	563'
Northwest corner Bldg No.3.			152°00L	862'
West bank of stream			166°30L	514'
West bank of stream			136°30L	417'
Center of R.R. bridge			113°05L	556'
West bank of stream			97°15L	844'
West bank of stream			93°25L	1318'
₵ of R.R. Main line			5°00L	480'
O3			109°20L	1669'
West shore of lake			45°00L	955'
East shore of lake			45°00L	438'
West shore of lake			51°32L	722'
East shore of lake			51°32L	480'
West bank of stream			60°00L	600'
East bank of stream			60°00L	555'
East bank of stream			89°15L	565'
₵ of west bridge on				
Washington St			105°15L	762'
North bank at confluence				
of streams			113°05L	940'

Fig. 25–38.   Survey notes, Map A.

Station	Azimuth	Obs. Dist.	Cor. Dist.	Vert. Angle	Diff. of Elev.		Elev.	
At Sta. 1	Elev. 698.8	H.I. 4.6			K = 100			
Shot 1	30°-30'		1130				690.2	All stations on this traverse are
2	" "		1025				693.1	the same as those in the
3	" "		608				694.5	previous survey.
4	64°-25'		1140				693.3	
5	" "		845				693.9	
6	" "		534				694.7	
7	90°-00'		1383				693.5	Note:– The azimuth of any line
8	" "		1010				693.8	is the angle which the line
9	" "		490				696.4	makes with a north and south
10	119°-15'		1308				693.6	line measured in a clockwise
11	" "		851				694.5	direction from the south.
12	142°-05'		1035				693.6	
13	" "		570				696.0	
14	165°-10'		1196				693.8	
15	" "		720				698.2	
16	" "		267				700.7	H.I. means height of
17	194°-45'		1198				704.2	instrument
18	" "		793				705.3	
19	221°-00'		1115				711.9	
20	" "		742				705.6	K is the stadia constant, a
21	240°-00'		838				705.6	factor used in computations
22	" "		687				702.1	
23	303°-00'		720				697.2	
△ 2	135°-55'	H.I. 4.7	1618				706.8	

The data in these columns have not been reproduced since they are not essential to plotting the map.

These notes to be read down the page.

Fig. 25–39.   Topography notes, Map A.

Station	Azimuth	Obs. Dist	Cor. Dist	Vert. Angle	Diff. of Elev.		Elev.	
At Sta. 2								
Shot 1	22°-45'		940'				691.0	
2	" "		642'				692.7	
3	31°-30'		500'				696.2	
4	46°-40'		250'				701.1	Water level of lake 692.3
5	90°-00'		358'				693.9	
6	" "		157'				701.3	
7	270°-00'		617'				693.6	
8	" "		310'				700.8	
9	335°-00'		251'				694.6	
10	" "		148'				698.9	
△ 3	26°-25'		1669'				697.2	
Shot 1	10°-00'		520'				699.2	
2	66°-50'		530'				706.2	
3	" "		259'				701.4	
4	137°-45'		710'				700.6	
5	154°-32'		1150'				694.6	
6	" "		512'				698.8	
7	171°-05'		1122'				694.5	
8	182°-09'		768'				696.0	
9	208°-00'		597'				693.6	
10	249°-03'		330'				693.4	
11	289°-15'		629'				693.2	
12	305°-55'		905'				696.1	
13	305°-55'		468'				694.0	

Fig. 25–40.   Topography notes, Map A.

Station			Defl. ∠s	Distance
West bank at confluence				
of north & south branches			128°30'R	1375'
North bank of south branch			83°45'R	730'
Center of highway bridge			58°30'R	680'
North bank of south branch			26°45'R	905'
West bank of north branch			140°30'L	1560'
South bank of north branch			120°30'L	2290'
North bank of south branch			8°30'R	1170'
⊙2			48°45'R	2700'
P.C. on R.R. line			137°40'R	2420'
P.C. on ₵ of highway			118°15'R	1495'
P.T. on R.R. line			85°00'R	1535'
₵ of R.R. line			7°20'L	1915'
⊙1			50°30'R	3040'
Center of highway bridge			180°00'R	250'
P.S. on R.R.			159°30'R	490'
P.T. on R.R. switch			128°45'R	940'
Southwest corner Bldg No.1			124°30'R	1005'
Northeast corner Bldg No.2			111°15'R	1365'
North bank of stream			107°00'R	550'
North bank of stream			94°45'R	940'
North bank of stream			139°00'L	400'
Locate Station 0, 400' from left and 1100'				
from top border line. Foresight north				
along section line which makes 30° with				
the left border line. Read notes up the page.				

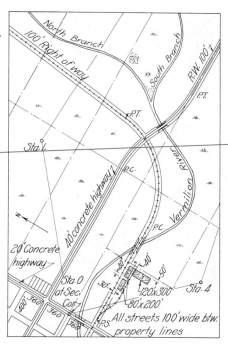

Fig. 25–41.   Survey notes, Map B.

Station			Defl. ∠s	Distance
Scale of map 1"=400'				
⊙0			66°00'R	2380'
Southeast cor. bldg No.3			83°00'R	870'
Northeast cor. bldg No.3			90°00'R	1150'
South bank of river			97°00'R	1460'
Center of R.R. bridge			109°00'R	1235'
South bank of river			135°20'R	1022'
South bank of river			163°30'R	1314'
⊙4			56°15'R	3040'
South bank of river			78°00'R	1370'
South bank of river			101°00'R	1185'
Center of highway bridge			118°30'R	1220'
P.T. on ₵ of highway			160°30'R	625'
Section corner			142°40'L	985'
⊙3			94°15'R	2190'

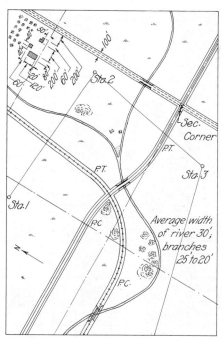

Fig. 25–42.   Survey notes, Map B.

Station	Azimuth	Obs.Dist.	Cor.Dist	Vert.Angle	Diff of Elev.	Elevation	
At Sta.0.	Elev. 448.7	H.I. 4.7		K=.98			
Shot 1	135°40'		720			452.1	Note:- The azimuth of a line is
2	194°30'		564			452.6	the angle which the line makes
3	" "		1430			460.0	with a north and south line
4	230°30'		898			455.0	measured in a clockwise
5	" "		1462			461.2	direction from the south.
6	" "		1690			469.1	
7	" "		2356			474.3	
8	331°30'		712			450.0	Elevation at water line under
9	" "		1344			459.1	highway bridge 447.4
Δ1	230°30'	H.I. 4.3	3040			478.2	
10	16°45'		1200			470.0	
11	" "		2000			457.5	Elevation at water line under
12	156°15'		520			481.3	railway bridge 452.5
13	230°20'		410			477.5	
14	" "		1420			470.0	
15	" "		2182			460.3	
16	254°15'		1955			462.5	The traverse of this survey
17	" "		2456			470.0	is the same as that used in
18	296°45'		984			473.9	the preceding survey.
19	" "		1714			460.0	
20	337°50'		720			475.0	
21	" "		1440			471.8	
22	" "		1749			465.0	
Δ2	279°15'	H.I. 4.6	2700			467.6	

These notes read down the page.

Fig. 25–43. Topographic notes, Map B.

Station	Azimuth	Obs.Dist.	Cor.Dist	Vert.Angle	Diff of Elev.	Elevation	
Shot 23	00°00'		361			463.7	
24	" "		1280			470.0	
25	58°30'		775			460.0	
26	175°00'		1889			472.0	
27	201°00'		508			472.4	
28	" "		1020			480.0	
29	243°00'		750			473.8	
30	264°45'		834			466.2	
31	284°15'		1100			460.0	
Δ3	13°30'	H.I. 4.8	2190			472.8	
32	58°35'		1770			462.9	
33	69°15'		1715			457.1	Elevation at water line under
34	121°30'		320			468.6	highway bridge 455.4
35	" "		760			463.2	
36	173°40'		978			462.0	
Δ4	69°45'	H.I. 4.3	3040			462.1	
37	16°30'		354			465.0	
38	" "		775			468.9	
39	" "		1120			472.0	
40	69°20'		682			460.2	
41	162°30'		450			457.3	
42	" "		1370			455.0	
43	210°00'		1835			458.4	
44	221°30'		1526			454.7	
45	233°00'		631			457.1	

The data belonging in the empty columns have not been reproduced since they are not needed in plotting the map.

Fig. 25–44. Topographic notes, Map B.

Station	Azimuth	Distance
O1 (check back for ∠ & distance	266°-0'	3485'-0"
West bank of stream	325°-30'	940'-0"
P.C. on highway ₵ (Rad.1000')	265°-30'	1245'-0"
₵ of 150' highway bridge	255°-50'	1020'-0"
Southeast corner of barn	197°-45'	1245'-0"
Southeast corner of house	188°-30'	1170'-0"
Intersection of highway ₵s	171°-50'	900'-0"
Northeast corner of house	135°-15'	534'-0"
Southwest corner of barn	108°-45'	610'-0"
O3	40°-30'	2945'-0"
Intersection of highway & R.R.₵s	91°-50'	2040'-0"
Northeast corner Bldg.No.1	38°-0'	810'-0"
Southeast corner Bldg.No.2	30°-30'	975'-0"
P.T. on R.R. switch (Rad.820')	28°-0'	836'-0"
P.R.C. on R.R. switch	359°-0'	635'-0"
P.S. on R.R. (Rad.820')	312°-45'	815'-0"
O2	142°-0'	2530'-0"
East bank of stream	168°-45'	1700'-0"
Intersection of highway & R.R.₵	168°-45'	1305'-0"
₵ of R.R. bridge (200' span)	155°-0'	1510'-0"
East bank of stream	142°-0'	1250'-0"
South bank of stream	104°-15'	1430'-0"
P.T. on ₵ of highway (Rad.1000')	104°-15'	895'-0"
O1 Locate Sta. No.1 100 ft from right border line & 900 ft from lower border line.		

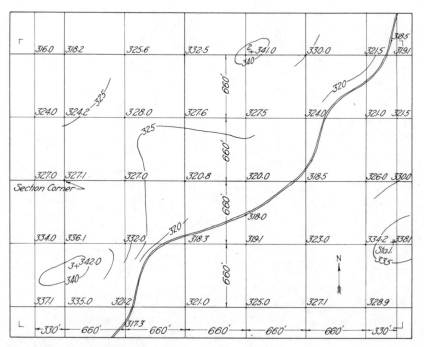

These notes read up the page

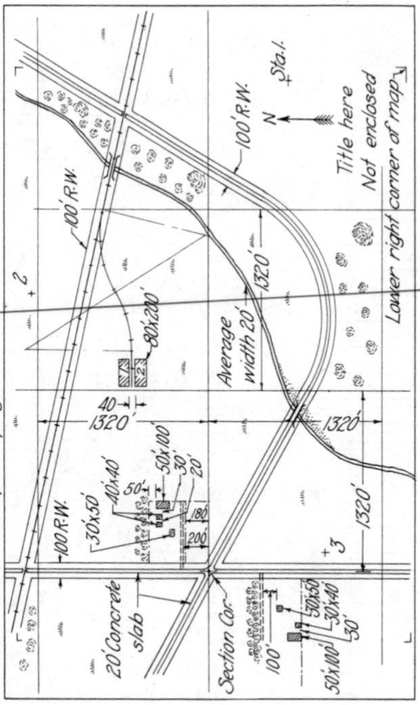

Fig. 25-45.   Survey notes, Map C.

Fig. 25-46.   Topography, Map C.

Station	Azimuth	Distance
O1 (check back ∠ & distance)	91° 0'	3020'-0"
Section Corner	223° 0'	575'-0"
P.T. on highway ₵ (1000' Rad)	192° 0'	432'-0"
P.C. on highway ₵	110° 0'	569'-0"
₵ of 200' highway bridge	84° 0'	900'-0"
P.T. on highway ₵	67° 30'	1775'-0"
East bank of stream	34° 0'	1051'-0"
O3	348° 30'	1640'-0"
Northwest corner of barn	298° 30'	1215'-0"
Northwest corner Bldg No.2	310° 45'	564'-0"
Southwest corner Bldg No.1	322° 15'	695'-0"
R.R. ₵	110° 0'	545'-0"
P.T. on R.R. switch	70° 35'	1390'-0"
P.S. on R.R. switch (1200' Rad)	72° 05'	2010'-0"
North bank of stream	47° 0'	1620'-0"
East bank of stream	30° 0'	1580'-0"
O2	240° 0'	3105'-0"
P.C. on highway ₵ (1000' Rad)	321° 0'	1230'-0"
Northwest corner of barn	311° 10'	502'-0"
Northeast corner of barn	295° 15'	780'-0"
South bank of stream	236° 0'	985'-0"
₵ of 150' R.R. bridge	214° 0'	970'-0"
West bank of stream	180° 0'	1060'-0"
West bank of stream	168° 0'	1550'-0"

O1 Locate Sta No.1 200'-0" from left border line & 1,200'-0" from the lower border line.

These notes read up the page.

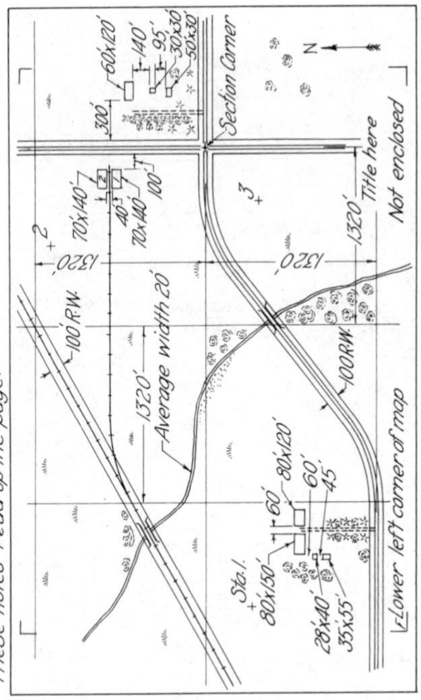

Fig. 25-47. Survey notes, Map D.

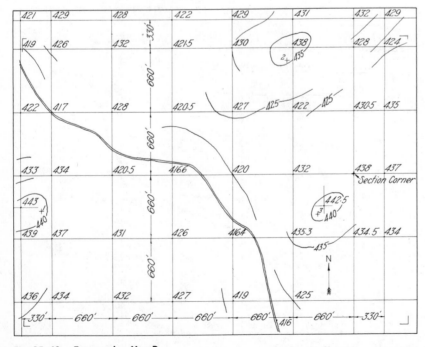

Fig. 25-48. Topography, Map D.

Photograph of model of U. S. Air Force Academy Chapel, Colorado Springs, Colorado (Skidmore, Owings & Merrill).

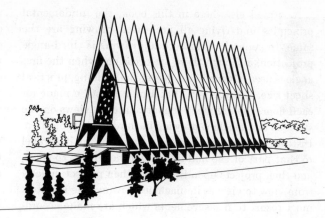

26

Architectural Drawing*

26.1 Introduction. Architecture is the art and science of building, and involves diverse types of structures. Many phases of engineering are integrated in building, construction, and design. These include electrical engineering for power, illumination, and communications; mechanical engineering for elevators, escalators, machinery, and power; and civil engineering for structural design, site planning, and services. Other fields of engineering must be considered for materials and methods, plumbing, heating, and ventilating. Every engineer will have occasion to use architectural drawings. An engineer may draw plans or write specifications for a building or some part of a building. Engineers have designed and built industrial buildings, multi-storied structures, bridges, and power projects, whose architecture is good because of the forthright engineered solution of the building's purpose and structure. Architecture constantly changes and advances with progress in science and engineering.

A building is essentially a structural frame which meets certain space requirements, and which will endure certain loading conditions. The designer of a building must understand human needs, space requirements, structural elements, form, scale, and proportion. This chapter is concerned with the working drawings or "plans" by which the architect conveys to the builder or contractor the necessary information to erect the complete structure. Building design, specifications, esthetics, and other aspects of architecture are beyond the scope of this book.

* This chapter was prepared by Professor Wayne L. Shick, Registered Architect.

As stated elsewhere in this book, the fundamental principles underlying all projection drawing are the same. In general, architectural drawing is third-angle projection, although there are occasions when the first angle is used. Owing to the size of the building, practical sheet size, and the fact that a plan must be made for each floor, the architect cannot relate his views on one sheet as in a machine drawing in third-angle projection. Instead, he uses one plane at a time, placing it parallel to that part of the building which he wishes to show, and then projects upon it. Rather than project directly from view to view as in machine drawing, the architect must resort to measurements which are made according to the rules of projection.

An architect's drawings may be divided into two general classes, namely, those which are used for study and consultation with clients, and those by means of which the building is actually erected. The latter are called working drawings. The former are further subdivided into two classes called preliminary sketches and display drawings. The preliminary sketches are made by the architect for his own study of the problem and to use in discussion with his client; the display drawings represent the completed solution which the architect submits in competition or for public display.

26.2 Preliminary sketches. The draftsman begins his study of a problem by making freehand sketches embodying different ideas which occur to him. From these he selects what appears to be the best, and works up a preliminary sketch in pencil to a small scale, say ¹⁄₁₆ or ⅛ inch to the foot, for presentation to his client. These sketches may include the main floor plans, an elevation, and a perspective. They are dimensioned for general sizes only and are sometimes embellished in such a way as to make them more attractive to the client. It is essential that they shall be easily understood, since frequently the person who is to inspect and approve them is not proficient at reading drawings. To this end, only the material which will show the general arrangement is included, and the details of construction are omitted. These drawings are often made on tracing paper so that comparison of different floor plans can be readily made by placing one over the other.

26.3 Display drawings. In some respects display drawings serve the same purpose as the preliminary sketches, since they make clear to others the general arrangement and appearance of the building. They are made to small scale, the exact choice depending upon the size of the building and the desired size of the finished drawing. They usually include a front elevation, the main floor plans, and a perspective. They are rendered in pencil, ink, or water colors, or in a combination of these, and include, besides the building itself, some imaginary background, such as trees, shrubbery, gardens, and clouds, the whole drawing being a problem in art, designed to secure the most pleasing effect and to show the building to the best advantage.

An ordinary front elevation may be made quite realistic by projecting the shades and shadows on the building, by material indication, colors in various tones, and by putting in a foreground in parallel perspective.

Display drawings are not dimensioned, but the scale is represented graphically. They contain very little information that could be used by the builder.

26.4 Working drawings. The working drawings developed from the architect's sketches and display drawings are the ones in which the engineer is particularly interested. The purpose of such drawings is to provide information from which, with the written specifications, accurate estimates of cost can be made and the building constructed. They must, therefore, be accurately drawn to scale and include all necessary details and dimensions.

A complete set of working drawings, or set of plans, as they are sometimes called, will include the following six or more sheets: plot plan; basement or foundation plan; floor plans in order—first, second, third, and so on, not duplicating, of course, where the floors are exactly alike; four elevations, if all views of the building are different; sections, as many as may be required; and details, as many as may be required. In addition, large buildings frequently require separate sets of plans for the structural framing, whether it be of timber, steel, or reinforced concrete, and separate plans for the mechanical, electrical, plumbing, heating, and ventilating work.

26.5 Plot plans. The first sheet of a complete set of plans is the plot plan. It shows the property lines and the relation of the proposed building to them. See Fig. 26–1. The building is sometimes represented by a cross-hatched area whose shape is that of the outside of the structure at the grade line. In addition, there should be shown the drainage sewers and water mains, utilities, walks and driveways, and any outbuildings to be constructed. If the building site is hilly, the elevations are shown by contour lines, and any grading which may be necessary is indicated. This sheet, like the others, contains in the lower right-hand corner the architect's standard title and, at some convenient place on the sheet, an arrow indicating the north point.

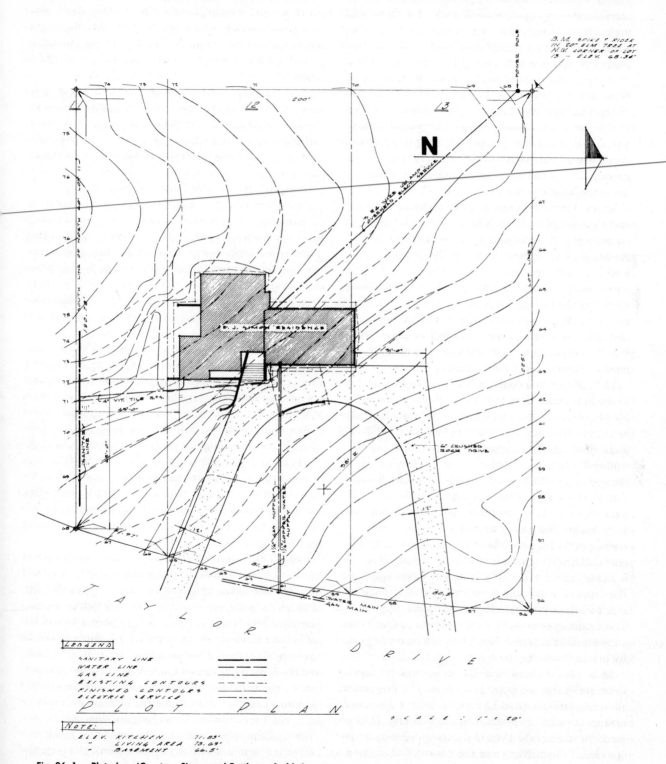

Fig. 26-1.   Plot plan. (Courtesy Simon and Rettberg, Arch's.)

26.6   Floor plans. The floor plan of a building, instead of being a top view as in machine drawing, is in reality a horizontal section as seen from above. The horizontal cutting plane is passed so that it will show the most detail; it need not be a single continuous plane, but may be offset to different heights above the floor at various places. The plan will, therefore, show all openings in the walls in the story through which it is passed. See Fig. 26–2 and Fig. 26–11. It will show interior walls and built-in features such as the plumbing fixtures, special cases, and cabinets. The location of heat outlets or ventilating ducts may also be shown, as well as the location of steam or hot-water radiators and their connecting lines where space must be provided for them by someone other than the heating contractor. The exact location of the water and drainage pipes for the plumbing is usually not shown on small jobs unless their location presents a problem the solution of which must be provided for in advance.

Stairways are indicated by showing approximately one-half of the full flight to the floors above and below, and by marking upon the drawing the full number of risers. An illustration is shown in the floor plans in Fig. 26–2. Two consecutive floor plans show completely the stairway connecting them. Stairways are frequently worked out to a large scale in order to make sure that they will properly fit in the space allowed. A common rule for proportioning the risers and treads is to make the sum of one riser and one tread approximately 17 inches. Seven to eight inches is a maximum height for a comfortable riser.

In addition to the items discussed above, which would actually appear in a projection made strictly according to theory, it is customary to indicate certain features which would not appear by the rules of projection. For example, beams and ornamental features, which appear in the ceiling above the floor shown, are indicated on the floor plan. The lintels over wall openings are also indicated, although they are above the cutting plane. In small buildings not requiring separate framing plans, the supporting members for the floor above are shown on the plan of the floor below. Thus, the beams or joists supporting the second floor would be indicated on the first-floor plan. This, of course, does not apply where a special set of framing plans is prepared. Ceiling lights and outlets are indicated in the same way, by locating them on the plan of the floor below. The precise location of the wiring is not given, unless openings must be allowed for it by others than those who do the wiring.

In reinforced concrete and steel work, for example, holes must be provided where wiring conduits and pipes pass through floors or beams, as the cutting of holes after the concrete is poured and set might damage its structural value. For reasons of economy also, space for conduits, piping, and ventilating ducts must be provided in advance.

It has become an established practice to draw the floor plans so that the front of the building is toward the bottom or right edge of the sheet, depending upon the shape and size of the building. Elevations should read from the bottom of the sheet, or the right-hand edge in some instances.

In making the floor plans of a building that has several stories, time may be saved by tracing from the first-floor plan the outside walls and interior columns which run through from floor to floor. This also avoids the possibility of error in the location of columns or piers, elevator shafts, and the like, which must line up from story to story.

26.7   Elevations. The elevation of a building is a projection of the building upon a vertical plane perpendicular to the direction from which the elevation is seen, and shows the story heights, all openings in the outside walls, and the nature of the outside finish, such as wood, stone, brick, metal, and glass. Unless the sides of a building are identical, each elevation should be drawn, see Figs. 26–3, 26–4, and 26–5. Where the wall material is erected in a certain pattern, the size, arrangement, and location of the material are shown on the elevation, and the exact construction is shown in a large-scale detail drawing. The outline of the building below the grade line is shown by invisible lines, as seen in Fig. 26–12, as are also roof lines which may be concealed behind parapet walls. On elevations of small buildings, stairways are sometimes drawn in invisible lines in order to save drawing a section. With these exceptions, the invisible line is not used on the elevation unless absolutely necessary. Dimensions on an elevation are practically limited to those in a vertical direction. See Fig. 26–12. Other dimensions belong on the floor plans and should not be placed on the elevation unless it is impossible to show them on the plans. The elevations are given life and snap by accented lines and touches of ruled-line rendering to suggest the texture of the surface. This ruled-line rendering must be soft and subdued, and not an attempt at a rigid representation, as in machine drawing.

In making elevations, the plan sheet is taped in proper projection position, either beneath the tracing

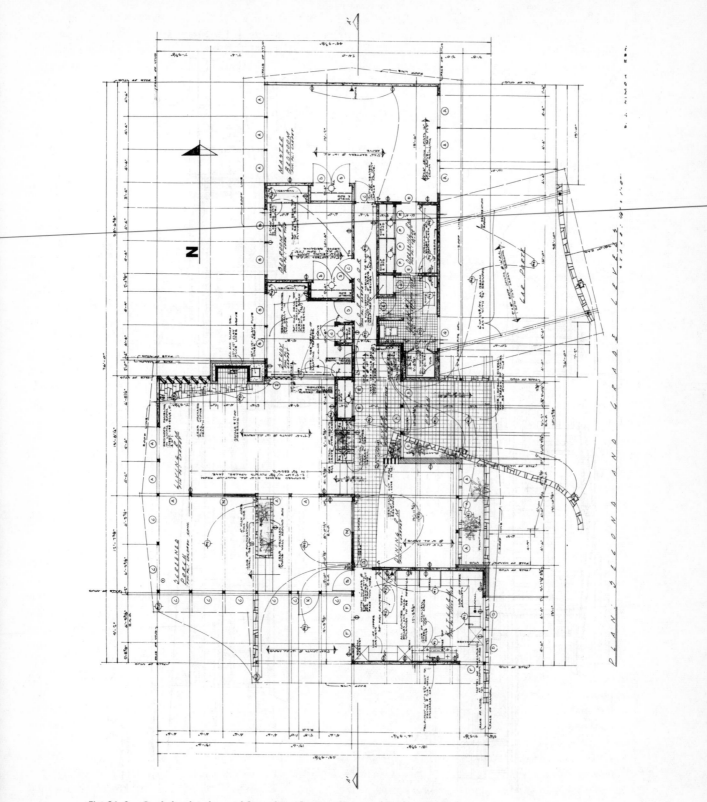

Fig. 26-2. Grade level and second floor plan. (Courtesy Simon and Rettberg, Arch's.)

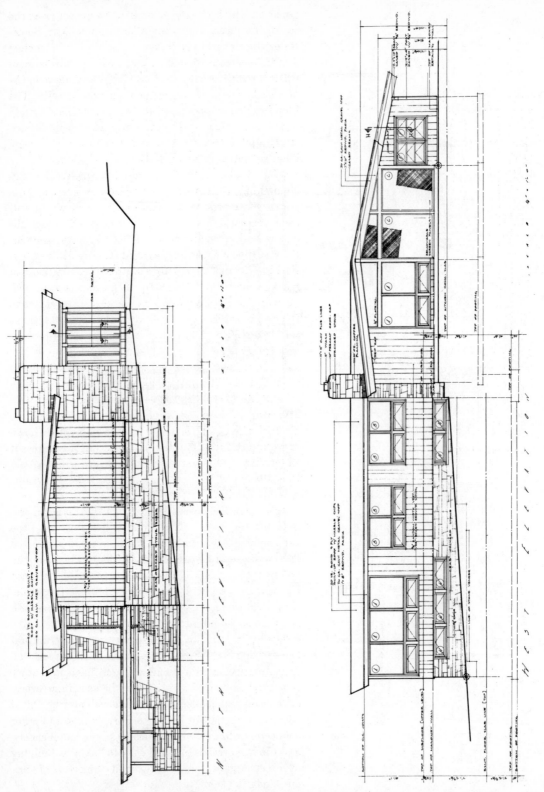

Fig. 26-3. North elevation. (Courtesy Simon and Rettberg, Arch's.)   **Fig. 26-4. West elevation. (Courtesy Simon and Rettberg, Arch's.)**

paper on which the elevation is to be drawn or at the top of the sheet, whichever is more convenient. Sometimes the elevation is drawn by reading the principal dimensions from the plan view, locating approximate window positions, and then drawing the windows in the best size, style, and arrangement on the elevation. The best fenestration is worked out by a coordinated study of the plan, elevations, and section. This coordinated study applies to the design and detailing of the entire building and its many parts.

26.8   Sections. The exact details of construction, different kinds of material, and the exact size and integrated placement of the materials are shown in cutaway drawings or sections. Sections cut across the narrow way of a building are called transverse sections, those cutting lengthwise are called longitudinal sections, as shown in Fig. 26-6. Other sections may be taken of parts of the building, showing with exactness the construction of the individual part and how it relates to the building. These sections are called detail sections, that is, a section of a foundation, a doorway, a fireplace, or stairway. The cutting plane for a section may be offset to take in the important features which it is desirable to show. The cutting plane may be shown edgewise on the floor plan by a heavy dash-and-dot line with arrows at the ends indicating the direction in which the view is taken. All parts cut by the plane are shown cross-hatched in some characteristic way to represent the material, as shown in Fig. 26-13. All parts behind the cutting plane are shown in the usual way. Invisible lines are avoided.

26.9   Standard details. Many of the details and materials and methods used in building construction have been standardized. An entire building could be erected of materials which are standard, uniformly manufactured and specified by the manufacturer, and erected by standard practices. Such things as brick, tile, structural steel, windows, and doors are furnished in certain standard sizes and fabrications.

The most common uses of brick are as a structural load-bearing wall or partition, or an outer screen wall or veneer facing to a building which has some other structural framing. The brick may be used in a variety of patterns and bonds, and the brick wall may be united with the structure by metal anchors, lintels, and other connectors. Precast concrete slabs, stone, metal sheets, and other materials are also used to "skin" a building over a structural frame, using metal connectors of various kinds.

a. Brick. Bricks may be obtained in several sizes,

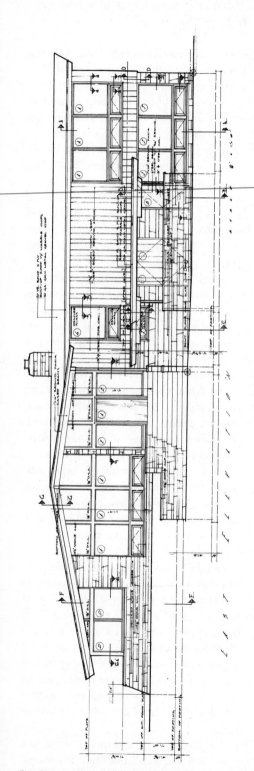

Fig. 26-5.   East elevation. (Courtesy Simon and Rettberg, Arch's.)

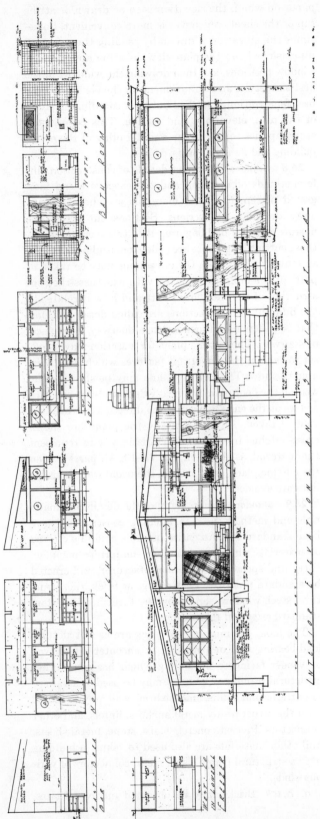

colors, and textures. Figure 26-7 illustrates two common types of bond, and some types of brick joints. Joints vary from ¼" to 1" thick usually by ⅛-" increments.

b. *Tile.* The word tile applies to two distinct classes of material, namely, the large hollow blocks or building tile, and the smaller solid units used for floors and the covering of walls which are subject to moisture, acid, or other abusive conditions, particularly in kitchens and bathrooms. Tile is also widely used in schools, industrial plants, public buildings, etc. Both kinds may be obtained in standardized dimensions. Figure 26-8 illustrates common building tile sizes.

c. *Structural steel.* A few of the common sizes and dimensions of standard steel beams, channels, and angles are given in the tables in the Appendix. For complete information, consult the American Institute of Steel Construction (AISC) handbook.

d. *Metal sash.* Metal windows are made in stock sizes and are specified by numbers which have the meanings indicated in Fig. 26-9. The details of construction of one type of sash are shown at the left of this figure. See the Metal Window Institute for a complete listing of standard metal window sizes and types.

e. *Wood sash.* Wood windows and metal windows are manufactured in the same types, namely, the projecting or awning types, casement—that is, vertically pivoted; double-hung—that is, sliding up and down and horizontal sliding. Windows can be had in any size of fixed sash. A millwork manufacturer or lumber yard should be consulted for a catalogue of standard types and dimensions of wood sash. For large window openings, the opening is broken up into two, three, or more sashes, separated by a slender vertical member called a mullion. Figure 26-10 gives standard sizes for three types of wood windows.

f. *Doors.* Doors may be obtained in wood, metal, or flexible material types. Common metal and wood doors are manufactured in stock sizes from 1'-8" to 3'-0" wide by increments of 2", and in 6'-6", 6'-8", and 7'-0" heights. The thickness may be 1⅜", 1¾", or for very large doors 2¼". Flush-panel doors having smooth flat faces are most commonly used, although doors panelled in various designs are available. Doors for large openings may be made up of several doors either hinged together or sliding on tracks, or they may be of a flexible folding type.

g. *Wood.* Wood is used in buildings in two ways, as a structural material and as a finish material. Structural lumber comes in several grades, the number 1 and num-

Fig. 26-6. Longitudinal section and details. (Courtesy Simon and Rettberg, Arch's.)

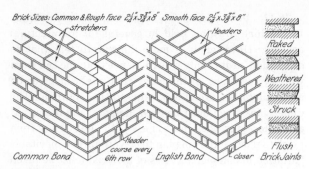

Brick Sizes: Common & Rough Face $2\frac{1}{4} \times 3\frac{3}{4} \times 8$" Smooth Face $2\frac{1}{4} \times 3\frac{3}{8} \times 8$"

Common Bond — English Bond

Brick Joints: Raked, Weathered, Struck, Flush

Fig. 26–7. Brick bond and joints.

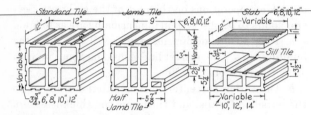

Fig. 26–8. Typical tile blocks.

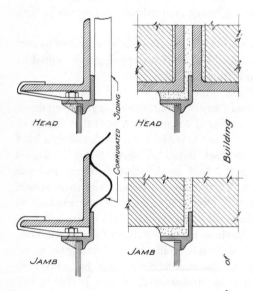

HEAD | HEAD

JAMB | JAMB

SILL | SILL

STEEL & CORRUGATED IRON CONSTRUCTION | MASONRY CONSTRUCTION

Fig. 26–9. Steel sash details and dimensions.

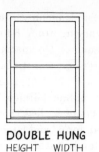

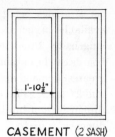

DOUBLE HUNG		CASEMENT (2 SASH)	
HEIGHT	WIDTH	HEIGHT	WIDTH
2'-10"	1'-8"	2'-2"	1'-10½"
3'-2"	2'-0"	2'-8 3/16"	3'-10¾"
3'-6"	2'-4"	3'-2 3/16"	5'-11"
3'-10"	2'-8"	4'-2 3/16"	7'-11¼"
4'-2"	3'-0"	5'-2 3/16"	9'-11½"
4'-6"	3'-4"		
4'-10"	3'-8"		
5'-2"			
5'-6"			

ONE MANUFACTURER MAKES 54 STOCK SIZES OF LISTED DIMENSIONS — MULLIONS ARE 3" WIDE — MUNTINS IN SEVERAL STOCK PATTERNS

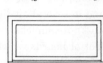

AWNING OR TRANSOM

HEIGHT	WIDTH
1'-0 5/8"	2'-4 5/8"
1'-4 5/8"	3'-2"
1'-8 1/8"	3'-10"
2'-0 1/8"	

WOOD WINDOWS – SASH SIZES
ALL WINDOWS MAY BE COMBINED WITH FIXED SASH (PICTURE WINDOWS) OF MANY STOCK SIZES-

Fig. 26–10. Wood window details and dimensions.

DIMENSIONS – METAL SASH
A TYPE – 20 × 16 BAR CENTERS
B TYPE – 22 × 16 BAR CENTERS

HEIGHT	WIDTH			
	1'-8 7/8"	3'-8 7/8"	5'-0 7/8"	6'-8 7/8"
2'-9"	A12	B22	A32	A42
4'-1"	A13	B23	A33	A43
5'-5"	A14	B24	A34	A44
6'-9"	A15	B25	A35	A45
8'-1"		B26	A36	A46
9'-5"		B27	A37	A47
10'-9"		B28	A38	A48
12'-1"		B29	A39	A49

MULTIPLE UNITS — OPENING WIDTHS:
BAR CENTER DIMENSION (1'-8", 3'-8", 5'-0", 6'-8")
TIMES NUMBER OF EACH UNIT, PLUS 4" FOR
EACH MULLION, PLUS ONE BRICK JOINT

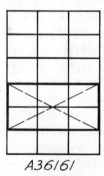

A36161

CODE FOR SASH NUMBERS

A-20×16

3-LIGHTS WIDE

6-LIGHTS HIGH

1-NO. VENTS.

6-LIGHTS IN VENT

1-LIGHTS UP TO VENT

ber 2 grades being most commonly used. Lumber is available in lengths varying from 8-foot to 24-foot lengths by 2-foot increments. On special order longer boards can be obtained. The cross-sectional dimensions in greatest demand are $2'' \times 4''$, $2'' \times 6''$, $2'' \times 8''$, $2'' \times 10''$, and $2'' \times 12''$. These are nominal dimensions, the exact dimensions of lumber being $\frac{3}{8}''$ less than the nominal dimensions up to $5''$, and, for $6''$ and larger, $\frac{1}{2}''$ less than the nominal. For example: a $2'' \times 4''$ is actually $1\frac{5}{8}'' \times 3\frac{5}{8}''$ in cross section, and a $6'' \times 8''$ is $5\frac{1}{2}'' \times 7\frac{1}{2}''$. One exception is the $1''$ board which is about $\frac{13}{16}''$ in thickness. As a finish material, wood is usually employed as boards $1''$ ($\frac{13}{16}''$) thick, of various widths and lengths, and in several qualities from nearly perfect boards with no knots, checks, or other defects to the most imperfect of boards which may be used for some decorative effect. Wood can be processed into several other types of finish material such as plywood which comes in many thicknesses and sheet sizes.

26.10 Details. Because of the small scale, it is impossible to show the exact construction of all parts of a building on any of the drawings just discussed. It is necessary, therefore, to draw typical details of all intricate parts of the building for which the construction is not self-evident or in accordance with standard practice. These details are made to a larger scale than the rest of the drawing and may vary from ½ inch to the foot up to full size, as shown in Fig. 26–13. It is quite evident that an architect cannot include everything that may need explanation, but his plans and specifications should embrace enough details to permit the making of an explicit contract. It would be manifestly unfair for him to insist upon some type of construction not fully shown in the plans and specifications, when the contractor had perhaps figured on some cheaper scheme. As the building operations proceed, however, the architect is required, from time to time, to furnish additional detail drawings, which must always be given a title showing clearly to what part of the building they apply.

The architect does not devise all the details which are shown in his plans, but depends upon the manufacturers of the different products which go to make up a building to supply him with information concerning their products. Such information has been collected in a set of volumes, called *Sweet's Architectural File*, published annually. A similar file for engineers is also on the market. The progressive architect or engineer also keeps a file of the catalogues of all the manufacturers of materials in which he is interested.

26.11 Dimensioning. The common rules which apply to machine drawing hold in general for architectural drawing. However, it is more difficult to tell what to dimension, as it is only by experience that one can learn which dimensions, of the many that might be given on a building plan, are of any value to the workman. The dimensions given must be clear, definite, and unmistakable. Moreover, they must check with one another from place to place and from plan to elevation. The inevitable variation in commercial sizes of material must be taken into consideration. This does not lessen the requirements for accuracy but demands an expert knowledge of building operations on the part of the architect. Several points to be observed in dimensioning are as follows:

a. Keep all outside dimension lines well away from the building lines. The nearest line should be about an inch away from the building line.

b. Dimension to center lines of interior walls or to the outside of walls, and then give the thickness also. Whenever possible, make a series of inside dimensions in one straight line clear across the building.

c. Dimension to the center lines of columns in both directions.

d. Dimension to the center lines of openings in outside walls, or to the sides of the opening, as required by the structural framing.

26.12 Notes. More notes are used in architectural drawing than in any other branch of engineering drawing. If the meaning of a symbol is doubtful, it should be made clear by a note. When a part is detailed, a brief note, such as "See detail on sheet No. 11," should be placed on the floor or elevation drawings near the part detailed. Then under the detail itself there should be a title stating what it is, and a note referring back to the place where the parts may be found in the drawings. In addition to these notes, the sizes of doors, windows, beams, girders, lintels, columns, etc., must be given. These might be classified as dimensions, but since they do not appear in dimension lines it is better to call them notes.

26.13 Specifications. The contract documents in any architectural project are the agreement, the general conditions of the contract, the drawings, and specifications. The architect prepares specifications to accompany each set of plans. Specifications begin with general statements and conditions, and proceed in a systematic way to consider the work of various trades and materials involved in the construction of the building. The specifications cover those points of construction which cannot be shown in a drawing, namely, kind and quality of

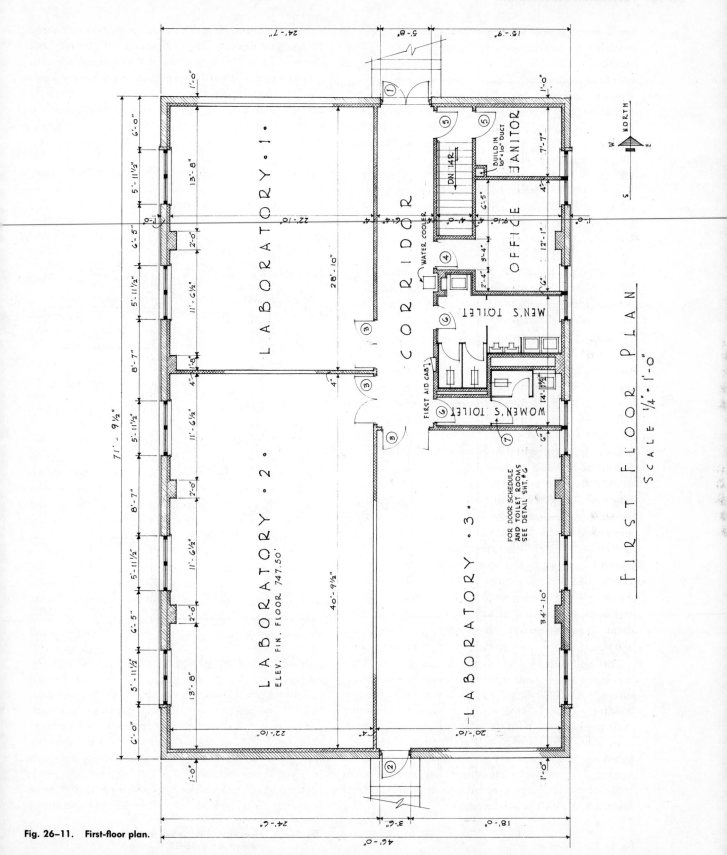

FIRST FLOOR PLAN
Scale ¼" = 1'-0"

Fig. 26-11. First-floor plan.

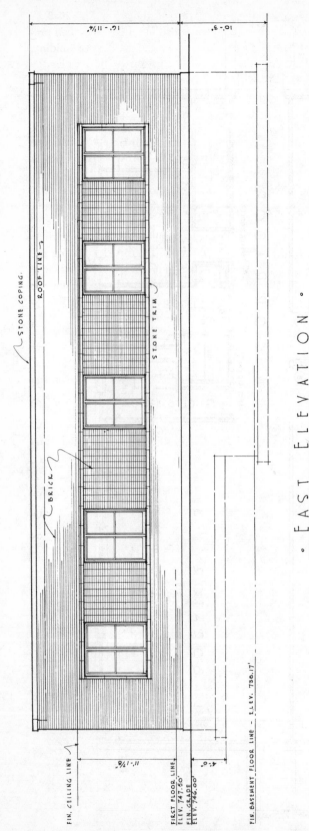

Fig. 26-12. Elevation.

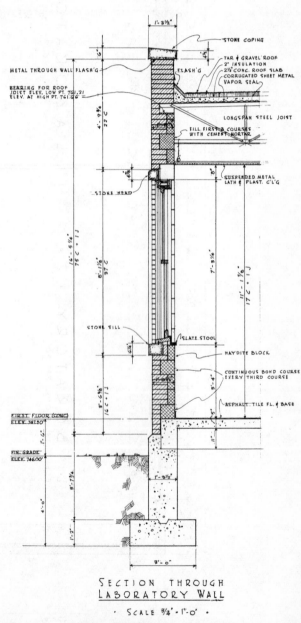

SECTION THROUGH
LABORATORY WALL

· SCALE ¾"·1'-0" ·

Fig. 26-13. Typical section through wall of building
shown in Fig. 26-12.

materials, manufacturer, type of finish, methods of construction, and in addition reemphasize such points as might be overlooked if the drawings alone were used.

The Federal Housing Authority has prepared a booklet on residential construction, *Minimum Property Requirements,* and a short-form type of specifications which are quite good for small-house work. *Architectural Specifications* by Sleeper, John Wiley & Sons, is a most comprehensive book on the subject, and the American Institute of Architects has prepared Specification Sheets as an aid in their writing. The specifications of individual manufacturers of building products and *Sweet's Architectural File* provide specific information.

26.14 Symbols. Since the plans and elevations of working drawings are made to a scale of ¼ or ⅛ inch to the foot, certain conventional representations are employed. These conventions have been generally standardized, and the parts of the building represented by given symbols are specifically described either by detail drawings, notes, or specifications. Windows are commonly indicated by an opening in the wall the width of the sash, and lines representing the glass and sill. Swinging doors are shown by breaking the wall the width of the door, and drawing the door ajar with an arc for the swing of the door. See Fig. 26–2 and Fig. 26–14. Windows and doors are usually coded by a letter in a circle, each window or door of the same kind and

size having the same letter as shown in Fig. 26–2. A chart or schedule of doors and of windows is then prepared describing each kind and size used in the building.

It is clear that the smaller the scale the simpler the symbol must become. A common fault of beginners is to make the symbol too large and cumbersome in proportion to the rest of the drawing. See Ramsey and Sleeper, *Architectural Graphic Standards,* for a comprehensive table of architectural indications. Equipment or material which is not standard or for which there is no definite symbol should be identified on the drawing by a noted circle or rectangle, and be explicitly described by note, detail, or specification in the drawings and specifications.

Various kinds of crosshatching indicate different materials as shown in Fig. 26–15. A key, showing the crosshatching and materials represented, may be placed on the drawing, particularly if the materials are uncommon and not generally recognizable. However, to one familiar with building plans and construction, crosshatchings commonly used are readily understood without such a key.

26.15 Electrical wiring. The electric outlets and switches which control outlets are shown either on the floor plan, or upon a simplified tracing of the floor plan, in their approximate locations. A line between an outlet and a switch indicates control of the outlet by that switch, as shown in Fig. 26–2. This simplified type

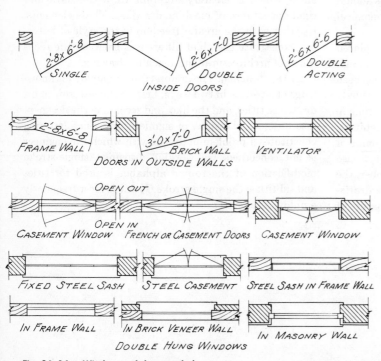

Fig. 26–14. Window and door symbols.

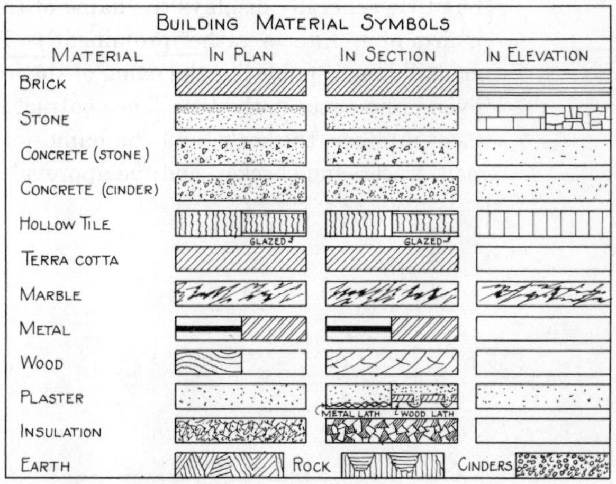

Fig. 26–15. Standard material symbols.

of electrical layout is generally used by architects. The type of service, method of wiring, number of circuits, types of fixtures, and other details are exactly described in the specifications. The precise location of outlets, routing of wire and conduit, and the grouping of outlets into circuits can best be accomplished after the structural shell of the building has been erected. This on-the-job location is worked out by the electrical contractor under the supervision of the architect. Such procedure is economic of drafting time and costs, avoids conflicts between the drawing and the practical installation, and gives the contractor a clear picture of the outlets to be installed which with the specifications enables him to figure the contract cost. The National Electrical Code governs the method of wiring and circuit design. Electrical symbols used in building construction are shown in Table 37 in the Appendix.

For buildings which are repeated many times, such as identical units in a housing project or prefabricated houses, or for very large structures in which duct and pipe spaces must be provided for wiring, the electrical layout problem should be integrated with the plan and the structural drawings. In such cases, it may be economical to predetermine the exact location of outlets, wiring, and the grouping of outlets into circuits. Even so, under practical installation difficulties, and unforeseen conditions, changes or deviations from the electrical layout will be made. A meticulous electrical design and layout could be made for any building, but this should be done only when it is a practical and economical procedure.

26.16 Titles. Architectural titles are usually placed in the lower right-hand corner of the sheet, although occasionally one will find a drawing whose title has been put in some other place. The style of lettering usually employed is a single-stroke, free imitation of the roman. The title generally displays the name of the architect, or firm of architects, rather prominently. The name of the building, if public, or the name of the owner, is also given prominence in the title. The contract number, the sheet number, the scale, and the names of the draftsman, tracer, and checker, and the approval signature of

the architect are also included. The same general title is placed on each sheet, with a change, of course, in the sheet number and other details where necessary. Other information concerning the drawing on the sheet is placed below the views, as, for example, First-Floor Plan, East Elevation, etc., and not in the title space itself.

26.17 Technique. The technique of architectural drawing is similar in many respects to that of machine drawing. Visible outlines, such as walls, beams, and columns, are made heavier than center lines, dimension lines, and crosshatching. All lines should be lighter than those generally used in a first-class machine drawing in order to show adequately the many small details. Contrast between the weights of lines will give the drawings a vigorous and workmanlike appearance.

There is, however, a little greater freedom in the architect's technique, by which he gives expression and life to the drawing, than is permissible in other fields of drawing, although greater freedom does not mean less accuracy. The overrunning of corners is a common practice not found in other engineering drawings, and, though it may speed up the work somewhat, care should be exercised not to overrun where confusion might result.

On elevations, accent lines and ruled-line rendering are used for embellishment of the drawing. There are also many details which the architect must put in freehand. These give character to the work, and produce an effect which is entirely different from the hard and rigid appearance of machine drawings. These elements, together with the greater freedom in the style of lettering, constitute the chief differences between the technique of architectural and machine drawing.

26.18 Lettering. The architect must employ his knowledge of lettering in two ways: first, in the lettering of his drawings, titles, and the like; and second, in the design of inscriptions and display or sign lettering. Such lettering constitutes a problem in design with which the engineer is not concerned. On working drawings, single-stroke modification of the roman alphabet is used for titles and subtitles; the single-stroke Gothic is most frequently employed for notes.

PROBLEMS

The plans shown in Figs. 26-17 and 26-19 to 26-29 show all walls, door openings, and rooms (some windows and prominent elements are also shown). Other plans may be selected from magazines and books, or a plan may be originally designed. Some variations have been suggested, and the student may develop and modify any particular plan to suit individual needs. Locate and determine the size of windows, built-in features, and other details. Select materials for construction, walls, and partitions. Determine the type of roof, whether flat, shed, gable, or hip. Locate electric outlets, plumbing fixtures, heating, etc., as required. Some details of construction can be worked out by inspection of the building shown in this chapter, and by information from reference books. Select the scale and sheet size to be used for each problem.

Each of the following problems may be applied to any one of the buildings shown in Figs. 26-16 to 26-29.

1. Draw the floor plan (or plans).

2. Draw the foundation or basement plan.

3. Draw a vertical section through the outside wall, roof, and foundation.

4. Draw one to four elevations, as assigned.

5. Draw four interior elevations and a plan of a selected room.

6. Draw a detail of some part of the building, such as fireplace, doorway, stairway, or counter and sections or elevations as needed.

7. Draw a transverse section through the entire building.

8. Draw the plot plan for the building.

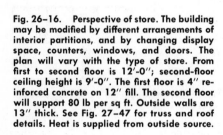

Fig. 26-16.   Perspective of store. The building may be modified by different arrangements of interior partitions, and by changing display space, counters, windows, and doors. The plan will vary with the type of store. From first to second floor is 12'-0"; second-floor ceiling height is 9'-0". The first floor is 4" reinforced concrete on 12" fill. The second floor will support 80 lb per sq ft. Outside walls are 13" thick. See Fig. 27-47 for truss and roof details. Heat is supplied from outside source.

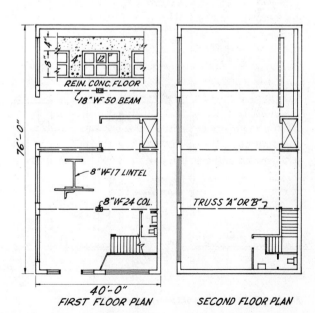

Fig. 26-17.   First- and second-floor plans of store shown in Fig. 26-16. The interior of the building may be divided by non-bearing partitions into desired spaces, i.e., washroom, office, stock room, sales room, etc.

Fig. 26-18.   Perspective of factory. Walls of masonry, concrete, or metal panels over masonry. Wall footings are reinforced concrete 2'-0" wide and 12" deep. Column footings are 3'-0" square and 15" deep. The gable end may have truck doors on each side with a large window in the middle. The monitor on top of the building may be extended the full length, or be omitted. See Fig. 27-48 for steel framing.

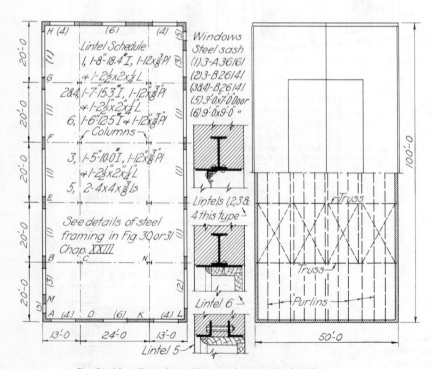

Fig. 26-19.   Floor plans of factory shown in Fig. 26-18.

Fig. 26-20.   First-floor plan of a two-story residence with basement. 30'-0" × 72'-0".

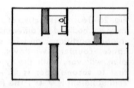

Fig. 26-21.   Floor plan of a one-story development house. 24'-0" × 40'-0".

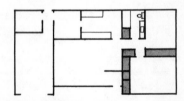

Fig. 26-22.   Floor plan of a two-bedroom house. 28'-0" × 56'-0".

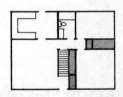

Fig. 26-23.   Floor plan of a one and one-half or two-story house with basement. 26'-0" × 36'-0".

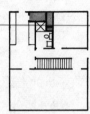

Fig. 26–24. Floor plan of a two-story house with basement. 27'-0" × 33'-0".

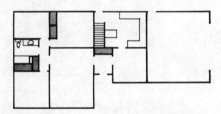

Fig. 26–25. Floor plan of a six-room house with basement. 32'-0" × 68'-0". Furniture and interior decoration should be considered. Minimum ceiling height is 10'-0".

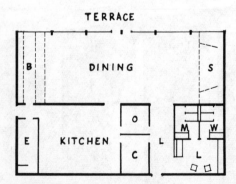

Fig. 26–26. Floor plan of a restaurant or cafe. The building may serve various types of business. Ceiling height is 12'-0" for larger spaces.

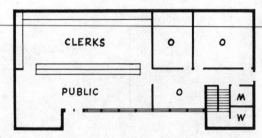

Fig. 26–27. Floor plan of a small office building. 40'-0" × 84'-0".

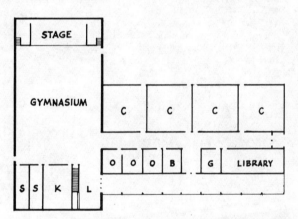

Fig. 26–28. Floor plan of a school. 128'''-0" × 188'-0". The gymnasium truss is 6'-0" deep and clears the floor by 24'-0". Roof structure over classrooms is 2'-0" deep. Ceiling height in all rooms but gymnasium is minimum of 10'-0".

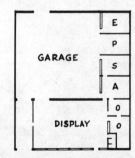

Fig. 26–29. Floor plan of a garage with sales room. Ceiling height in garage and sales room is 14'-0" minimum. Smaller spaces have 9'-0" ceilings. Trusses in garage portion average 6'-0" deep.

Reinforced concrete bridges (Hamilton Wright Organization).

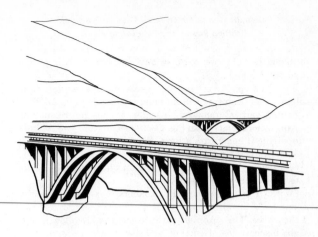

27

Structural Drawing

27.1 Introduction. Structural drawing includes all layout and detail drawings connected with the design and construction of buildings, bridges, viaducts, and similar structures in which structural steel, timber, concrete, and other building materials are used. Certain standard practices and conventions have been developed in this field of drafting quite unlike those prevailing in machine drawing, although merging somewhat with those found in architectural drawing.

Steel and reinforced-concrete structures are treated here from the drafting viewpoint only. No attempt is made to deal with engineering design of any structure, but the information gained in studying methods of framing, clearances required, and the technical terminology forms an excellent basis for later design courses.

Although a sufficient number of tables are given in the Appendix to solve the problems of this chapter, it is desirable that the student have access to the *Steel Construction Manual* of the American Institute of Steel Construction.

27.2 Definition of terms. In order that the meaning of certain terms used in the later portions of this chapter may be clear, a glossary of the more common terms used in structural work is given below. Where the term member is used in these definitions, a unit part of some larger structure is meant. This unit part itself may be constructed of numerous pieces of steel, but it functions as a single piece and is designated as such. Thus, any part of a structural framework, such as a floor beam or post in a steel bridge, may be spoken of as a member of that particular structure.

Definitions of Common Terms Used in Structural Drafting Rooms and Fabricating Plants

Batten Plate. A small plate used near the ends of built-up members to hold two parts of any member in their proper position. See Fig. 27–1.

Bay. The space between two consecutive sets or tiers of columns and beams, or columns and trusses. See Fig. 27–2.

Bent. A vertical framework, usually columns and beams supporting other members. In Fig. 27–2, the truss and two columns supporting it constitute a bent. Figure 27–3 shows a bent as used in railroad trestles or on viaducts.

Cantilever. A beam, girder, or truss in which one end or both ends project beyond the supports.

Chord. The top or bottom members of a truss. See Fig. 27–2.

Clearance. The space left between members to allow for the slight inaccuracies of cutting, and also to facilitate erection. See Fig. 27–4.

Clip angle. A small angle used to fasten light connections. See angles on top chord of truss in Fig. 27–33.

Column. A vertical compression member, usually supporting beams and girders. See Fig. 27–2.

Cope. To cut out a part of the top or bottom flange of a beam or channel so that it may fit another. See Fig. 27–4.

Cover plate. A plate riveted to the flanges of a compression member to give it greater area. The plates on the top flange of a plate girder are perhaps the most common examples. See Fig. 27–5.

Filler plate. A plate used to fill in empty spaces through which rivets must pass, as, for example, under stiffeners on a plate girder. See Fig. 27–5.

Flange. The top and bottom projection or outstanding parts of a beam, channel, or girder. See Figs. 27–4 and 27–5.

Gage line. The line along which rivet holes are punched in structural members. See Fig. 27–4.

Girder. A member designed to carry bending stress, usually supporting other members. Figure 27–5 shows one end and a section of a girder.

Gusset plate. A plate connecting the several members of a truss or other structural framework. See Fig. 27–4.

Lattice bar or lacing bar. One of a series of short diagonal bars used to connect the several parts of a member. See Fig. 27–1.

Lintel. A structural member designed to carry the wall over a window, door, or other opening. See Fig. 27–6.

Panel. The space between two purlins in a roof or between two vertical members in a bridge truss. See Fig. 27–2.

Pitch. The ratio of the height of a gabled roof to its width.

Purlin. The horizontal members spanning from truss to truss, upon which the roof is carried. See Fig. 27–2.

Stiffener. An angle riveted to a plate to prevent it from buckling. See Fig. 27–5.

Truss. A steel framework whose members take only tension or compression stresses. See Figs. 27–2 and 27–33.

Web. The portion of an I-beam, channel, or girder, between the upper and lower flanges. See Figs. 27–4 and 27–5.

Web member. The members of a truss between the top and bottom chords. See Fig. 27–2.

27.3 Number and location of views. As in machine drawing, third-quadrant projections are used entirely, and two or three views of an object are drawn, as may be required. The top view appears above the front view, and the end view to the right or left of the front view. If the top member is inclined, the top view will be an auxiliary projection rather than a projection on the horizontal plane, as, for example, the top chord of the truss in Fig. 27–33. Frequently, however, for very simple pieces, only one view is necessary, since the shapes of the pieces in the other direction are known to have a certain standard form. In blocking out the views, care should be taken to allow ample space for dimensions, more space being required between views for this purpose than is ordinarily necessary in machine drawing.

27.4 Bottom view. In addition to the usual three

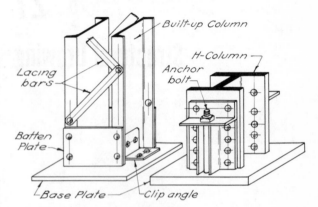

Fig. 27–1. Column bases.

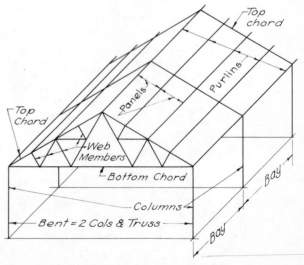

Fig. 27–2. Line diagram, mill building.

views, it is frequently necessary to show a bottom view of structural members. In structural drafting, such a bottom view is made as a horizontal section looking down, instead of the regular bottom view, such as would be made in machine drawing. The horizontal cutting plane is passed to show as little other detail beside the bottom members as possible. An illustration of this practice is shown in Figs. 27–5 and 27–33. The purpose of this practice is to show the front and back details of a girder, for instance, on the same side of the horizontal center lines in both the top and bottom views. This arrangement shows their actual relation to each other better than if a theoretical bottom view were taken.

27.5   Details. In machine drawing it is customary, in making a detail working drawing to separate the parts of a machine and detail them individually, whereas in structural drafting the opposite may be said to be the common practice. In other words, all the parts of a member are detailed as far as possible in the place they occupy in the structure. For example, the members of an ordinary roof truss are detailed in their proper places in the truss, as are the parts of a plate girder, or the large posts and chords of a bridge. That is to say, beams and girders are detailed horizontally on the sheet, and columns are detailed vertically, unless they are too long to be placed in that position, in which case the bottom end is placed at the left of the sheet and the column detailed horizontally. Inclined or sloping members are sometimes detailed in the position which they occupy, as indicated in Fig. 27–7. When they cannot be conveniently detailed in this manner, they are placed horizontally in the position in which they would fall.

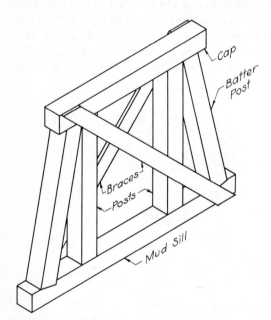

Fig. 27–3.   Railroad trestle bent.

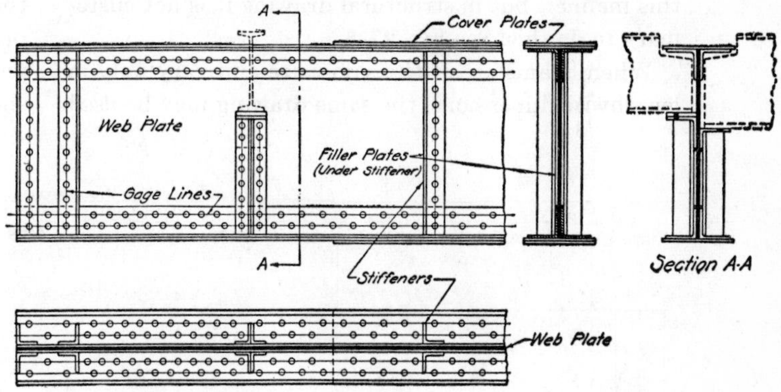

Fig. 27–5.   Plate girder.

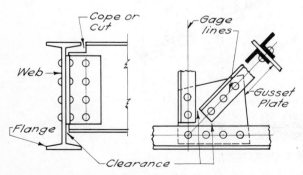

Fig. 27–4.   Structural riveted connections.

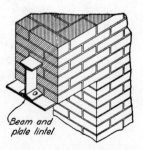

Fig. 27–6.   Steel lintel.

If the member detailed is a part of a larger structure, its position in the completed structure is shown by a heavy line in a small sketch on the sheet, as shown in Fig. 27–7. This holds true for all except plain building work. When connections occur in building work upon the detailing of which other framing depends, sketches are made showing the member connecting with the one detailed, in order to work out dimensions. Connecting members are not shown on the final shop drawing.

27.6   Scales. Structural drawing differs from machine drawing again in that on simple pieces the drawing is not scaled in one direction. Thus, in Fig. 27–8, the end view is made to scale in both directions and the other view is likewise to scale in all dimensions except the overall length. The details at the ends are made to scale lengthwise, but the total length is not. In machine drawing a break is indicated across a figure which is shortened in this manner, but in structural drawing it is not customary to do this. See Fig. 27–8.

When beams are of the same size and vary only in lengthwise dimensions, the same drawing may be used for several beams by putting on a set of dimensions for each beam as shown in Fig. 27–8. Many companies have printed forms showing the front, top, bottom, and end views of a beam, or any combination of these views which best suits their purpose. On these sheets it is only necessary for the draftsman to put in the details and dimensions.

In structural drawing the architect's scales are the only ones employed. They range from ¼″ = 1′-0″ for framing plans, to 3″ = 1′-0″ for the layout of joints. Almost any combination between these limits may be used. The more common ones, however, are ¾″ = 1′-0″ and 1″ = 1′-0″.

27.7   Symmetrical members. If large members such as trusses and plate girders are symmetrical about a center line perpendicular to their longest dimension, only one-half is detailed. It is the standard practice to show the left half when looking toward the side having the principal connections. For a railroad plate girder, this requires that the inside left end of the far girder be shown as the front view. Figure 27–33 illustrates this

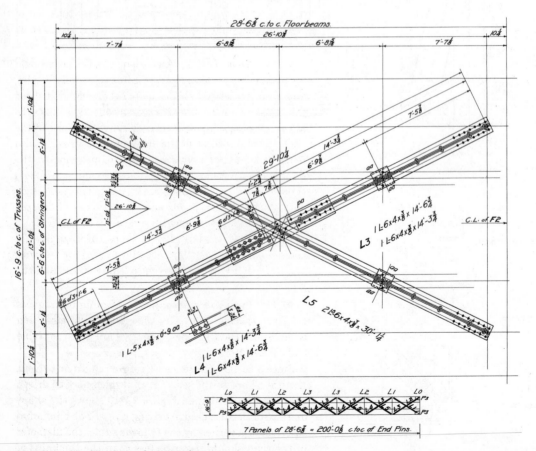

Fig. 27–7.   Wind bracing and erection diagram.

for a roof truss. As may be noted, the detail should be carried far enough past the center line to show any variation that may occur at the center. In no case should the detail be stopped exactly on the center line, even though there may be no variation beyond. The member should be broken off beyond the center by a ragged or wavy line, or the lines of the drawing may be simply stopped at the same place. The wavy line should be drawn only where there are members actually broken off and not through the space between members.

27.8   Sectional views. Sections are frequently necessary in structural drawing and may be made in the positions occupied by end views or interpolated sections in machine drawing. When several sections of the same piece are necessary, these may be put in convenient places on the sheet and noted as sections taken at some particular plane, as, for example, Section *AA*. The place where this section is taken is then indicated on the drawing by a line *AA*, with arrows on the end of it to indicate the direction of sight, as in Fig. 27–5. Standard practice as regards cross-hatching is also shown in Fig.

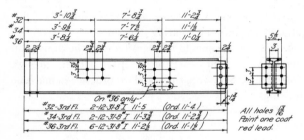

Fig. 27–8.   Detail for a series of beams.

WF BEAM   I BEAM   CHANNEL   ANGLES   Z-BAR   ROLLED TEE

Fig. 27–9.   Structural rolled sections.

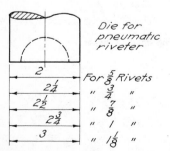

Fig. 27–10.   Rivet die.

27–5. The main part of the member cut is usually made solid black, although cross-section lines may be used. Filler plates, stiffeners, etc., need not be cross-sectioned.

27.9   Standard details. Through long years of practice and experience, certain details of steel construction have become standardized. The draftsman and detailer should adhere to these standard details unless it is impossible to do so, or unless some particular advantage is to be gained by departing therefrom. Some of the more important and common standards are discussed in the following paragraphs.

27.10   Standard structural shapes. The shape, dimensions, and consequently the weight of structural sections are thoroughly standardized, and the general dimensions of the more common pieces should be familiar to the draftsman. Figure 27–9 shows cross sections of the more common shapes, the sizes of which vary through a wide range although the general proportions remain about the same. Thus, I-beams may be obtained in sizes from 3 to 36 inches in height, and for each height there are a number of standard weights. The *Steel Construction Manual* lists all of these completely, and the student is referred to it for further information. A list of the standard light sections is given in Tables 26 to 29 in the Appendix.

27.11   Gage lines. The lines along which rivets should be placed in the flanges of I-beams, channels, angles, and other structural shapes have become standardized through long usage. These lines are called gage lines. In angles, the gage line is measured from the back of the angle. The gage line in the flange of a channel is also measured from the back of the channel, but in the flanges of an I-beam the gage lines are measured from the center. Edge distances are not given because they vary along the same beam, and they also vary in shapes of different weight, whereas the distance measured from the back or center line always keeps the gage lines in the same relative position. Standard gages for I-beams, channels, and angles are given in Table 26 to 29 in the Appendix.

27.12   Rivet size and spacing.   Minimum distances for rivet spacing along the gage lines have also been established. Data on these spacings are given in Table 30 in the Appendix.

Since a certain clearance is required in driving rivets, there is a limit to the size of rivets which may be driven in the standard shapes. Figure 27–10 shows the shape and size of the dies used in driving rivets. The minimum-size rivet is governed by the following rule: the diameter of the rivet should never be less than the thickness of metal to be punched. That is to say, a hole for a ½-inch rivet should not be punched through ¾-inch metal.

When drawing rivet heads the diameter is made equal to $1\frac{1}{2}D + \frac{1}{8}$ inch where D is the rivet diameter.

27.13 Beam connections. The angles for connecting beams to columns or girders have been standardized in six series designated as A, H, HH, B, K and KK to accommodate different loadings and rivet sizes. A portion of the B series for ¾ rivets is shown in Table 31 in the Appendix. The rivet spacings shown should be adhered to.

27.14 Conventional symbols. The use of conventional signs and symbols is limited almost entirely to the representation of rivets. The standard symbols and their meaning are shown in Fig. 27–11. It will be noted that, where the operation is to be performed on the near side or outside of the piece, the designating marks are on the outside of the circle, whereas, to indicate the same operation on the far side or inside, the marks are on the inside of the circle.

When there is a long line of rivets uniformly spaced, not all the rivets need be drawn in. Usually only those at the beginning and end of a series of uniform spaces need be indicated. The side view of a rivet is not shown except when it will add to the clearness of the drawing.

A departure from the above rule must be observed with field rivets. All field rivets must be shown. They are also shown in the side view unless this will confuse the drawing.

27.15 Billing materials. In making a bill of material or in notes, the following symbols are used as abbreviations: the wide-flanged beams are indicated by WF; I-beam is indicated by the capital letter I; the channel by a symbol similar to the cross section of a channel lying on its back to prevent confusion with the symbol for the I-beam if carelessly made; and angle, T-bar, and Z-bar are indicated in the same way by symbols representing their cross section. The proper method of billing the various shapes is shown in Fig. 27–12. The weight per foot, or thickness in the case of the angle, must always be given, as all the structural shapes are made in several weights for the same general dimensions.

27.16 Dimensions. Since a single detail may be sufficient for the fabrication of several tons of steel, it is quite evident that a single error in dimensions may spoil tons of steel, not to mention the waste in labor and time and the loss of a reputation for reliability. Placing of the dimensions is perhaps the most difficult single problem. An examination of the illustrations in this chapter will give a basis upon which judgment can be formed as to the best placing of dimensions. The rules given apply particularly to drawings which are completely detailed in all respects. The following rules should be observed and applied with common sense and judgment.

27.17 Techniques. *a.* Dimension lines should be light, solid, black lines terminating in arrows.

b. The figures should be placed above the dimension lines at or near the center of the space between arrows. *Note:* This differs from the standard practice in machine drawing.

c. Dimensions should be given as shown in *A*, Fig. 27–13.

d. Where a dimension line runs through a rivet whose location it does not give, the dimension line should be broken and an arc drawn around the rivet, as shown in

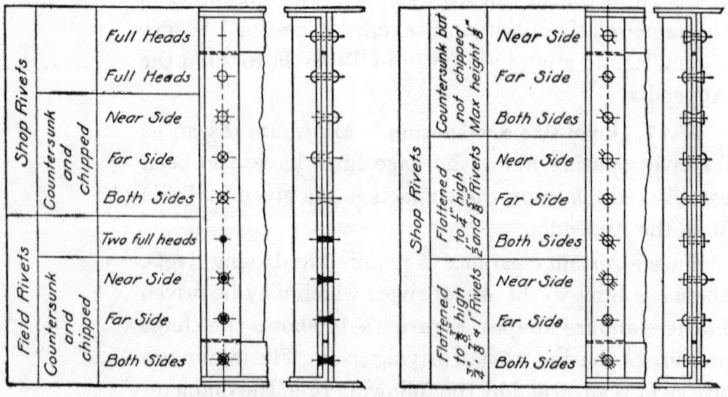

Fig. 27–11. Conventional symbols for rivets.

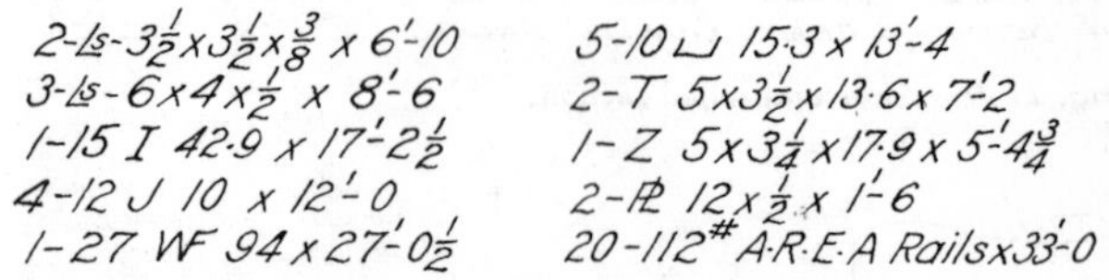

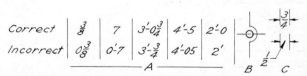

$2-\text{L}s-3\frac{1}{2}x3\frac{1}{2}x\frac{3}{8} \; x \; 6'-10$ $5-10 \text{L} \; 15\cdot3 \; x \; 13'-4$

$3-\text{L}s-6x4x\frac{1}{2} \; x \; 8'-6$ $2-\text{T} \; 5x3\frac{1}{2}x13\cdot6 \; x \; 7'-2$

$1-15 \; \text{I} \; 42\cdot9 \; x \; 17'-2\frac{1}{2}$ $1-\text{Z} \; 5x3\frac{1}{4}x17\cdot9 \; x \; 5'-4\frac{3}{4}$

$4-12 \; \text{J} \; 10 \; x \; 12'-0$ $2-\text{IL} \; 12x\frac{1}{2} \; x \; 1'-6$

$1-27 \; \text{WF} \; 94 \; x \; 27'-0\frac{1}{2}$ $20-112^{\#} \; \text{A·R·E·A Rails} \; x \; 33'-0$

Fig. 27–12. Method of specifying standard shapes.

Correct	$\frac{3}{8}$	7	$3'-0\frac{3}{4}$	$4'-5$	$2'-0$	
Incorrect	$0\frac{3}{8}$	$0\cdot7$	$3'-\frac{3}{4}$	$4'-05$	$2'$	
			A			B C

Fig. 27–13. Method of dimensioning.

B, Fig. 27–13. Avoid this situation whenever possible.

e. The division line in fractions should always be made parallel to the dimension line.

f. When the space between the arrowheads is very limited, the dimension may be put in as shown in *C,* Fig. 27–13.

27.18   Placing dimensions. *a.* On truss members, detail dimensions should be placed in a continuous row from end to end of the member, no dimension being omitted.

b. An overall dimension should accompany each set of detail dimensions.

c. Where two or more lines of dimensions are given for the same piece, they should not be placed closer together than ⁵⁄₁₆ inch, and the first line should not be closer to the piece than double this distance. It may be farther away when circumstances demand. Above all things, dimensions should not be crowded upon one another or upon the object drawn.

d. The lettered figures of a dimension should not fall upon the outline of any member, since this makes it almost impossible to read. When other methods fail, a leader should be used and the dimension placed in the clear, where it will be legible.

27.19   Fabricating dimensions. *a.* Dimensions should be calculated to the nearest sixteenth of an inch, except for bevels when it is frequently advisable to work to the nearest thirty-second of an inch.

b. The detail dimensions should always be added to see that they check with the overall dimension.

c. The work is completely detailed only when it is unnecessary for the workman to add, subtract, multiply, or perform any other mathematical operation to obtain an essential dimension.

d. The slope of all members should be given in run and rise and not by angles. One of the dimensions of the run and rise should always be 12 inches. The run is the horizontal distance and the rise the vertical distance. See Figs. 27–32 and 27–33.

e. Before the work is submitted to the checker, it should be examined from the point of view of the shop man. All the dimensions and other information needed to lay out the work should be checked.

f. On beams and girders, the position of successive and independent details may be dimensioned consecutively from the left end in one line of dimensions as in Figs. 27–8 and 27–14. Chain dimensioning may be used when the details are continuous from end to end as in Fig. 27–23.

g. End distances and edge distance are usually given by note on light truss members. They are dimensioned on beams, columns, and girders. Gage lines should be dimensioned even though they are standard.

h. Field rivets should be dimensioned independently even though they are located with a series of detail dimensions.

i. The size of each piece is given close to the piece itself.

In dimensioning, as with standard details, many fabricating companies have adopted certain standard practices for their draftsmen to observe, which have been developed through experience in the shop. These vary

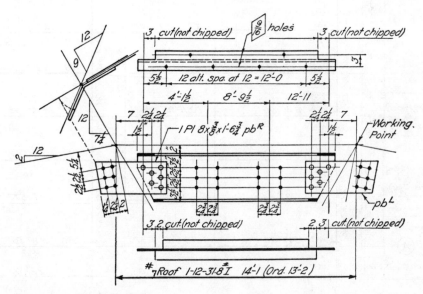

Fig. 27–14.   Roof purlin detail.

somewhat in different shops.

27.20 Rectangular framed structures. Structural steel fabrication may be roughly divided into two major categories, namely, rectangular framed structures such as tall buildings and those involving triangular framework such as roof trusses and bridges. The framing of buildings consists mainly of vertical and horizontal members which are connected at right angles to each other.

27.21 Design drawings or layouts. The structural draftsman usually works from design layouts or framing plans which show the arrangement of columns, girders, and beams for each floor of a building. This layout gives the size of each member and its location relative to others both horizontally and vertically. The horizontal distances are shown by dimensions and the vertical distances by elevations as shown in Fig. 27–15. A note indicates the distance of the major portion of the framing below the finished floor line. Departure from this general level will be called out as plus or minus distances above or below the finished floor level as noted for beam *K3* in Fig. 27–15.

27.22 Marking. In order to provide a systematic procedure for detailing, fabricating, and erection, each member of a structure is given a mark on the design drawing. This mark on the layout is placed on the detail drawing of the piece, painted on the piece in the shop, and used by the erector in the field to place the member in the structure.

In addition to these marks, which can be called erection marks, and which must appear on the final finished piece, other marks must be placed upon each piece of steel used to make the composite. These latter marks are for the purpose of assembling the member in the shop and may be called assembly marks.

Each company has its own system in both categories. A common method is to assign capital letters as erection marks to the horizontal members. The letter is followed by a number. This number may refer to the sheet or drawing number on which the member is detailed or it may refer to a floor number.

Columns may be numbered in consecutive order in some systematic arrangement on the plan, or the rows of columns may be given letters in one direction and numbers in the direction at right angles to the first as shown in Fig. 27–15. Any column is then designated by the intersection of the lettered and numbered rows, as for example, *B-2, C-3,* etc., in Fig. 27–15. Since a column will have the same number throughout its entire height, but must be erected in sections, each section must be given a distinguishing mark, as for example, *B-2* Tier One or *B-2* (*0-2*). Tier one would be the mark of the first columns to be erected, usually through two stories. The mark (*0-2*) would indicate the same thing, namely, that the column extended from the footing through story two.

It is customary in many shops to use small letters for

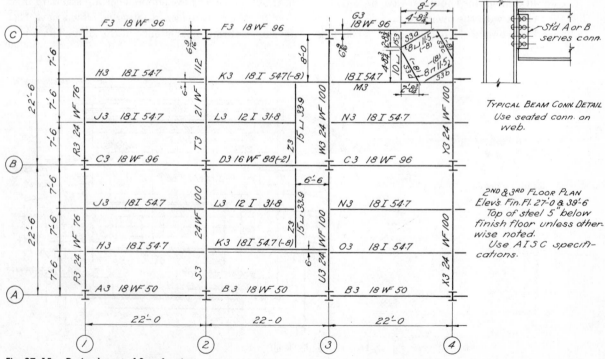

Fig. 27–15. Design layout of floor framing.

assembly marks. The assembly marks originate with the detailer whereas the erection marks are placed on the layout by the designer. The detailer should observe the following rules.

a. Each separate piece should be given a mark.

b. When two or more pieces are identical, they should be given the same mark and need to be detailed only once.

c. When two pieces are similar in all respects except that one is left and the other right, they may be given the same mark with the suffix *R* and *L*. The one drawn is usually marked *R*.

d. The letters *i* and *l* should be avoided since it is difficult to distinguish them on a drawing or in the shop. The prime mark should not be used.

27.23 Detail sketches. Before beginning the detail of a member, except perhaps the simplest, it is advisable to make a sketch with straight edge and pencil, or freehand, to work out the connections to other members. The controlling dimensions such as elevations above or below floor levels, line-up with other members, and actual rather than nominal member sizes form the basis for working out these sketches. Use standard beam connections wherever possible.

Thus for the left end of the beam in Fig. 27–16, which is a sketch of beam *H-3* in Fig. 27–15, a sketch is hardly necessary. But for the right end it is essential to work out the connection very carefully so that beams *H-3*

and *K-3* may be erected without difficulty. Note that the top of *K-3* is below *H-3* and also offset horizontally. Such connections may tax the ingenuity of the detailer.

In beginning this sketch, the engineer would first select a standard beam connection. From page 190 of the *AISC Manual,* the load that the beam *H-3* will carry on a span of 22 feet is 54,000 pounds. One-half of this load is supported at each end. From the table on page 257, *AISC Manual,* connection *B-4* will be more than ample since it will carry an end reaction of 53,000 pounds, almost double that required. A *B-3* connection would have the necessary strength, but the detailer will normally use the standard for the beam size unless the designer has authorized lighter connections.

The location of this connection on beam *H-3* depends upon the size of the beam and type of supporting member. From Table 27 in the Appendix we find that the first rivet cannot be closer than 2¾ inches to the top of the support beam. When possible this distance is made 3 inches to facilitate the use of multiple punches. Since the top of the flange is usually at a specified height, it is customary to dimension rivets from the top flange. This line of dimensions should not be tied in to the bottom flange. The completed shop drawing of beam *H-3* is shown in Fig. 27–17.

A second detail sketch for a seated connection on a column is shown in Fig. 27–18. This is a detail of beam *C-3* in Fig. 27–15. When a beam must fit between the flanges of a column, standard beam connections are usually not practicable. For the inexperienced draftsman it is a satisfactory rule to make the number of rivets in the seat equal to the number in the outstanding flanges

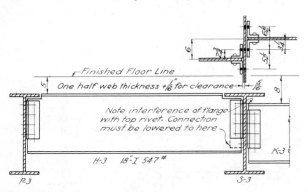

Fig. 27–16. Sketch for detailing beam.

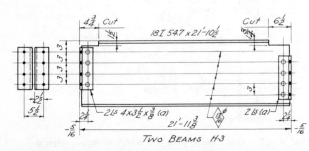

Fig. 27–17. Floor beam detail of Fig. 22–16.

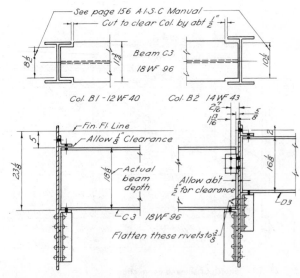

Fig. 27–18. Sketch of beam and column connections.

of a standard connection for the size of beam involved. Actually the number of rivets must be carefully computed in design.

The clip angle at the top of the left end of the beam in Fig. 27-18 is used for stability only. On the right end the clip was placed on the web to avoid interference with the connecting beam on the opposite side of the column. The shop drawing of beam *C-3* is shown in Fig. 27-19. Note the −⅝ at each end of the overall dimension. This is the distance from the center line of the column to the end of the beam and gives a check on the center-to-center distance of columns. The 1¹³⁄₁₆″ end distance to rivet

holes is obtained as shown in the sketch at the right in Fig. 27-18. The actual clearance is approximately ⁷⁄₁₆ inch instead of ½ inch.

The ±⅛ inch shown opposite the ends of the beam in Fig. 27-19 indicates that the length of beam may be allowed to vary by this amount. In other words, a beam with a minimum length of 21'-10½″ or a maximum of 21'-11″ could be used. The shop would adjust the 1¹³⁄₁₆″ dimension to suit. The net distance between holes as shown on the drawing cannot be varied.

27.24 Non-rectangular connections. Structural members may be skewed, that is, at an angle of other than

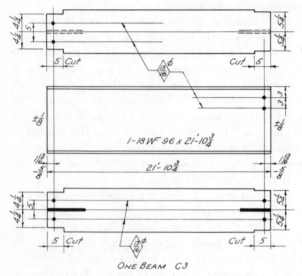

Fig. 27-19.   Beam detail of Fig. 27-18.

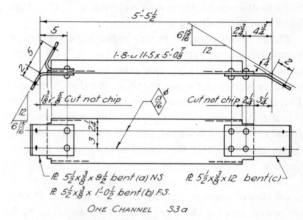

Fig. 27-21.   Detail of skewed beam of Fig. 27-20.

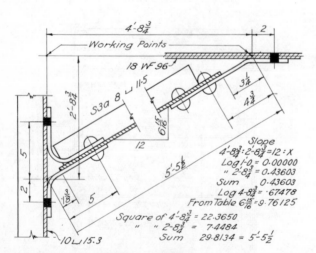

Fig. 27-20.   Sketch of skewed connection.

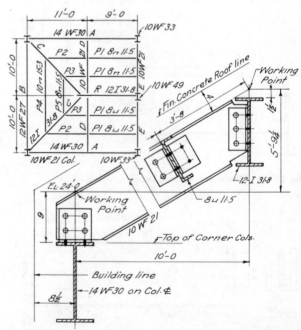

Fig. 27-22.   Roof framing plan and sketch of sloping rafter D.

90° with each other, as, for example, the 8″ channels in the upper right-hand part of Fig. 27–15. Members may also have a slope with the horizontal, as, for example, the roof rafters *D* and *E* in Fig. 27–22. The hip rafters *C* in this figure have both skew and slope. If the purlins *P1, P2,* etc., had their webs in a vertical plane, they would be canted relative to their supporting members.

Non-rectangular connections usually require some trigonometric calculations in making the layout. In order that these computations may be accurately controlled, working points are established.

27.25 Working points. Working points are commonly taken at the intersection of the center lines of members or in the case of trusses at the intersection of gage lines. See Fig. 27–33. It is not necessary that center lines be used. The lines used, however, must be parallel to the center lines. Thus in Fig. 27–20, which is a detail sketch of the channel *S3a* in Fig. 27–15, the center line of the 18 WF 96 beam, and the back of the channels were used to establish the working points. In Fig. 27–22, the intersection of the center lines of the ridge and side beams with the top of the sloping beam were used.

27.26 Detailing skewed members. Using the channel *S3a* of Fig. 27–15 as an illustration, the sketch of Fig. 27–20 can be made. The diagonal length between working points is obtained by taking the square root of the sum of the squares of the two legs of the right-angle triangle, as shown at the bottom of the figure. The squares were obtained from Inskip Table of Squares.

Using the same tables, the bevel of the member is found to be 12 to $6^{15}/_{16}$ as shown in the computations in the figure. Minimum bends and rivet distances have been standardized as given in Table 32 in the Appendix. With these data the shop drawing of the channel was made as in Fig. 27–21.

27.27 Detailing sloping members. A roof framing plan together with a sketch of the end connections of a rafter is shown in Fig. 27–22. From consideration of the architect's plans the working points were chosen in the plane of the top of the rafter, as shown. The ridge rafter was then located 1½ inches below the working point so that its edge would lie approximately in the plane of the top of the rafter. In a similar manner the top of the side beam and top of the corner column were located to give a reasonable connection. From this sketch the shop detail shown in Fig. 27–23 was prepared.

In some shops sloping members are detailed in the position they occupy. Likewise the elevation of working points rather than the vertical distance between them is sometimes given. The slope of the member is given by the usual right-angle triangle shown on the member.

In other shops the member is drawn horizontally, in which case the slope or bevel would be given on the end connections as shown in Fig. 27–24. In this figure the purlins have been shown canted for purpose of illustration. Note that the holes for the purlin connections have been kept in lines parallel and perpendicular to the length of the member. This is desirable in multiple-

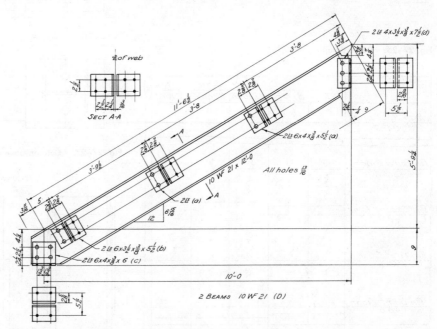

Fig. 27–23. Detail of roof rafter of Fig. 27–22.

punch operations. Figure 27–25 shows the purlin detail for this situation.

27.28   Column details. Since the lower-story columns are the first structural pieces to be erected and footings with anchor bolts and base plates must be in position before erection can begin, it is necessary to detail columns first. In order to facilitate detailing, the designer makes a column schedule as illustrated in Fig. 27–26. This schedule shows the elevation of each floor, the size and composition of each column, the point at which the columns are spliced, the elevation of the base plate, and the size of the base plate.

When base plates are shipped loose, as is usually the case, these are detailed separately with proper provision

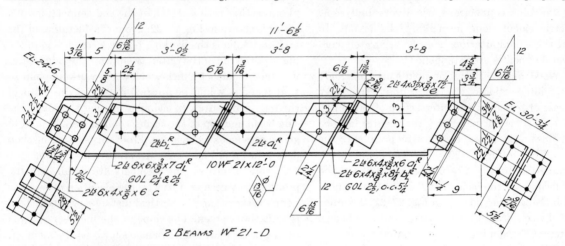

Fig. 27–24.   Detail of Fig. 27–23 drawn horizontally.

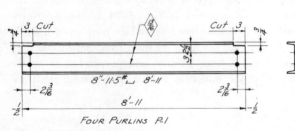

Fig. 27–25.   Purlin detail.

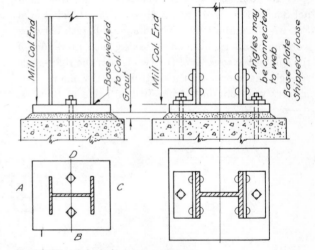

Fig. 27–27.   Column-base connections.

		COLUMN	SCHEDULE		
	A1	B1 to F1	A2 to A6	B2 to B6	C2 to C6
High Roof line 64-9					
Fin.Third Floor +39'-6	10 WF 21	12 WF 27	12 WF 27	12 WF 40	12 WF 40
		1'-3	1'-6		
Fin.Second Floor +27'-0					
Fin.First Floor +14'-6	10 WF 33	12 WF 40	12 WF 40	14 WF 43	14 WF 43
	12"	12	12 1'-6	14	14
Fin. Bsmt Floor +0.0					
COL. BASE PLATE	16x1½x18	16x1½x20	16x1½x20	16x1½x22	16x1½x22

Fig. 27–26.   Column schedule.

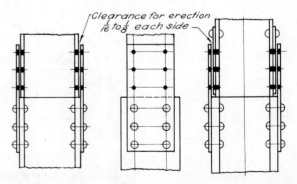

Fig. 27–28.   Column splices.

for anchor bolt holes, grouting holes if necessary, and planed surfaces on heavy plates to give full bearing to the milled end of the column. Two typical column bases are shown in Fig. 27–27.

27.29 Column splices. Since the load which columns carry increases from the top downward the size of columns must be increased accordingly. This is usually done at intervals of two stories, beginning at the bottom. In buildings with an odd number of stories the top section may be either one or three stories in height. Column splices are usually placed far enough above the floor level to clear all beam connections. Two typical splices are shown in Fig. 27–28. Further details are shown in *Structural Shop Drafting,* Vol. I, AISC.

27.30 Right- and left-hand columns. Situations sometimes occur in which columns and other members are similar in detail except that they are in right- and left-hand arrangement as shown for Columns *A2* and *B2* in the upper part of Fig. 27–29. Right- and left-hand arrangements are always relative to a vertical plane, never a horizontal plane.

In situations of this kind considerable drafting time can be saved by detailing one column and calling it out as shown and then by note calling out the second column as opposite hand, as indicated in the lower part of Fig. 27–29.

In the shop it is customary to mark the faces of a column by the letters *A, B, C,* and *D* in counterclockwise order, looking down on the column and always begin-

ning with the letter *A* on a flange face as shown in Fig. 27–29. Shop details should show the faces so marked. The direction of one face, as for example, the north side, should be so marked.

A shop detail of Column *B2* in the framing plan of Fig. 27–15 and the column schedule of Fig. 27–26 is shown in Fig. 27–30.

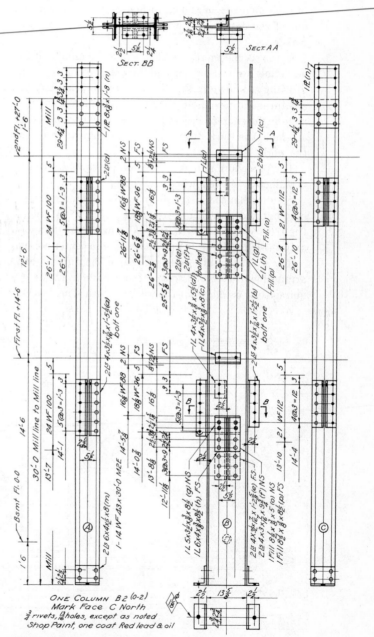

Fig. 27–29. Right- and left-hand details.

Fig 27–30. Column detail.

The columns having been detailed, the beams framing into them must be detailed to fit.

27.31   Detailing a truss. In designing trusses, line diagrams similar to the one shown in Fig. 27–31 are used as the bases for the computation of stresses. The intersections of these lines give the working points used in detailing the truss.

Two general schemes for making roof truss details are in use. In one of these only the dimensions between working points are given along with the size of members, the slopes of members, and the number of rivets in each member, as shown in Fig. 27–32. The working out of the details of the joints is left to the template maker.

In the second method which is more commonly used, all details are worked out and dimensioned on the shop drawing as shown in Fig. 27–33. This method has the advantage of permitting the template maker and the men in the shop to proceed at once to cut, punch, and assemble the work. It also gives a permanent record of the work.

The procedure in making a complete shop drawing is explained in the following paragraphs.

Assume that complete information is given the draftsman in the design sketch, as shown in Fig. 27–31. Since the truss is symmetrical, it will be necessary to show only the left half, up to and including the center points.

The first step, after deciding upon the number and arrangement of views and selecting a scale to fit the requirements, is to lay out the working lines. These working lines correspond to the gage lines shown in Fig. 27–33, which form a group of triangular figures the dimensions of which can be readily computed. It will be noted that all dimensions in Fig. 27–33 are based on the working points. After the working lines are laid out, the members of the truss may be laid out around these lines as gage lines to the same scale, or to a slightly larger one if desired. For example, the bottom chord is composed of two 3″ × 2½″ × ¼″ angles placed back to back with the long legs vertical. The standard gage for a 3″ angle, as obtained from the tables, is 1¾″. Hence, we scale down from the working line for the bottom chord a distance of 1¾″, and draw a line parallel to the working line which represents the bottom of the angles. A second line, drawn just a little above the first, represents the thickness of the angle. From the bottom line,

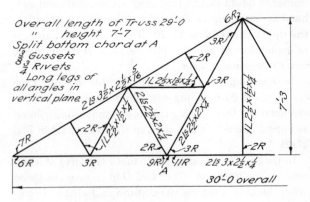

Fig. 27–31.   Design diagram of steel truss.

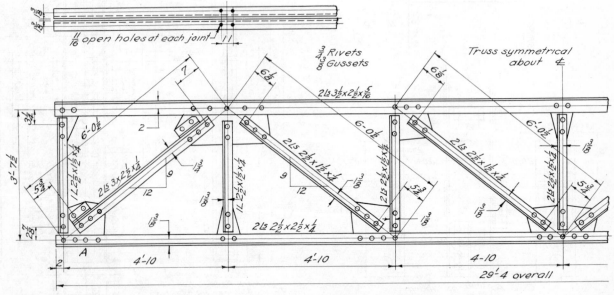

Fig. 27–32.   Sketch detail of flat truss.

we may now scale upward a distance of 3″, and draw a line which will represent the top edge of the vertical leg of the angle. These three lines, which together represent the angle, can be marked off with one setting of the scale and then drawn in very quickly.

In the same way the other angles may be drawn around their corresponding working lines. The ends of the angles should usually be shown cut off at right angles to their length as a matter of economy. When all the angles have been drawn, the proper number of rivets may be put in at each point to the same scale as that used in laying out the angles. The rivet spacings may be scaled from the end of the angles, using the standard end distance and standard spacing called for by the design. After all the rivets have been properly located, the gusset plates may be drawn in to scale, care being taken

to provide the proper edge distance from the last rivets. This is done by drawing a circle of the proper radius—equal to the specified edge distance—around the outstanding rivets in each member and then drawing the lines representing the edges of the gusset plate tangent to these circles. Gusset plates must be cut from rectangular pieces, and hence it is desirable to make as few cuts as possible to obtain the proper shape for the plates. In no case may re-entrant angles be used. When the gusset plates have been drawn, the truss is ready for dimensioning. The rules for dimensioning are given in Arts. 27.16 to 27.18.

27.32 Layout of a joint. Where structural members meet at an angle other than 90°, the distance from the working point to the first rivet in the sloping member is determined by making a large-scale layout right on the

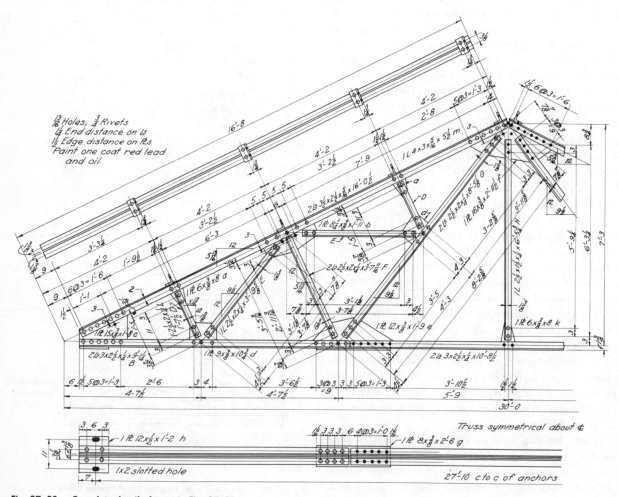

Fig. 27-33. Complete detail of truss in Fig. 27-31.

truss detail, as illustrated for one joint in Fig. 27–34, which represents joint *A* on Fig. 27–32. The truss detail is usually made to a scale of $1'' = 1'\text{-}0''$, and the joint layout to a scale of $3'' = 1'\text{-}0''$. The needed dimensions are then scaled off. Although all lines of the large-scale layout have been shown in Fig. 27–34, only those which are useful in obtaining the desired dimensions need be drawn.

To make such a layout, the principal working lines of the joint, as indicated by the lines marked *1, 2,* and *3,* are used. These are the gage lines of the members which form the joint. Around these lines the members are then drawn in to large scale, beginning with the member which runs through the joint, as, for example, the bottom member in Fig. 27–34. The bottom chord, which is composed of two $2\frac{1}{2}'' \times 2\frac{1}{2}'' \times \frac{1}{4}''$ angles, is laid out around line *1* by measuring down at right angles to the line a distance of $1\frac{3}{8}''$, which is the standard gage for the $2\frac{1}{2}''$ leg. With the bottom line of the angle thus determined, the whole angle may now be drawn in. Then, to scale, ½ inch above the top edge, draw a line for clearance. Draw the angles around the working lines *2* and *3*. The sloping member on line *3* is composed of two $3'' \times 2\frac{1}{2}'' \times \frac{1}{4}''$ angles, and the standard gage for the $3''$ leg is $1\frac{1}{4}''$. The angle may then be laid out around the working line as a gage line in the same manner as the bottom chord. The line representing the lower edge of the angle is extended until it intersects the clearance line of the bottom chord, and at the intersection a line is drawn at right angles to line *3*. This last line represents the end of the angle. The first rivet may be put in $1\frac{1}{4}''$ from this line, and then its distance to the working point *B* may be scaled and put down on the detail drawing. From the first rivet, the location of the last one may be scaled off, and a circle with a radius equal to the standard edge distance for gusset plates drawn around it. In a similar manner, the rivets farthest from the working point *B* in each member may be drawn, and then the edges of the gusset plate may be drawn tangent to the edge distance circles around these rivets. Any required distance may now be scaled from this layout, and the size of the gusset plate determined. Such a layout must be made for each different joint, and, although the type of connection may be quite different from the one shown, the general principle is just the same.

27.33 Welding. In some structures welding is being used in lieu of rivets for fastening members together. As with riveted structures, some of the welding is done in the shop and other portions upon erection in the field. For the correct use of welding symbols and the dimen-

sioning thereof the reader is referred to Chapter 29, Welding Drawing.

27.34 Reinforced concrete. Only the general principles of detailing reinforced-concrete structures can be covered in this brief treatment, since reinforced concrete is used for such a wide variety of structures each of which involves details not covered in others. The following paragraphs cover items which must always be included. All data, symbols, abbreviations, etc., shown in this section are approved and shown in the *Manual of Standard Practice for Detailing Reinforced Concrete Structures* published by the American Concrete Institute.

27.35 Symbols and abbreviations. The following symbols and abbreviations are recommended by the ACI.

#	To indicate size of deformed bar member
∅	Round—mainly for plain round bars
□	Square
⟶	Direction in which bars extend
Pl	Plain bar
Bt	Bent
St	Straight
Stir	Stirrup
Sp	Spiral
CT	Column tie
IF	Inside face
OF	Outside face
NF	Near face
FF	Far face
EF	Each face
Bot	Bottom
E.W.	Each way
T	Top

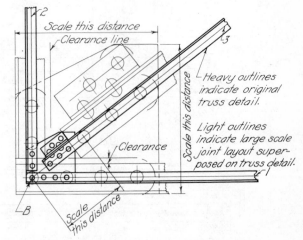

Fig. 27–34.   Large-scale joint layout for obtaining detail dimensions.

Round deformed bars are specified by number from #2 to #8. The number corresponds to the diameter in eighths of an inch. Thus a #3 bar is approximately ⅜ inch in diameter. The nominal diameter of a deformed bar is the same as a plain bar having the same weight per foot.

27.36   Engineering drawings. These are the general plans of the structure. They must give all information necessary to build the forms, detail the reinforcing steel, and make the steel placement drawings. Beside the general floor plan showing the location and size of girders, beams, joists, columns, etc., this will require some details, usually sectional views, and typical bar diagrams as shown in Fig. 27–35. In buildings of this type, beam and joist schedules are also required as illustrated in Fig. 27–36. Note that, although these schedules give all necessary information, they are not adequate for bending the steel.

Reinforcement for walls and slabs must be shown either in schedules or on the plans or elevations. A spe-

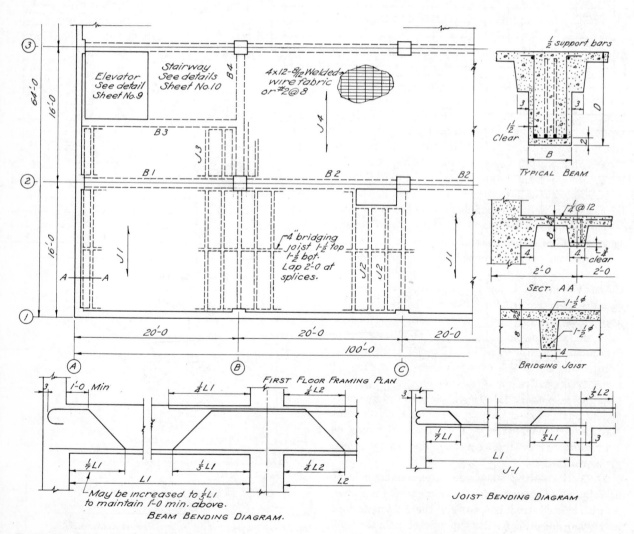

Fig. 27-35.   Reinforced-concrete framing plan.

cial detail of this type is shown in Fig. 27–37.

The steel for columns is usually shown in schedules together with sufficient detail views to show the typical arrangement of steel, as illustrated in Figs. 27–38 and 27–39.

Typical column splices are shown in Fig. 27–40.

Footings are shown on the general plans as illustrated in Fig. 27–41 and detailed as in Fig. 27–42.

Accessories such as beam bolsters, chairs, etc., which support the reinforcing may be shown on the drawing but are usually given by note, referring to some stand-

ard, covering the placement of such items.

Anchors for architectural work, such as suspended ceilings, and elevators which require placement before pouring the concrete, must be shown or noted as well as all openings to be provided for plumbing, heating, ventilating, and the like.

27.37 Placement drawings. The instructions in this article are quoted, by permission, from the *ACI Manual of Standard Practice* with such modifications as are necessary to make them fit the illustrations of this textbook.

BEAM SCHEDULE

Mark	BxD	Tee	Reinforcing		Stirrups				Stirrup support
			Bent	Str	No.	Size	Spacing each end		bar at top
B1	12x25	2 sides	2-$\frac{7}{8}$	2-$\frac{7}{8}$	10	$\frac{1}{2}$	6,2@8,10,12		2-$\frac{1}{2}$
B2	12x25	2 sides	2-$\frac{7}{8}$	2-$\frac{7}{8}$	12	$\frac{1}{2}$	5,2@7,9,12,12		
B3	10x17	1 side	2-$\frac{3}{4}$	2-$\frac{3}{4}$	8	$\frac{3}{8}$	6,8,10,12		
B4	12x20	2 sides	2-$\frac{7}{8}$	2-$\frac{7}{8}$	10	$\frac{3}{8}$	6,2@8,10,12		
B5	14x25	2 sides	2-1ϕ	2-1ϕ	14	$\frac{1}{2}$	5,2@7,2@9,2@12		

B = Breadth of beam and D = Depth overall.

JOIST SCHEDULE

Mark	B	D	Reinforcing	
			Bent	Str.
J-1	4	8+2$\frac{1}{2}$	1-$\frac{3}{4}$	1-$\frac{3}{4}$
J-2	4	8+2$\frac{1}{2}$	1-$\frac{3}{4}$	1-$\frac{3}{4}$
J-3	4	8+2$\frac{1}{2}$	1-$\frac{5}{8}$	1-$\frac{1}{2}$
J-4	4	8+2$\frac{1}{2}$	1-$\frac{3}{4}$	1-$\frac{3}{4}$

Fig. 27–36. Beam and joist schedules.

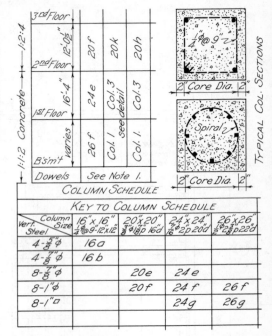

Fig. 27–38. Column schedule.

KEY TO COLUMN SCHEDULE

Vert. Steel \ Column Size	16"x16" 4-$\frac{7}{8}$@9-12x12	20"x20" 8-$\frac{3}{4}$@18p 16d	24"x24" 16-$\frac{7}{8}$@2p 20d	26x26 16-$\frac{7}{8}$@2$\frac{3}{4}$p22d
4-$\frac{5}{8}\phi$	16a			
4-$\frac{7}{8}\phi$	16b			
8-$\frac{7}{8}\phi$		20e	24e	
8-1"ϕ		20f	24f	26f
8-1"$\square$			24g	26g

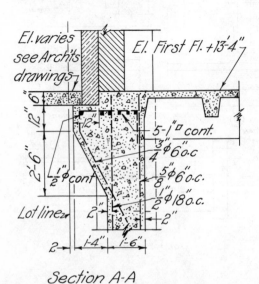

Fig. 27–37. Special reinforcing detail.

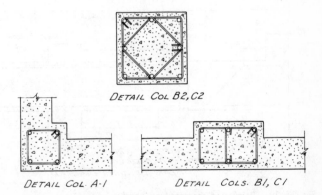

Fig. 27–39. Detail of column reinforcing.

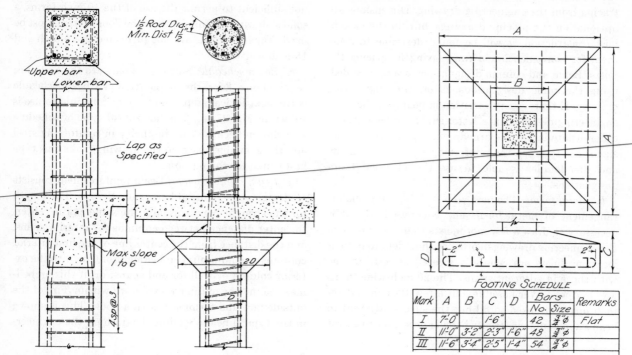

Fig. 27-40. Column reinforcing splices.

Fig. 27-42. Column footing schedule.

FOOTING SCHEDULE

Mark	A	B	C	D	Bars		Remarks
					No.	Size	
I	7'-0"		1'-6"		42	3/4"φ	Flat
II	11'-0"	3'-2"	2'-3"	1'-6"	48	3/4"φ	
III	11'-6"	3'-4"	2'-5"	1'-4"	54	3/4"φ	

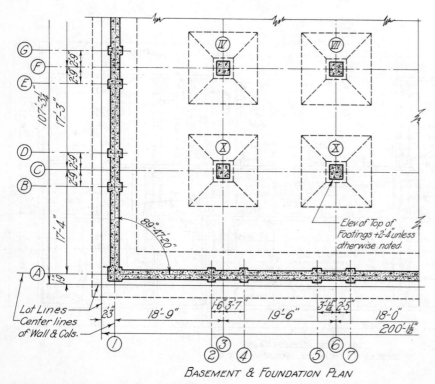

BASEMENT & FOUNDATION PLAN

Fig. 27-41. Column and wall footing plan.

a. Outline drawing. The detailer should first draw the outline of the floor, which can usually be done by tracing from the engineering drawing. Dimensions are optional on the placing drawings, but, in the case of joist construction, it will be found desirable to show them for convenience and time saving in spacing the joists. Beam and column designations are then added, using the same designations as on the engineering drawing. If there is any variation in beams of the same engineering designation, a letter suffix can be added to differentiate it. On the drawing in Fig. 27–43, the designer has foreseen the reinforcing steel requirements and the detailer is able to use the identical beam designations.

b. Metal forms. The next step is the spacing and arrangement of metal forms and concrete joists. It is necessary to draw a few more joists than are shown on the engineering drawing in order to show definitely their location. Joists are generally located directly in line with those in adjacent spans. The 20-inch-wide forms are used wherever possible, but a few 10-inch and 15-inch forms are used to fill out the spaces adjacent to beams and double joists or wherever necessary to adjust

the joist spacing to provide continuity. Only these two narrow widths should be used, and, where a space is not sufficient to permit the use of the 10-inch forms, a solid slab with the full depth of the floor system must be used. Tapered forms are not furnished in 10-inch and 15-inch widths.

c. Beam schedule. Since beam bars are the first ones required on a floor, the preparation of a beam schedule is the next logical step. The form of schedule to use is shown in Fig. 27–44. The horizontal type of schedule was chosen because the simplicity in reinforcing steel and the available space on the drawing make this type best suited for the purpose.

d. Beam reinforcement. Beam reinforcement consists of straight bars, trussed bars, and stirrups. The length for the straight bars is usually the same as the center-to-center distance between columns for interior spans, and the distance from the center line of the first interior columns to a minimum embedment of 6 in. into the exterior column or wall for end spans; or, if this embedment cannot be obtained, extend to within 3 in. of the outside face and terminate with a hook. This is shown in the typical beam-bending diagram on the engineer-

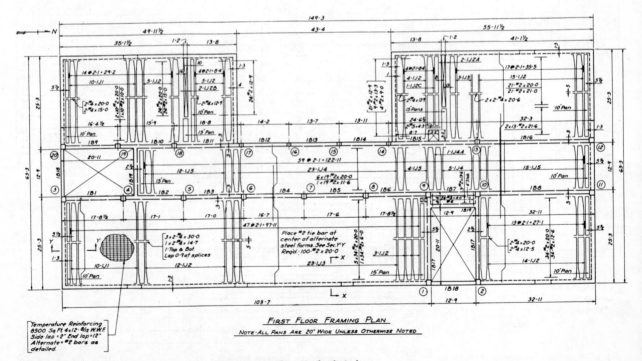

Fig. 27–43.   Steel placement drawing. (Courtesy American Concrete Institute.)

ing drawing in Fig. 27-35. Bending dimensions for truss bars are calculated from information given on the engineering drawing.

Consider beam *1B9* in Fig. 27-43 as an example. The detailer should draw a simple line detail to show the width of supports and clear span for the beam, as shown in Fig. 27-45, filling in the other dimensions as they are determined.

The various dimensions of the bars are then calculated according to the typical beam-bending diagram and inserted on the line detail. These dimensions are then added up and inserted in the proper space provided in the beam schedule. The height of bend is obtained by deducting the top and bottom concrete protection from the beam depth, in this case, 25 inches less 4 inches (2 inches at bottom for fireproofing and 2 inches at top for fireproofing and joist bars) or 21 inches. The slope dimension is then computed or selected from a table.

e. Stirrups. Dimensions for stirrups are obtained from the size of the beam by deducting the concrete protection, in this case, 1½ inches from the top, bottom, and sides of the beam. Thus 3 inches is deducted from both the width and depth of the beam. For beam *1B9* which is a 12 × 25 beam, the stirrup dimensions become 9 × 22. The detailer must also determine the direction in which hooks are to extend and indicate this in his schedule. It is usually desirable to turn hooks out into a slab unless prevented from doing so by openings; when used in spandrel beams, one hook is turned in and the other out. In this case, the length of stirrup support bars are specified as approximately the length of the clear span. These support bars are frequently specified as covering the stirrup spacing only.

f. Joists. When spacing the joists, it is best to select

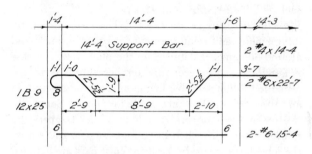

Fig. 27-45. Bending computation diagram. (Courtesy American Concrete Institute.)

	BEAM			STRAIGHT			BENT													STIRRUPS						SUPPORT BARS			2" CHAIRS	
MARK	No	B	D	No.	SIZE	LGTH.	No.	SIZE	LGTH.	MARK	TYPE	HOOK						HOOK	H	O	No.	SIZE	LGTH.	MARK	DIM.	TYPE	SPACING EACH END	No.	SIZE	LGTH.	No.	TYPE
1B1	1	12	25	2	#6	16·8	2	#6	24·3	1B600	⌒	8	2·2	2·5½	9·9	2·5½	6·9		1·9		13	#4	4·11	U400	9/22	⊔	4,2●6, 2●10, 12 Col·3 / 5,2●8, 2●10,12,15 Col·4	2	#4	15·8	4	BB
1B2	1	12	25	2	#7	16·7	2	#7	27·9	1B700	⌒		7·6	2·5½	7·10	2·5½	7·6		1·9		7 / 6	#4 / #4	4·11 / 4·11	U400 / U401	9/22 / 9/22	⊔	5,2●8, 2●10, 12, 15 Col·4 / 6,2●8, 10,12,15 Col·5	2		15·7	4	BB
1B3	1	12	23	2	#6	16·6	2	#6	27·8	1B601	⌒		7·8	2·3	7·10	2·3	7·8		1·7		16	#3	4·7	U301	9/20	⊔	4,3●6, 2●8, 10, 12	2		15·6	4	BB
1B4	1	12	23	2	#6	16·1	2	#6	27·5	1B602	⌒		7·8	2·3	7·7	2·3	7·8		1·7		16	#3	4·7	U301	9/20	⊔	Do.	2		15·1	4	BB
1B5	1	12	23	2	#6	17·0	2	#6	28·4	1B603	⌒		7·11	2·3	8·0	2·3	7·11		1·7		16	#3	4·7	U301	9/20	⊔	Do.	2		16·0	4	BB
1B6	1	12	23	2	#7	16·6	2	#7	27·0	1B701	⌒		7·9	2·3	7·10	2·3	6·11		1·7		16	#3	4·7	U301	9/20	⊔	Do.	2		15·6	4	BB
1B7	1	12	23	2 / 2	#6 / #7	13·9 / 27·6			Bot. In Top			Extend	7·8	Into Beam 1B8							10	#3	4·7	U301	9/20	⊔	5, 2●7, 10, 12				3	BB
*1B8	1	12	33	3	#8	30·8	3	#8	38·6	1B800	—		8·7	3·2	19·6	3·2	3·2	1·1	2·3		20	#4	6·3	U402	9/30	⊔	6,3●8, 2●12, 2●15, 2●18	2		29·9	4 / 6	BB+1 / BB
1B9	1	12	25	2	#6	15·4	2	#6	22·7	1B604	⌒	8	2·1	2·5½	8·9	2·5½	6·2		1·9		12	#4	4·11	U400	9/22	⊔	5, 2●7, 2●10, 13	2		14·4	3	BB

BEAM SCHEDULE

	JOIST			STRAIGHT			BENT													3/4"
MARK	No.	B	D	No.	SIZE	LGTH.	No.	SIZE	LGTH.	MARK	TYPE	HOOK						HOOK	H	O	CHAIRS
1J1	20	5	8+2½	1	#7	24·0	1	#6	26·2	1J600	⌒	8	3·4	1·0½	16·6	1·0½	3·7		9	24·11	5
1J2	58	5		1	#6	24·0	1	#6	44·11	1J603	⌒		3·7	1·0½	15·2	1·0½	24·1		9		5
1J2A	2	Var.		2	#6	24·0	2	#6	31·6	1J607	⌒		3·7	1·0½	15·2	1·0½	10·8		9		10
1J2B	2	Var.		2	#6	24·0	1	#6	44·11	1J603	⌒		3·7	1·0½	15·2	1·0½	24·1		9		10
1J2C	1	5		1	#6	20·2	1	#6	22·0	1J606	⌒	8	2·6	1·0½	13·8	1·0½	3·1		9	20·9	4
1J3	26	5		1	#6	24·0	1	#6	31·6	1J607	⌒		3·7	1·0½	15·2	1·0½	10·8		9		5
1J4	28	5		1	#6	13·9	1	#6	21·4	1J604	⌒		8·4	1·0½	8·4	1·0½	1·11	8	9		3
1J4A	1	5		1	#6	13·9	1	#6	16·4	1J605	⌒	8	1·11	1·0½	9·1	1·0½	1·11	8	9	14·5	3
1J5	31	5	8+2½	1	#5	13·9															

JOIST SCHEDULE

Fig. 27-44. Beam and joist schedules for Fig. 27-43. (Courtesy American Concrete Institute.)

a principal panel of the floor, then align all other joists in adjoining panels by the use of narrow-width forms where necessary. It is obvious that on the floor shown in Fig. 27–43 the detailer would select the panel bounded by columns *3, 9,* and *1.*

The general procedure for calculating lengths and bending diagrams for joist bars is the same as for beams except that the typical bending diagrams for joists, as shown on the engineering drawings, are to be followed. The joist schedule is similar to the beam schedule except that stirrups and stirrup support bars are not usually required. Variations in the typical joists shown on the engineering drawings are indicated by suffixes such as *J2, J2A, J2B,* and *J2C.*

g. Temperature reinforcement. The temperature reinforcement, and reinforcement for bridging joists and around openings, is detailed on the plan view. For ease in handling, and for economy, temperature bars are detailed in 20-foot lengths, using only one odd length in any run with an allowance made for splices. Some fabricators and erectors prefer to have all #2 temperature reinforcement furnished in 20-foot lengths and cut on the job where necessary. Bridging joist bars are detailed in the same manner, except that the bars, being of a larger size, make it more economical to specify greater

lengths. In determining the number of lines of temperature steel, the lines adjacent to beams or walls are located about one-half the standard spacing away from the beam or wall.

Frequently, wire mesh is used for temperature reinforcement instead of straight bars, as the ease of placing often compensates for any difference in cost. The method of indicating the areas to be covered is plainly shown on the placing drawing in Fig. 27–43. Similar methods of detailing can be used wherever wire-mesh temperature reinforcement is required.

27.38   Column-placement schedules. The placement of steel for columns is usually shown in schedules, and bar-bending lists as shown in Fig. 27–46. The straight bars are ordered directly from the schedule, and all bent bars, ties, spirals, etc., are shown in the bar-bending lists. Bent bars are numbered in both schedules to correspond.

27.39   Other types of construction. The foregoing discussion has applied directly to the beam and joist type of construction. The general principles are the same in all construction, but for specific cases involving other types such as flat slab construction the reader is referred to the *Manual of Standard Practice for Detailing Reinforced Concrete Structures* ACI 315–51.

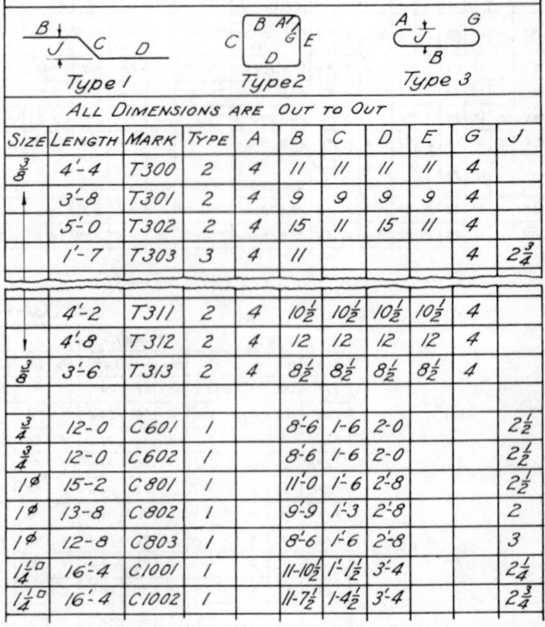

Fig. 27-46.   Column reinforcing schedule.

PROBLEMS

The problems for rectangular framed parts and skewed and sloping members are referred to Figs. 27–15 and 27–26 which are to be used together. The truss problem in Figs. 27–47 to 27–48 are for building shown in Figs. 26–16 and 26–18 of the preceding chapter. These should be referred to where necessary.

Beam problems can normally be detailed on an A-size sheet (8½ × 11). Column details will require the B-size sheet (11 × 17), and truss details require the C-size sheet (17 × 22). A scale of 1″ = 1′-0″ should normally be used.

Although only a few problems have been stated verbally, the selection of beams and columns available make it possible to assign each student in a class of 25 a different problem if desired.

Standard connections can be found in the Appendix.

Where a sketch is called for in the following problems, a pencil layout made with instruments but omitting unessential elements is meant.

Square Framed Beams

1. Make a detail sketch of the connections required for a beam assigned from Fig. 27–15. Refer to Fig. 27–26 for column sizes. Standard beam connections are shown in the Appendix. Study your problem carefully to see that the connection you make can be assembled in the shop and erected in the field.

2. Make a complete detail of the beam assigned and sketched in Problem 1.

Skewed Beams

3. Make a sketch of the connections required in an assigned skewed channel in the upper right corner of Fig. 27–15.

4. Make a complete detail of the channel sketched in Problem 3.

Sloping Beams

5. Make a sketch of the connections for the sloping rafter E in Fig. 27–22.

6. Make a complete detail of rafter E sketched in Problem 5.

7. Make a sketch of connections required for the hip rafter C in Fig. 27–22. Note that a double auxiliary layout is required to obtain the angle of bend of the connections.

8. Make a complete detail of the hip rafter C sketched in Problem 7.

Purlins

9. Make a complete detail of a purlin assigned from Fig. 27–22. Notes should cover number required which are exactly alike.

Trusses

10. Make a complete detail of the truss shown in Fig. 27–47 at the top of the figure. This is an architect's drawing. You are not to copy it but to make a detail for fabrication in the shop.

11. Same as Problem 10, using lower truss of Fig. 27–47.

12. Make a complete detail of the truss shown in Fig. 27–48. Scale ¾″ = 1′-0″.

Columns

13. Make a complete detail of a column assigned from Fig. 27–26. For beam connections to these columns, see Fig. 27–15. Assume first-floor beams to be the same as second-floor beams.

Reinforced Concrete

The following data supplements that given in Figs. 27–49, 27–50, and 27–51.

Columns C-3, C-6, F-3, and F-6 are 24 inches square. The reinforcing consists of eight 1-inch square bars with proper ties.

Column A-1 is 30 inches square and has eight ¾-inch bars.

Columns A-2, A-4, A-5, A-7, B-1, D-1, E-1, and G-1 are 18 × 30 inches in cross section, and each has six ⅞-inch bars.

The first-story height floor to floor is 14 feet. The columns above the second floor are 4 inches smaller on each dimension. Except for Column A-1 they are centered over the column below. Column A-1 has its outside faces flush for the entire height. Reinforcing rods in the second story are ⅛ inch less in diameter than in the first story.

14. Make a typical cross section of any assigned column.

15. Make a typical detail of second-story splice for any assigned column.

16. Make a bar-bending schedule for beams B-101 and B-102. See Figs. 27–49 and 27–50.

17. Make a bar-bending schedule for joists J-101, J-103, J-104, and J-105. See Figs. 27–49 and 27–51.

18. Make an engineering drawing (floor framing plan) for the second floor of the building shown in Figs. 26–16 and 26–17. Use 20-inch metal pans instead of tile to form joists. Each joist shall have two ⅝-diameter rods, one bent and one straight. See ACI Manual for details of framing concrete to steel beams.

19. Make a typical detail of the joists of Problem 18.

20. Make a typical cross-section detail through the 18″-WF 50 pound beam, showing the placing of joist reinforcing rods. See ACI Manual for suggestions.

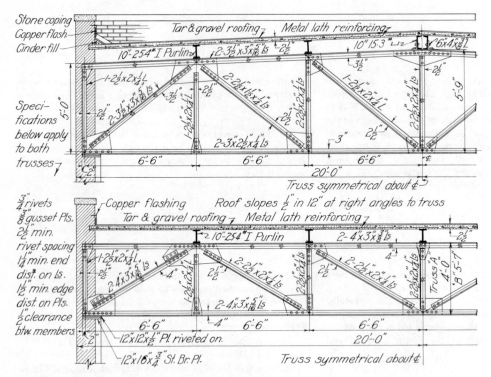

Fig. 27-47. Truss detail for building shown in Figs. 26-16 and 26-17.

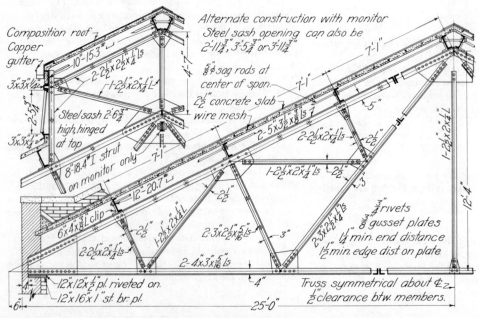

Fig. 27-48. Truss detail for building shown in Figs. 26-18 and 26-19.

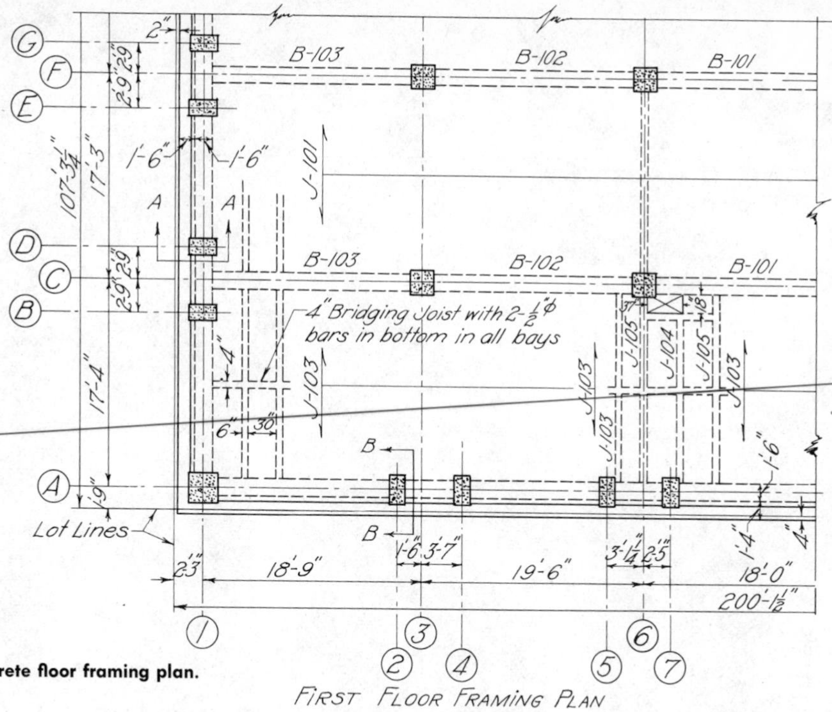

Fig. 27–49. Concrete floor framing plan.

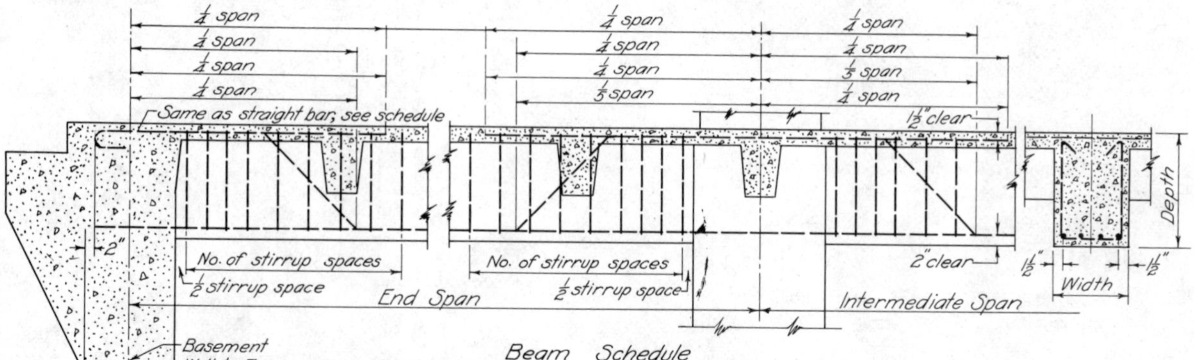

Beam Schedule

Mark	Size	T	Steel		Stirrups			Remarks
			Straight	Bent	No.	Size & Shape	Spaces (each end)	
B-101	13"x22"	–	2-1"φ	2-1"φ	16	½"φ ⊔	4@5", 3@10"	
B-102	15"x22"	–	2-1⅛"□	2-1"□	22	½"φ ⊔	3@4", 3@6", 4@8"	

Fig. 27–50. Beam detail.

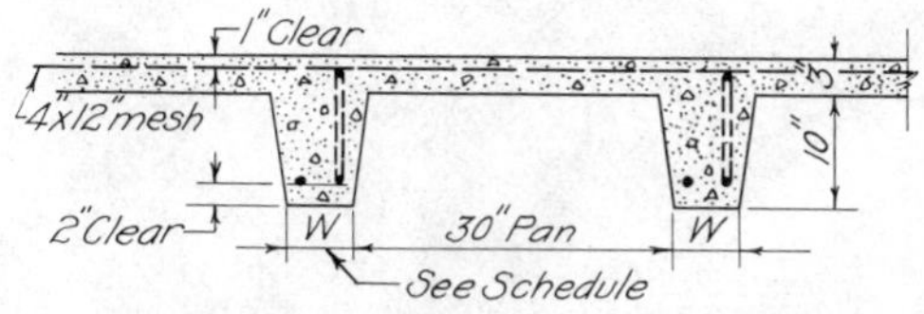

JOIST SCHEDULE

Mark	Size		Steel		Stirrups			Remarks
	Width	Depth	Stright	Bent	No.	Size + Shape	Spacing	
J-101	6"	10"+3"	1-⅞"φ	1-¾"φ	20	¼"φ ⊔	3@3", 6@6"	
J-102	6"	10"+3"	1-1"φ	1-⅞"φ	18	¼"φ ⊔	3@3, 5@6"	
J-103	6"	10"+3"	1-⅞"φ	1-⅞φ	18	¼"φ ⊔	3@3, 5@6"	
J-109	5"	10"+3	1-⅝"φ	1-½"φ	4	¼"φ ⊔	3@5"	
All straight bars to extend 1'-0" past ℄ of support								
Bent bars shall extend to the ¼" point of the next span.								

Fig. 27–51. Joist detail.

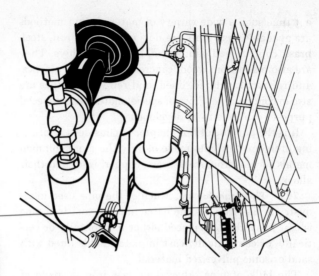

28

Pipe Drawing*

28.1 Introduction. Some form of piping is used in most projects with which the engineer is concerned. For that reason he should understand the general functions and characteristics of piping systems. He should also know the proper methods of representation and location of pipes and pipe fittings.

Pipes are normally used for conveying liquids, gases, and solids such as water, oil, steam, air, and minerals. They are sometimes used as structural elements, such as columns and beams.

The material of which pipes are made covers a wide range. In general, they are round but other shapes are frequently used. Sizes range from very small to very large and thickness of walls ranges from very thin to very thick.

The material, shape, size, and wall thickness are not necessarily dependent one upon the other but each depends upon the purpose for which the pipe is used.

In general, a piping system of any extent consists of a succession of individual pieces connected in such a manner as to maintain continuity of flow. Volume of flow is controlled by various devices developed to meet the specific need. Fixtures used to control direction and volume of flow are generally classified as fittings and valves. Fittings and valves may or may not be made of the same material as the pipes to which they are attached.

28.2 Pipe material. In ancient times pipe material was limited to bamboo, wood, and stone. As civilization progressed metals came into common use. At the pres-

* This chapter was prepared by Professor L. D. Walker of the University of Illinois.

◀ Interior view of a chemical plant (Martin Iger).

ent time such a wide variety of materials and methods are available that pipes are now made from iron, steel, brass, copper, lead, aluminum, and metal alloys. They are also made from wood, concrete, clay, glass, plastics, and rubber. Insulated, lined, and reinforced pipes are also in common use. Pipes of special materials for special purposes continue to be developed.

It is the purpose of this chapter to consider the drafting problems for pipes made of only the more common metals such as iron, steel, brass, copper, lead, and their alloys.

28.3   Pipe manufacture. Much of the pipe used in industry is cast iron. As the name implies, cast iron pipe is cast in sand molds placed either horizontally or vertically, or centrifugally cast in metal molds lined with sand or some pulverized material.

The bulk of pipe other than cast iron is made of wrought metal such as steel, iron, brass, or copper. In principle the methods of manufacture of wrought metal pipe differ widely from those of making cast iron pipe. In one common method, pipe-length strips of metal are rolled into cylindrical shapes and the edges are welded together. The electric-weld method is used quite extensively. Another common method is to bring a cylindrically shaped piece of metal to a high forging temperature, force a hole through the center of the cylinder, and then roll it down to the desired wall thickness. In general, copper tubing is made by the cold-drawn process.

28.4   Pipe sizes and specifications. Inside diameter depends mainly upon the volume of flow desired. Wall thickness depends upon a number of variables such as internal and external pressure, shock, vacuum, and thermal expansion.

Careful consideration must be given to the meaning of pipe sizes, which are usually indicated simply as ½ inch, 1 inch, 2 inch, etc. When such reference is made to the size of steel or wrought-iron pipe up to 12 inch, the specified size refers to the nominal inside diameter because this is close to, but not, the exact inside diameter. For example, the inside diameter of a nominal 1-inch "standard weight" steel pipe is 1.049 inches, "extra-strong" is .957 inch, and "double-strong" is .599

inch, yet the outside diameter in each case is 1.315 inches. The great advantage in keeping the outside diameter the same for each nominal diameter, regardless of wall thickness, is the adaptability of standard valves and fixtures to pipes, regardless of the thickness of walls. Figure 28–1 shows the outside diameter, inside diameter, and wall thickness of typical 1-inch steel pipe. See Table 38 in the Appendix for dimensions of wrought-steel pipe.

When reference is made to standard steel or wrought-iron pipe sizes larger than 12 inches, such as 14-inch, 16-inch, etc., the specified size now refers to the outside diameter. Such large pipe is often called O.D. pipe. When outside diameter is used to designate the pipe size, thickness of walls must also be stated so that inside diameter can be determined.

Cast iron pipe is available in a wide variety of standard sizes and weights with the bell-and-spigot joint. It is also available in sizes 1¼ inches to 12 inches with threaded ends. Nominal size of cast iron pipe always indicates inside diameter regardless of size. Terms such as "strong" and "extra-strong" are not commonly used in connection with cast iron pipe; consequently wall thickness or outside diameter or both should be indicated in connection with nominal size. See Table 39 of Appendix for common characteristics of bell-and-spigot-end cast iron pipe.

Brass and copper pipes are available in sizes from ⅛ inch to 12 inches and in two weights called "regular" and "extra-strong." They are very similar in wall thickness and inside diameter to steel pipe classified as "standard" and "extra-strong." Outside diameters are exactly the same as outside diameters of corresponding

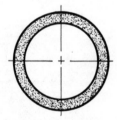
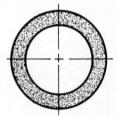

Fig. 28–2.   Sections of 1-inch brass pipe.

Fig. 28–1.   Sections of 1-inch steel pipe.

Fig. 28–3.   Sections of 1-inch copper water tubing.

nominal sizes of steel pipe. Figure 28–2 shows outside diameter, inside diameter, and wall thickness of 1-inch "regular" and "extra-strong" brass pipe. See Table 40 of the Appendix for dimensions of brass and copper pipe.

Copper water tubing is available in sizes from ⅛ inch to 12 inches. Its wall thickness is considerably less than that of most other piping material. Nominal size indicates neither outside diameter nor inside diameter. Actual outside diameter is consistently .125 inch greater than nominal size. Consequently, in specifying size of tubing, outside diameter and wall thickness must be given. Three wall thicknesses are available. Figure 28–3 shows outside diameter, inside diameter, and wall thickness of 1-inch Type K, Type L, and Type M copper water tubing. See Table 41 of Appendix for sizes of copper water tubing.

Specifications and recommendations for manufacture, composition, strength, use, size, etc., of pipe and pipe products have been developed by such organizations as the American Water Works Association, American Gas Association, American Petroleum Institute, American Society for Testing Materials, American Standards Association, and others. The American Standards Association is working toward a unification of all pipe specifications in an attempt to eliminate odd sizes and varieties and to develop some coordination applicable to all common types and sizes. Printed copies of complete standards for pipes and pipe products may be obtained from the American Standards Association.

Pipe standards, piping handbooks, manufacturers' manuals, and catalogues are available to supplement the limited amount of data in tables in the Appendix.

28.5 Pipe joints. In order to join properly pipe lengths, fittings, and valves, suitable connections must be provided. These connections must withstand pressures, shock, and stresses to which the pipes, fittings, and valves are subjected.

One of the most common methods of connecting cast iron pipe is by the conventional bell-and-spigot joint. This joint is suitable where there is relatively low pressure and little vibration such as in underground installations. Lead, cement, sulfur compounds, oakum, and jute are the usual packing materials.

Other joints used on cast iron pipe may be classed as mechanical joints because of the manner in which the jointing material is forced into place. In this type of joint, the jointing material is rolled or pushed along the outside of the inserted spigot end of one pipe into the bell end of the other, either by bolt action or screw action. This type of joint usually requires some modifications of the conventional bell-shaped end of the pipe. This joint will withstand greater pressure and vibration, and allows for greater lateral deflection and thermal expansion than the conventional bell-and-spigot joint. Additional packing materials especially adaptable to mechanical joints are rubber, composition materials, and bituminous compounds. Frequently these materials are pre-formed before use.

Still other methods of connecting cast-iron pipe include the use of mechanical joints such as the gland type, ball-and-socket and universal joints, sleeve couplings, and welding. Screwed couplings and fittings similar to those used for steel pipe are not uncommon where small size cast iron pipe is used. The conventional bell-and-spigot joint is illustrated in Fig. 28–4.

Standard steel and wrought-iron pipes are usually

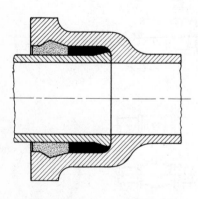

BELL & SPIGOT JOINT

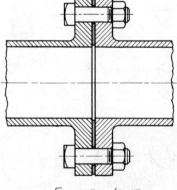

FLANGED JOINT

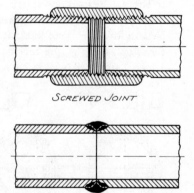

SCREWED JOINT

WELDED JOINT

Fig. 28–4. Pipe joints.

connected by flanges, threaded couplings, or welds.

The flange joint can be quite readily disassembled and may be designed to withstand high pressures. Flanges are attached to the pipe ends either by being screwed on, welded, or lapped. To complete the joint the flange faces are drawn tightly together with bolts. Flange design, face type and finish, gasket design and composition, and bolt load are all important factors in this type of joint. One of the more simple flange joints is illustrated in Fig. 28–4.

Welded joints and connections are not uncommon in high-pressure pipe assemblies. They are becoming more common in low-pressure assemblies as less expensive low-pressure valves and fixtures are being developed. Butt welds with conventional modifications are most frequently used. See Fig. 28–4.

Threaded couplings are simply short cylinders, threaded on the inside at each end to form pressure-tight joints for end-threaded pipe. This type of joint is illustrated in Fig. 28–4. These joints are not so readily

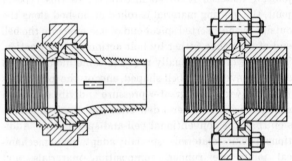

Fig. 28–5.   Screwed and flanged unions.

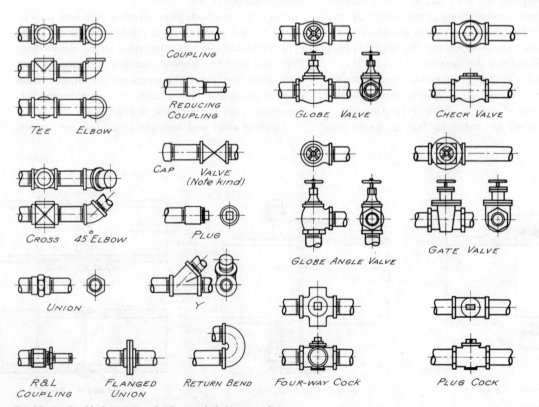

Fig. 28–6.   Double-line pipe and valve symbols for screw fittings.

disassembled as flange joints. They may be designed to withstand relatively high pressures. The thread design of the coupling must conform to the thread design of the pipes to be connected. For pipe sizes over 2 inches the threads are tapered 1 inch in 16 or .75 inch per foot measured on the diameter and along the axis. See Fig. 10–34. For pipe sizes of 2 inches and under, straight threads are frequently used on both ends of the coupling. Straight threads on one end and tapered threads on the other, or left-hand threads on one end and right-hand threads on the other are not unusual. To expedite disassembly in a threaded pipe system, couplings called pipe unions are used. See Fig. 28–5 for conventional screwed and flanged unions.

Soldered joints are frequently used on copper and brass tubing, but pressure and temperature restrict the extensive use of solder as a jointing material.

28.6   Pipe fittings. In order to control and change direction of flow in a piping system of any extent, a number of pipe fittings are necessary. Elbows, tees, crosses, laterals, return bends, and reducers are some of many in use. They are made of cast iron, steel, malleable iron, brass, and sometimes of special materials. They are not necessarily made of the same material as the pipe to which they are attached. Connections of these fittings to pipes and valves are made by flanges, screw fittings, welding, soldering, or jointing materials. A number of screw fittings are shown in Fig. 28–6.

Most pipe fittings are specified by material, name, and nominal pipe size. Some fittings such as tees, laterals, and crosses are sometimes used to connect pipes of different sizes. When this occurs, the fitting is called a reducing fitting and sizes of openings must be properly indicated. In the case of the reducing tee, lateral, and cross, the size of the largest opening is given first and then the size of the opening at the opposite end. When the fitting is a tee or a lateral, the third dimension is that of the outlet. When the fitting is a cross, the third dimension is the largest outlet opening and the fourth is the opposite opening. Figure 28–7 indicates the method of specifying sizes of reducing fittings.

28.7   Valves. Volume of flow in pipes is controlled primarily by valves. The more common types are the gate valve, globe valve, and check valve. Many other types such as the angle valve, relief valve, needle valve, pressure-reducing valve, butterfly valve, and plug valve are not uncommon.

Most valve bodies in the smaller sizes are made of brass or bronze. Those in the larger sizes are usually made of cast iron for intermediate pressures, and cast steel or cast alloy for high pressures. They are not necessarily made of the same material as the pipes to which they are attached. Connections to pipes and fittings are usually made by flanges, screw fittings, or welding.

The gate valve is used more frequently than any other valve. When open it offers little restriction to straight-line flow. It is used on lines conveying water and other liquids.

If the design is such that the gate moves out of the body of the valve with the stem, it is called a rising-stem valve. If the gate moves out of the body of the valve along the stem, it is called a non-rising-stem valve. Consideration of the mechanics of these two styles of gate valves is important. The rising-stem type requires more space for stem clearance than does the non-rising-stem type, but an open or closed position of the gate is clearly indicated by the position of the stem.

The globe valve is less expensive than the gate valve. It is used extensively for throttling on steam lines and where close regulation of volume of flow of liquids is necessary. In general, the design requires two changes

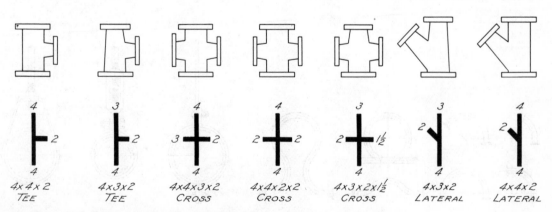

Fig. 28–7.   Method of designating sizes of reducing fittings.

of direction of flow which causes some loss of pressure in the system. All globe valves are of the rising-stem type. Ample space must be provided for operation to open completely.

The check valve is used to prevent reversal of the direction of flow. The design is usually quite simple, and in most cases gravity plays a part in its operation. The swing check and lift check, with variations, are the two principal types of check valves in common use.

Conventional gate, globe, and check valves are shown in Fig. 28-8.

28.8 Pipe bends. Where conventional long-turn elbows are not suitable for high velocity flow, fabricated pipe bends are frequently used. Lineal expansion and space limitations may also require their use. They may be obtained in almost any size and shape but require-

ments must be described to the manufacturer in the form of complete drawings and specifications.

Some conventional pipe bends are shown in Fig. 28-9.

28.9 Pipe supports and accessories. Pipe lines of any considerable extent require hangers and supports to provide for dead weight and stresses due to thermal expansion and vibration. Provision must also be made for adequate drainage of the line. Location, type, and spacing of supports are all important factors which must be given careful consideration. For horizontal runs, rods or straps are usually adequate where the pipes are relatively small. They are usually attached to joists or steel work in the ceiling. For long vertical runs of considerable weight, bottom supports set on the floor are frequently used. Many types of supports with recommendations for spacing and slope are available from pipe

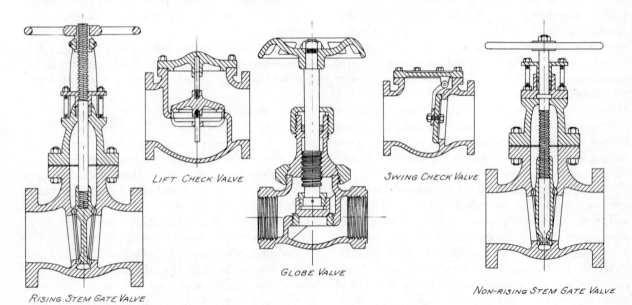

LIFT CHECK VALVE

GLOBE VALVE

SWING CHECK VALVE

RISING STEM GATE VALVE

NON-RISING STEM GATE VALVE

Fig. 28–8. Sections of valves.

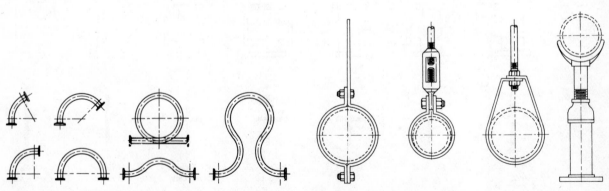

Fig. 28–9. Typical pipe bends.

Fig. 28–10. Typical pipe supports.

manufacturers. Their recommendations should be carefully considered. A few types of pipe hangers are shown in Fig. 28–10.

In steam lines, special provision must be made for drainage of condensation. The slope of piping in these lines should be in the direction of steam flow. Drip pockets, steam separators, and steam traps are some of the devices used in this connection. A few of the more common accessories on steam and cold water lines are shown in Fig. 28–11. Many other accessories to pipelines are illustrated in manufacturers' catalogues.

28.10 Pipe symbols. Pipes, fittings, valves, fixtures, and accessories common to piping systems are most frequently represented on drawings by accepted standard symbols. The standard single-line symbols used on small-scale drawings are shown in Fig. 28–12. Shown in

the Appendix are standard symbols for plant equipment and plumbing fixtures. These standard symbols are from the American Standards Association. Complete copies of graphical symbols may be purchased from the American Standards Association.

28.11 Pipe drawings and diagrams. The purpose of pipe drawings is to show the location and size of pipes and the location and identification of valve fixtures and apparatus which go to make up all or parts of piping systems large or small. In general they are much like other engineering drawings. Orthographic, oblique, and axonometric are the types of projection most commonly used in pipe drawing. The use of either double-line or single-line representation of pipes, valves, and pipe fixtures is approved.

Orthographic one-, two-, or three-view projections are

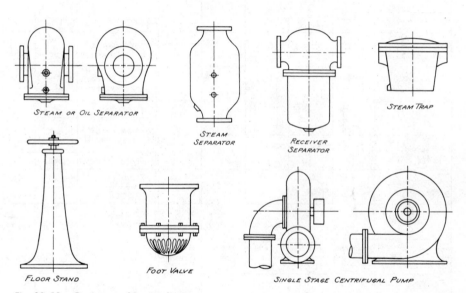

Fig. 28–11.   Devices used in pipe lines.

used in drawings of many installations. Double-line representation is ordinarily used where the system is made up principally of large pipe and where the drawings may be used a number of times as reference on similar projects. Such a drawing is shown in Fig. 28–13. Single-line representation of small pipe is permissible on double-line pipe drawings. Where the number of pipe-

lines in a system is large it is good practice to make up several sheets for the same plant layout. One or more sheets might properly show the main lines only, others return lines, and still others laterals, etc. Such drawings should be made upon tracing paper or cloth so they can be checked one over the other to see that no conflicts in the system exist.

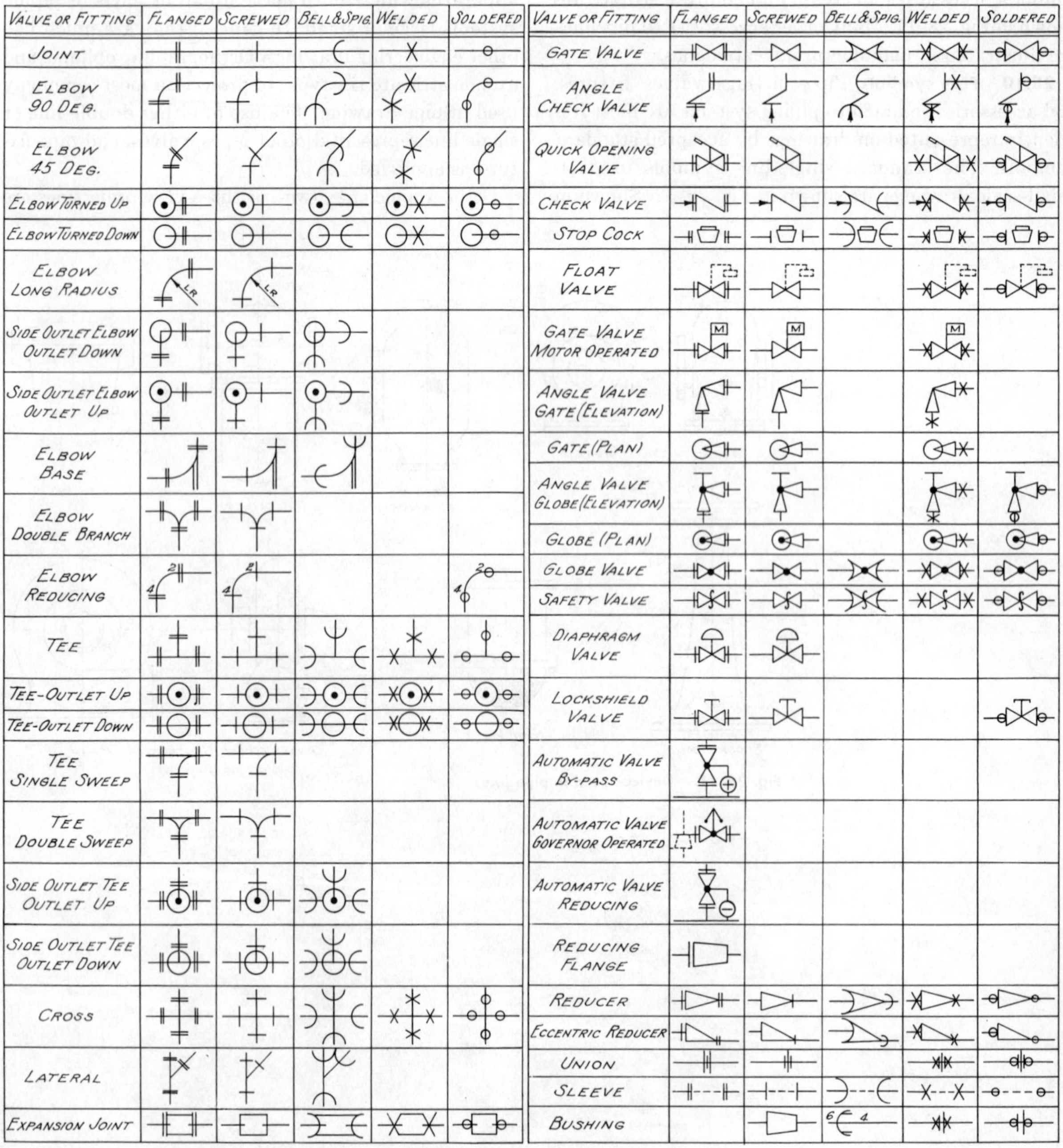

Fig. 28–12. American Standard single-line pipe and valve symbols.

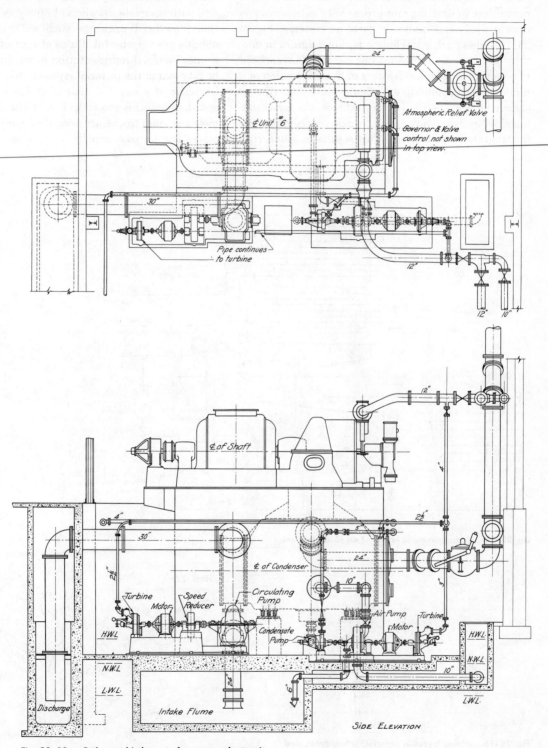

Fig. 28-13. Orthographic layout of a power plant unit.

For systems in which relatively small pipe is used it is good practice to represent all the pipes and pipe fixtures by single-line representation. This scheme saves much time in drafting and proves very satisfactory in drawings of small units or parts of systems. Figure 28–14 shows such a single-line piping diagram in one-view projection. A modification of the conventional two-view orthographic drawing of a small section of a piping system, sometimes called a developed view, is shown in Fig. 28–15. In this scheme the pipes are imagined to be revolved into a single plane, either the horizontal or the vertical. This results in a one-view

drawing and proves very effective on small-job studies and estimates.

For preliminary layouts and for reference in connection with complete drawings of piping systems, conventional pictorial drawings such as axonometric and oblique are very useful. Rules of projection governing proper pictorial representation of machine parts must be followed in the pictorial representation of piping. An isometric of a small section of piping both single-line and double-line is shown in Fig. 28–16. Single-line isometric is more frequently used than double-line since it serves the purpose equally well in most cases and is

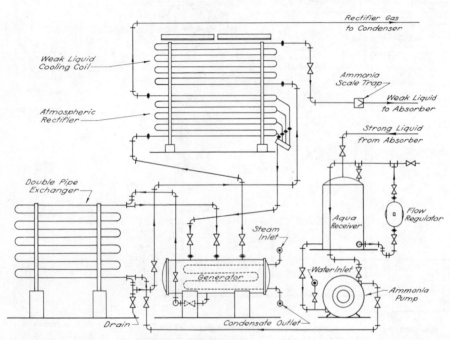

Fig. 28–14.   A diagrammatic layout of an absorption unit.

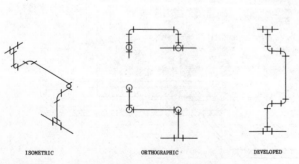

Fig. 28–15.   Piping layout in pictorial, orthographic, and developed form.

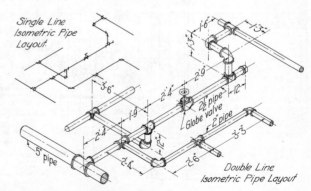

Fig. 28–16.   Isometric pipe layout.

much more easily done.

Single-line oblique drawings may be used for the same purpose as isometrics and have advantages in allowable modifications that isometrics do not have. An oblique of a small heat distribution system is shown in Fig. 28–17. It should be noted that the usual method of oblique projection has been modified to allow a clear interpretation of the location of risers and returns in this layout. Such modifications of oblique are used only when necessary to add clearness to the drawing. On almost all pictorial drawings and diagrams of pipe layouts the single-line representation of pipes and pipe fixtures is used regardless of changes of pipe sizes in the system. In single-line pipe drawings for heating systems, the weight of the line representing supply is usually heavier than that representing return. See Fig. 28–17.

28.12 Dimensions on pipe drawings. The general rules for dimensioning orthographic, axonometric, and

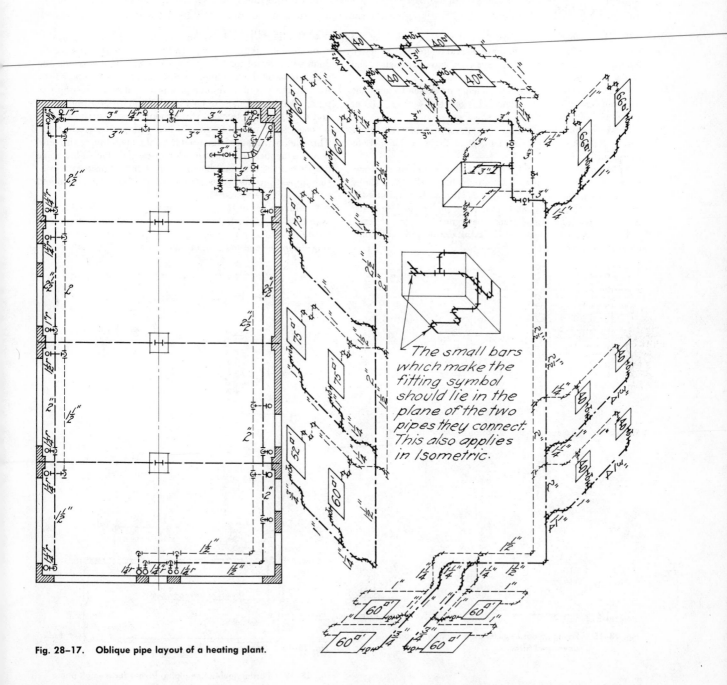

The small bars which make the fitting symbol should lie in the plane of the two pipes they connect. This also applies in Isometric.

Fig. 28–17. Oblique pipe layout of a heating plant.

oblique apply to pipe drawings. All lengths of straight runs of pipe must be dimensioned. The pipe sizes are indicated by writing the nominal pipe diameter near the side of the pipe, using leaders when necessary. Practically all other dimensions are location dimensions; consequently center lines of pipes, fixtures, and apparatus must be used freely. Overall dimensions of valves and fixtures are seldom shown since their sizes are standard.

Valves and apparatus are frequently identified by name or manufacturer's number on the drawing. The material of which the pipes, pipe fixtures, and valves are made is usually indicated in general specifications. Sizes of flanges, length of threads, and similar details are indicated on the drawing by conventional representation. On most pipe drawings, the dimensions are written on the dimension line rather than in a break in the line.

PROBLEMS

The following problems are typical of many that can be assigned. Excellent sources of material and references are actual building plans, water treatment systems, valve catalogues, and trade journals.

Sheet sizes, scales, paper, etc., should be chosen to meet the requirements of the problems. In general, 8½″ × 11″ or 11″ × 17″ should be a suitable sheet size.

1. Make a one-view freehand sketch of a gate valve, globe valve, or check valve for either flange or threaded connections as assigned.

2. Make an orthographic two-view double-line piping drawing of a section of a piping system to include 5 elbows, 3 valves (cross, check, and angle), 2 couplings (R. and L. and union), 1 cross, 1 reducer, 1 plug, and connecting pipe runs. Use either flanged or threaded connections as assigned.

3. Make a single-line isometric layout of the section of piping described in Problem 2.

4. In Fig. 28–18 is shown an isometric single-line piping diagram for a small pump house. In Fig. 28–19 is shown a partial double-line layout for the same system. Standard wrought-iron pipe is to be used in the interior. Standard cast-iron pipe is to be used underground. Five-inch pipe is to be used from supply to pump. All other pipe is to be 4 inch. Standard cast iron valves and fittings are to be used throughout. Flange fittings are to be used from pump to supply and pump to storage tank. Threaded fittings are to be used from the main line to the compound chamber and return. Complete the double-line pipe drawing of the system. Show pipe sizes and all necessary location dimensions and elevations necessary for construction and operation of the system.

5. Make a list of the pipe and fittings to be ordered for the system in Problem 4. Arrange the list in tabular form under headings of size, pipe lengths, valves (number and kind), fittings (number and kind), material, remarks.

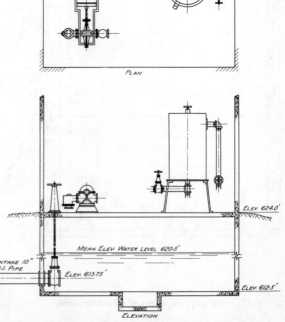

Fig. 28–19.   Partial double-line piping layout for a small pump house.

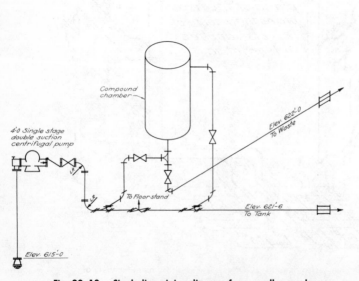

Fig. 28–18.   Single-line piping diagram for a small pump house.

6. Following are some typical piping layouts. Make an isometric single-line layout of all, or assigned, portions from any of the given layouts in Figs. 28–20 to 28–22.

7. Make a two-view orthographic drawing of portions as-signed in Problem 6. Show pipe sizes and all necessary location dimensions.

8. Make a pipe and fittings list for portions assigned in Problem 6. Arrange as suggested in Problem 5.

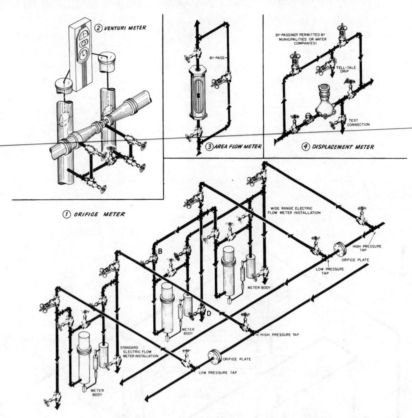

Fig. 28–20. Typical meter connections. (Courtesy Jenkins Bros., manufacturers of valves.)

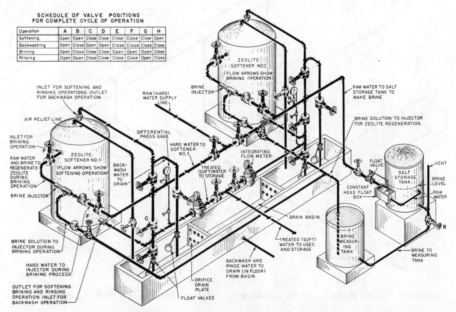

Fig. 28–21. Typical water-softening system layouts. (Courtesy Jenkins Bros., manufacturers of valves.)

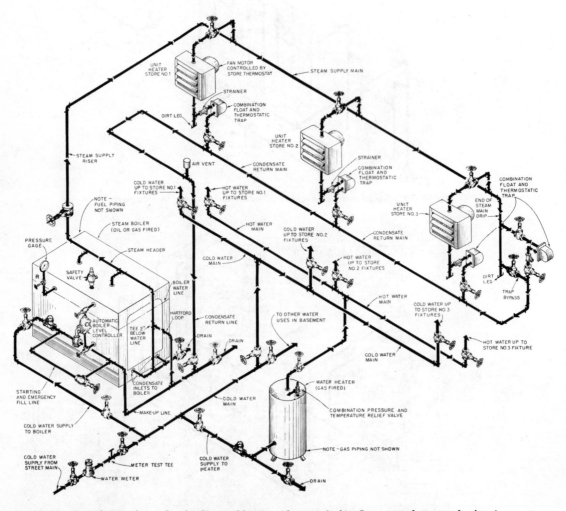

Fig. 28-22. Typical piping layout for plumbing and heating. (Courtesy Jenkins Bros., manufacturers of valves.)

Welding (Robert M. Mottar).

29
Welding Drawing

29.1 Introduction. For permanent fastening of parts of a structure, welding is a very important method. Many machine parts are now being constructed by welding various units together, thus making a built-up structure to replace a complicated casting or riveted part.

The earliest form of welding consisted of heating the parts and pounding them together on an anvil until they were joined together. From this stage the process of welding has been developed to its present state of perfection where almost any kind of metal may be satisfactorily welded. The two principal kinds of welding now generally used are fusion welding and forge welding.

a. Fusion welding is the term applied to the method of joining two pieces of metal by melting metal into a joint that has been raised to the melting temperature. Thus a fusion weld is actually a process whereby two parts are joined by bringing the metal of each part to a liquid state and adding extra molten metal which forms the joint when cooled.

b. Forge welding is the term applied to the method of joining two pieces of metal by heating them to the plastic state and then forcing the parts together either by pressure or by a blow of a hammer. In modern welding various kinds of machines are used to apply the pressure or the hammer blow.

29.2 Methods of welding. Welding may also be classified according to the method of applying the heat. Under this group there are four main divisions, gas welding, arc welding, resistance welding, and Thermit welding.

29.2.1   *Gas welding* is that type in which the heat is supplied by burning acetylene or hydrogen gas. The gas under pressure is mixed with oxygen and ignited. This creates a very hot flame which can be regulated to give various characteristics by adjusting the flow of the gas or the oxygen. Temperatures as high as 6000° F may be obtained with the oxyacetylene torch.

29.2.2   *Arc welding* is that type in which the heat is applied by means of an electric arc. Usually the parts to be welded are wired as one pole of the arc with the electrode held by the operator forming the other pole. Sometimes this is a carbon electrode, in which case the extra metal for the weld is supplied by a welding rod held in the arc in a manner similar to gas welding. More frequently the welding rod is used as the electrode so that the electrode itself gradually melts away, thus supplying the extra metal for the weld. Sometimes the arc is formed between two tungsten points, neither of which touches the metal being welded, in which case extra metal must be supplied by a filler rod. This latter method is used in atomic-hydrogen arc welding. The temperature of the arc is about 6000° F.

29.2.3   *Resistance welding.* Electric current is also used as a source of heat in a type of welding known as resistance welding. This is usually considered the easiest and cheapest method of fastening the pieces of metal together permanently. It is based on the fact that electric current flowing through metal will heat the metal when the resistance increases. Therefore, since current flowing from one plate to another will encounter the greatest resistance at the joint, whether it be a lap joint or a butt joint, the tendency is to heat the metal at the joint. The temperature at the joint may be regulated by the amount of the current. When the proper temperature is attained, pressure applied by some kind of machine will create a forge weld, thus fastening the two pieces together. This may be done over the entire joint, forming a butt or seam weld, or at particular points forming a spot weld. The term flash weld is sometimes used when the ends of two parts are joined by resistance welding.

29.2.4   *Thermit welding* is a method based on the strong affinity of aluminum for oxygen. A mixture of finely divided aluminum and iron oxide may be ignited at one spot, and it will then burn rapidly at a very high temperature, leaving a quantity of molten metal and aluminum oxide slag in the container. The temperature resulting from this reaction is about 4500° F. The reaction must be started by lighting a small quantity of special ignition powder.

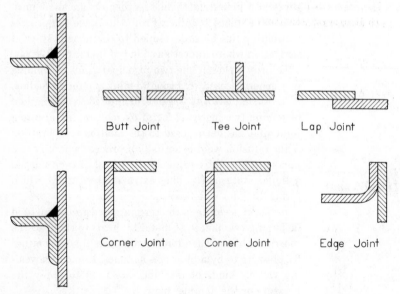

Butt Joint   Tee Joint   Lap Joint

Corner Joint   Corner Joint   Edge Joint

Fig. 29–1.   **Types of joints.**

For the fusion method of Thermit welding, it is first necessary to build a wax mold around the break or joint. A refractory sand mold is then constructed around the wax, which is dried out and preheated by some method such as blowing vaporized kerosene and air into the mold. During this preheating process the wax is burned out, leaving a space into which the metal melted by the Thermit reaction may be poured. This molten metal fuses with the parts to be joined together and upon cooling leaves a welded joint.

In some cases, such as the Thermit pipe weld, only the heat of the Thermit metal and slag is used to make a forge weld. With the ends of the pipe faced and butted together, the slag and the Thermit metal are poured around the joint. The heat of the metal raises the temperature of the pipe to a point where the forge weld can be made by pressing the two pieces together. After cooling the Thermit metal can be broken off because the slag forms a coating on the pipe which prevents the Thermit metal from sticking to the pipe.

29.3 Types of joints. One very valuable feature of welding is that the parts may be fastened together in almost any relative position. However, there are certain standard joints that are most frequently encountered in welding operations. Figure 29-1 shows the joints most commonly found in practice.

29.3.1 *Cross section of joint.* The thickness of the parts to be joined will have a large bearing on the cross section of the joint. If the plates are thin the plain butt joint may be used as shown in Fig. 29-2(*a*). Plates with a little greater thickness might be prepared with a single *V* butt joint as in Fig. 29-2(*b*) or a *Y* type butt joint as in Fig. 29-2(*c*). Still greater thickness might require a double V butt joint with the welding being done from both sides. See Fig. 29-2(*d*). Other methods of preparing the parts for welding are shown in Figs. 29-2(*e*) to (*m*).

29.4 Welding symbols for fusion welding. There are so many different conditions under which welding is done and so much information to be conveyed from the office to the welding operator that the American Welding Society has devised a composite symbol by means of which all this information may be transmitted. This symbol is in the general form of an arrow on which other symbols, letters, and marks may be placed to give complete instructions for fusion welding. The form of this arrow as well as the kind and position of other symbols is given in Fig. 29-3.

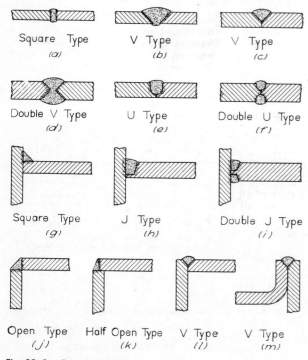

Fig. 29-2. Types of welds.

29.5   Welding legend for fusion welding. When fusion welding is specified on a drawing by means of the welding symbols, a legend should be placed on the drawing to aid in interpreting the symbols. This legend is shown in Fig. 29-4. To further aid in clarifying the use of the welding symbol, many of the figures shown in Fig. 29-2 are repeated in Fig. 29-5 together with the proper welding symbols.

These symbols may be made either mechanically or freehand.

Fillet, bevel and groove weld symbols should always be shown with the perpendicular leg to the left.

The size dimension should be to the left of the symbol with length and spacing of increments to the right.

The finish of a weld may be indicated as shown in Fig. 29-5(*k*). The letters *C, G,* and *M* are used to indicate chip, grind, or machine. The standard finish mark *f* may also be used.

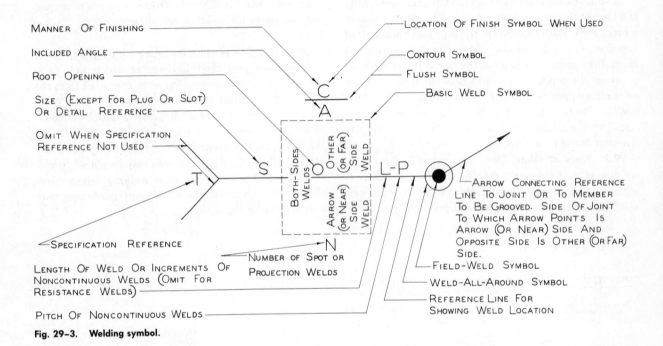

Fig. 29–3.   Welding symbol.

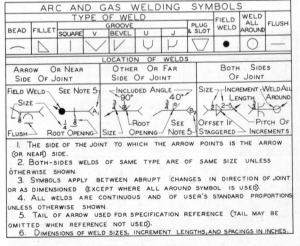

Fig. 29–4.   Arc and gas welding symbols.

When only one member is to be grooved, it is important that the arrow point specifically to that member as in Fig. 29–5(*h*) or (*i*).

For complete instructions for making these symbols, see the booklet entitled "Welding Symbols" by the American Welding Society, 29 West 39th Street, New York City.

29.6 Welding legend for resistance welding. When resistance welding is specified there must be some differ-

ence in the symbols because there is no significance to the terms "arrow" side or "other" side, since the weld always occurs between the two parts. Consequently the symbols are centered on the arrow as shown in Fig. 29–6. Instead of size of the fillet, the weld is specified by strength as indicated in Fig. 29–6. Sometimes the symbol is placed on the arrow and sometimes shown on the drawing in its actual position which may be dimensioned. Figure 29–6 shows the legend to be placed on

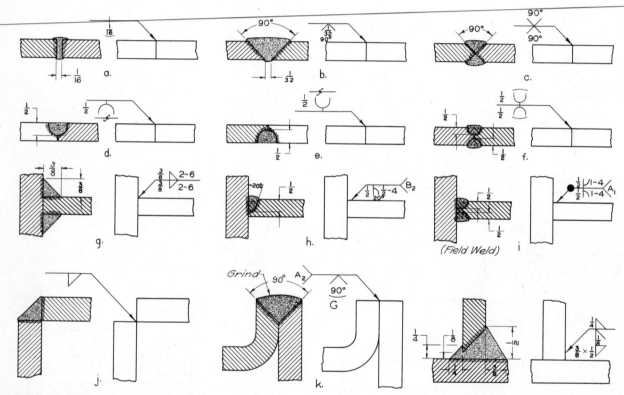

Fig. 29–5. Application of welding symbol.

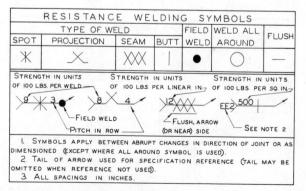

Fig. 29–6. Resistance welding symbols.

the drawing when resistance welds are to be specified.

The use of resistance weld symbols is shown in Fig. 29-7. Note that when the welding symbol is placed on the drawing, only the strength specification is placed on the arrow.

29.7   Other methods of specifying welds. Although the symbols of the American Welding Society are being used in many industries, welds are still being specified by other means. Probably the most common is to show cross hatching on the drawing at the place where the weld is to be placed. In that case notes and dimensions on the drawing give the required information about the weld. This method is illustrated in Fig. 29-8.

29.8   Welding symbols on working drawings. An application of fusion welding symbols to a working drawing of a machine part is shown in Fig. 29-9. A second application to a structural joint of a truss is shown in Fig. 29-10.

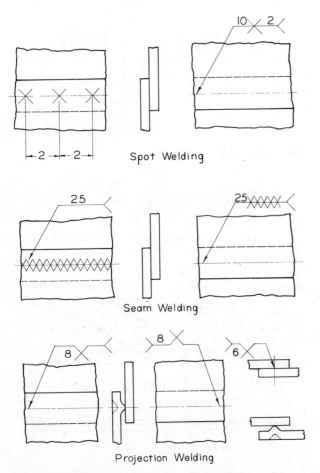

Spot Welding

Seam Welding

Projection Welding

Fig. 29-7.   Application of resistance welding symbol.

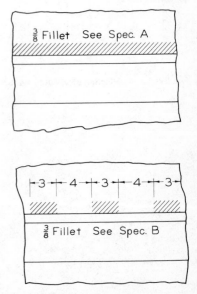

$\frac{3}{8}$ Fillet   See Spec. A

$\frac{3}{8}$ Fillet   See Spec. B

Fig. 29-8.   Alternate method of showing welds.

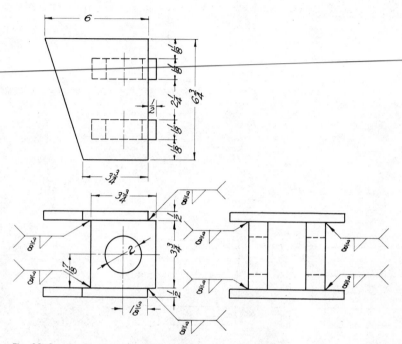

Fig. 29–9.   Application of welding symbol to a machine part.

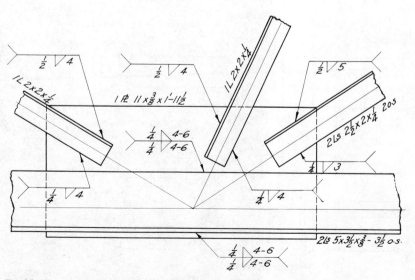

Fig. 29–10.   Application of welding symbol to a structural connection.

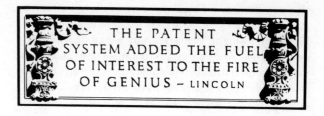

30

Patent Office Drawings

30.1 Meaning of patents. * The patent, as a physical entity (more properly "Letters Patent"), is a document stating the "grant" and including a "specification" describing the invention concerned and ending with one or more claims defining specifically the novel features of the invention. There must also be a drawing, if the invention permits of illustration, which drawing is fully described in the specification.

The Statute limits the field of patentable inventions (other than growing plants and designs) to processes, machines, manufactures, and compositions of matter. It also requires that the invention be "new and useful." It does not define the term "invention" other than to state that it means "invention or discovery." Many courts have tried to pass upon the degree of "genius" that must be displayed in the thing patented in order to amount to "invention." Some have said there must be a sudden inspiration, or a "flash of genius." In most cases, however, it has been regarded as sufficient if there is shown a degree of ingenuity beyond that to be expected of an average worker "skilled in the art."

The new Code tries to elucidate the matter by stating, Section 103, that a patent may not be granted "if the differences between the subject matter sought to be patented and the prior art are such that the subject matter as a whole would have been obvious at the time when the invention was made to a person having ordinary skill in the art to which said subject matter pertains."

Let us assume that an inventor has perceived a need

* This article was abstracted by permission from a paper by George A. Lovett, formerly Patent Attorney, General Motors Corporation.

◄ Entranceway to the Patent Office, the Department of Commerce Building (U. S. Department of Commerce).

or a possible use for something new falling within the statutory classes noted above. By careful study or by a "happy thought," he arrives at a way in which the desired object or result may be obtained or a mechanism may be constructed by which an improvement may be effected. So far, this may have been only a mental process and, if so, no matter how definite his idea or how certain he may be that he has a solution to the problem in hand, he has not "made an invention" in the legal sense. He has only a "conception" and no means of proving even that.

If he then makes some sketches of the device or writes a description or both and signs and dates them, he now has available something in the nature of proof of the conception, but still no "invention." Furthermore, these documents need one or more witnesses who can testify that they saw the documents at a certain time. Accordingly, the cautious inventor will take the matter up with someone able to understand the device, explain it to him, and have the papers dated and signed. Now we have "corroboration," a highly important element in establishing an inventor's dates. These steps should be taken at the earliest possible time.

After "conception" the next step is to reduce the invention to practice. Without this the invention is not regarded as "completed." "Reduction to practice" may be accomplished in one of two ways, either by "actual" reduction, i.e., by making and operating the structure and actual carrying out of a process, or by filing an application for patent thereon in the Patent Office. Such filing is regarded, by a sort of legal fiction, as fully equivalent to actual reduction and is termed "constructive" reduction to practice.

"Actual" reduction to practice requires successful use under substantially the same conditions as those for which the device is designed. As an example, a man had devised a stoplight for automobiles but his only test had been by mounting the mechanism on a bench and operating it by a lever. He was held not to have "reduced to practice" since the device was not used on an automobile. This may be an extreme case but it illustrates the principle.

In order to prove actual reduction to practice one should have witnesses and records similar to those required in proof of conception. The device used in demonstrating successful use should be preserved if possible.

30.2   Application for patents. Applications for patents must be made to the Commissioner of Patents. A complete application comprises: (1) a petition or request for a patent; (2) a specification, including a claim or claims; (3) an oath; (4) drawings, when necessary;

(5) the prescribed filing fee.

30.3   Specifications. The specifications accompanying a patent petition should be arranged in the following order:

a. Title of the invention; or a preamble stating the name, citizenship, and residence of the applicant and the title of the invention may be used.

b. Brief summary of the invention.

c. Brief description of the several views of the drawing, if there are drawings.

d. Detailed description.

e. Claim or claims.

f. Signature.

30.4   Drawings. The drawings required by the Patent Office differ somewhat from those used in engineering practice. Before beginning the drawings the inventor should secure a copy of "Rules of Practice of the United States Patent Office" from the Supt. of Documents, Washington 25, D. C. The cost is $.40. Stamps are not acceptable in payment. The drawings used for patents are made according to the usual rules of orthographic projection, but it is not necessary that they appear in projection with each other nor on one sheet. The following rules quoted verbatim from "Rules of Practice of the United States Patent Office" must be followed exactly. They are illustrated in Fig. 30–1.

Drawings required. The applicant for patent is required by statute to furnish a drawing of his invention whenever the nature of the case admits of it; this drawing must be filed with the application. Illustrations facilitating an understanding of the invention (for example, flow sheets in cases of processes, and diagrammatic views) may also be furnished in the same manner as drawings, and may be required by the Office when considered necessary or desirable.

Signature to drawing. The drawing must either be signed by the applicant in person or have the name of the applicant placed thereon followed by the signature of the attorney or agent as such.

Content of drawing. The drawing must show every feature of the invention specified in the claims. When the invention consists of an improvement on an old machine the drawing must when possible exhibit, in one or more views, the improved portion itself, disconnected from the old structure, and also in another view, so much only of the old structure as will suffice to show the connection of the invention therewith.

Standards for drawings. The complete drawing is printed and published when the patent issues, and a copy is attached to the patent. This work is done by the photolithographic process, the sheets of drawings being reduced about one-third in size. In addition, a reduction of a selected portion of the drawing of each application is published in the *Official Gazette.* It is therefore necessary for these and other reasons that the character of each drawing be brought as nearly as possible to a uniform standard of execution and excellence, suited to the requirements of the reproduction process and of the use of the draw-

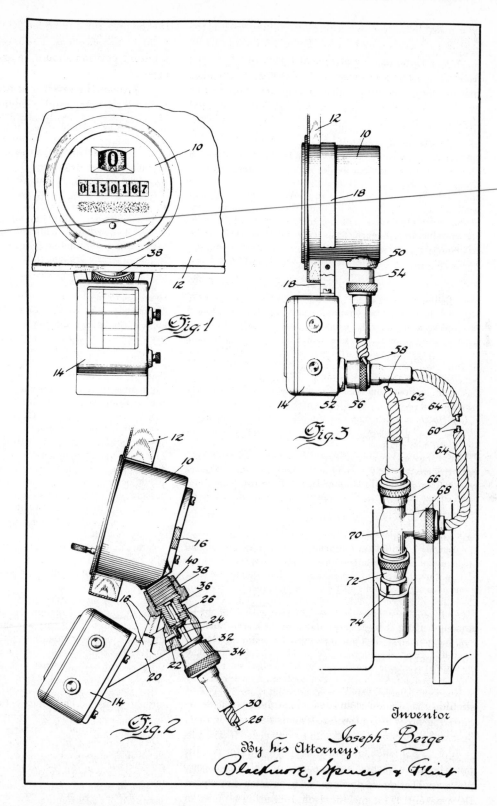

Fig. 30–1. Patent Office drawing.

ings, to give the best results in the interest of inventors, of the Office, and of the public. The following regulations with respect to drawings are accordingly prescribed:

(a) *Paper and ink.* Drawings must be made upon pure white paper of a thickness corresponding to two-ply or three-ply Bristol board. The surface of the paper must be calendered and smooth and of a quality which will permit erasure and correction. India ink alone must be used for pen drawings to secure perfectly black solid lines. The use of white pigment to cover lines is not acceptable.

(b) *Size of sheet and margins.* The size of a sheet on which a drawing is made must be exactly 10 by 15 inches. One inch from its edges a single marginal line is to be drawn, leaving the "sight" precisely 8 by 13 inches. Within this margin all work and signatures must be included. One of the shorter sides of the sheet is regarded as its top, and, measuring down from the marginal line, a space of not less than 1¼ inches is to be left blank for the heading of title, name, number, and date, which will be applied subsequently by the Office in a uniform style.

(c) *Character of lines.* All drawings must be made with drafting instruments or by photolithographic process which will give them satisfactory reproduction characteristics. Every line and letter (signatures included) must be absolutely black. This direction applies to all lines however fine, to shading, and to lines representing cut surfaces in sectional views. All lines must be clean, sharp, and solid, and fine or crowded lines should be avoided. Solid black should not be used for sectional or surface shading. Free-hand work should be avoided wherever it is possible to do so.

(d) *Hatching and shading.* Hatching should be made by oblique parallel lines, which may be not less than about one-twentieth inch apart.

Heavy lines on the shaded side of the object should be used except where they tend to thicken the work and obscure reference characters. The light should come from the upper left-hand corner at an angle of 45°. Surface delineations should be shown by proper shading, which should be open.

(e) *Scale.* The scale to which a drawing is made ought to be large enough to show the mechanism without crowding when the drawing is reduced in reproduction, and views of portions of the mechanism on a larger scale should be used when necessary to show details clearly; two or more sheets should be used if one does not give sufficient room to accomplish this end, but the number of sheets should not be more than is necessary.

(f) *Reference characters.* The different views should be consecutively numbered figures. Reference numerals (and letters, but numerals are preferred) must be plain, legible and carefully formed, and not be encircled. They should, if possible, measure at least one-eighth of an inch in height so that they may bear reduction to one twenty-fourth of an inch; and they may be slightly larger when there is sufficient room. They must not be so placed in the close and complex parts of the drawing as to interfere with a thorough comprehension of the same, and therefore should rarely cross or mingle with the lines. When necessary grouped around a certain part, they should be placed at a little distance, at the closest point where there is available space, and connected by lines with the parts to which they refer. They should not be placed upon hatched or shaded surfaces but when necessary, a blank space may be left in the hatching or shading where the character occurs so that it shall

appear perfectly distinct and separate from the work. The same part of an invention appearing in more than one view of the drawing must always be designated by the same character, and the same character must never be used to designate different parts.

(g) *Symbols, legends.* Graphical drawing symbols for conventional elements may be used when appropriate, subject to approval by the Office. The elements for which such symbols are used must be adequately identified in the specification. While descriptive matter on drawings is not permitted, suitable legends may be used, or may be required in proper cases, as in diagrammatic views and flow sheets. The lettering should be as large as, or larger than, the reference characters.

(h) *Location of signature and names.* The signature of the applicant, or the name of the applicant and signature of the attorney or agent, should be placed in the lower right-hand corner of each sheet within the marginal line. Signatures of witnesses are not required. The title of the invention must not be placed on the drawing but may be written in pencil below the lower marginal line.

(i) *Views.* The drawing must contain as many figures as may be necessary to show the invention; the figures should be consecutively numbered if possible, in the order in which they appear. The figures may be plan, elevation, section, or perspective views, and detail views of portions or elements, on a larger scale if necessary may also be used. Exploded views, with the separated parts of the same figure embraced by a bracket to show the relationship or order of assembly of various parts, are permissible. When necessary a view of a large machine or device in its entirety may be broken and extended over several sheets if there is no loss of facility of understanding the view (the different parts should be identified by the same figure number but followed by the letters, *a, b, c,* etc., for each part). The plane upon which a sectional view is taken should be indicated on the general view by a broken line, the ends of which should be designated by numerals corresponding to the figure number of the sectional view and have arrows applied to indicate the direction in which the view is taken. A moved position may be shown by a broken line superimposed upon a suitable figure if this can be done without crowding, otherwise a separate figure must be used for this purpose. Modified forms of construction can only be shown in separate figures. Views should not be connected by projection lines nor should center lines be used.

(j) *Arrangement of views.* All views on the same sheet must stand in the same direction and should, if possible, stand so that they can be read with the sheet held in an upright position. If views longer than the width of the sheet are necessary for the clearest illustration of the invention, the sheet may be turned on its side. The space for a heading must then be reserved at the right and the signatures placed at the left, occupying the same space and position on the sheet as in the upright views and being horizontal when the sheet is held in an upright position. One figure must not be placed upon another or within the outline of another.

(k) *Figure for Official Gazette.* The drawing should, as far as possible, be so planned that one of the views will be suitable for publication in the *Official Gazette* as the illustration of the invention.

(l) *Extraneous matter.* An agent's or attorney's stamp, or address, or other extraneous matter, will not be permitted upon the face of a drawing, within or without the marginal line, except that the title of the invention in pencil and identifying indicia, to distinguish from other drawings filed at the same time, may be placed below the lower margin.

(*m*) *Transmission of drawings.* Drawings transmitted to the Office should be sent flat, protected by a sheet of heavy binder's board, or may be rolled for transmission in a suitable mailing tube; but must never be folded. If received creased or mutilated, new drawings will be required.

See rule 152 for design drawings, 165 for plant drawings, and 174 for reissue drawings.

Informal drawings. The requirements of rule 84 relating to drawings will be strictly enforced. A drawing not executed in conformity thereto may be admitted for the purpose of examination, but in such case the drawing must be corrected or a new one furnished, as required. The necessary corrections will be made by the Office upon applicant's request and at his expense. (See rule 21.)

Draftsman to make drawings. Applicants are advised to employ competent draftsmen to make their drawings.

The Office may furnish the drawings at the applicant's expense as promptly as its draftsmen can make them, for applicants who can not otherwise conveniently procure them. (See rule 21.)

Return of drawings. The drawings of an accepted application will not be returned to the applicant except for signature.

A photographic print is made of the drawing of an accepted application.

Use of old drawings. If the drawings of a new application are to be identical with the drawings of a previous application of the applicant on file in the Office, or with part of such drawings, the old drawings or any sheets thereof may be used if the prior application is, or is about to be, abandoned, or if the sheets to be used are cancelled in the prior application. The new application must be accompanied by a letter requesting the transfer of the drawings, which should be completely identified.

30.5   Symbols. The symbols to be used on patent drawings may be found in the "Rules of Practice" quoted above. Other symbols may be used if their meaning is clear and unequivocal.

Appendix

TABLE 1. STANDARD STRAIGHT SHANK TWIST DRILL SIZES

Fractional letter number	Decimal	Drill diam. tolerance	Fractional letter number	Decimal	Drill diam. tolerance
80	0.0135		12	0.189	
1/64	0.0156		10	0.1935	
77	0.018		8	0.199	
75	0.021		13/64	0.2031	
73	0.024		5	0.2055	
72	0.025		3	0.213	Plus 0.0000
70	0.028	Plus 0.000	7/32	0.2188	
68	0.031		2	0.221	
1/32	0.0312		A	0.234	Minus 0.0010
66	0.033		15/64	0.2344	
65	0.035	Minus 0.0006	B	0.238	
63	0.037		C	0.242	
62	0.038		D	0.246	
60	0.040		E and 1/4	0.250	
58	0.042				
57	0.043		F	0.257	
3/64	0.0469		G	0.261	
			17/64	0.2656	
55	0.052		H	0.266	
53	0.0595		I	0.272	
1/16	0.0625		J	0.277	
52	0.0635		K	0.281	
50	0.070		9/32	0.2812	
48	0.076		L	0.290	
5/64	0.0781		M	0.295	
47	0.0785	Plus 0.0000	19/64	0.2969	
45	0.082		N	0.302	
43	0.089		5/16	0.3125	Plus 0.0000
42	0.0935		O	0.316	
3/32	0.0938	Minus 0.0008	P	0.323	
40	0.098		21/64	0.3281	
38	0.1015		Q	0.332	
37	0.104		R	0.339	Minus 0.0015
7/64	0.1094		11/32	0.3438	
35	0.110		S	0.348	
33	0.113		T	0.358	
32	0.116		23/64	0.3594	
1/8	0.1250		U	0.368	
			3/8	0.375	
30	0.1285		V	0.377	
28	0.1405		W	0.386	
9/64	0.1406		25/64	0.3906	
27	0.144		X	0.397	
25	0.1495		Y	0.404	
23	0.154	Plus 0.0000	Z	0.413	
5/32	0.1562		27/64 to 3/4 by 1/64 intervals	0.750	
22	0.157				
20	0.161		3/4 to 1¼ by 1/64 intervals	1.250	Plus 0.0000
18	0.1695	Minus 0.0010			Minus 0.0020
11/64	0.1719		1¼ to 1½ by 1/32 intervals	1.500	
17	0.173				
15	0.180		1½ to 2 by 1/16 intervals	2.000	Plus 0.0000
13	0.185				Minus 0.0025
3/16	0.1875				

Courtesy ASA

TABLE 2. UNIFIED AND AMERICAN THREADS

Coarse-Threaded Series—UNC and NC (Basic Dimensions)

Sizes	Basic major diameter, D	Thds. per inch, n	Basic pitch diameter,* E	Minor diameter ext. thds. K_s	Minor diameter int. thds. K_n	Lead angle at basic pitch diameter, λ		Section at minor diameter at $D - 2h_b$	Stress area†	Tap drill number or size
	Inches		Inches	Inches	Inches	Deg	Min	Sq in.	Sq in.	
1(.073)	0.0730	64	0.0629	0.0538	0.0561	4	31	0.0022	0.0026	53
2(.086)	0.0860	56	0.0744	0.0641	0.0667	4	22	0.0031	0.0036	50
3(.099)	0.0990	48	0.0855	0.0734	0.0764	4	26	0.0041	0.0048	47
4(.112)	0.1120	40	0.0958	0.0813	0.0849	4	45	0.0050	0.0060	43
5(.125)	0.1250	40	0.1088	0.0943	0.0979	4	11	0.0067	0.0079	38
6(.138)	0.1380	32	0.1177	0.0997	0.1042	4	50	0.0075	0.0090	36
8(.164)	0.1640	32	0.1437	0.1257	0.1302	3	58	0.0120	0.0139	29
10(.190)	0.1900	24	0.1629	0.1389	0.1449	4	39	0.0145	0.0174	26
12(.216)	0.2160	24	0.1889	0.1649	0.1709	4	1	0.0206	0.0240	16
1/4	0.2500	20	0.2175	0.1887	0.1959	4	11	0.0269	0.0317	7
5/16	0.3125	18	0.2764	0.2443	0.2524	3	40	0.0454	0.0522	F
3/8	0.3750	16	0.3344	0.2983	0.3073	3	24	0.0678	0.0773	5/16
7/16	0.4375	14	0.3911	0.3499	0.3602	3	20	0.0933	0.1060	U
1/2	0.5000	13	0.4500	0.4056	0.4167	3	7	0.1257	0.1416	27/64
9/16	0.5625	12	0.5084	0.4603	0.4723	2	59	0.1620	0.1816	31/64
5/8	0.6250	11	0.5660	0.5135	0.5266	2	56	0.2018	0.2256	17/32
3/4	0.7500	10	0.6850	0.6273	0.6417	2	40	0.3020	0.3340	21/32
7/8	0.8750	9	0.8028	0.7387	0.7547	2	31	0.4193	0.4612	49/64
1	1.0000	8	0.9188	0.8466	0.8647	2	29	0.5510	0.6051	7/8
1⅛	1.1250	7	1.0322	0.9497	0.9704	2	31	0.6931	0.7627	63/64
1¼	1.2500	7	1.1572	1.0747	1.0954	2	15	0.8898	0.9684	1⁷⁄₆₄
1⅜	1.3750	6	1.2667	1.1705	1.1946	2	24	1.0541	1.1538	1¹³⁄₆₄
1½	1.5000	6	1.3917	1.2955	1.3196	2	11	1.2938	1.4041	1¹¹⁄₃₂
1¾	1.7500	5	1.6201	1.5046	1.5335	2	15	1.7441	1.8983	1⁹⁄₁₆
2	2.0000	4½	1.8557	1.7274	1.7594	2	11	2.3001	2.4971	1²⁵⁄₃₂
2¼	2.2500	4½	2.1057	1.9774	2.0094	1	55	3.0212	3.2464	2¹⁄₃₂
2½	2.5000	4	2.3376	2.1933	2.2294	1	57	3.7161	3.9976	2¼
2¾	2.7500	4	2.5876	2.4433	2.4794	1	46	4.6194	4.9326	2½

* British: Effective diameter.
† The stress area is the assumed area of an externally threaded part which is used for the purpose of computing the tensile strength.

Courtesy ASA

TABLE 3. UNIFIED AND AMERICAN THREADS

Fine-Thread Series—UNF and NF (Basic Dimensions)

Sizes	Basic major diameter, D	Thds. per inch, n	Basic pitch diameter,* E	Minor diameter ext. thds. K_s	Minor diameter int. thds. K_n	Lead angle at basic pitch diameter, λ		Section at minor diameter at $D-2h_b$	Stress area†	Tap drill number or size
	Inches		Inches	Inches	Inches	Deg	Min	Sq in.	Sq in.	
0(.060)	0.0600	80	0.0519	0.0447	0.0465	4	23	0.0015	0.0018	3/64
1(.073)	0.0730	72	0.0640	0.0560	0.0580	3	57	0.0024	0.0027	53
2(.086)	0.0860	64	0.0759	0.0668	0.0691	3	45	0.0034	0.0039	50
3(.099)	0.0990	56	0.0874	0.0771	0.0797	3	43	0.0045	0.0052	45
4(.112)	0.1120	48	0.0985	0.0864	0.0894	3	51	0.0057	0.0065	42
5(.125)	0.1250	44	0.1102	0.0971	0.1004	3	45	0.0072	0.0082	37
6(.138)	0.1380	40	0.1218	0.1073	0.1109	3	44	0.0087	0.0101	33
8(.164)	0.1640	36	0.1460	0.1299	0.1339	3	28	0.0128	0.0146	29
10(.190)	0.1900	32	0.1697	0.1517	0.1562	3	21	0.0175	0.0199	22
12(.216)	0.2160	28	0.1928	0.1722	0.1773	3	22	0.0226	0.0257	14
1/4	0.2500	28	0.2268	0.2062	0.2113	2	52	0.0326	0.0362	3
5/16	0.3125	24	0.2854	0.2614	0.2674	2	40	0.0524	0.0579	I
3/8	0.3750	24	0.3479	0.3239	0.3299	2	11	0.0809	0.0876	Q
7/16	0.4375	20	0.4050	0.3762	0.3834	2	15	0.1090	0.1185	25/64
1/2	0.5000	20	0.4675	0.4387	0.4459	1	57	0.1486	0.1597	29/64
9/16	0.5625	18	0.5264	0.4943	0.5024	1	55	0.1888	0.2026	33/64
5/8	0.6250	18	0.5889	0.5568	0.5649	1	43	0.2400	0.2555	37/64
3/4	0.7500	16	0.7094	0.6733	0.6823	1	36	0.3513	0.3724	11/16
7/8	0.8750	14	0.8286	0.7874	0.7977	1	34	0.4805	0.5088	13/16
1	1.0000	12	0.9459	0.8978	0.9098	1	36	0.6245	0.6624	59/64
1⅛	1.1250	12	1.0709	1.0228	1.0348	1	25	0.8118	0.8549	1³⁄₆₄
1¼	1.2500	12	1.1959	1.1478	1.1598	1	16	1.0237	1.0721	1¹¹⁄₆₄
1⅜	1.3750	12	1.3209	1.2728	1.2848	1	9	1.2602	1.3137	1¹⁹⁄₆₄
1½	1.5000	12	1.4459	1.3978	1.4098	1	3	1.5212	1.5799	1²⁷⁄₆₄

* British: Effective diameter.

† The stress area is the assumed area of an externally threaded part which is used for the purpose of computing the tensile strength.

Courtesy ASA

TABLE 4. SLOTTED HEAD MACHINE SCREWS (AMERICAN STANDARD)

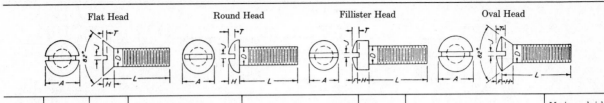

Flat Head   Round Head   Fillister Head   Oval Head

Nominal size	Maximum Diameter	Threads per inch (coarse Series)	Maximum diameter of head			Maximum height of head			Maximum width of slot	Maximum depth of slot				Maximum height of the head	
			Flat and oval	Round	Fillister	Flat and oval	Round	Fillister		Flat	Round	Fillister	Oval	Oval	Fillister
	(D)		(A)	(A)	(A)	(H)	(H)	(H)	(J)	(T)	(T)	(T)	(T)	(F)	(F)
2	0.086	56	0.172	0.162	0.140	0.051	0.070	0.055	0.036	0.023	0.048	0.037	0.045	0.036	0.028
3	.099	48	.199	.187	.161	.059	.078	.063	.038	.027	.053	.043	.052	.038	.032
4	.112	40	.225	.211	.183	.067	.086	.072	.040	.030	.058	.048	.059	.040	.35
5	.125	40	.252	.236	.205	.075	.095	.081	.043	.034	.062	.054	.067	.043	.039
6	.138	32	.279	.260	.226	.083	.103	.089	.045	.038	.067	.060	.074	.045	.043
8	.164	32	.352	.309	.270	.100	.119	.106	.050	.045	.076	.071	.088	.050	.050
10	.190	24	.385	.359	.313	.116	.136	.123	.055	.053	.086	.083	.103	.055	.057
12	.216	24	.438	.408	.357	.132	.152	.141	.059	.060	.095	.094	.117	.059	.064
1/4	.250	20	.507	.472	.414	.153	.174	.163	.066	.070	.108	.109	.136	.066	.074
5/16	.3125	18	.636	.591	.519	.192	.214	.205	.077	.088	.130	.137	.171	.077	.092
3/8	.375	16	.762	.708	.622	.230	.254	.246	.088	.106	.153	.164	.206	.088	.109

TABLE 5. SLOTTED AND HEXAGONAL-HEAD CAP SCREWS (AMERICAN STANDARD)

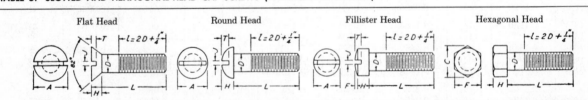

Flat Head   Round Head   Fillister Head   Hexagonal Head

Nominal size	Maximum diameter	Threads per inch	Maximum diameter of head			Maximum height of head			Maximum width of slot	Maximum depth of slot			Maximum height of fillister head oval	Finished hexagonal-head cap screw		
			Flat	Round	Fillister	Flat (Nominal)	Round	Fillister		Flat	Round	Fillister		Maximum width across flats	Minimum width across corners	Maximum height
	(D)		(A)	(A)	(A)	(H)	(H)	(H)	(J)	(T)	(T)	(T)	(F)	(F)	(C)	(H)
1/4	0.2500	20	0.500	0.437	0.375	0.140	0.191	0.172	0.075	0.068	0.117	0.097	0.044	0.4375	0.488	0.163
5/16	0.3125	18	.625	.562	.437	.177	.245	.203	.084	.086	.151	.115	.050	0.5000	0.577	.211
3/8	0.3750	16	.750	.625	.562	.210	.273	.250	.094	.103	.168	.142	.064	0.5625	0.628	.243
7/16	0.4375	14	.813	.750	.625	.210	.328	.297	.094	.103	.202	.168	.071	0.6250	0.698	.291
1/2	0.5000	13	0.875	0.812	0.750	0.210	0.354	0.328	0.106	0.103	0.218	0.193	0.084	0.7500	0.840	0.323
9/16	0.5625	12	1.000	.937	.812	.244	.409	.375	.118	.120	.252	.213	.091	0.8125	0.910	.371
5/8	0.6250	11	1.125	1.000	.875	.281	.437	.422	.133	.137	.270	.239	.099	0.8750	0.980	.403
3/4	0.7500	10	1.325	1.250	1.000	.352	.546	.500	.149	.171	.338	.283	.112	1.0000	1.121	.483
7/8	0.8750	9	1.625		1.125	0.423		0.594	0.167	0.206	.334	.126		1.1250	1.261	0.563
1	1.0000	8	1.875		1.312	.494		.656	.188	.240	.371	.146		1.3125	1.473	.627
1⅛	1.1250	7	2.062			.529				.257				1.5000	1.684	.718
1¼	1.2500	7	2.312			.600				.291				1.6875	1.896	.813

TABLE 6. REGULAR SQUARE BOLTS

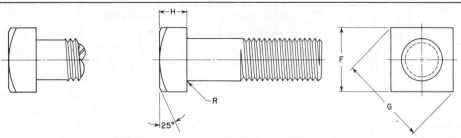

Nominal size or basic major diameter of thread		Body diam.	Width across flats F			Width across corners G		Height H			Radius of fillet R
		Max.	Max (basic)		Min	Max	Min	Nom	Max	Min	Max
1/4	0.2500	0.260	3/8	0.3750	0.362	0.530	0.498	11/64	0.188	0.156	0.031
5/16	0.3125	0.324	1/2	0.5000	0.484	0.707	0.665	13/64	0.220	0.186	0.031
3/8	0.3750	0.388	9/16	0.5625	0.544	0.795	0.747	1/4	0.268	0.232	0.031
7/16	0.4375	0.452	5/8	0.6250	0.603	0.884	0.828	19/64	0.316	0.278	0.031
1/2	0.5000	0.515	3/4	0.7500	0.725	1.061	0.995	21/64	0.348	0.308	0.031
5/8	0.6250	0.642	15/16	0.9375	0.906	1.326	1.244	27/64	0.444	0.400	0.062
3/4	0.7500	0.768	1⅛	1.1250	1.088	1.591	1.494	1/2	0.524	0.476	0.062
7/8	0.8750	0.895	1⁵⁄₁₆	1.3125	1.269	1.856	1.742	19/32	0.620	0.568	0.062
1	1.0000	1.022	1½	1.5000	1.450	2.121	1.991	21/32	0.684	0.628	0.093
1⅛	1.1250	1.149	1¹¹⁄₁₆	1.6875	1.631	2.386	2.239	3/4	0.780	0.720	0.093
1¼	1.2500	1.277	1⅞	1.8750	1.812	2.652	2.489	27/32	0.876	0.812	0.093
1⅜	1.3750	1.404	2¹⁄₁₆	2.0625	1.994	2.917	2.738	29/32	0.940	0.872	0.093
1½	1.5000	1.531	2¼	2.2500	2.175	3.182	2.986	1	1.036	0.964	0.093
1⅝	1.6250	1.658	2⁷⁄₁₆	2.4375	2.356	3.447	3.235	1³⁄₃₂	1.132	1.056	0.125

Courtesy ASA

TABLE 7. REGULAR SQUARE NUTS

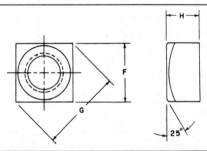

Nominal size or basic major diameter of thread		Width across flats F		Min	Width across corners G		Thickness H		
		Max (basic)		Min	Max	Min	Nom	Max	Min
1/4	0.2500	7/16	0.4375	0.425	0.619	0.584	7/32	0.235	0.203
5/16	0.3125	9/16	0.5625	0.547	0.795	0.751	17/64	0.283	0.249
3/8	0.3750	5/8	0.6250	0.606	0.884	0.832	21/64	0.346	0.310
7/16	0.4375	3/4	0.7500	0.728	1.061	1.000	3/8	0.394	0.356
1/2	0.5000	13/16	0.8125	0.788	1.149	1.082	7/16	0.458	0.418
5/8	0.6250	1	1.0000	0.969	1.414	1.330	35/64	0.569	0.525
3/4	0.7500	1⅛	1.1250	1.088	1.591	1.494	21/32	0.680	0.632
7/8	0.8750	1⁵⁄₁₆	1.3125	1.269	1.856	1.742	49/64	0.792	0.740
1	1.0000	1½	1.5000	1.450	2.121	1.991	7/8	0.903	0.847
1⅛	1.1250	1¹¹⁄₁₆	1.6875	1.631	2.386	2.239	1	1.030	0.970
1¼	1.2500	1⅞	1.8750	1.812	2.652	2.489	1³⁄₃₂	1.126	1.062
1⅜	1.3750	2¹⁄₁₆	2.0625	1.994	2.917	2.738	1¹³⁄₆₄	1.237	1.169
1½	1.5000	2¼	2.2500	2.175	3.182	2.986	1⁵⁄₁₆	1.348	1.276

Courtesy ASA

TABLE 8. REGULAR HEXAGON BOLTS

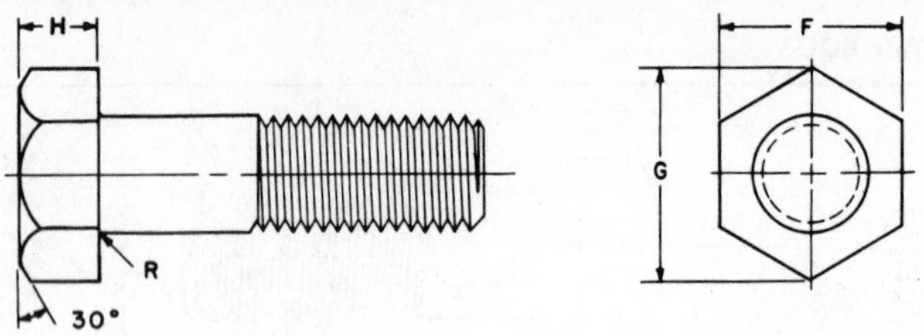

Nominal size or basic major diameter of thread		Body diam.	Width across flats F			Width across corners G		Height H			Radius of fillet R
		Max.	Max (basic)		Min	Max	Min	Nom	Max	Min	Max
1/4	0.2500	0.260	7/16	0.4375	0.425	0.505	0.484	11/64	0.188	0.150	0.031
5/16	0.3125	0.324	1/2	0.5000	0.484	0.577	0.552	7/32	0.235	0.195	0.031
3/8	0.3750	0.388	9/16	0.5625	0.544	0.650	0.620	1/4	0.268	0.226	0.031
7/16	0.4375	0.452	5/8	0.6250	0.603	0.722	0.687	19/64	0.316	0.272	0.031
1/2	0.5000	0.515	3/4	0.7500	0.725	0.866	0.826	11/32	0.364	0.302	0.031
5/8	0.6250	0.642	15/16	0.9375	0.906	1.083	1.033	27/64	0.444	0.378	0.062
3/4	0.7500	0.768	1⅛	1.1250	1.088	1.299	1.240	1/2	0.524	0.455	0.062
7/8	0.8750	0.895	1 5/16	1.3125	1.269	1.516	1.447	37/64	0.604	0.531	0.062
1	1.0000	1.022	1½	1.5000	1.450	1.732	1.653	43/64	0.700	0.591	0.093
1⅛	1.1250	1.149	1 11/16	1.6875	1.631	1.949	1.859	3/4	0.780	0.658	0.093
1¼	1.2500	1.277	1⅞	1.8750	1.812	2.165	2.066	27/32	0.876	0.749	0.093
1⅜	1.3750	1.404	2 1/16	2.0625	1.994	2.382	2.273	29/32	0.940	0.810	0.093
1½	1.5000	1.531	2¼	2.2500	2.175	2.598	2.480	1	1.036	0.902	0.093
1¾	1.7500	1.785	2⅝	2.6250	2.538	3.031	2.893	1 5/32	1.196	1.054	0.125

Courtesy ASA

TABLE 9. REGULAR HEXAGON AND HEXAGON-JAM NUTS

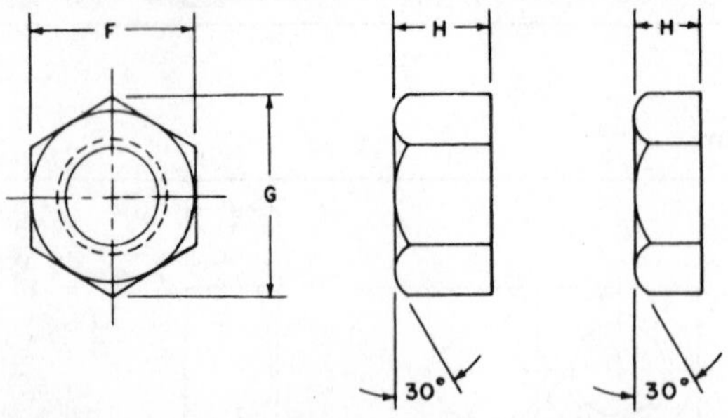

Nominal size or basic major diameter of thread		Width across flats F			Width across corners G		Thickness regular nuts H			Thickness regular jam nuts H		
		Max (basic)		Min	Max	Min	Nom	Max	Min	Nom	Max	Min
1/4	0.2500	7/16	0.4375	0.425	0.505	0.484	7/32	0.235	0.203	5/32	0.172	0.140
5/16	0.3125	9/16	0.5625	0.547	0.650	0.624	17/64	0.283	0.249	3/16	0.204	0.170
3/8	0.3750	5/8	0.6250	0.606	0.722	0.691	21/64	0.346	0.310	7/32	0.237	0.201
7/16	0.4375	3/4	0.7500	0.728	0.866	0.830	3/8	0.394	0.356	1/4	0.269	0.231
1/2	0.5000	13/16	0.8125	0.788	0.938	0.898	7/16	0.458	0.418	5/16	0.332	0.292
9/16	0.5625	7/8	0.8750	0.847	1.010	0.966	1/2	0.521	0.479	11/32	0.365	0.323
5/8	0.6250	1	1.0000	0.969	1.155	1.104	35/64	0.569	0.525	3/8	0.397	0.353
3/4	0.7500	1⅛	1.1250	1.088	1.299	1.240	21/32	0.680	0.632	7/16	0.462	0.414
7/8	0.8750	1 5/16	1.3125	1.269	1.516	1.447	49/64	0.792	0.740	1/2	0.526	0.474
1	1.0000	1½	1.5000	1.450	1.732	1.653	7/8	0.903	0.847	9/16	0.590	0.534
1⅛	1.1250	1 11/16	1.6875	1.631	1.949	1.859	1	1.030	0.970	5/8	0.655	0.595
1¼	1.2500	1⅞	1.8750	1.812	2.165	2.066	1 3/32	1.126	1.062	3/4	0.782	0.718
1⅜	1.3750	2 1/16	2.0625	1.994	2.382	2.273	1 13/64	1.237	1.169	13/16	0.846	0.778
1½	1.5000	2¼	2.2500	2.175	2.598	2.480	1 5/16	1.348	1.276	7/8	0.911	0.839

Courtesy ASA

TABLE 10. REGULAR SEMIFINISHED HEXAGON BOLTS

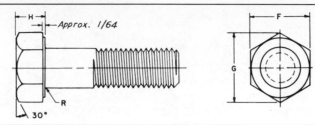

Nominal size or basic major diameter of thread		Body diam.	Width across flats F			Width across corners G		Height H			Radius of fillet R	
		Max.	Max (basic)		Min	Max	Min	Nom	Max	Min	Max	Min
1/4	0.2500	0.260	7/16	0.4375	0.425	0.505	0.484	5/32	0.163	0.150	0.009	0.031
5/16	0.3125	0.324	1/2	0.5000	0.484	0.577	0.552	13/64	0.211	0.195	0.009	0.031
3/8	0.3750	0.388	9/16	0.5625	0.544	0.650	0.620	15/64	0.243	0.226	0.009	0.031
7/16	0.4375	0.452	5/8	0.6250	0.603	0.722	0.687	9/32	0.291	0.272	0.009	0.031
1/2	0.5000	0.515	3/4	0.7500	0.725	0.866	0.826	5/16	0.323	0.302	0.009	0.031
5/8	0.6250	0.642	15/16	0.9375	0.906	1.083	1.033	25/64	0.403	0.378	0.021	0.062
3/4	0.7500	0.768	1⅛	1.1250	1.088	1.299	1.240	15/32	0.483	0.455	0.021	0.062
7/8	0.8750	0.895	1 5/16	1.3125	1.269	1.516	1.447	35/64	0.563	0.531	0.031	0.062
1	1.0000	1.022	1½	1.5000	1.450	1.732	1.653	39/64	0.627	0.591	0.062	0.093
1⅛	1.1250	1.149	1 11/16	1.6875	1.631	1.949	1.859	11/16	0.718	0.658	0.062	0.093
1¼	1.2500	1.277	1⅞	1.8750	1.812	2.165	2.066	25/32	0.813	0.749	0.062	0.093
1⅜	1.3750	1.404	2 1/16	2.0625	1.994	2.382	2.273	27/32	0.878	0.810	0.062	0.093
1½	1.5000	1.531	2¼	2.2500	2.175	2.598	2.480	15/16	0.974	0.902	0.062	0.093
1¾	1.7500	1.785	2⅝	2.6250	2.538	3.031	2.893	1 3/32	1.134	1.054	0.078	0.125

Courtesy ASA

TABLE 11. REGULAR SEMIFINISHED HEXAGON AND HEXAGON-JAM NUTS

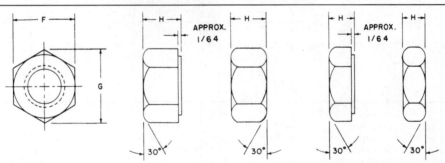

Nominal size or basic major diameter of thread		Width across flats F		Width across corners G		Thickness regular nuts H			Thickness regular jam nuts H		
		Max (basic)	Min	Max	Min	Nom	Max	Min	Nom	Max	Min
1/4	0.2500	7/16	0.4375	0.425	0.505	0.485	13/64	0.219	0.187	9/64	0.157	0.125
5/16	0.3125	9/16	0.5625	0.547	0.650	0.624	1/4	0.267	0.233	11/64	0.189	0.155
3/8	0.3750	5/8	0.6250	0.606	0.722	0.691	5/16	0.330	0.294	13/64	0.221	0.185
7/16	0.4375	3/4	0.7500	0.728	0.866	0.830	23/64	0.378	0.340	15/64	0.253	0.215
1/2	0.5000	13/16	0.8125	0.788	0.938	0.898	27/64	0.442	0.402	19/64	0.317	0.277
9/16	0.5625	7/8	0.8750	0.847	1.010	0.966	31/64	0.505	0.463	21/64	0.349	0.307
5/8	0.6250	1	1.0000	0.969	1.155	1.104	17/32	0.553	0.509	23/64	0.381	0.337
3/4	0.7500	1⅛	1.1250	1.088	1.299	1.240	41/64	0.665	0.617	27/64	0.446	0.398
7/8	0.8750	1 5/16	1.3125	1.269	1.516	1.447	3/4	0.776	0.724	31/64	0.510	0.458
1	1.0000	1½	1.5000	1.450	1.732	1.653	55/64	0.887	0.831	35/64	0.575	0.519
1⅛	1.1250	1 11/16	1.6875	1.631	1.949	1.859	31/32	0.999	0.939	39/64	0.639	0.579
1¼	1.2500	1⅞	1.8750	1.812	2.165	2.066	1 1/16	1.094	1.030	23/32	0.751	0.687
1⅜	1.3750	2 1/16	2.0625	1.994	2.382	2.273	1 11/64	1.206	1.138	25/32	0.815	0.747
1½	1.5000	2¼	2.2500	2.175	2.598	2.480	1 9/32	1.317	1.245	27/32	0.880	0.808
1⅝	1.6250	2 7/16	2.4375	2.356	2.815	2.686	1 25/64	1.429	1.353	29/32	0.944	0.868
1¾	1.7500	2⅝	2.6250	2.538	3.031	2.893	1½	1.540	1.460	31/32	1.009	0.929

Courtesy ASA

TABLE 12. FINISHED HEXAGON BOLTS

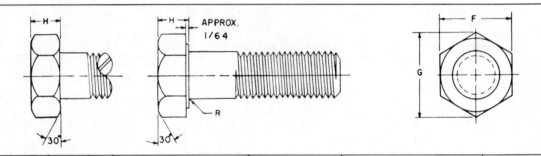

Nominal size or basic major diameter of thread		Body diameter min (maximum equal to nominal size)	Width across flats F			Width across corners G		Height H			Radius of fillet R	
			Max (basic)		Min	Max	Min	Nom	Max	Min	Min	Max
1/4	0.2500	0.2450	7/16	0.4375	0.428	0.505	0.488	5/32	0.163	0.150	0.009	0.023
5/16	0.3125	0.3065	1/2	0.5000	0.489	0.577	0.557	13/64	0.211	0.195	0.009	0.023
3/8	0.3750	0.3690	9/16	0.5625	0.551	0.650	0.628	15/64	0.243	0.226	0.009	0.023
7/16	0.4375	0.4305	5/8	0.6250	0.612	0.722	0.698	9/32	0.291	0.272	0.009	0.023
1/2	0.5000	0.4930	3/4	0.7500	0.736	0.866	0.840	5/16	0.323	0.302	0.009	0.023
9/16	0.5625	0.5545	13/16	0.8125	0.798	0.938	0.910	23/64	0.371	0.348	0.021	0.041
5/8	0.6250	0.6170	15/16	0.9375	0.922	1.083	1.051	25/64	0.403	0.378	0.021	0.041
3/4	0.7500	0.7410	1⅛	1.1250	1.100	1.299	1.254	15/32	0.483	0.455	0.021	0.041
7/8	0.8750	0.8660	1⁵⁄₁₆	1.3125	1.285	1.516	1.465	35/64	0.563	0.531	0.041	0.062
1	1.0000	0.9900	1½	1.5000	1.469	1.732	1.675	39/64	0.627	0.591	0.062	0.093
1⅛	1.1250	1.1140	1¹¹⁄₁₆	1.6875	1.631	1.949	1.859	11/16	0.718	0.658	0.062	0.093
1¼	1.2500	1.2390	1⅞	1.8750	1.812	2.165	2.066	25/32	0.813	0.749	0.062	0.093
1⅜	1.3750	1.3630	2¹⁄₁₆	2.0625	1.994	2.382	2.273	27/32	0.878	0.810	0.062	0.093
1½	1.5000	1.4880	2¼	2.2500	2.175	2.598	2.480	15/16	0.974	0.902	0.062	0.093
1¾	1.7500	1.7380	2⅝	2.6250	2.538	3.031	2.893	1³⁄₃₂	1.134	1.054	0.062	0.093

Note: Boldface indicates products unified dimensionally with British and Canadian Standards.

Courtesy ASA

TABLE 13. FINISHED HEXAGON AND HEXAGON-JAM NUTS

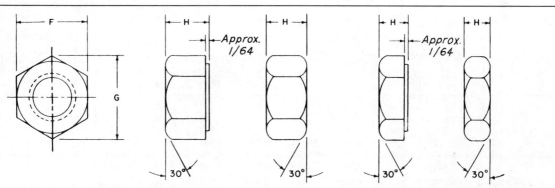

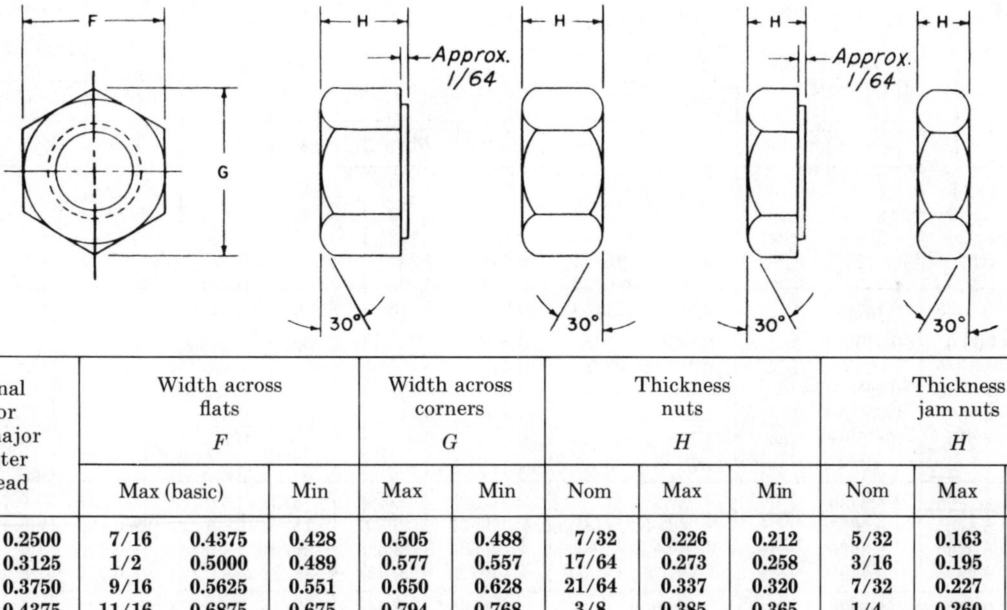

Nominal size or basic major diameter of thread		Width across flats F			Width across corners G		Thickness nuts H			Thickness jam nuts H		
		Max (basic)		Min	Max	Min	Nom	Max	Min	Nom	Max	Min
1/4	0.2500	7/16	0.4375	0.428	0.505	0.488	7/32	0.226	0.212	5/32	0.163	0.150
5/16	0.3125	1/2	0.5000	0.489	0.577	0.557	17/64	0.273	0.258	3/16	0.195	0.180
3/8	0.3750	9/16	0.5625	0.551	0.650	0.628	21/64	0.337	0.320	7/32	0.227	0.210
7/16	0.4375	11/16	0.6875	0.675	0.794	0.768	3/8	0.385	0.365	1/4	0.260	0.240
1/2	0.5000	3/4	0.7500	0.736	0.866	0.840	7/16	0.448	0.427	5/16	0.323	0.302
9/16	0.5625	7/8	0.8750	0.861	1.010	0.982	31/64	0.496	0.473	6/16	0.324	0.301
5/8	0.6250	15/16	0.9375	0.922	1.083	1.051	35/64	0.559	0.535	3/8	0.387	0.363
3/4	0.7500	1⅛	1.1250	1.088	1.299	1.240	41/64	0.665	0.617	27/64	0.446	0.398
7/8	0.8750	1⁵⁄₁₆	1.3125	1.269	1.516	1.447	3/4	0.776	0.724	31/64	0.510	0.458
1	1.0000	1½	1.5000	1.450	1.732	1.653	55/64	0.887	0.831	35/64	0.575	0.519
1⅛	1.1250	1¹¹⁄₁₆	1.6875	1.631	1.949	1.859	31/32	0.999	0.939	39/64	0.639	0.579
1¼	1.2500	1⅞	1.8750	1.812	2.165	2.066	1¹⁄₁₆	1.094	1.030	23/32	0.751	0.687
1⅜	1.3750	2¹⁄₁₆	2.0625	1.994	2.382	2.273	1¹¹⁄₆₄	1.206	1.138	25/32	0.815	0.747
1½	1.5000	2¼	2.2500	2.175	2.598	2.480	1⁹⁄₃₂	1.317	1.245	27/32	0.880	0.808
1¾	1.7500	2⅝	2.6250	2.538	3.031	2.893	1½	1.540	1.460	31/32	1.009	0.929

Note: Boldface indicates products unified dimensionally with British and Canadian Standards.

Courtesy ASA

TABLE 14. SQUARE HEAD SET SCREWS

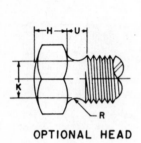

OPTIONAL HEAD

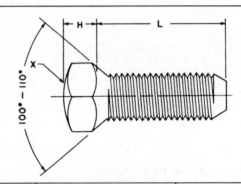

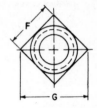

Nominal size		F Width across flats		G Width across corners	H Height of head			K Diameter of neck relief		X Radius of head	R Rad. of neck relief	U Width of neck relief
		Max	Min	Min	Nom	Max	Min	Max	Min	Nom	Max	Min
#10	0.190	0.1875	0.180	0.247	9/64	0.148	0.134	0.145	0.140	15/32	0.027	0.083
#12	0.216	0.216	0.208	0.292	5/32	0.163	0.147	0.162	0.156	35/64	0.029	0.091
1/4	0.250	0.250	0.241	0.331	3/16	0.196	0.178	0.185	0.170	5/8	0.032	0.100
5/16	0.3125	0.3125	0.302	0.415	15/64	0.245	0.224	0.240	0.225	25/32	0.036	0.111
3/8	0.3750	0.375	0.362	0.497	9/32	0.293	0.270	0.294	0.279	15/16	0.041	0.125
7/16	0.4375	0.4375	0.423	0.581	21/64	0.341	0.315	0.345	0.330	1 3/32	0.046	0.143
1/2	0.500	0.500	0.484	0.665	3/8	0.389	0.361	0.400	0.385	1 1/4	0.050	0.154
9/16	0.5625	0.5625	0.545	0.748	27/64	0.437	0.407	0.454	0.439	1 13/32	0.054	0.167
5/8	0.6250	0.625	0.606	0.833	15/32	0.485	0.452	0.507	0.492	1 9/16	0.059	0.182
3/4	0.750	0.750	0.729	1.001	9/16	0.582	0.544	0.620	0.605	1 7/8	0.065	0.200
7/8	0.875	0.875	0.852	1.170	21/32	0.678	0.635	0.731	0.716	2 3/16	0.072	0.222
1	1.000	1.000	0.974	1.337	3/4	0.774	0.726	0.838	0.823	2 1/2	0.081	0.250
1 1/8	1.125	1.125	1.096	1.505	27/32	0.870	0.817	0.939	0.914	2 13/16	0.092	0.283
1 1/4	1.250	1.250	1.219	1.674	15/16	0.966	0.908	1.064	1.039	3 1/8	0.092	0.283
1 3/8	1.375	1.375	1.342	1.843	1 1/32	1.063	1.000	1.159	1.134	3 7/16	0.109	0.333
1 1/2	1.500	1.500	1.464	2.010	1 1/8	1.159	1.091	1.284	1.259	3 3/4	0.109	0.333

All dimensions given in inches.

Threads shall be coarse-, fine-, or 8-thread series, class 2A; unless otherwise specified, coarse-thread series will be furnished. Square head set screws 1/4 in. size and larger are normally stocked in coarse thread series only.

Tolerance on screw length for sizes up to and including 5/8 in. shall be; minus 1/32 in. for lengths up to and including 1 in.; minus 1/16 in. for lengths over 1 in. to and including 2 in.; and minus 3/32 in. for lengths over 2 in. The tolerance shall be doubled for larger size screws of comparable length.

Square head set screws shall be made from alloy or carbon steel suitably hardened. Screws made from nonferrous material or corrosion-resisting steel shall be made from a material mutually agreed upon by manufacturer and user.

Courtesy ASA

TABLE 15. SQUARE HEAD SET SCREW POINTS

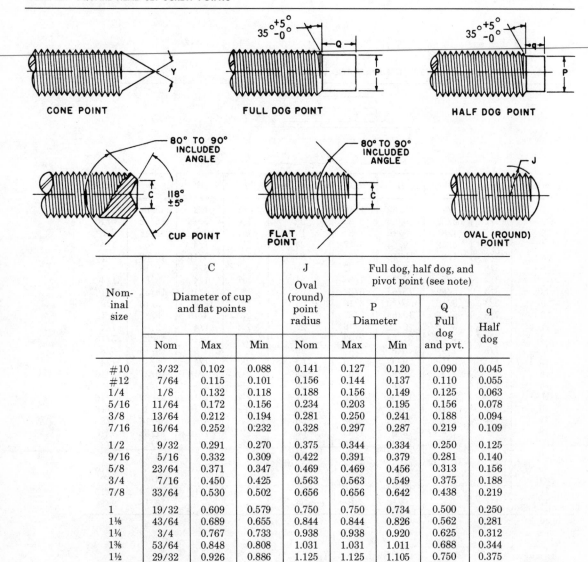

Nominal size	C Diameter of cup and flat points			J Oval (round) point radius	Full dog, half dog, and pivot point (see note)			
					P Diameter		Q Full dog and pvt.	q Half dog
	Nom	Max	Min	Nom	Max	Min		
#10	3/32	0.102	0.088	0.141	0.127	0.120	0.090	0.045
#12	7/64	0.115	0.101	0.156	0.144	0.137	0.110	0.055
1/4	1/8	0.132	0.118	0.188	0.156	0.149	0.125	0.063
5/16	11/64	0.172	0.156	0.234	0.203	0.195	0.156	0.078
3/8	13/64	0.212	0.194	0.281	0.250	0.241	0.188	0.094
7/16	16/64	0.252	0.232	0.328	0.297	0.287	0.219	0.109
1/2	9/32	0.291	0.270	0.375	0.344	0.334	0.250	0.125
9/16	5/16	0.332	0.309	0.422	0.391	0.379	0.281	0.140
5/8	23/64	0.371	0.347	0.469	0.469	0.456	0.313	0.156
3/4	7/16	0.450	0.425	0.563	0.563	0.549	0.375	0.188
7/8	33/64	0.530	0.502	0.656	0.656	0.642	0.438	0.219
1	19/32	0.609	0.579	0.750	0.750	0.734	0.500	0.250
1⅛	43/64	0.689	0.655	0.844	0.844	0.826	0.562	0.281
1¼	3/4	0.767	0.733	0.938	0.938	0.920	0.625	0.312
1⅜	53/64	0.848	0.808	1.031	1.031	1.011	0.688	0.344
1½	29/32	0.926	0.886	1.125	1.125	1.105	0.750	0.375

All dimensions are given in inches.

Pivot points are similar to full dog point except that the point is rounded by a radius equal to J.

Where usable length of thread is less than the nominal diameter, half-dog point shall be used.

When length equals nominal diameter or less, $Y = 118$ deg ± 2 deg; when length exceeds nominal diameter, $Y = 90$ deg ± 2 deg.

Courtesy ASA

TABLE 16. PROPORTIONS OF KEYS IN THE PRATT AND WHITNEY SYSTEM

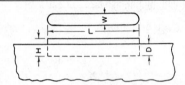

No. of key	L	W	H	D	No. of key	L	W	H	D
1	1/2	1/16	3/32	1/16	22	1⅜	1/4	3/8	1/4
2	1/2	3/32	9/64	3/32	23	1⅜	5/16	15/32	5/16
3	1/2	1/8	3/16	1/8	F	1⅜	3/8	9/16	3/8
4	5/8	3/32	9/64	3/32	24	1½	1/4	3/8	1/4
5	5/8	1/8	3/16	1/8	25	1½	5/16	15/32	5/16
6	5/8	5/32	15/64	5/32	G	1½	3/8	9/16	3/8
7	3/4	1/8	3/16	1/8	51	1¾	1/4	3/8	1/4
8	3/4	5/32	15/64	5/32	52	1¾	5/16	15/32	5/16
9	3/4	3/16	9/32	3/16	53	1¾	3/8	9/16	3/8
10	7/8	5/32	15/64	5/32	26	2	3/16	9/32	3/16
11	7/8	3/16	9/32	3/16	27	2	1/4	3/8	1/4
12	7/8	7/32	21/64	7/32	28	2	5/16	15/32	5/16
A	7/8	1/4	3/8	1/4	29	2	3/8	9/16	3/8
13	1	3/16	9/32	3/16	54	2¼	1/4	3/8	1/4
14	1	7/32	21/64	7/32	55	2¼	5/16	15/32	5/16
15	1	1/4	3/8	1/4	56	2¼	3/8	9/16	3/8
B	1	5/16	15/32	5/16	57	2¼	7/16	21/32	7/16
16	1⅛	3/16	9/32	3/16	58	2½	5/16	15/32	5/16
17	1⅛	7/32	21/64	7/32	59	2½	3/8	9/16	3/8
18	1⅛	1/4	3/8	1/4	60	2½	7/16	21/32	7/16
C	1⅛	5/16	15/32	5/16	61	2½	1/2	3/4	1/2
19	1¼	3/16	9/32	3/16	30	3	3/8	9/16	3/8
20	1¼	7/32	21/64	7/32	31	3	7/16	21/32	7/16
21	1¼	1/4	3/8	1/4	32	3	1/2	3/4	1/2
D	1¼	5/16	15/32	5/16	33	3	9/16	27/32	9/16
E	1¼	3/8	9/16	3/8	34	3	5/8	15/16	5/8

TABLE 17.   WOODRUFF KEYS

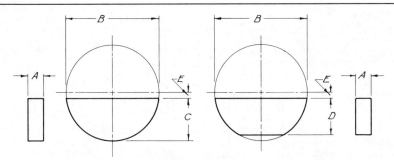

Woodruff Key Dimensions

Key* number	Nominal key size $A \times B$	Width of key A		Diam. of key B		Height of key				Distance below center E
		Max	Min	Max	Min	C		D		
						Max	Min	Max	Min	
204	1/16 × 1/2	0.0635	0.0625	0.500	0.490	0.203	0.198	0.194	0.188	3/64
304	3/32 × 1/2	.0948	.0938	0.500	0.490	.203	.198	.194	.188	3/64
305	3/32 × 5/8	.0948	.0938	0.625	0.615	.250	.245	.240	.234	1/16
404	1/8 × 1/2	.1260	.1250	0.500	0.490	.203	.198	.194	.188	3/64
405	1/8 × 5/8	.1260	.1250	0.625	0.615	.250	.245	.240	.234	1/16
406	1/8 × 3/4	.1260	.1250	0.750	0.740	.313	.308	.303	.297	1/16
505	5/32 × 5/8	.1573	.1563	0.625	0.615	.250	.245	.240	.234	1/16
506	5/32 × 3/4	.1573	.1563	0.750	0.740	.313	.308	.303	.297	1/16
507	5/32 × 7/8	.1573	.1563	0.875	0.865	.375	.370	.365	.359	1/16
606	3/16 × 3/4	.1885	.1875	0.750	0.740	.313	.308	.303	.297	1/16
607	3/16 × 7/8	.1885	.1875	0.875	0.865	.375	.370	.365	.359	1/16
608	3/16 × 1	.1885	.1875	1.000	0.990	.438	.433	.428	.422	1/16
609	3/16 × 1⅛	.1885	.1875	1.125	1.115	.484	.479	.475	.469	5/64
807	1/4 × 7/8	.2510	.2500	0.875	0.865	.375	.370	.365	.359	1/16
808	1/4 × 1	.2510	.2500	1.000	0.990	.438	.433	.428	.422	1/16
809	1/4 × 1⅛	.2510	.2500	1.125	1.115	.484	.479	.475	.469	5/64
810	1/4 × 1¼	.2510	.2500	1.250	1.240	.547	.542	.537	.531	5/64
811	1/4 × 1⅜	.2510	.2500	1.375	1.365	.594	.589	.584	.578	3/32
812	1/4 × 1½	.2510	.2500	1.500	1.490	.641	.636	.631	.625	7/64

All dimensions given in inches.

* Note: Key numbers indicate the nominal key dimensions. The last two digits give the nominal diameter (B) in eighths of an inch and the digits preceding the last two give the nominal width (A) in thirty-seconds of an inch. Thus, 204 indicates a key ²⁄₃₂ × ⁴⁄₈ or ¹⁄₁₆ × ½ inches; 1210 indicates a key ¹²⁄₃₂ × ¹⁰⁄₈ or ⅜ × 1¼ inches.

Courtesy ASA

TABLE 18. PLAIN PARALLEL STOCK KEYS

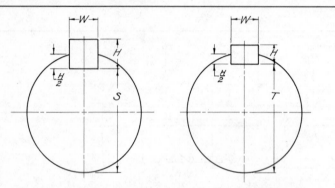

Dimensions of Square and Flat Plain Parallel Stock Keys

Shaft diameter	Square key $W \times H$	Flat key $W \times H$	Tolerance on W and H (−)	Bottom of keyseat to opposite side of shaft	
				Square key S	Flat key T
1/2	1/8 × 1/8	1/8 × 3/32	0.0020	0.430	0.445
9/16	1/8 × 1/8	1/8 × 3/32	.0020	0.493	0.509
5/8	3/16 × 3/16	3/16 × 1/8	.0020	0.517	0.548
11/16	3/16 × 3/16	3/16 × 1/8	.0020	0.581	0.612
3/4	3/16 × 3/16	3/16 × 1/8	.0020	0.644	0.676
13/16	3/16 × 3/16	3/16 × 1/8	.0020	0.708	0.739
7/8	3/16 × 3/16	3/16 × 1/8	.0020	0.771	0.802
15/16	1/4 × 1/4	1/4 × 3/16	.0020	0.796	0.827
1	1/4 × 1/4	1/4 × 3/16	.0020	0.859	0.890
1 1/16	1/4 × 1/4	1/4 × 3/16	.0020	0.923	0.954
1 1/8	1/4 × 1/4	1/4 × 3/16	.0020	0.986	1.017
1 3/16	1/4 × 1/4	1/4 × 3/16	.0020	1.049	1.081
1 1/4	1/4 × 1/4	1/4 × 3/16	.0020	1.112	1.144
1 5/16	5/16 × 5/16	5/16 × 1/4	.0020	1.137	1.169
1 3/8	5/16 × 5/16	5/16 × 1/4	.0020	1.201	1.232
1 7/16	3/8 × 3/8	3/8 × 1/4	.0020	1.225	1.288
1 1/2	3/8 × 3/8	3/8 × 1/4	.0020	1.289	1.351
1 9/16	3/8 × 3/8	3/8 × 1/4	.0020	1.352	1.415
1 5/8	3/8 × 3/8	3/8 × 1/4	.0020	1.416	1.478
1 11/16	3/8 × 3/8	3/8 × 1/4	.0020	1.479	1.542
1 3/4	3/8 × 3/8	3/8 × 1/4	.0020	1.542	1.605

Courtesy ASA

TABLE 19. DIMENSIONS OF TAPER PINS

Number	7/0	6/0	5/0	4/0	3/0	2/0	0	1	2	3	4	5	6	7	8	9	10
Size (large end)	0.0625	0.0780	0.0940	0.1090	0.1250	0.1410	0.1560	0.1720	0.1930	0.2190	0.2500	0.2890	0.3410	0.4090	0.4920	0.5910	0.7060
Length, L																	
0.375	X	X															
0.500	X	X	X	X	X	X	X										
0.625	X	X	X	X	X	X	X										
0.750		X	X	X	X	X	X	X	X	X							
0.875					X	X	X	X	X	X							
1.000			X	X	X	X	X	X	X	X	X	X					
1.250						X	X	X	X	X	X	X	X				
1.500							X	X	X	X	X	X	X				
1.750								X	X	X	X	X	X				
2.000								X	X	X	X	X	X	X	X		
2.250									X	X	X	X	X	X	X		
2.500									X	X	X	X	X	X	X		
2.750										X	X	X	X	X	X	X	
3.000										X	X	X	X	X	X	X	
3.250													X	X	X	X	
3.500													X	X	X	X	X
3.750													X	X	X	X	X
4.000													X	X	X	X	X
4.250															X	X	X
4.500															X	X	X
4.750															X	X	X
5.000															X	X	X
5.250																X	X
5.500																X	X
5.750																X	X
6.000																X	X

All dimensions are given in inches.
Standard reamers are available for pins given above the line.
Pins Nos. 11 (size 0.8600), 12 (size 1.032), 13 (size 1.241), and 14 (1.523) are special sizes—hence their lengths are special.
To find small diameter of pin, multiply the length by 0.02083 and subtract the result from the large diameter.

TYPES	COMMERCIAL TYPE	PRECISION TYPE
Sizes	7/0 to 14	7/0 to 10
Tolerance on diameter	(+0.0013, −0.0007)	(+0.0013, −0.0007)
Taper	¼ in. per ft	¼ in. per ft
Length tolerance	(±0.030)	(±0.030)
Concavity tolerance	None	0.0005 up to 1 in. long
		0.001 1¹⁄₁₆ to 2 in. long
		0.002 2¹⁄₁₆ and longer

TABLE 20. RUNNING AND SLIDING FITS

Limits are in thousandths of an inch.
Limits for hole and shaft are applied algebraically to the basic size to obtain the limits of size for the parts.
Data are in accordance with ABC agreements.
Symbols H5, g5, etc., are Hole and Shaft designations used in ABC System.

Nominal size range inches		Class RC 1			Class RC 2			Class RC 3			Class RC 4		
		Limits of clearance	Standard limits		Limits of clearance	Standard limits		Limits of clearance	Standard limits		Limits of clearance	Standard limits	
over	to		Hole H5	Shaft g4		Hole H6	Shaft g5		Hole H6	Shaft f6		Hole H7	Shaft f7
0.04–	0.12	0.1 0.45	+0.2 0	−0.1 −0.25	0.1 0.55	+0.25 0	−0.1 −0.3	0.3 0.8	+0.25 0	−0.3 −0.55	0.3 1.1	+0.4 0	−0.3 −0.7
0.12–	0.24	0.15 0.5	+0.2 0	−0.15 −0.3	0.15 0.65	+0.3 0	−0.15 −0.35	0.4 1.0	+0.3 0	−0.4 −0.7	0.4 1.4	+0.5 0	−0.4 −0.9
0.24–	0.40	0.2 0.6	+0.25 0	−0.2 −0.35	0.2 0.85	+0.4 0	−0.2 −0.45	0.5 1.3	+0.4 0	−0.5 −0.9	0.5 1.7	+0.6 0	−0.5 −1.1
0.40–	0.71	0.25 0.75	+0.3 0	−0.25 −0.45	0.25 0.95	+0.4 0	−0.25 −0.55	0.6 1.4	+0.4 0	−0.6 −1.0	0.6 2.0	+0.7 0	−0.6 −1.3
0.71–	1.19	0.3 0.95	+0.4 0	−0.3 −0.55	0.3 1.2	+0.5 0	−0.3 −0.7	0.8 1.8	+0.5 0	−0.8 −1.3	0.8 2.4	+0.8 0	−0.8 −1.6
1.19–	1.97	0.4 1.1	+0.4 0	−0.4 −0.7	0.4 1.4	+0.6 0	−0.4 −0.8	1.0 2.2	+0.6 0	−1.0 −1.6	1.0 3.0	+1.0 0	−1.0 −2.0
1.97–	3.15	0.4 1.2	+0.5 0	−0.4 −0.7	0.4 1.6	+0.7 0	−0.4 −0.9	1.2 2.6	+0.7 0	−1.2 −1.9	1.2 3.6	+1.2 0	−1.2 −2.4

Nominal size range inches		Class RC 5			Class RC 6			Class RC 7			Class RC 8			Class RC 9		
		Limits of clearance	Standard limits		Limits of clearance	Standard limits		Limits of clearance	Standard limits		Limits of clearance	Standard limits		Limits of clearance	Standard limits	
over	to		Hole H7	Shaft e7		Hole H8	Shaft e8		Hole H9	Shaft d8		Hole H10	Shaft c9		Hole H11	Shaft
0.04–	0.12	0.6 1.4	+0.4 0	−0.6 −1.0	0.6 1.8	+0.6 0	−0.6 −1.2	1.0 2.6	+1.0 0	−1.0 −1.6	2.5 5.1	+1.6 0	−2.5 −3.5	4.0 8.1	+2.5 0	− 4.0 − 5.6
0.12–	0.24	0.8 1.8	+0.5 0	−0.8 −1.3	0.8 2.2	+0.7 0	−0.8 −1.5	1.2 3.1	+1.2 0	−1.2 −1.9	2.8 5.8	+1.8 0	−2.8 −4.0	4.5 9.0	+3.0 0	− 4.5 − 6.0
0.24–	0.40	1.0 2.2	+0.6 0	−1.0 −1.6	1.0 2.8	+0.9 0	−1.0 −1.9	1.6 3.9	+1.4 0	−1.6 −2.5	3.0 6.6	+2.2 0	−3.0 −4.4	5.0 10.7	+3.5 0	− 5.0 − 7.2
0.40–	0.71	1.2 2.6	+0.7 0	−1.2 −1.9	1.2 3.2	+1.0 0	−1.2 −2.2	2.0 4.6	+1.6 0	−2.0 −3.0	3.5 7.9	+2.8 0	−3.5 −5.1	6.0 12.8	+4.0 0	− 6.0 − 8.8
0.71–	1.19	1.6 3.2	+0.8 0	−1.6 −2.4	1.6 4.0	+1.2 0	−1.6 −2.8	2.5 5.7	+2.0 0	−2.5 −3.7	4.5 10.0	+3.5 0	−4.5 −6.5	7.0 15.5	+5.0 0	− 7.0 −10.5
1.19–	1.97	2.0 4.0	+1.0 0	−2.0 −3.0	2.0 5.2	+1.6 0	−2.0 −3.6	3.0 7.1	+2.5 0	−3.0 −4.6	5.0 11.5	+4.0 0	−5.0 −7.5	8.0 18.0	+6.0 0	− 8.0 −12.0
1.97–	3.15	2.5 4.9	+1.2 0	−2.5 −3.7	2.5 6.1	+1.8 0	−2.5 −4.3	4.0 8.8	+3.0 0	−4.0 −5.8	6.0 13.5	+4.5 0	−6.0 −9.0	9.0 20.5	+7.0 0	− 9.0 −13.5

Courtesy ASA

TABLE 21. CLEARANCE LOCATIONAL FITS

Limits are in thousandths of an inch.
Limits for hole and shaft are applied algebraically to the basic size to obtain the limits of size for the parts.
Data are in accordance with ABC agreements.
Symbols H6, h5, etc., are Hole and Shaft designations used in ABC System.

Nominal size range inches over	to	Class LC 1 Limits of clearance	Standard limits Hole H6	Shaft h5	Class LC 2 Limits of clearance	Standard limits Hole H7	Shaft h6	Class LC 3 Limits of clearance	Standard limits Hole H8	Shaft h7	Class LC 4 Limits of clearance	Standard limits Hole H9	Shaft h9	Class LC 5 Limits of clearance	Standard limits Hole H7	Shaft g6
0.04–	0.12	0 0.45	+0.25 −0	+0 −0.2	0 0.65	+0.4 −0	+0 −0.25	0 1	+0.6 −0	+0 −0.4	0 2.0	+1.0 −0	+0 −1.0	0.1 0.75	+0.4 −0	−0.1 −0.35
0.12–	0.24	0 0.5	+0.3 −0	+0 −0.2	0 0.8	+0.5 −0	+0 −0.3	0 1.2	+0.7 −0	+0 −0.5	0 2.4	+1.2 −0	+0 −1.2	0.15 0.95	+0.5 −0	−0.15 −0.45
0.24–	0.40	0 0.65	+0.4 −0	+0 −0.25	0 1.0	+0.6 −0	+0 −0.4	0 1.5	+0.9 −0	+0 −0.6	0 2.8	+1.4 −0	+0 −1.4	0.2 1.2	+0.6 −0	−0.2 −0.6
0.40–	0.71	0 0.7	+0.4 −0	+0 −0.3	0 1.1	+0.7 −0	+0 −0.4	0 1.7	+1.0 −0	+0 −0.7	0 3.2	+1.6 −0	+0 −1.6	0.25 1.35	+0.7 −0	−0.25 −0.65
0.71–	1.19	0 0.9	+0.5 −0	+0 −0.4	0 1.3	+0.8 −0	+0 −0.5	0 2	+1.2 −0	+0 −0.8	0 4	+2.0 −0	+0 −2.0	0.3 1.6	+0.8 −0	−0.3 −0.8
1.19–	1.97	0 1.0	+0.6 −0	+0 −0.4	0 1.6	+1.0 −0	+0 −0.6	0 2.6	+1.6 −0	+0 −1	0 5	+2.5 −0	+0 −2.5	0.4 2.0	+1.0 −0	−0.4 −1.0
1.97–	3.15	0 1.2	+0.7 −0	+0 −0.5	0 1.9	+1.2 −0	+0 −0.7	0 3	+1.8 −0	+0 −1.2	0 6	+3 −0	+0 −3	0.4 2.3	+1.2 −0	−0.4 −1.1

Nominal size range inches over	to	Class LC 6 Limits of clearance	Standard limits Hole H8	Shaft f8	Class LC 7 Limits of clearance	Standard limits Hole H9	Shaft e9	Class LC 8 Limits of clearance	Standard limits Hole H10	Shaft d9	Class LC 9 Limits of clearance	Standard limits Hole H11	Shaft c11	Class LC 10 Limits of clearance	Standard limits Hole H12	Shaft	Class LC 11 Limits of clearance	Standard limits Hole H13	Shaft
0.04–	0.12	0.3 1.5	+0.6 −0	−0.3 −0.9	0.6 2.6	+1.0 −0	−0.6 −1.6	1.0 3.6	+1.6 −0	−1.0 −2.0	2.5 7.5	+2.5 −0	−2.5 −5.0	4 12	+4 −0	−4 −8	5 17	+6 −0	−5 −11
0.12–	0.24	0.4 1.8	+0.7 −0	−0.4 −1.1	0.8 3.2	+1.2 −0	−0.8 −2.0	1.2 4.2	+1.8 −0	−1.2 −2.4	2.8 8.8	+3.0 −0	−2.8 −5.8	4.5 14.5	+5 −0	−4.5 −9.5	6 20	+7 −0	−6 −13
0.24–	0.40	0.5 2.3	+0.9 −0	−0.5 −1.4	1.0 3.8	+1.4 −0	−1.0 −2.4	1.6 5.2	+2.2 −0	−1.6 −3.0	3.0 10.0	+3.5 +0	−3.0 −6.5	5 17	+6 −0	−5 −11	7 25	+9 −0	−7 −16
0.40–	0.71	0.6 2.6	+1.0 −0	−0.6 −1.6	1.2 4.4	+1.6 −0	−1.2 −2.8	2.0 6.4	+2.8 −0	−2.0 −3.6	3.5 11.5	+4.0 −0	−3.5 −7.5	6 20	+7 −0	−6 −13	8 28	+10 −0	−8 −18
0.71–	1.19	0.8 3.2	+1.2 −0	−0.8 −2.0	1.6 5.6	+2.0 −0	−1.6 −3.6	2.5 8.0	+3.5 −0	−2.5 −4.5	4.5 14.5	+5.0 −0	−4.5 −9.5	7 23	+8 −0	−7 −15	10 34	+12 −0	−10 −22
1.19–	1.97	1.0 4.2	+1.6 −0	−1.0 −2.6	2.0 7.0	+2.5 −0	−2.0 −4.5	3.0 9.5	+4.0 −0	−3.0 −5.5	5 17	+6 −0	−5 −11	8 28	+10 −0	−8 −18	12 44	+16 −0	−12 −28
1.97–	3.15	1.2 4.8	+1.8 −0	−1.2 −3.0	2.5 8.5	+3.0 −0	−2.5 −5.5	4.0 11.5	+4.5 −0	−4.0 −7.0	6 20	+7 −0	−6 −13	10 34	+12 −0	−10 −22	14 50	+18 −0	−14 −32

Courtesy ASA

TABLE 22. TRANSITION LOCATIONAL FITS

Limits are in thousandths of an inch.
Limits for hole and shaft are applied algebraically to the basic size to obtain the limits of size for the mating parts.
Data are in accordance with ABC agreements.
"Fit" represents the maximum interference (minus values) and the maximum clearance (plus values).
Symbols H8, j6, etc., are Hole and Shaft designations used in ABC System.

Nominal size range inches		Class LT 1			Class LT 2			Class LT 3			Class LT 4			Class LT 6			Class LT 7		
		Fit	Standard limits		Fit	Standard limits		Fit	Standard limits		Fit	Standard limits		Fit	Standard limits		Fit	Standard limits	
over	to		Hole H7	Shaft j6		Hole H8	Shaft j7		Hole H7	Shaft k6		Hole H8	Shaft k7		Hole H8	Shaft m7		Hole H7	Shaft n6
0.04–	0.12	−0.15	+0.4	+0.15	−0.3	+0.6	+0.3							−0.55	+0.6	+0.55	−0.5	+0.4	+0.5
		+0.5	−0	−0.1	+0.7	−0	−0.1							+0.45	−0	+0.15	+0.15	−0	+0.25
0.12–	0.24	−0.2	+0.5	+0.2	−0.4	+0.7	+0.4							−0.7	+0.7	+0.7	−0.6	+0.5	+0.6
		+0.6	−0	−0.1	+0.8	−0	−0.1							+0.5	−0	+0.2	+0.2	−0	+0.3
0.24–	0.40	−0.3	+0.6	+0.3	−0.4	+0.9	+0.4	−0.5	+0.6	+0.5	−0.7	+0.9	+0.7	−0.8	+0.9	+0.8	−0.8	+0.6	+0.8
		+0.7	−0	−0.1	+1.1	−0	−0.2	+0.5	−0	+0.1	+0.8	−0	+0.1	+0.7	−0	+0.2	+0.2	−0	+0.4
0.40–	0.71	−0.3	+0.7	+0.3	−0.5	+1.0	+0.5	−0.5	+0.7	+0.5	−0.8	+1.0	+0.8	−1.0	+1.0	+1.0	−0.9	+0.7	+0.9
		+0.8	−0	−0.1	+1.2	−0	−0.2	+0.6	−0	+0.1	+0.9	−0	+0.1	+0.7	−0	+0.3	+0.2	−0	+0.5
0.71–	1.19	−0.3	+0.8	+0.3	−0.5	+1.2	+0.5	−0.6	+0.8	+0.6	−0.9	+1.2	+0.9	−1.1	+1.2	+1.1	−1.1	+0.8	+1.1
		+1.0	−0	−0.2	+1.5	−0	−0.3	+0.7	−0	+0.1	+1.1	−0	+0.1	+0.9	−0	+0.3	+0.2	−0	+0.6
1.19–	1.97	−0.4	+1.0	+0.4	−0.6	+1.6	+0.6	−0.7	+1.0	+0.7	−1.1	+1.6	+1.1	−1.4	+1.6	+1.4	−1.3	+1.0	+1.3
		+1.2	−0	−0.2	+2.0	−0	−0.4	+0.9	−0	+0.1	+1.5	−0	+0.1	+1.2	−0	+0.4	+0.3	−0	+0.7
1.97–	3.15	−0.4	+1.2	+0.4	−0.7	+1.8	+0.7	−0.8	+1.2	+0.8	−1.3	+1.8	+1.3	−1.7	+1.8	+1.7	−1.5	+1.2	+1.5
		+1.5	−0	−0.3	+2.3	−0	−0.5	+1.1	−0	+0.1	+1.7	−0	+0.1	+1.3	−0	+0.5	+0.4	−0	+0.8

Courtesy ASA

TABLE 23. INTERFERENCE LOCATIONAL FITS

Limits are in thousandths of an inch.
Limits for hole and shaft are applied algebraically to the basic size to obtain the limits of size for the parts.
Data are in accordance with ABC agreements.
Symbols H7, p6, etc., are Hole and Shaft designations used in ABC System.

Nominal size range inches		Class LN 2			Class LN 3		
		Limits of interference	Standard limits		Limits of interference	Standard limits	
over	to		Hole H7	Shaft p6		Hole H7	Shaft r6
0.04–	0.12	0	+0.4	+0.65	0.1	+0.4	+0.75
		0.65	−0	+0.4	0.75	−0	+0.5
0.12–	0.24	0	+0.5	+0.8	0.1	+0.5	+0.9
		0.8	−0	+0.5	0.9	−0	+0.6
0.24–	0.40	0	+0.6	+1.0	0.2	+0.6	+1.2
		1.0	−0	+0.6	1.2	−0	+0.8
0.40–	0.71	0	+0.7	+1.1	0.3	+0.7	+1.4
		1.1	−0	+0.7	1.4	−0	+1.0
0.71–	1.19	0	+0.8	+1.3	0.4	+0.8	+1.7
		1.3	−0	+0.8	1.7	−0	+1.2
1.19–	1.97	0	+1.0	+1.6	0.4	+1.0	+2.0
		1.6	−0	+1.0	2.0	−0	+1.4
1.97–	3.15	0.2	+1.2	+2.1	0.4	+1.2	+2.3
		2.1	−0	+1.4	2.3	−0	+1.6

Courtesy ASA

TABLE 24. FORCE AND SHRINK FITS

Limits are in thousandths of an inch.
Limits for hole and shaft are applied algebraically to the basic size to obtain the limits of size for the parts.
Data are in accordance with ABC agreements.
Symbols H7, s6, etc., are Hole and Shaft designations used in ABC System.

Nominal size range inches		Class FN 1			Class FN 2			Class FN 3			Class FN 4			Class FN 5		
		Limits of interference	Standard limits		Limits of interference	Standard limits		Limits of interference	Standard limits		Limits of interference	Standard limits		Limits of interference	Standard limits	
over	to		Hole H6	Shaft		Hole H7	Shaft s6		Hole H7	Shaft t6		Hole H7	Shaft u6		Hole H7	Shaft x7
0.04–	0.12	0.05 0.5	+0.25 −0	+0.5 +0.3	0.2 0.85	+0.4 −0	+0.85 +0.6				0.3 0.95	+0.4 −0	+0.95 +0.7	0.5 1.3	+0.4 −0	+1.3 +0.9
0.12–	0.24	0.1 0.6	+0.3 −0	+0.6 +0.4	0.2 1.0	+0.5 −0	+1.0 +0.7				0.4 1.2	+0.5 −0	+1.2 +0.9	0.7 1.7	+0.5 −0	+1.7 +1.2
0.24–	0.40	0.1 0.75	+0.4 −0	+0.75 +0.5	0.4 1.4	+0.6 −0	+1.4 +1.0				0.6 1.6	+0.6 −0	+1.6 +1.2	0.8 2.0	+0.6 −0	+2.0 +1.4
0.40–	0.56	0.1 0.8	+0.4 −0	+0.8 +0.5	0.5 1.6	+0.7 −0	+1.6 +1.2				0.7 1.8	+0.7 −0	+1.8 +1.4	0.9 2.3	+0.7 −0	+2.3 +1.6
0.56–	0.71	0.2 0.9	+0.4 −0	+0.9 +0.6	0.5 1.6	+0.7 −0	+1.6 +1.2				0.7 1.8	+0.7 −0	+1.8 +1.4	1.1 2.5	+0.7 −0	+2.5 +1.8
0.71–	0.95	0.2 1.1	+0.5 −0	+1.1 +0.7	0.6 1.9	+0.8 −0	+1.9 +1.4				0.8 2.1	+0.8 −0	+2.1 +1.6	1.4 3.0	+0.8 −0	+3.0 +2.2
0.95–	1.19	0.3 1.2	+0.5 −0	+1.2 +0.8	0.6 1.9	+0.8 −0	+1.9 +1.4	0.8 2.1	+0.8 −0	+2.1 +1.6	1.0 2.3	+0.8 −0	+2.3 +1.8	1.7 3.3	+0.8 −0	+3.3 +2.5
1.19–	1.58	0.3 1.3	+0.6 −0	+1.3 +0.9	0.8 2.4	+1.0 −0	+2.4 +1.8	1.0 2.6	+1.0 −0	+2.6 +2.0	1.5 3.1	+1.0 −0	+3.1 +2.5	2.0 4.0	+1.0 −0	+4.0 +3.0
1.58–	1.97	0.4 1.4	+0.6 −0	+1.4 +1.0	0.8 2.4	−1.0 −0	+2.4 +1.8	1.2 2.8	+1.0 −0	+2.8 +2.2	1.8 3.4	+1.0 −0	+3.4 +2.8	3.0 5.0	+1.0 −0	+5.0 +4.0
1.97–	2.56	0.6 1.8	+0.7 −0	+1.8 +1.3	0.8 2.7	+1.2 −0	+2.7 +2.0	1.3 3.2	+1.2 −0	+3.2 +2.5	2.3 4.2	+1.2 −0	+4.2 +3.5	3.8 6.2	+1.2 −0	+6.2 +5.0
2.56–	3.15	0.7 1.9	+0.7 −0	+1.9 +1.4	1.0 2.9	+1.2 −0	+2.9 +2.2	1.8 3.7	+1.2 −0	+3.7 +3.0	2.8 4.7	+1.2 −0	+4.7 +4.0	4.8 7.2	+1.2 −0	+7.2 +6.0

Courtesy ASA

TABLE 25. DIMENSIONS OF PLAIN WASHERS

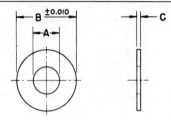

Type A

Inside diameter A*	Outside diameter B	Thickness, C			Inside diameter A*	Outside diameter B	Thickness, C		
		Nom	Max	Min			Nom	Max	Min
5/64	3/16	0.020	0.025	0.016	5/8	1½	0.109	0.132	0.086
3/32	7/32	0.020	0.025	0.016	5/8	2⅛	0.134	0.160	0.108
3/32	1/4	0.020	0.025	0.016	21/32	1⁵⁄₁₆	0.095	0.121	0.074
1/8	1/4	0.022	0.028	0.017	11/16	1½	0.134	0.160	0.108
1/8	5/16	0.032	0.040	0.025	11/16	1¾	0.134	0.160	0.108
5/32	5/16	0.035	0.048	0.027	11/16	2⅜	0.165	0.192	0.136
5/32	3/8	0.049	0.065	0.036	13/16	1½	0.134	0.160	0.108
11/64	13/32	0.049	0.065	0.036	13/16	1¾	0.148	0.177	0.122
3/16	3/8	0.049	0.065	0.036	13/16	2	0.148	0.177	0.122
3/16	7/16	0.049	0.065	0.036	13/16	2⅞	0.165	0.192	0.136
13/64	15/32	0.049	0.065	0.036	15/16	1¾	0.134	0.160	0.108
7/32	7/16	0.049	0.065	0.036	15/16	2	0.165	0.192	0.136
7/32	1/2	0.049	0.065	0.036	15/16	2¼	0.165	0.192	0.136
15/64	17/32	0.049	0.065	0.036	15/16	3⅜	0.180	0.213	0.153
1/4	1/2	0.049	0.065	0.036	1¹⁄₁₆	2	0.134	0.160	0.108
1/4*	9/16	0.049	0.065	0.036	1¹⁄₁₆	2¼	0.165	0.192	0.136
1/4*	9/16	0.065	0.080	0.051	1¹⁄₁₆	2½	0.165	0.192	0.136
17/64	5/8	0.049	0.065	0.036	1¹⁄₁₆	3⅞	0.238	0.280	0.210
9/32	5/8	0.065	0.080	0.051	1³⁄₁₆	2½	0.165	0.192	0.136
5/16	3/4	0.065	0.080	0.051	1¼	2¾	0.165	0.192	0.136
5/16	7/8	0.065	0.080	0.051	1⁵⁄₁₆	2¾	0.165	0.192	0.136
11/32	11/16	0.065	0.080	0.051	1⅜	3	0.165	0.192	0.136
3/8	3/4	0.065	0.080	0.051	1⁷⁄₁₆	3	0.180	0.213	0.153
3/8	7/8	0.083	0.104	0.064	1½	3¼	0.180	0.213	0.153
3/8	1⅛	0.065	0.080	0.051	1⁹⁄₁₆	3¼	0.180	0.213	0.153
13/32	13/16	0.065	0.080	0.051	1⅝	3½	0.180	0.213	0.153
7/16	7/8	0.083	0.104	0.064	1¹¹⁄₁₆	3½	0.180	0.213	0.153
7/16	1	0.083	0.104	0.064	1¾	3¾	0.180	0.213	0.153
7/16	1⅜	0.083	0.104	0.064	1¹³⁄₁₆	3¾	0.180	0.213	0.153
15/32	59/64	0.065	0.080	0.051	1⅞	4	0.180	0.213	0.153
1/2	1⅛	0.083	0.104	0.064	1¹⁵⁄₁₆	4	0.180	0.213	0.153
1/2	1¼	0.083	0.104	0.064	2	4¼	0.180	0.213	0.153
1/2	1⅝	0.083	0.104	0.064	2¹⁄₁₆	4¼	0.180	0.213	0.153
17/32	1¹⁄₁₆	0.095	0.121	0.074	2⅛	4½	0.180	0.213	0.153
9/16	1¼	0.109	0.132	0.086	2⅜	4¾	0.220	0.248	0.193
9/16	1⅜	0.109	0.132	0.086	2⅝	5	0.238	0.280	0.210
9/16	1⅞	0.109	0.132	0.086	2⅞	5¼	0.259	0.310	0.228
19/32	1³⁄₁₆	0.095	0.121	0.074	3⅛	5½	0.284	0.327	0.249
5/8	1⅜	0.109	0.132	0.086					

All dimensions are given in inches.

* Tolerance ±0.005 on inside diameter to and including ⁷⁄₃₂ inside diameter; ±0.010 on inside diameter greater than ⁷⁄₃₂ with exception of two ¼ x ⁹⁄₁₆ sizes marked with an asterisk on which two sizes the tolerance is ±0.005.

Courtesy ASA

TABLE 26. WF SHAPES

Dimensions for Detailing

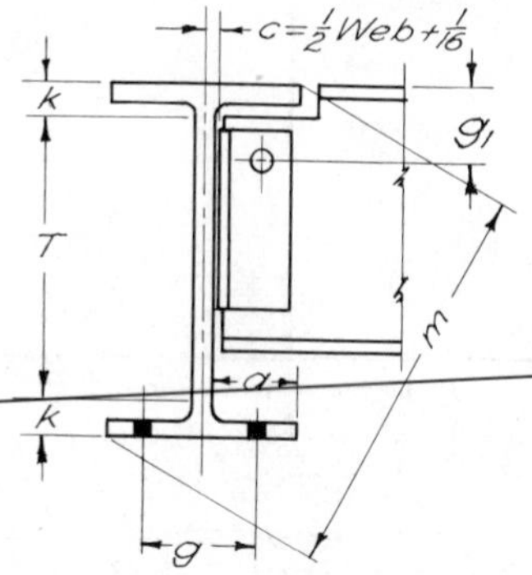

Nominal size	Weight per foot	Depth	Flange		Web		Distance						Usual gage g
			Width	Thick-ness	Thick-ness	Half thick-ness	a	T	k	m	g_1	c	
In.	Lb.	In.	In.	In.	In.	In.	In.	In.	In.	In.	In.	In.	In.
36 × 16½	230	35⅞	16½	1¼	3/4	3/8	7⅞	31⅛	2⅜	39½	3½	7/16	5½
36 × 12	150	35⅞	12	15/16	5/8	5/16	5⅝	32¼	1 13/16	37⅞	3	3/8	5½
33 × 15¾	200	33	15¾	1⅛	3/4	3/8	7½	28⅝	2 3/16	36⅝	3½	7/16	5½
33 × 11½	130	33⅛	11½	7/8	9/16	5/16	5½	29¾	1 11/16	35⅛	3	3/8	5½
30 × 15	172	29⅞	15	1 1/16	11/16	5/16	7⅛	25¾	2 1/16	33½	3¼	3/8	5½
30 × 10½	108	29⅞	10½	3/4	9/16	5/16	5	26⅞	1½	31⅝	2¾	3/8	5½
24 × 14	130	24¼	14	7/8	9/16	5/16	6¾	20¾	1¾	28	3	3/8	5½
24 × 12	100	24	12	3/4	1/2	1/4	5¾	20⅞	1 9/16	26⅞	2¾	5/16	5½
24 × 9	76	23⅞	9	11/16	7/16	1/4	4¼	21⅜	1¼	25⅝	2½	5/16	5½
21 × 13	112	21	13	7/8	9/16	1/4	6¼	17¾	1⅝	24¾	3	5/16	5½
21 × 9	82	20⅞	9	13/16	1/2	1/4	4¼	18	1 7/16	22¾	2¾	5/16	5½
21 × 8¼	62	21	8¼	5/8	3/8	3/16	4	18⅝	1 3/16	22⅝	2½	1/4	5½
18 × 11¾	96	18⅛	11¾	13/16	1/2	1/4	5⅝	15⅛	1½	21¾	2¾	5/16	5½
18 × 8¾	64	17⅞	8¾	11/16	7/16	3/16	4⅛	15⅜	1¼	20	2½	1/4	5½
18 × 7½	50	18	7½	9/16	3/8	3/16	3⅝	15⅞	1 1/16	19½	2¼	1/4	3½
16 × 11½	88	16⅛	11½	13/16	1/2	1/4	5½	13⅛	1½	19⅞	2¾	5/16	5½
16 × 8½	58	15⅞	8½	5/8	7/16	1/4	4	13⅜	1¼	18	2½	5/16	5½
16 × 7	36	15⅞	7	7/16	5/16	3/16	3⅜	14	15/16	17⅜	2¼	1/4	3½
14 × 12	78	14	12	11/16	7/16	1/4	5¾	11⅜	1 5/16	18½	2½	5/16	5½
14 × 10	61	13⅞	10	5/8	3/8	3/16	4¾	11⅜	1¼	17⅛	2½	1/4	5½
14 × 8	43	13⅝	8	1/2	5/16	3/16	3⅞	11⅜	1⅛	15⅞	2½	1/4	5½
12 × 10	53	12	10	9/16	3/8	3/16	4⅞	9¾	1 3/16	15⅝	2½	1/4	5½
12 × 8	40	12	8	1/2	5/16	3/16	3⅞	9¾	1⅛	14⅜	2½	1/4	5½
12 × 6½	27	12	6½	3/8	1/4	1/8	3⅛	10⅜	13/16	13⅝	2¼	3/16	3½
10 × 8	33	9¾	8	7/16	5/16	3/16	3⅞	7⅞	15/16	12⅝	2¼	1/4	5½
10 × 5¾	21	9⅞	5¾	5/16	1/4	1/8	2¾	8½	11/16	11½	2	3/16	2¾
8 × 6½	24	7⅞	6½	3/8	1/4	1/8	3⅛	6⅜	3/4	10¼	2¼	3/16	3½
8 × 5¼	17	8	5¼	5/16	1/4	1/8	2½	6¾	5/8	9⅝	2¼	3/16	2¾

Courtesy *AISC Manual*

TABLE 27. AMERICAN STANDARD I BEAMS

Dimensions for Detailing

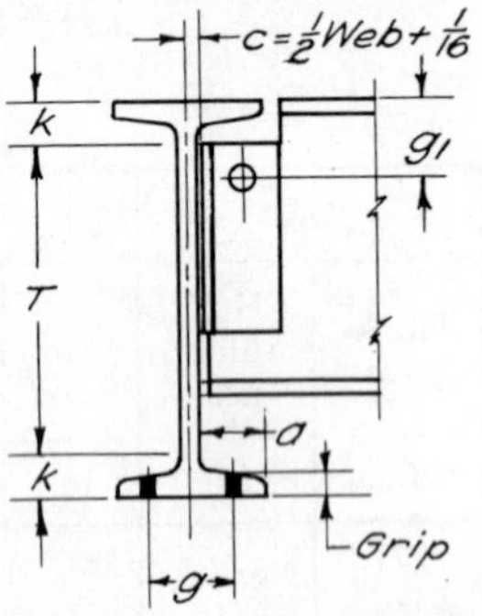

Depth of section	Weight per foot	Flange		Web		Distance					Grip	Max. flange rivet	Usual gage g
		Width	Mean thickness	Thickness	Half thickness	a	T	k	g_1	c			
In.	Lb.	In.	In.	In.	In.	In.	In.	In.	In.	In.	In.	In.	In.
24	79.9	7	7/8	1/2	1/4	3¼	20¾	1⅝	3	5/16	7/8	1	4
20	65.4	6¼	13/16	1/2	1/4	2⅞	16⅞	1 9/16	3	5/16	3/4	7/8	3½
18	54.7	6	11/16	1/2	1/4	2¾	15¼	1⅜	2¾	5/16	11/16	7/8	3½
15	42.9	5½	5/8	7/16	1/4	2½	12½	1¼	2¾	5/16	9/16	3/4	3½
12	31.8	5	9/16	3/8	3/16	2⅜	9¾	1⅛	2½	1/4	1/2	3/4	3
10	25.4	4⅝	1/2	5/16	3/16	2⅛	8	1	2½	1/4	1/2	3/4	2¾
8	18.4	4	7/16	5/16	1/8	1⅞	6¼	7/8	2¼	3/16	7/16	3/4	2¼
7	15.3	3⅝	3/8	1/4	1/8	1¾	5⅜	13/16	2	3/16	3/8	5/8	2¼
6	12.5	3⅜	3/8	1/4	1/8	1½	4½	3/4	2	3/16	5/16		
5	10.0	3	5/16	1/4	1/8	1⅜	3⅝	11/16	2	3/16	5/16	1/2	1¾
4	7.7	2⅝	5/16	3/16	1/8	1¼	2¾	5/8	2	3/16	5/16		
3	5.7	2⅜	1/4	3/16	1/8	1⅛	1⅞	9/16		3/16	1/4	3/8	1½

Courtesy *AISC Manual*

TABLE 28. STANDARD GAGES FOR ANGLES, INCHES

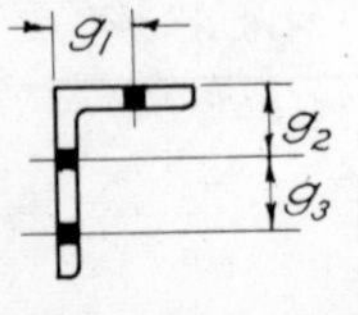

Leg	8	7	6	5	4	3½	3	2½	2	1¾	1½	1⅜	1¼	1	3/4
g_1	4½	4	3½	3	2½	2	1¾	1⅜	1⅛	1	7/8	7/8	3/4	5/8	1/2
g_2	3	2½	2¼	2											
g_3	3	3	2½	1¾											
Max. rivet	1⅛	1	7/8	7/8	7/8	7/8	7/8	3/4	5/8	1/2	3/8	3/8	3/8	1/4	1/4

Courtesy *AISC Manual*

TABLE 29. AMERICAN STANDARD CHANNELS   APP–23

Dimensions for Detailing

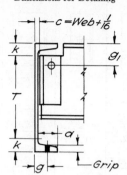

Depth of section	Weight per foot	Flange		Web		Distance					Grip	Max. flange rivet	Usual gage g
		Width	Mean thickness	Thickness	Half thickness	a	T	k	g_1	c			
In.	Lb.	In.	In.	In.	In.	In.	In.	In.	In.	In.	In.	In.	In.
15	33.9	3⅜	5/8	7/16	3/16	3	12⅜	1 5/16	2¾	1/2	5/8	1	2
12	20.7	3	1/2	5/16	1/8	2⅝	9⅞	1 1/16	2½	3/8	1/2	7/8	1¾
10	15.3	2⅝	7/16	1/4	1/8	2⅜	8⅛	15/16	2½	5/16	7/16	3/4	1½
9	13.4	2⅜	7/16	1/4	1/8	2¼	7¼	7/8	2½	5/16	3/8	3/4	1⅜
8	11.5	2¼	3/8	1/4	1/8	2	6⅜	13/16	2¼	5/16	3/8	3/4	1⅜
7	9.8	2⅛	3/8	1/4	1/8	1⅞	5⅝	13/16	2	5/16	3/8	5/8	1¼
6	8.2	1⅞	3/8	3/16	1/8	1¾	4½	3/4	2	1/4	5/16	5/8	1⅛
5	6.7	1¾	5/16	3/16	1/8	1½	3⅝	11/16	2	1/4	5/16	1/2	1⅛
4	5.4	1⅝	5/16	3/16	1/8	1⅜	2¾	5/8	2	1/4	1/4	1/2	1
3	4.1	1⅜	1/4	3/16	1/8	1¼	1¾	5/8		1/4	1/4		

Courtesy AISC Manual

TABLE 30. RIVET SPACING

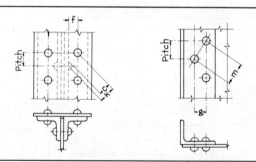

Minimum Pitch for Machine Riveting

Dia. of rivet	c	k	Distance, f, Inches													
			1⅛	1¼	1⅜	1½	1⅝	1¾	1⅞	2	2⅛	2¼	2⅜	2½	2¾	3
3/8	7/8	1 3/16	1/4	0												
1/2	1	1⅜	3/4	1/2	0											
5/8	1⅛	1 9/16	1⅛	1	3/4	3/8	0									
3/4	1¼	1¾	...	1¼	1⅛	1	3/4	0								
7/8	1⅜	2	...	...	1½	1⅜	1⅛	7/8	5/8	0						
1	1½	2 3/16	...	...	...	1⅝	1½	1⅜	1⅛	7/8	1/2	0				
1⅛	1⅝	2⅜	...	...	...	...	1¾	1⅝	1½	1⅜	1⅛	7/8	0			
1¼	1¾	2⅝	...	...	...	...	...	2	1⅞	1¾	1½	1¼	1	5/8	0	
1⅜	1⅞	2 13/16	...	...	...	...	...	...	2⅛	2	1⅞	1¾	1½	1¼	1/2	0
1½	2	3	...	...	...	...	...	...	...	2¼	2⅛	2	1⅞	1⅝	1⅛	0

Courtesy AISC Manual

TABLE 31. STANDARD BEAM CONNECTIONS—SERIES B AISC MANUAL

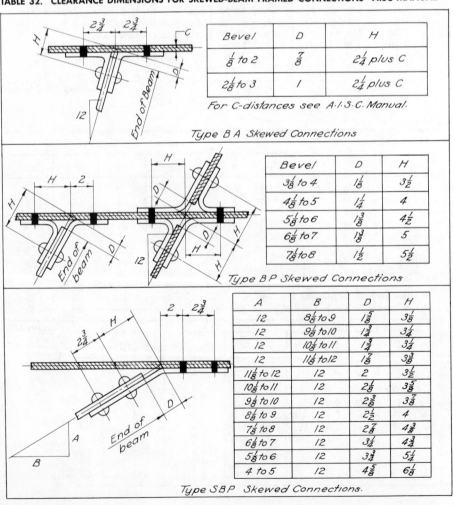

	B6	B5	B4	B-3	B-2	B1
BEAM SIZES	24 WF 160 to 84, 76 24 I All	21 WF 142 to 73,68,62 20 I All	18 WF to 77 16 WF 18 I & 15 I	14 WF, 12 WF 12 I	10 WF 8 WF 10 I & 8 I	7 I, 6 I 5 I
RIVETS IN OUTSTANDING LEGS	12	10	8	6	4	2
SHEAR (OUTSTD LEG) (X 1000 lbs)	79.5	66.3	53	39.8	26.5	13.3
BEARING IN WEB LEGS	180 t	150 t	120 t	90 t	120 t	60 t
MIN. SPAN IN FT. (LIGHT SECT. ONLY)	WF 14.8 I 14.6	WF 14.0 I 11.8	WF 13.8 & 10.5 I 11.1 & 8.0	WF 11.5 & 10.5 I 7.6	WF 5.4 & 3.9 I 6.1 & 3.6	I 5.2, 3.7 & 2.5
WEIGHT (SHOP RIV. ONLY)	34	28	20	14	13	7

TABLE 32. CLEARANCE DIMENSIONS FOR SKEWED-BEAM FRAMED CONNECTIONS—AISC MANUAL

Bevel	D	H
$\frac{1}{8}$ to 2	$\frac{7}{8}$	$2\frac{1}{4}$ plus C
$2\frac{1}{8}$ to 3	1	$2\frac{1}{4}$ plus C

For C-distances see A.I.S.C. Manual.

Type B A Skewed Connections

Bevel	D	H
$3\frac{1}{8}$ to 4	$1\frac{1}{8}$	$3\frac{1}{2}$
$4\frac{1}{8}$ to 5	$1\frac{1}{4}$	4
$5\frac{1}{8}$ to 6	$1\frac{3}{8}$	$4\frac{1}{2}$
$6\frac{1}{8}$ to 7	$1\frac{3}{8}$	5
$7\frac{1}{8}$ to 8	$1\frac{1}{2}$	$5\frac{1}{2}$

Type B P Skewed Connections

A	B	D	H
12	$8\frac{1}{8}$ to 9	$1\frac{5}{8}$	$3\frac{1}{8}$
12	$9\frac{5}{8}$ to 10	$1\frac{1}{4}$	$3\frac{1}{4}$
12	$10\frac{5}{8}$ to 11	$1\frac{1}{2}$	$3\frac{1}{4}$
12	$11\frac{5}{8}$ to 12	$1\frac{7}{8}$	$3\frac{3}{8}$
$11\frac{1}{8}$ to 12	12	2	$3\frac{1}{2}$
$10\frac{5}{8}$ to 11	12	$2\frac{1}{8}$	$3\frac{5}{8}$
$9\frac{5}{8}$ to 10	12	$2\frac{3}{8}$	$3\frac{7}{8}$
$8\frac{5}{8}$ to 9	12	$2\frac{1}{2}$	4
$7\frac{5}{8}$ to 8	12	$2\frac{7}{8}$	$4\frac{3}{8}$
$6\frac{5}{8}$ to 7	12	$3\frac{1}{4}$	$4\frac{3}{4}$
$5\frac{5}{8}$ to 6	12	$3\frac{3}{4}$	$5\frac{1}{4}$
4 to 5	12	$4\frac{5}{8}$	$6\frac{1}{8}$

Type SBP Skewed Connections.

TABLE 33. MAXIMUM SPACING OF COLUMN TIES

Vertical bar size	Size and spacing of ties, in. Maximum spacing not to exceed least column dimension		
	#2	#3	#4
#5	10	10	10
#6	12	12	12
#7	12	14	14
#8	12*	16	16
#9	12*	18	18
#10	12*	18	20
#11	12*	18	22

* #2 ties are not recommended for #8 or larger verticals.

Courtesy ACI

TABLE 34. MAXIMUM NUMBER OF COLUMN BARS FOR ROUND COLUMNS

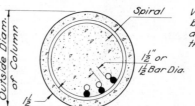

Diameter of column	Spiral size	Bar size						
		#5	#6	#7	#8	#9	#10	#11
14	3/8	12	11	10	9	7	6	
15	3/8	13	12	11	10	8	7	6
16	3/8	15	13	12	11	9	8	6
17	3/8	16	15	14	12	11	9	7
18	3/8	18	16	15	14	12	10	8
19	3/8	19	18	16	15	13	11	9
20	3/8	21	19	18	16	14	12	10
21	1/2	22	20	19	17	15	13	11
22	1/2	23	22	20	18	16	14	11
23	1/2	25	23	21	20	17	15	12
24	1/2	26	24	22	21	18	16	13

Courtesy ACI

TABLE 35. LAPPING OF BARS

Inches of lap corresponding to number of bar diameters (figured to next largest whole inch)

Number of diameters	Size of bar								
	#3	#4	#5	#6	#7	#8	#9	#10	#11
20	..	..	13	15	18	20	23	26	29
21	..	..	14	16	19	21	24	27	30
22	..	..	14	17	20	22	25	28	31
23	..	12	15	18	21	23	26	30	33
24	..	12	15	18	21	24	28	31	34
25	..	13	16	19	22	25	29	32	36
26	..	13	17	20	23	26	30	33	37
27	..	14	17	21	24	27	31	35	39
28	..	14	18	21	25	28	32	36	40
29	..	15	19	22	26	29	33	37	41
30	12	15	19	23	27	30	34	39	43
32	12	16	20	24	28	32	36	41	45
34	13	17	22	26	30	34	39	44	48
36	14	18	23	27	32	36	41	46	51
38	15	19	24	29	34	38	43	49	54
40	15	20	25	30	35	40	46	51	57

Minimum lap equals 12 in.

Courtesy ACI

TABLE 36. MINIMUM BEAM WIDTHS—ACI CODE

Size of bars	Number of bars in single layer of reinforcing							Add for each added bar
	2	3	4	5	6	7	8	
#4	5¾	7¼	8¾	10¼	11¾	13¼	14¾	1½
#5	6	7¾	9¼	11	12½	14¼	15¾	1⅝
#6	6¼	8	9¾	11½	13¼	15	16¾	1¾
#7	6½	8½	10¼	12¼	14	16	17¾	1⅞
#8	6¾	8¾	10¾	12¾	14¾	16¾	18¾	2
#9	7¼	9½	11¾	14	16¼	18½	20¾	2¼
#10	7¾	10¼	12¾	15¼	17¾	20¼	23	2⅝
#11	8	11	13¾	16½	19½	22¼	25	2⅞

Table shows minimum beam widths when #3 stirrups are used; if no stirrups are
    required, deduct ¾ in. from figures shown.

For additional bars, add dimension in last column for each added bar.

For bars of different sizes, determine from table the beam width which would be
    required for the given number of smaller size bars, and then add last column
    figure for each larger bar used.

Clear space between bars should be at least 1⅓ times the maximum size of coarse
    aggregate, which often requires increased beam width when aggregate
    exceeds ¾ in.

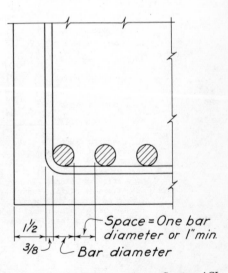

Space = One bar diameter or 1" min.

Bar diameter

1½

3/8

Courtesy ACI

TABLE 37. ELECTRICAL SYMBOLS

ASA Z32.9-1943

Ceiling	Wall	GENERAL OUTLETS
◯	◯	Outlet.
Ⓑ	Ⓑ	Blanked Outlet.
Ⓓ	Ⓓ	Drop Cord.
Ⓔ	Ⓔ	Electrical Outlet; for use only when circle used alone might be confused with columns, plumbing symbols, etc.
Ⓕ	Ⓕ	Fan Outlet.
Ⓙ	Ⓙ	Junction Box.
Ⓛ	Ⓛ	Lamp Holder.
Ⓛ$_{PS}$	Ⓛ$_{PS}$	Lamp Holder with Full Switch.
Ⓢ	Ⓢ	Pull Switch.
Ⓥ	Ⓥ	Outlet for Vapor Discharge Lamp.
Ⓧ	Ⓧ	Exit Light Outlet.
Ⓒ	Ⓒ	Clock Outlet. (Specify Voltage)

CONVENIENCE OUTLETS

⊖ Duplex Convenience Outlet.

⊖$_{1,3}$ Convenience Outlet other than Duplex. 1 = Single, 3 = Triplex, etc.

⊖$_{WP}$ Weatherproof Convenience Outlet.

⊖$_R$ Range Outlet.

⊖$_S$ Switch and Convenience Outlet.

⊖Ⓡ Radio and Convenience Outlet.

⬤ Special Purpose Outlet. (Des. in Spec.)

⊙ Floor Outlet.

SWITCH OUTLETS

S Single Pole Switch.

S$_2$ Double Pole Switch.

S$_3$ Three Way Switch.

S$_4$ Four Way Switch.

S$_D$ Automatic Door Switch.

S$_E$ Electrolier Switch.

S$_K$ Key Operated Switch.

S$_P$ Switch and Pilot Lamp.

S$_{CB}$ Circuit Breaker.

S$_{WCB}$ Weatherproof Circuit Breaker.

S$_{MC}$ Momentary Contact Switch.

S$_{RC}$ Remote Control Switch.

S$_{WP}$ Weatherproof Switch.

S$_F$ Fused Switch

S$_{WF}$ Weatherproof Fused Switch.

SPECIAL OUTLETS

◯a, b, c, etc.
⊖a, b, c, etc.
S a, b, c, etc.

Any Standard Symbol as given above with the addition of a lower case subscript letter may be used to designate some special variation of Standard Equipment of particular interest in a specific set of Architectural Plans.

When used they must be listed in the Key of Symbols on each drawing and if necessary further described in the specifications.

PANELS, CIRCUITS, AND MISCELLANEOUS

▰ Lighting Panel.

▨ Power Panel.

──── Branch Circuit; Concealed in Ceiling or Wall.

- - - - Branch Circuit; concealed in Floor.

- - - - - Branch Circuit; Exposed.

•→ Home Run to Panel Board. Indicate number of Circuits by number of arrows.

Note: Any circuit without further designation indicates a two-wire circuit. For a greater number of wires indicate as follows:

⊣⊦⊦ (3 wires) ⊣⊦⊦⊦ (4 wires), etc.

──── Feeders. Note: Use heavy lines and designate by number corresponding to listing in Feeder Schedule.

⊐⊏ Underfloor Duct and Junction Box. Triple System. Note: For double or single systems eliminate one or two lines. This symbol is equally adaptable to auxiliary system layouts.

Ⓖ Generator.

Ⓜ Motor.

Ⓘ Instrument.

Ⓣ Power Transformer. (Or draw to scale.)

⊠ Controller.

⊡ Isolating Switch.

AUXILIARY SYSTEMS

⊡ Push Button.

⊏⊓ Buzzer.

⊏⊐ Bell.

◇ Annunciator.

◀ Outside Telephone.

◁ Interconnecting Telephone.

◁⊦ Telephone Switchboard.

Ⓣ Bell Ringing Transformer.

Ⓓ Electric Door Opener.

Ⓕ Fire Alarm Bell.

Ⓕ Fire Alarm Station.

⬛ City Fire Alarm Station.

FA Fire Alarm Central Station.

FS Automatic Fire Alarm Device.

W Watchman's Station.

W̄ Watchman's Central Station.

H Horn.

N Nurse's Signal Plug.

M Maid's Signal Plug.

R Radio Outlet.

SC Signal Central Station.

▢ Interconnection Box.

||||| Battery.

- - - - - Auxiliary System Circuits.
Note: Any line without further designation indicates a 2-Wire System. For a greater number of wires designate with numerals in manner similar to --. --12-No. 18W-3/4"C., or designate by number corresponding to listing in Schedule.

▢a, b, c Special Auxiliary Outlets. Subscript letters refer to notes on plans or detailed description in specifications.

Courtesy ASA

TABLE 38. AMERICAN STANDARD STEEL PIPE DATA

(All dimensions in inches. Weights in pounds.)

Nominal size	Actual outside diameter	Standard weight (40)*			Extra-strong (80)†			Double-extra strong‡		
		Inside diameter	Wall thickness	Weight per foot§	Inside diameter	Wall thickness	Weight per foot	Inside diameter	Wall thickness	Weight per foot
1/8	0.405	0.269	0.068	0.244	0.215	0.095	0.314	. . . . .	. . . . .	. . . . .
1/4	0.540	0.364	.088	0.424	0.302	.119	0.535	. . . . .	. . . . .	. . . . .
3/8	0.675	0.493	.091	0.567	0.423	.126	0.738	. . . . .	. . . . .	. . . . .
1/2	0.840	0.622	.109	0.850	0.546	.147	1.087	0.252	0.294	1.714
3/4	1.050	0.824	.113	1.130	0.742	.154	1.473	0.434	.308	2.440
1	1.315	1.049	.133	1.678	0.957	.179	2.171	0.599	.358	3.659
1¼	1.660	1.380	.140	2.272	1.278	.191	2.996	0.896	.382	5.214
1½	1.900	1.610	.145	2.717	1.500	.200	3.631	1.100	.400	6.408
2	2.375	2.067	.154	3.652	1.939	.218	5.022	1.503	.436	9.029
2½	2.875	2.469	.203	5.79	2.323	.276	7.66	1.771	.552	13.70
3	3.500	3.068	.216	7.58	2.900	.300	10.25	2.300	.600	18.58
3½	4.000	3.548	.226	9.11	3.364	.318	12.51	. . . . .	. . . . .	. . . . .
4	4.500	4.026	.237	10.79	3.826	.337	14.98	3.152	.674	27.54
5	5.563	5.047	.258	14.62	4.813	.375	20.78	4.063	.750	38.55
6	6.625	6.065	.280	18.97	5.761	.432	28.57	4.897	.864	53.16
8	8.625	7.981	.322	28.55	7.625	.500	43.39	6.875	.875	72.42
10	10.750	10.020	.365	40.48	9.750	.500	54.74	. . . . .	. . . . .	. . . . .
12	12.750	12.000	.375	49.56	11.750	.500	65.42	. . . . .	. . . . .	. . . . .

* Same as ASA B36.10—"Schedule 40" except 12-inch diameter.
† Same as ASA B36.10—"Schedule 80" except 10- and 12-inch diameter.
‡ Not identified with ASA Schedule number, but available as indicated.
§ Plain ends.

TABLE 39. AGA STANDARD CAST-IRON BELL-AND-SPIGOT PIPE DATA

(All dimensions in inches.   Approx. weights in pounds.)

Nominal size inside diameter	Outside diameter of pipe	Pipe wall thickness	Inside diameter of socket	Depth of socket	Thickness of joint	Weight per foot, 12-foot lengths*
4	4.80	0.40	5.80	4.00	0.50	19.5
6	6.90	0.43	7.90	4.00	.50	30.58
8	9.05	0.45	10.05	4.00	.50	42.42
10	11.10	0.49	12.10	4.00	.50	55.91
12	13.20	0.54	14.20	4.50	.50	73.83
16	17.40	0.62	18.40	4.50	.50	112.58
20	21.60	0.68	22.85	4.50	.63	153.83
24	25.80	0.76	27.05	5.00	.63	206.41
30	31.74	0.85	32.99	5.00	.63	284.00
36	37.96	0.95	39.21	5.00	.63	379.25
42	44.20	1.07	45.45	5.00	.63	497.66
48	50.50	1.26	51.75	5.00	.63	663.50

* Including bell-and-spigot bead.

TABLE 40. ASTM STANDARD BRASS AND COPPER PIPE DATA

(All dimensions in inches.   Weights in pounds.)

Nominal size	Outside diameter	Regular				Extra-strong		
		Wall thickness	Weight per foot			Wall thickness	Weight per foot	
			Red brass	Copper			Red brass	Copper
1/8	0.405	0.062	0.253	0.259		0.100	0.363	0.371
1/4	0.540	0.082	0.447	0.457		0.123	0.611	0.625
3/8	0.675	0.090	0.627	0.641		0.127	0.829	0.847
1/2	0.840	0.107	0.934	0.955		0.149	1.23	1.25
3/4	1.050	0.114	1.27	1.30		0.157	1.67	1.71
1	1.315	0.126	1.78	1.82		0.182	2.46	2.51
1¼	1.660	0.146	2.63	2.69		0.194	3.39	3.46
1½	1.900	0.150	3.13	3.20		0.203	4.10	4.19
2	2.375	0.156	4.12	4.22		0.221	5.67	5.80
2½	2.875	0.187	5.99	6.12		0.280	8.66	8.85
3	3.500	0.219	8.56	8.75		0.304	11.6	11.8
3½	4.000	0.250	11.2	11.4		0.321	14.1	14.4
4	4.500	0.250	12.7	12.9		0.341	16.9	17.3
5	5.562	0.250	15.8	16.2		0.375	23.2	23.7
6	6.625	0.250	19.0	19.4		0.437	32.2	32.9
8	8.625	0.312	30.9	31.6		0.500	48.4	49.5
10	10.750	9.365	45.2	46.2		0.500	61.1	62.4
12	12.750	0.375	55.3	56.5				

TABLE 41. ASTM STANDARD COPPER WATER TUBE DATA

(All dimensions in inches.   Weights in pounds.)

Nominal size	Outside diameter	Type K		Type L		Type M	
		Wall thickness	Weight per foot	Wall thickness	Weight per foot	Wall thickness	Weight per foot
1/8	0.250	0.032	0.085	0.025	0.068	0.025	0.068
1/4	0.375	0.032	0.134	0.030	0.126	0.025	0.107
3/8	0.500	0.049	0.269	0.035	0.198	0.025	0.145
1/2	0.625	0.049	0.344	0.040	0.285	0.028	0.204
5/8	0.750	0.049	0.418	0.042	0.362	0.030	0.263
3/4	0.875	0.065	0.641	0.045	0.455	0.032	0.328
1	1.125	0.065	0.839	0.050	0.655	0.035	0.465
1¼	1.375	0.065	1.04	0.055	0.884	0.042	0.682
1½	1.625	0.072	1.36	0.060	1.14	0.049	0.940
2	2.125	0.083	2.06	0.070	1.75	0.058	1.46
2½	2.625	0.095	2.93	0.080	2.48	0.065	2.03
3	3.125	0.109	4.00	0.090	3.33	0.072	2.68
3½	3.625	0.120	5.12	0.100	4.29	0.083	3.58
4	4.125	0.134	6.51	0.110	5.38	0.095	4.66
5	5.125	0.160	9.67	0.125	7.61	0.109	6.66
6	6.125	0.192	13.9	0.140	10.2	0.122	8.92
8	8.125	0.271	25.9	0.200	19.3	0.170	16.5
10	10.125	0.338	40.3	0.250	30.1	0.212	25.6
12	12.125	0.405	57.8	0.280	40.4	0.254	36.7

TABLE 42. AMERICAN STANDARD TAPER PIPE THREAD DATA

(All dimensions in inches.   Weights in pounds.)

Nominal size	Outside diameter	Inside diameter	Threads per inch	Tap drill	Weight per foot thds. and couplings	Normal engagement by hand
1/8	0.405	0.269	27	11/32	0.245	0.180
1/4	0.540	0.364	18	7/16	0.425	0.200
3/8	0.675	0.493	18	37/64	0.568	0.240
1/2	0.840	0.622	14	23/32	0.852	0.320
3/4	1.050	0.824	14	59/64	1.134	0.339
1	1.315	1.049	11½	1⁵⁄₃₂	1.684	0.400
1¼	1.660	1.380	11½	1½	2.281	0.420
1½	1.900	1.610	11½	1⁴⁷⁄₆₄	2.731	0.420
2	2.375	2.067	11½	2⁷⁄₃₂	3.678	0.436
2½	2.875	2.469	8	2⅝	5.82	0.682
3	3.500	3.068	8	3¼	7.62	0.766
3½	4.000	3.548	8	3¾	9.20	0.821
4	4.500	4.026	8	4¼	10.89	0.844
5	5.563	5.047	8	5⁵⁄₁₆	14.81	0.937
6	6.625	6.065	8	6⁵⁄₁₆	19.18	0.958
8	8.625	7.981	8		29.35	1.063
10	10.750	10.020	8		41.85	1.210
12	12.750	12.000	8		51.15	1.360

TABLE 43. STANDARD FLANGED FITTINGS

(125 lb per sq in. pressure.)

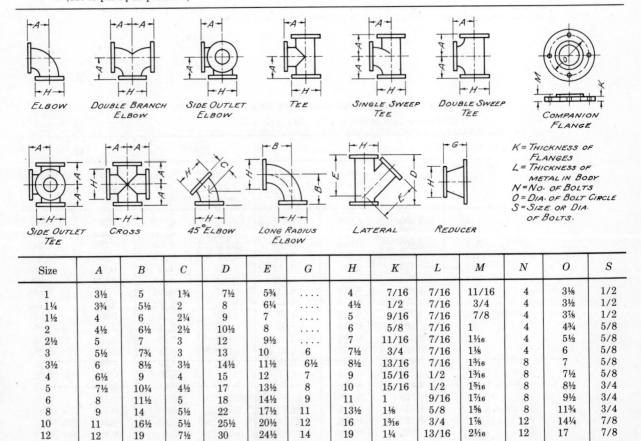

ELBOW   DOUBLE BRANCH ELBOW   SIDE OUTLET ELBOW   TEE   SINGLE SWEEP TEE   DOUBLE SWEEP TEE   COMPANION FLANGE

SIDE OUTLET TEE   CROSS   45° ELBOW   LONG RADIUS ELBOW   LATERAL   REDUCER

K = THICKNESS OF FLANGES
L = THICKNESS OF METAL IN BODY
N = NO. OF BOLTS
O = DIA. OF BOLT CIRCLE
S = SIZE OR DIA. OF BOLTS.

Size	A	B	C	D	E	G	H	K	L	M	N	O	S
1	3½	5	1¾	7½	5¾	....	4	7/16	7/16	11/16	4	3⅛	1/2
1¼	3¾	5½	2	8	6¼	....	4½	1/2	7/16	3/4	4	3½	1/2
1½	4	6	2¼	9	7	....	5	9/16	7/16	7/8	4	3⅞	1/2
2	4½	6½	2½	10½	8	....	6	5/8	7/16	1	4	4¾	5/8
2½	5	7	3	12	9½	....	7	11/16	7/16	1¹⁄₁₆	4	5½	5/8
3	5½	7¾	3	13	10	6	7½	3/4	7/16	1⅛	4	6	5/8
3½	6	8½	3½	14½	11½	6½	8½	13/16	7/16	1³⁄₁₆	8	7	5/8
4	6½	9	4	15	12	7	9	15/16	1/2	1³⁄₁₆	8	7½	5/8
5	7½	10¼	4½	17	13½	8	10	15/16	1/2	1⁵⁄₁₆	8	8½	3/4
6	8	11½	5	18	14½	9	11	1	9/16	1⁷⁄₁₆	8	9½	3/4
8	9	14	5½	22	17½	11	13½	1⅛	5/8	1⅝	8	11¾	3/4
10	11	16½	5½	25½	20½	12	16	1³⁄₁₆	3/4	1⅞	12	14¼	7/8
12	12	19	7½	30	24½	14	19	1¼	13/16	2¹⁄₁₆	12	17	7/8

TABLE 44. STANDARD CAST-IRON SCREW FITTINGS
(125 lb per sq in. pressure.)

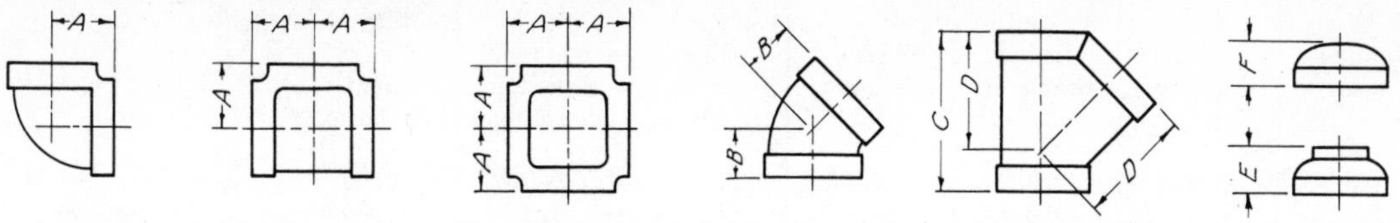

Size inches	Dimensions in inches					
	A	B	C	D	E	F
1/4	13/16	3/4				
3/8	15/16	13/16				
1/2	1 1/8	7/8	2 1/2	1 7/8		
3/4	1 5/16	1	3	2 1/4		
1	1 7/16	1 1/8	3 1/2	2 3/4		
1 1/4	1 3/4	1 5/16	4 1/4	3 1/4	2 1/8	
1 1/2	1 15/16	1 7/16	4 7/8	3 13/16	2 1/4	
2	2 1/4	1 11/16	5 3/4	4 1/4	2 7/16	
2 1/2	2 11/16	1 15/16	6 3/4	5 3/16	2 11/16	
3	3 1/8	2 3/16	7 7/8	6 1/8	2 15/16	
3 1/2	3 7/16	2 3/8	8 7/8	6 7/8	3 1/8	
4	3 3/4	2 5/8	9 3/4	7 5/8	3 3/8	2 1/16
5	7 7/16	3 1/16	11 5/8	9 1/4	3 7/8	2 3/8
6	5 1/8	3 7/16	13 7/16	10 3/4	4 3/8	2 5/8
8	6 1/2	4 1/4	16 15/16	13 5/8	5 1/4	3 1/8
10	8 1/16	5 3/16	20 11/16	16 3/4	6 3/16	3 5/8
12	9 1/2	6	24 1/8	19 5/8	7 1/8	4 1/4

Fractional dimensions are nominal. See ASA Bulletin for decimal dimensions.

TABLE 45. DIMENSIONS OF STANDARD GLOBE, ANGLE, AND CROSS VALVES
(All dimensions in inches.)

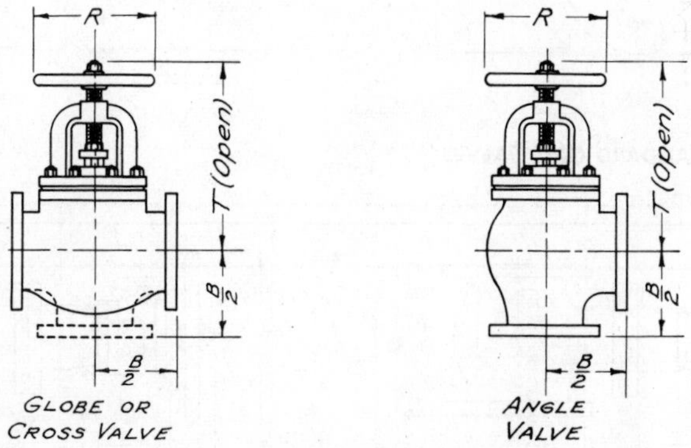

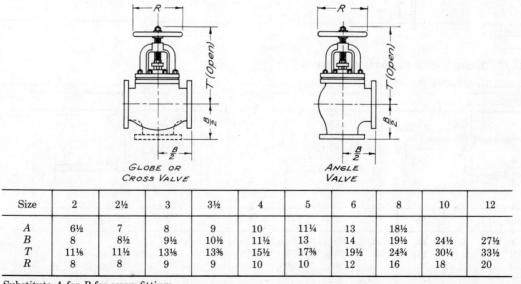

Size	2	2 1/2	3	3 1/2	4	5	6	8	10	12
A	6 1/2	7	8	9	10	11 1/4	13	18 1/2		
B	8	8 1/2	9 1/2	10 1/2	11 1/2	13	14	19 1/2	24 1/2	27 1/2
T	11 1/8	11 1/2	13 1/8	13 3/8	15 1/2	17 3/8	19 1/2	24 3/4	30 1/4	33 1/2
R	8	8	9	9	10	10	12	16	18	20

Substitute *A* for *B* for screw fittings.

TABLE 46. DIMENSIONS OF STANDARD LIFT AND SWING VALVES

(All dimensions in inches.)

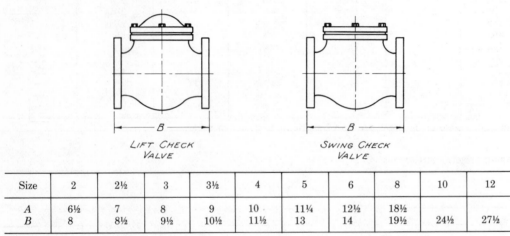

LIFT CHECK VALVE

SWING CHECK VALVE

Size	2	2½	3	3½	4	5	6	8	10	12
A	6½	7	8	9	10	11¼	12½	18½		
B	8	8½	9½	10½	11½	13	14	19½	24½	27½

Substitute *A* for *B* for screw fittings.

TABLE 47. DIMENSIONS OF STANDARD GATE VALVES

(All dimensions in inches.)

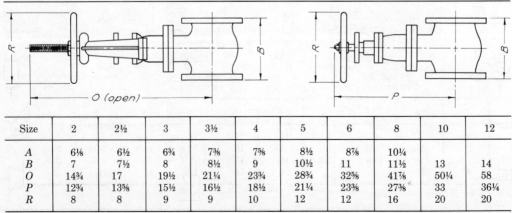

Size	2	2½	3	3½	4	5	6	8	10	12
A	6⅛	6½	6¾	7⅜	7⅝	8½	8⅞	10¼		
B	7	7½	8	8½	9	10½	11	11½	13	14
O	14¾	17	19½	21¼	23¾	28¾	32⅝	41⅞	50¼	58
P	12¾	13⅜	15½	16½	18½	21¼	23⅝	27⅜	33	36¼
R	8	8	9	9	10	12	12	16	20	20

Substitute *A* for *B* for screw fittings.

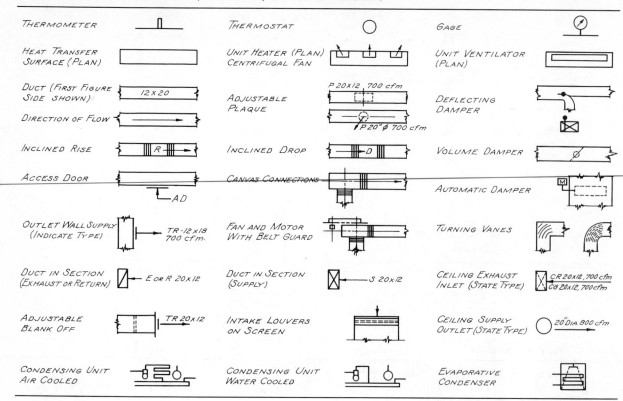

TABLE 49. ASA GRAPHIC SYMBOLS FOR PIPING

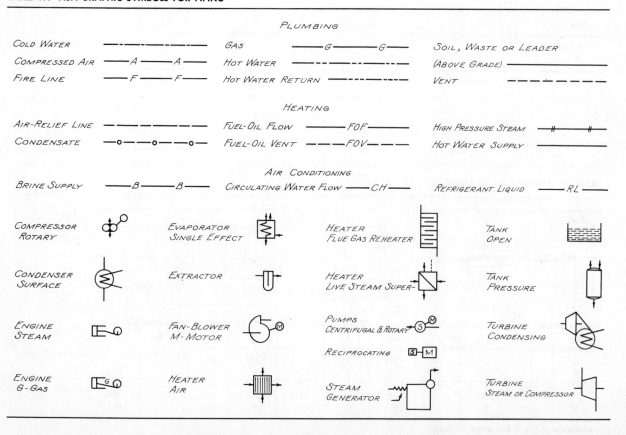

TABLE 50. PLUMBING SYMBOLS

BATH (RECESSED)	BATH (ROLL RIM)	CLEANOUT	DISHWASHER	DRAIN	DRAIN (WITH VALVE)
DRINKING FOUNTAIN WALL TYPE	DRINKING FOUNTAIN PEDESTAL TYPE	DRINKING FOUNTAIN TROUGH TYPE	GAS OUTLET	GAS RANGE	GREASE SEPARATOR
HOSE BIBB	HOSE RACK	HOT WATER	LAUNDRY TRAY	LAVATORY (CORNER)	LAVATORY (DENTAL)
LAVATORY (MANICURE)	LAVATORY (PEDESTAL)	LAVATORY (WALL)	METER	OIL SEPARATOR	ROOF SUMP
PLAN ELEV. SHOWER (HEAD)	SHOWER (STALL)	SINK & DISHWASHER	SINK & LAUNDRY TRAY	SINK (KITCHEN)	SINK (KITCHEN) (WITH DRAINBOARDS)
SINK (SERVICE)	SINK (SERVICE) (FLOOR TYPE)	SINK (WASH) (FREE STANDING)	SINK (WASH) (WALL TYPE)	URINAL (STALL)	URINAL (TROUGH)
URINAL (WALL)	VACUUM OUTLET	WATER CLOSET (LOW TANK)	WATER CLOSET (NO TANK)	WASH FOUNTAIN (HALF CIRCULAR)	WATER HEATER

Courtesy Ramsey & Sleeper

TABLE 51. BALL BEARING DATA

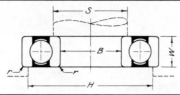

Brg. no.	Bore B	Dia. D	Width W	Balls Dia.	Balls No.	Rad. R	Shoulder dia. Shaft S	Shoulder dia. Housing H	Radial load at rpm 500	Radial load at rpm 1000	Radial load at rpm 2000
34	0.1575	0.6299	0.1969	1/8	6	0.016	0.222	0.550	99	83	66
35	0.1969	0.7480	.2362	9/64	6	.016	0.261	0.668	119	100	80
36	0.2362	0.7480	.2362	9/64	6	.016	0.300	0.668	119	100	80
37	0.2756	0.8661	.2756	5/32	7	.016	0.341	0.786	160	133	106
38	0.3150	0.8661	.2756	5/32	7	.016	0.379	0.786	160	133	106
39	0.3543	1.0236	.3150	3/16	7	.025	0.454	0.899	230	195	155
3L00	0.3937	1.0236	.3150	3/16	7	.016	0.500	0.920	230	195	155
3L01	0.4724	1.1024	.3150	3/16	8	.016	0.570	1.000	255	215	170
3L02	0.5906	1.2598	.3543	3/16	9	.016	0.690	1.15	275	230	185
3L03	0.6693	1.3780	.3937	3/16	10	.016	0.780	1.27	295	245	195
3L04	0.7874	1.6535	.4724	1/4	9	.025	0.940	1.50	505	425	340
3L05	0.9843	1.8504	.4724	1/4	10	.025	1.14	1.69	545	455	360
3L06	1.1811	2.1654	.5118	9/32	11	.040	1.37	1.94	750	630	500
3L07	1.3780	2.4409	.5512	5/16	11	.040	1.58	2.21	935	785	625
3L08	1.5748	2.6772	.5906	5/16	12	.040	1.78	2.44	990	835	665

Courtesy New Departure Division, General Motors Corp.

TABLE 52. DIMENSIONS OF SINGLE ROW, STRAIGHT-BORE TYPE-S ROLLER BEARINGS

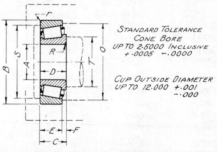

STANDARD TOLERANCE
CONE BORE
UP TO 2.5000 INCLUSIVE
+.0005 −.0000

CUP OUTSIDE DIAMETER
UP TO 12.000 +.001
−.000

Bore A	Outside dia. B	Width C	Rating at 500 rpm Radial lb	Rating at 500 rpm Thrust lb	Cone Radius R	Cone Length D	Cone Stand-out F	Cone Shoulder dia. T	Cup Radius R	Cup Length E	Cup Shoulder dia. S	Cup Shoulder dia. O
0.3750	1.2595	0.3940	255	205	3/64	0.4246	0.0815	11/16	3/64	0.3125	1	1⅛
0.4720	1.2595	.3940	255	205	1/32	.4246	.0815	3/4	3/64	.3125	1	1⅛
0.5000	1.3775	.4330	290	255	3/64	.4326	.0893	3/4	3/64	.3437	1⅛	1¼
0.5900	1.3775	.4330	290	255	1/32	.4326	.0893	27/32	3/64	.3437	1⅛	1¼
0.6250	1.5745	.4730	300	310	3/64	.4391	.0980	7/8	3/64	.3750	1 5/16	1 13/32
0.6690	1.5745	.4730	300	310	1/32	.4391	.0980	7/8	3/64	.3750	1 5/16	1 13/32
0.7500	1.5745	.4730	300	310	0.040	.4391	.0980	1	3/64	.3750	1 5/16	1 13/32
0.8125	1.9380	.7813	960	610	1/16	.7813	.1563	1 3/16	1/16	.6250	1 19/32	1 25/32
0.8750	1.9687	.5313	610	480	3/64	.5614	.1563	1 7/32	0.040	.3750	1 11/16	1⅞
0.9375	2.2400	.7625	1010	610	1/32	.7810	.1375	1¼	3/64	.6250	1 15/16	1 31/32
1.000	2.2500	.6875	885	600	3/64	.6875	.1563	1 11/32	1/16	.5313	1⅞	2 1/16
1.125	2.3750	.7813	1010	650	1/32	.7620	.1563	1 7/16	3/64	.6250	2	2 3/32
1.250	2.7500	.9375	1715	920	1/32	.9983	.1875	1 9/16	3/64	.7500	2 13/32	2 15/32

Courtesy Timken Roller Bearing Co.

TABLE 53. NATURAL TRIGONOMETRIC FUNCTIONS

Degrees	SINES							Cosines
	0′	10′	20′	30′	40′	50′	60′	
0	0.00000	0.00291	0.00582	0.00873	0.01164	0.01454	0.01745	89
1	.01745	.02036	.02327	.02618	.02908	.03199	.03490	88
2	.03490	.03781	.04071	.04362	.04653	.04943	.05234	87
3	.05234	.05524	.05814	.06105	.06395	.06685	.06976	86
4	.06976	.07266	.07556	.07846	.08136	.08426	.08716	85
5	.08716	.09005	.09295	.09585	.09874	.10164	.10453	84
6	.10453	.10742	.11031	.11320	.11609	.11898	.12187	83
7	.12187	.12476	.12764	.13053	.13341	.13629	.13917	82
8	.13917	.14205	.14493	.14781	.15069	.15356	.15643	81
9	.15643	.15931	.16218	.16505	.16792	.17078	.17365	80
10	.17365	.17651	.17937	.18224	.18509	.18795	.19081	79
11	.19081	.19366	.19652	.19937	.20222	.20507	.20791	78
12	.20791	.21076	.21360	.21644	.21928	.22212	.22495	77
13	.22495	.22778	.23062	.23345	.23627	.23910	.24192	76
14	.24192	.24474	.24756	.25038	.25320	.25601	.25882	75
15	.25882	.26163	.26443	.26724	.27004	.27284	.27564	74
16	.27564	.27843	.28123	.28402	.28680	.28959	.29237	73
17	.29237	.29515	.29793	.30071	.30348	.30625	.30902	72
18	.30902	.31178	.31454	.31730	.32006	.32282	.32557	71
19	.32557	.32832	.33106	.33381	.33655	.33929	.34202	70
20	.34202	.34475	.34748	.35021	.35293	.35565	.35837	69
21	.35837	.36108	.36379	.36650	.36921	.37191	.37461	68
22	.37461	.37730	.37999	.38268	.38537	.38805	.39073	67
23	.39073	.39341	.39608	.39875	.40142	.40408	.40674	66
24	.40674	.40939	.41204	.41469	.41734	.41998	.42262	65
25	.42262	.42525	.42788	.43051	.43313	.43575	.43837	64
26	.43837	.44098	.44359	.44620	.44880	.45140	.45399	63
27	.45399	.45658	.45917	.46175	.46433	.46690	.46947	62
28	.46947	.47204	.47460	.47716	.47971	.48226	.48481	61
29	.48481	.48735	.48989	.49242	.49495	.49748	.50000	60
30	.50000	.50252	.50503	.50754	.51004	.51254	.51504	59
31	.51504	.51753	.52002	.52250	.52498	.52745	.52992	58
32	.52292	.53238	.53484	.53730	.53975	.54220	.54464	57
33	.54464	.54708	.54951	.55194	.55436	.55678	.55919	56
34	.55919	.56160	.56401	.56641	.56880	.57119	.57358	55
35	.57358	.57596	.57833	.58070	.58307	.58543	.58779	54
36	.58779	.59014	.59248	.59482	.59716	.59949	.60182	53
37	.60183	.60414	.60645	.60876	.61107	.61337	.61566	52
38	.61566	.61795	.62024	.62251	.62479	.62706	.62932	51
39	.62932	.63158	.63383	.63608	.63832	.64056	.64279	50
40	.64279	.64501	.64723	.64945	.65166	.65386	.65606	49
41	.65606	.65825	.66044	.66262	.66480	.66697	.66913	48
42	.66913	.67129	.67344	.67559	.67773	.67987	.68200	47
43	.68200	.68412	.68624	.68835	.69046	.69256	.69466	46
44	.69466	.69675	.69883	.70091	.70298	.70505	.70711	45
Sines	60′	50′	40′	30′	20′	10′	0′	Degrees
				COSINES				

TABLE 53. NATURAL TRIGONOMETRIC FUNCTIONS (*Continued*)

Degrees	COSINES							Sines
	0′	10′	20′	30′	40′	50′	60′	
0	1.00000	1.00000	0.99998	0.99996	0.99993	0.99989	0.99985	89
1	0.99985	0.99979	.99973	.99966	.99958	.99949	.99939	88
2	0.99939	0.99929	.99917	.99905	.99892	.99878	.99863	87
3	0.99863	0.99847	.99831	.99813	.99795	.99776	.99756	86
4	0.99756	0.99736	.99714	.99692	.99668	.99644	.99619	85
5	0.99619	0.99594	.99567	.99540	.99511	.99482	.99452	84
6	0.99452	0.99421	.99390	.99357	.99324	.99290	.99255	83
7	0.99255	0.99219	.99182	.99144	.99106	.99067	.99027	82
8	0.99027	0.98986	.98944	.98902	.98858	.98814	.98769	81
9	0.98769	0.98723	.98676	.98629	.98580	.98531	.98481	80
10	0.98481	0.98430	.98378	.98325	.98272	.98218	.98163	79
11	0.98163	0.98107	.98050	.97992	.97934	.97875	.97815	78
12	0.97815	0.97754	.97692	.97630	.97566	.97502	.97437	77
13	0.97437	0.97371	.97304	.97237	.97169	.97100	.97030	76
14	0.97030	0.96959	.96887	.96815	.96742	.96667	.96593	75
15	0.96593	0.96517	.96440	.96363	.96285	.96206	.96126	74
16	0.96126	0.96046	.95964	.95882	.95799	.95715	.95630	73
17	0.95630	0.95545	.95459	.95372	.95284	.95195	.95106	72
18	0.95106	0.95015	.94924	.94832	.94740	.94646	.94552	71
19	0.94552	0.94457	.94361	.94264	.94167	.94068	.93969	70
20	0.93969	0.93869	.93769	.93667	.93565	.93462	.93358	69
21	0.93358	0.93253	.93148	.93042	.92935	.92827	.92718	68
22	0.92718	0.92609	.92499	.92388	.92276	.92164	.92050	67
23	0.92050	0.91936	.91822	.91706	.91590	.91472	.91355	66
24	0.91355	0.91236	.91116	.90996	.90875	.90753	.90631	65
25	0.90631	0.90507	.90383	.90259	.90133	.90007	.89879	64
26	0.89879	0.89752	.89623	.89493	.89363	.89232	.89101	63
27	0.89101	0.88968	.88835	.88701	.88566	.88431	.88295	62
28	0.88295	0.88158	.88020	.87882	.87743	.87603	.87462	61
29	0.87462	0.87321	.87178	.87036	.86892	.86748	.86603	60
30	0.86603	0.86457	.86310	.86163	.86015	.85866	.85717	59
31	0.85717	0.85567	.85416	.85264	.85112	.84959	.84805	58
32	0.84805	0.84650	.84495	.84439	.84182	.84025	.83867	57
33	0.83867	0.83708	.83549	.83389	.83228	.83066	.82904	56
34	0.82904	0.82741	.82577	.82413	.82248	.82082	.81915	55
35	0.81915	0.81748	.81580	.81412	.81242	.81072	.80902	54
36	0.80902	0.80730	.80558	.80386	.80212	.80038	.79864	53
37	0.79864	0.79688	.79512	.79335	.79158	.78980	.78801	52
38	0.78801	0.78622*	.78442	.78261	.78079	.77897	.77715	51
39	0.77715	0.77531	.77347	.77162	.76977	.76791	.76604	50
40	0.76604	0.76417	.76229	.76041	.75851	.75661	.75471	49
41	0.75471	0.75280	.75088	.74896	.74703	.74509	.74314	48
42	0.74314	0.74120	.73924	.73728	.73531	.73333	.73135	47
43	0.73135	0.72937	.72737	.72537	.72337	.72136	.71934	46
44	0.71934	0.71732	.71529	.71325	.71121	.70916	.70711	45
Cosines	60′	50′	40′	30′	20′	10′	0′	Degrees

SINES

TABLE 54. NATURAL TRIGONOMETRIC FUNCTIONS

Degrees	TANGENTS							Cotangents
	0′	10′	20′	30′	40′	50′	60′	
0	0.00000	0.00291	0.00582	0.00873	0.01164	0.01455	0.01746	89
1	.01746	.02036	.02328	.02619	.02910	.03201	0.03492	88
2	.03492	.03783	.04075	.04366	.04658	.04949	0.05241	87
3	.05241	.05533	.05824	.06116	.06408	.06700	0.06993	86
4	.06993	.07285	.07578	.07870	.08163	.08456	0.08749	85
5	.08749	.09042	.09335	.09629	.09923	.10216	0.10510	84
6	.10510	.10805	.11099	.11394	.11688	.11983	0.12278	83
7	.12278	.12574	.12869	.13165	.13461	.13758	0.14054	82
8	.14054	.14351	.14648	.14945	.15243	.15540	0.15838	81
9	.15838	.16137	.16435	.16734	.17033	.17333	0.17633	80
10	.17633	.17933	.18233	.18534	.18835	.19136	0.19438	79
11	.19438	.19740	.20042	.20345	.20648	.20952	0.21256	78
12	.21256	.21560	.21864	.22169	.22475	.22781	0.23087	77
13	.23087	.23393	.23700	.24008	.24316	.24624	0.24933	76
14	.24933	.25242	.25552	.25862	.26172	.26483	0.26795	75
15	.26795	.27107	.27419	.27732	.28046	.28360	0.28675	74
16	.28675	.28990	.29305	.29621	.29938	.30255	0.30573	73
17	.30573	.30891	.31210	.31530	.31850	.32171	0.32492	72
18	.32492	.32814	.33136	.33460	.33783	.34108	0.34433	71
19	.34433	.34758	.35085	.35412	.35740	.36068	0.36397	70
20	.36397	.36727	.37057	.37388	.37720	.38053	0.38386	69
21	.38386	.38721	.39055	.39391	.39727	.40065	0.40403	68
22	.40403	.40741	.41081	.41421	.41763	.42105	0.42447	67
23	.42447	.42791	.43136	.43481	.43828	.44175	0.44523	66
24	.44523	.44872	.45222	.45573	.45924	.46277	0.46631	65
25	.46631	.46985	.47341	.47698	.48055	.48414	0.48773	64
26	.48773	.49134	.49495	.49858	.50222	.50587	0.50953	63
27	.50953	.51320	.51688	.52057	.52427	.52798	0.53171	62
28	.53171	.53545	.53920	.54296	.54674	.55051	0.55431	61
29	.55431	.55812	.56194	.56577	.56962	.57348	0.57735	60
30	.57735	.58124	.58513	.58905	.59297	.59691	0.60086	59
31	.60086	.60483	.60881	.61280	.61681	.62083	0.62487	58
32	.62487	.62892	.63299	.63707	.64117	.64528	0.64941	57
33	.64941	.65355	.65771	.66189	.66608	.67028	0.67451	56
34	.67451	.67875	.68301	.68728	.69157	.69588	0.70021	55
35	.70021	.70455	.70891	.71329	.71769	.72211	0.72654	54
36	.72654	.73100	.73547	.73996	.74447	.74900	0.75355	53
37	.75355	.75812	.76272	.76733	.77196	.77661	0.78129	52
38	.78129	.78598	.79070	.79544	.80020	.80498	0.80978	51
39	.80978	.81461	.81946	.82434	.82923	.83415	0.83910	50
40	.83910	.84407	.84906	.85408	.85912	.86419	0.86929	49
41	.86929	.87441	.87955	.88473	.88992	.89515	0.90040	48
42	.90040	.90569	.91099	.91633	.92170	.92709	0.93252	47
43	.93252	.93797	.94345	.94896	.95451	.96008	0.96569	46
44	.96569	.97133	.97700	.98270	.98843	.99420	1.00000	45
Tangents	60′	50′	40′	30′	20′	10′	0′	Degrees
	COTANGENTS							

TABLE 54. NATURAL TRIGONOMETRIC FUNCTIONS (Continued)

Degrees	COTANGENTS							Tangents
	0′	10′	20′	30′	40′	50′	60′	
0	∞	343.77371	171.88540	114.58865	85.93979	68.75009	57.28996	89
1	57.28996	49.10388	42.96408	38.18846	34.36777	31.24158	28.63625	88
2	28.63625	26.43160	24.54176	22.90377	21.47040	20.20555	19.08114	87
3	19.08114	18.07498	17.16934	16.34986	15.60478	14.92442	14.30067	86
4	14.30067	13.72674	13.19688	12.70621	12.25051	11.82617	11.43005	85
5	11.43005	11.05943	10.71191	10.38540	10.07803	9.78817	9.51436	84
6	9.51436	9.25530	9.00983	8.77689	8.55555	8.34496	8.14435	83
7	8.14435	7.95302	7.77035	7.59575	7.42871	7.26873	7.11537	82
8	7.11537	6.96823	6.82694	6.69116	6.56055	6.43484	6.31375	81
9	6.31375	6.19703	6.08444	5.97576	5.87080	5.76937	5.67128	80
10	5.67128	5.57638	5.48451	5.39552	5.30928	5.22566	5.14455	79
11	5.14455	5.06584	4.98940	4.91516	4.84300	4.77286	4.70463	78
12	4.70463	4.63825	4.57363	4.51071	4.44942	4.38969	4.33148	77
13	4.33148	4.27471	4.21933	4.16530	4.11256	4.06107	4.01078	76
14	4.01078	3.96165	3.91364	3.86671	3.82083	3.77595	3.73205	75
15	3.73205	3.68909	3.64705	3.60588	3.56557	3.52609	3.48741	74
16	3.48741	3.44951	3.41236	3.37594	3.34023	3.30521	3.27085	73
17	3.27085	3.23714	3.20406	3.17159	3.13972	3.10842	3.07768	72
18	3.07768	3.04749	3.01783	2.98869	2.96004	2.93189	2.90421	71
19	2.90421	2.87700	2.85023	2.82391	2.79802	2.77254	2.74748	70
20	2.74748	2.72281	2.69853	2.67462	2.65109	2.62791	2.60509	69
21	2.60509	2.58261	2.56046	2.53865	2.51715	2.49597	2.47509	68
22	2.47509	2.45451	2.43422	2.41421	2.39449	2.37504	2.35585	67
23	2.35585	2.33693	2.31826	2.29984	2.28167	2.26374	2.24604	66
24	2.24604	2.22857	2.21132	2.19430	2.17749	2.16090	2.14451	65
25	2.14451	2.12832	2.11233	2.09654	2.08094	2.06553	2.05030	64
26	2.05030	2.03526	2.02039	2.00569	1.99116	1.97680	1.96261	63
27	1.96261	1.94858	1.93470	1.92098	1.90741	1.89400	1.88073	62
28	1.88073	1.86760	1.85462	1.84177	1.82907	1.81649	1.80405	61
29	1.80405	1.79174	1.77955	1.76749	1.75556	1.74375	1.73205	60
30	1.73205	1.72047	1.70901	1.69766	1.68643	1.67530	1.66428	59
31	1.66428	1.65337	1.64256	1.63185	1.62125	1.61074	1.60033	58
32	1.60033	1.59002	1.57981	1.56969	1.55966	1.54972	1.53987	57
33	1.53987	1.53010	1.52043	1.51084	1.50133	1.49190	1.48256	56
34	1.48256	1.47330	1.46411	1.45501	1.44598	1.43703	1.42815	55
35	1.42815	1.41934	1.41061	1.40195	1.39336	1.38484	1.37638	54
36	1.37638	1.36800	1.35968	1.35143	1.34323	1.33511	1.32704	53
37	1.32704	1.31904	1.31110	1.30323	1.29541	1.28764	1.27994	52
38	1.27994	1.27230	1.26471	1.25717	1.24969	1.24227	1.23490	51
39	1.23490	1.22758	1.22031	1.21310	1.20593	1.19882	1.19175	50
40	1.19175	1.18474	1.17777	1.17085	1.16398	1.15715	1.15037	49
41	1.15037	1.14363	1.13694	1.13029	1.12369	1.11713	1.11061	48
42	1.11061	1.10414	1.09770	1.09131	1.08496	1.07864	1.07237	47
43	1.07237	1.06613	1.05994	1.05378	1.04766	1.04158	1.03553	46
44	1.03553	1.02952	1.02355	1.01761	1.01170	1.00583	1.00000	45
Cotangents	60′	50′	40′	30′	20′	10′	0′	Degrees

TANGENTS

TABLE 55. RADII OF RAILROAD AND HIGHWAY CURVES

Degree of curvature	Radius, feet	Degree of curvature	Radius, feet	Degree of curvature	Radius, feet
0° 0′	∞	5° 0′	1146.28	10° 0′	573.69
10	34377.5	10	1109.33	10	564.31
20	17188.8	20	1074.68	20	555.23
30	11459.2	30	1042.14	30	546.44
40	8594.42	40	1011.51	40	537.92
50	6875.55	50	982.64	50	529.67
1° 0′	5729.65	6° 0′	955.37	11° 0′	521.67
10	4911.15	10	929.57	10	513.91
20	4297.28	20	905.13	20	506.38
30	3819.83	30	881.95	30	499.06
40	3437.87	40	859.92	40	491.96
50	3125.36	50	838.97	50	485.05
2° 0′	2864.93	7° 0′	819.02	12° 0′	478.34
10	2644.58	10	800.00	30	459.28
20	2455.70	20	781.84		
30	2292.01	30	764.49	13° 0′	441.68
40	2148.79	40	747.89	30	425.40
50	2022.41	50	732.01		
				14° 0′	410.28
3° 0′	1910.08	8° 0′	716.78	30	396.20
10	1809.57	10	702.18		
20	1719.12	20	688.16	15° 0′	383.06
30	1637.28	30	674.69	30	370.78
40	1562.88	40	661.74		
50	1494.95	50	649.27	16° 0′	359.26
				30	348.45
4° 0′	1432.69	9° 0′	637.27		
10	1375.40	10	625.71	17° 0′	338.27
20	1322.53	20	614.56	30	328.68
30	1273.57	30	603.80		
40	1228.11	40	593.42	18° 0′	319.62
50	1185.78	50	583.38	30	311.06

Note. The degree of curvature is the angle subtended at the center of the arc by a chord of 100 feet. The length of a curve is the length measured in 100-feet chords plus fractional 100-feet chords at the ends from P.C. to P.T.

TABLE 56. METRIC CONVERSION TABLES

Inches to centimeters—1 in. = 2.540005 cm

Units tens	0	1	2	3	4	5	6	7	8	9
0		2.540	5.080	7.620	10.160	12.700	15.240	17.780	20.320	22.860
1	25.400	27.940	30.480	33.020	35.560	38.100	40.640	43.180	45.720	48.260
2	50.800	53.340	55.880	58.420	60.960	63.500	66.040	68.580	71.120	73.660
3	76.200	78.740	81.280	83.820	86.360	88.900	91.440	93.980	96.520	99.060
4	101.600	104.140	106.680	109.220	111.760	114.300	116.840	119.380	121.920	124.460
5	127.00	129.540	132.080	134.620	137.160	139.700	142.240	144.780	147.320	149.860
6	152.400	154.940	157.480	160.020	162.560	165.100	167.640	170.180	172.720	175.260
7	177.800	180.340	182.880	185.420	187.960	190.500	193.040	195.580	198.120	200.660
8	203.200	205.740	208.280	210.820	213.360	215.900	218.440	220.980	223.520	226.060
9	228.600	231.140	233.680	236.220	238.760	241.300	243.840	246.380	248.920	251.460

Centimeters to inches—1 cm = 0.3937 in.

Units tens	0	1	2	3	4	5	6	7	8	9
0		0.3937	0.7874	1.1811	1.5748	1.9685	2.3622	2.7559	3.1496	3.5433
1	3.9370	4.3307	4.7244	5.1181	5.5118	5.9055	6.2992	6.6929	7.0866	7.4803
2	7.8740	8.2677	8.6614	9.0551	9.4488	9.8425	10.2362	10.6299	11.0236	11.4173
3	11.8110	12.2047	12.5984	12.9921	13.3858	13.7795	14.1732	14.5669	14.9606	15.3543
4	15.7480	16.1417	16.5354	16.9291	17.3228	17.7165	18.1102	18.5039	18.8976	19.2913
5	19.6850	20.0787	20.4724	20.8661	21.2598	21.6535	22.0472	22.4409	22.8346	23.2283
6	23.6220	24.0157	24.4094	24.8031	25.1968	25.5905	25.9842	26.3779	26.7716	27.1653
7	27.5590	27.9527	28.3464	28.7401	29.1338	29.5275	29.9212	30.3149	30.7086	31.1023
8	31.4960	31.8897	32.2834	32.6671	33.0708	33.4645	33.8582	34.2519	34.6456	35.0393
9	35.4330	35.8267	36.2204	36.6141	37.0078	37.4015	37.7952	38.1889	38.5826	38.9763

TABLE 57. WIRE GAGES

There has come about, through lack of standardization, a great deal of confusion concerning wire gages to be specified on the engineer's drawings. Until wire manufacturers have agreed to some national standard it would be well to specify on the drawing the exact diameter of the wire wanted. In the case of steel wires, the Bureau of Standards at Washington has recommended that the American Steel and Wire Co.'s gage be adopted as the Steel Wire Gage. This gage is given in the table below in decimals of an inch, and is the same as the Washburn & Moen gage. When there is danger of confusion with the British gage, it should be called the United States Steel Wire Gage.

In the case of copper wire, the American Wire Gage is standard throughout the United States and is the same as the Brown & Sharpe gage. It is also given in the table below in decimals of an inch.

Sheet and Plate Metal Gage

Congress legalized the United States Standard Gage for sheet and plate iron and steel, March 3, 1893. The various gage sizes are given in decimals of an inch in the table below.

WIRE AND SHEET METAL GAGES

No. of gage	Steel wire gage	American copper or B. & S. wire gage	British imperial wire gage	U. S. St'd. gage for plate	No. of gage	Steel wire gage	American wire gage	British imperial wire gage	U. S. St'd. gage for plate
0000000	0.4900	. . . . . .	0.5000	0.5000	23	0.0258	0.0226	0.0240	0.0281
000000	0.4615	0.5800	0.4640	0.4688	24	0.0230	0.0201	0.0220	0.0250
00000	0.4305	0.5165	0.4320	0.4375	25	0.0204	0.0179	0.0200	0.0219
0000	0.3938	0.4600	0.4000	0.4063	26	0.0181	0.0159	0.0180	0.0188
000	0.3625	0.4096	0.3720	0.3750	27	0.0173	0.0142	0.0164	0.0172
00	0.3310	0.3648	0.3480	0.3438	28	0.0162	0.0126	0.0148	0.0156
0	0.3065	0.3249	0.3240	0.3125	29	0.0150	0.0113	0.0136	0.0141
1	0.2830	0.2893	0.3000	0.2813	30	0.0140	0.0100	0.0124	0.0125
2	0.2625	0.2576	0.2760	0.2656	31	0.0132	0.0089	0.0116	0.0109
3	0.2437	0.2294	0.2520	0.2500	32	0.0128	0.0080	0.0108	0.0102
4	0.2253	0.2043	0.2320	0.2344	33	0.0118	0.0071	0.0100	0.0094
5	0.2070	0.1819	0.2120	0.2188	34	0.0104	0.0063	0.0092	0.0086
6	0.1920	0.1620	0.1920	0.2031	35	0.0095	0.0056	0.0084	0.0078
7	0.1770	0.1443	0.1760	0.1875	36	0.0090	0.0050	0.0076	0.0070
8	0.1620	0.1285	0.1600	0.1719	37	0.0085	0.0045	0.0068	0.0066
9	0.1483	0.1144	0.1440	0.1563	38	0.0080	0.0040	0.0060	0.0063
10	0.1350	0.1019	0.1280	0.1406	39	0.0075	0.0035	0.0052	. . . . . .
11	0.1205	0.0907	0.1160	0.1250	40	0.0070	0.0031	0.0048	. . . . . .
12	0.1055	0.0808	0.1040	0.1094	41	0.0066	0.0028	0.0044	. . . . . .
13	0.0915	0.0720	0.0920	0.0938	42	0.0062	0.0025	0.0040	. . . . . .
14	0.0800	0.0641	0.0800	0.0781	43	0.0060	0.0022	0.0036	. . . . . .
15	0.0720	0.0571	0.0720	0.0703	44	0.0058	0.0020	0.0032	. . . . . .
16	0.0625	0.0508	0.0640	0.0625	45	0.0055	0.00176	0.0028	. . . . . .
17	0.0540	0.0453	0.0560	0.0563	46	0.0052	0.00157	0.0024	. . . . . .
18	0.0475	0.0403	0.0480	0.0500	47	0.0050	0.00140	0.0020	. . . . . .
19	0.0410	0.0359	0.0400	0.0438	48	0.0048	0.00124	0.0016	. . . . . .
20	0.0348	0.0320	0.0360	0.0375	49	0.0046	0.00099	0.0012	. . . . . .
21	0.0317	0.0285	0.0320	0.0344	50	0.0044	0.00088	0.0010	. . . . . .
22	0.0286	0.0253	0.0280	0.0313					

TABLE 58. DECIMAL EQUIVALENTS OF FRACTIONS OF AN INCH

1/32	1/64	Decimal	Fraction	1/32	1/64	Decimal	Fraction
	1	0.015625			33	0.515625	
1	2	.03125		17	34	0.53125	
	3	.046875			35	0.546875	
2	4	.0625	1/16	18	36	0.5625	9/16
	5	.078125			37	0.578125	
3	6	.09375		19	38	0.59375	
	7	.109375			39	0.609375	
4	8	.125	1/8	20	40	0.625	5/8
	9	.140625			41	0.640625	
5	10	.15625		21	42	0.65625	
	11	.171875			43	0.671875	
6	12	.1875	3/16	22	44	0.6875	11/16
	13	.203125			45	0.703125	
7	14	.21875		23	46	0.71875	
	15	.234375			47	0.734375	
8	16	.25	1/4	24	48	0.75	3/4
	17	.265625			49	0.765625	
9	18	.28125		25	50	0.78125	
	19	.296875			51	0.796875	
10	20	.3125	5/16	26	52	0.8125	13/16
	21	.328125			53	0.828125	
11	22	.34375		27	54	0.84375	
	23	.359375			55	0.859375	
12	24	.375	3/8	28	56	0.875	7/8
	25	.390625			57	0.890625	
13	26	.40625		29	58	0.90625	
	27	.421875			59	0.921875	
14	28	.4375	7/16	30	60	0.9375	15/16
	29	.453125			61	0.953125	
15	30	.46875		31	62	0.96875	
	31	.48375			63	0.984375	
16	32	.5	1/2	32	64	1	1

TABLE 59. AREAS AND VOLUMES

Figure	Area	Figure	Surface	Figure	Volume
TRIANGLE	$Area = \frac{1}{2}bh$ $= \frac{1}{2}ab\sin C$	REGULAR RIGHT PRISMS	$Surface\ Area = nah$ $n = number\ of\ sides$	REGULAR RIGHT PRISMS	$Volume = Bh$ $B = area\ of\ base$
RECTANGLE	$Area = bh$	REGULAR RIGHT PYRAMIDS	$Surface\ Area = \frac{1}{2}san$ $n = number\ of\ sides$ $s = h/\sin\alpha$	REGULAR RIGHT PYRAMID	$Volume = \frac{1}{3}Bh$
PARALLELOGRAM	$Area = bh$ $= ab\sin C$	RIGHT CIRCULAR CYLINDER	$Surface\ Area = 2\pi rh$	RIGHT CIRCULAR CYLINDER	$Volume = \pi r^2 h$
TRAPEZOID	$Area = \frac{1}{2}(a+b)h$ $A = \frac{1}{2}d_1 d_2 \sin C$	SEGMENT OF CYLINDER	For Area of end segment see 1st Col.	SEGMENT OF CYLINDER	$Volume = Bl$ $B = area\ of\ segment$ see bottom of Col. I.
ANY REGULAR POLYGON	$Area = \frac{1}{2}nbh$ $n = number\ of\ sides$ $h = (b/2)(\tan\alpha$ $\alpha = (n-2/2n)180°$			HOLLOW CYLINDER	$Volume = \pi l(R^2 - r^2)$
CIRCLE	$Circum. = \pi d = 2\pi r$ $Area = \pi r^2 = \frac{\pi}{4}d^2$	RIGHT CIRCULAR CONE	$Surface\ Area = \pi rs$	RIGHT CIRCULAR CONE	$Volume = \frac{1}{3}\pi r^2 h$
ANNULUS	$Area = \pi(R^2 - r^2)$ $= \frac{\pi}{4}(D^2 - d^2)$	FRUSTUM OF CONE	$Surface\ Area = \pi s(R+r)$	FRUSTUM OF CONE	$Volume = \frac{1}{3}\pi h(R^2 + Rr + r^2)$
SECTOR OF CIRCLE	$Area = \frac{1}{2}rs$ $= \pi r^2 (\alpha/360°)$ $s = 2\pi r(\alpha/360°)$	SPHERE	$Surface\ Area = 4\pi r^2$	SPHERE	$Volume = \frac{4}{3}\pi r^3$
SEGMENT OF CIRCLE	$Area = \frac{1}{2}[r(s-c)+ch]$ $c = 2r\sin\alpha$ $s = 4\pi r(\alpha/360°)$ $\cos\alpha = (r-h)/r$	SPHERICAL SEGMENT	$Surface\ Area = 2\pi rh$	SPHERICAL SEGMENT	$Volume = \frac{1}{6}\pi h(3a^2 + h^2)$ $a^2 = (h(2r-h))$

TABLE 60. STANDARD BEND RADII

Material thickness	Aluminum alloy							Magnesium alloy		Steel			
	2SO 3SO 52SO 53SO	2S½H 3S¼H 4SO 52S¼H 53S¼H	2S¾H 3S½H 4S¼H 52S½H 53S½H	3S¾H 4S½H 17SO 24SO 52S¾H 53S¾H 61SO	4S¾H 17ST 24ST 53ST 53SW 61ST 61SW	75SO	27ST 75ST	Cold formed	Hot formed	Low carbon X4130 annealed	Stainless		
											annealed	¼ Hard	½ Hard
0 through 0.013	0.031	0.031	0.031	0.031	0.062	0.031	0.062	0.062	0.031	0.031	0.031	0.062	0.062
0.014 through .017	.031	.031	.031	.031	.062	.031	0.062	0.062	.031	.031	.031	.062	.062
.018 through .022	.031	.031	.031	.031	.062	.062	0.094	0.094	.031	.031	.031	.062	.062
.023 through .027	.031	.031	.031	.062	.094	.062	0.125	0.125	.062	.031	.031	.062	.062
.028 through .035	.062	.062	.062	.062	.125	.062	0.156	0.156	.062	.031	.031	.062	.094
.036 through .044	.062	.062	.062	.062	.125	.094	0.219	0.219	.094	.062	.062	.094	.125
.045 through .054	.062	.062	.094	.094	.156	.125	0.250	0.250	.125	.062	.062	.094	.125
.055 through .068	.062	.094	.094	.125	.219	.125	0.312	0.312	.156	.062	.062	.125	.188
.069 through .075	.094	.094	.125	.125	.250	.156	0.375	0.375	.188	.062	.062	.125	.188
.076 through .084	.094	.094	.156	.125	.281	.188	0.406	0.406	.219	.094	.094	.156	.219
.085 through .097	.094	.094	.188	.125	.312	.188	0.469	0.469	.250	.094	.094	.188	.250
.098 through .113	.125	.125	.188	.156	.375	.219	0.531	0.625	.250	.125	.125	.219	.312
.114 through .139	.125	.156	.219	.188	.438	.281	0.688	0.750	.312	.125	.188		
.140 through .172	.156	.188	.250	.250	.562	.375	0.875	1.000	.375	.156	.188		
.173 through .219	.188	.250	.375	.312	.750	.438	1.062	1.250	.500	.188	.188		
.220 through .262	.250	.312	.500	.469	.938	.531	1.250	1.500	.625	.250	.250		

TABLE 61

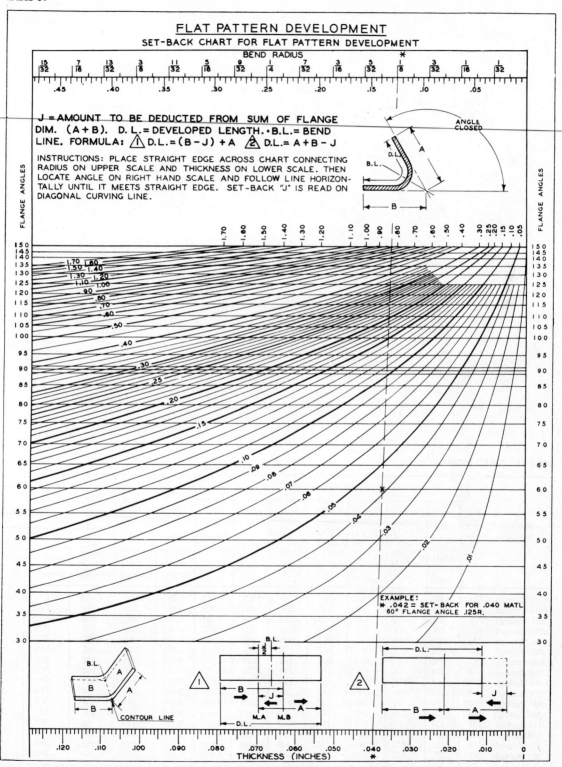

Courtesy McDonnell Aircraft Co.

Index